Silvabr...

Car & Motorcycle Restoration

Selection of processed material

- Brass
- Bronze
- Aluminium
- Steel
- Mazak
- Modern Die Cast
- Most Ferrous & Non Ferrous Metals

...olishing facilities
...teel and Aluminium

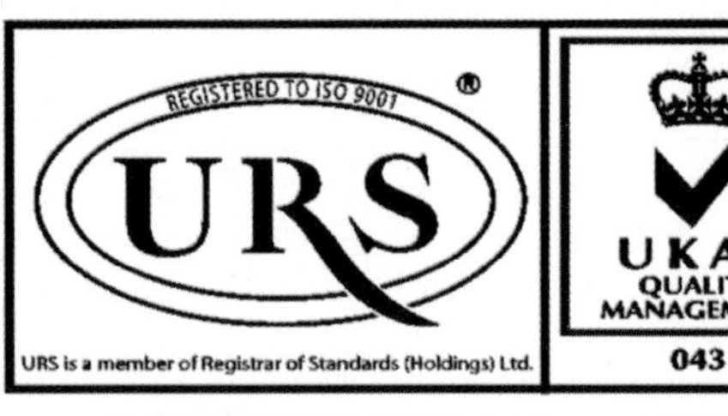

CERTIFICATE NO. 1373

Classic Car Show *Birmingham NEC*

Best Car in Show Daimler SP250

Practical Classics - Car of the Year 2006

Austin Sheerline

Owner - Colin Cummings

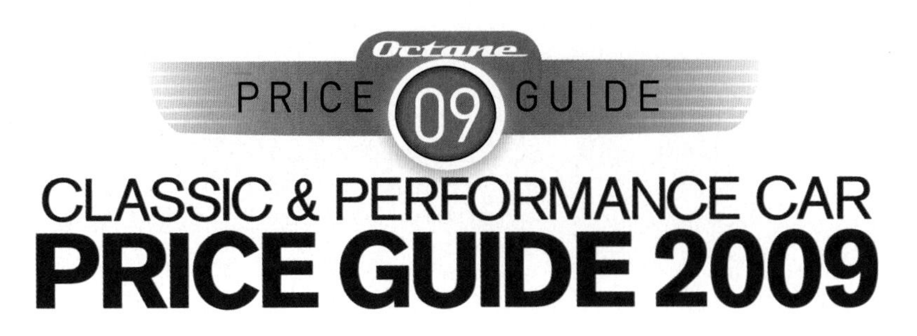

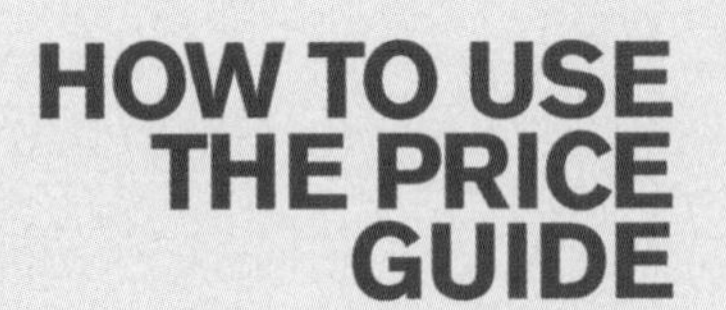

EXCELLENT
The sort of cars you'll see at concours events, and which command absolute top-dollar on the dealers' forecourts. Generally restored or with near zero mileage, you're looking at cars as good as, and sometimes better than, new.

GOOD
Excellent all-round condition requiring no money to be spent on them. Original condition or restored earlier in their life to factory-spec, and not far from concours condition. The best private cars usually fit into this category.

AVERAGE
Good, useable cars with an MoT and plenty of history and generally ready to go. Some cosmetic problems and, perhaps, the odd mechanical issue, but nothing that compromises driving the car.

PROJECT
A complete, running car, but in need of substantial work in order to get back into a driveable condition. Barn finds, restoration projects or accident damaged cars will fall into this category.
Buy with your eyes open.

Octane PRICE 09 GUIDE

CLASSIC & PERFORMANCE CAR
PRICE GUIDE 2009

Editorial office
Octane, 1 Tower Court, Irchester Road,
Wollaston, Northants NN29 7PJ, UK
Tel: +44 (0)207 907 6585. Fax: +44 (0)1933 663367
Email: info@octane-magazine.com
Website: www.octane-magazine.com

Advertising office
Octane Media Advertising Dept, 19 Highfield Lane,
Maidenhead, Berkshire SL6 3AN, UK
Tel: +44 (0)1628 510080. Fax: +44 (0)1628 510090
Email: ads@octane-magazine.com

Managing editor: David Lillywhite
Art editor: Rob Gould
Production: Nigel Grimshaw, Sarah Bradley, Ben Field, Simon Johnston, Richard Heseltine
Contributors Russ Smith, Richard Gunn, Keith Adams, Matthew Hayward

Advertising director: Sanjay Seetanah
Advertising sales: Mark Wibberley
Advertising production: Anisha Mogra, Kerem Kolcak

Publishing director Geoff Love
Newstrade director Martin Belson
Marketing manager Juliette Cooper
Managing director Ian Westwood
Group finance director Ian Leggett
COO Brett Reynolds
CEO James Tye
Chairman Felix Dennis

Repro by Octane Repro **Printed by** Wyndeham Heron
Distribution Seymour, 2 East Poultry Avenue, London EC1A 9PT. Tel: +44 (0)207 429 400

Periodicals Postage paid @ Emigsville, PA.
Postmaster: send address corrections to Octane Media c/o 3330 Pacific Ave, Suite 404, Virginia Beach, VA 23451

THE ULTIMATE GUIDE TO YOUR NEXT CAR...

'From just a few hundred pounds to tens of thousands, the possibilities are seemingly endless'

So many cars, so little time. It's easy to forget just how much is out there, but flick through this guide and you'll find over 1000 classic and performance cars from the early 1920s to the present day.

Every car in this guide is accurately described, with performance figures and specification, and valued using the latest market data – you'll soon see that there really is something for every pocket, as dreadful a cliché as that is. From just a few hundred pounds to tens of thousands, the buying possibilities are seemingly endless.

Our team consists of some of the most experienced classic car journalists in the UK, and they've all worked hard to give you the most complete guide to classic and performance car values seen for many years. It's difficult not to idly leaf through the pages and come across a long-forgotten model that suddenly seems like the ideal car to spend your money on.

And if you do get that feeling, then you'll find thousands of cars for sale on our website, www.octane-magazine.com.

David Lillywhite

CONTRIBUTORS

RICHARD DREDGE
The original 'data dad', for *Top Gear* magazine, and founder of online picture library Magic Car Pics, Richard's huge personal archive has been stretched putting together our price guide.

RUSS SMITH
A freelance contributor and former editor of several classic car magazines, Russ Smith has been writing about classics for 20 years, as well as driving and getting his hands dirty on them.

RICHARD GUNN
Richard Gunn is a writer and photographer with several books to his credit. Has a strange softness for Volvos, and is currently the editor-at-large of *Classic Car Weekly*.

KEITH ADAMS
Assistant editor of *Octane* magazine and self-confessed car geek, Keith's encyclopaedic knowledge of classic cars came in handy when putting together the more obscure entries.

MATTHEW HAYWARD
Online contributor for both *MG Enthusiast* and *Octane* magazines. Matthew's been ultra-busy sourcing pictures, researching specification data and writing potted histories.

BUYING A CLASSIC

A good classic sports car is something you'll love for years. A bad one will drive you mad, so read this and choose carefully

Words: Richard Dredge Photography: www.magiccarpics.co.uk

What to buy

» Your budget will dictate what classic you can buy, but in any price band there will be all sorts of car types available. You need to work out whether you want something fun or practical, mainstream or off-beat.

» Continue to narrow down your field by working out what sort of age your classic should be. Many classics are surprisingly usable on an everyday basis; if the car is more than a toy you'll need something reasonably practical and frugal.

» If you want something that's really off-beat such as a low-volume sportscar or an American import, bear in mind that specialists will be few and far between. Also parts could be harder to get and may be more costly.

» You can't beat the buzz of driving a convertible on a sunny day, but most cheap open-topped classics leak like sieves. A leaky classic that's stored outside is a recipe for disaster, so be wary unless you've got a garage.

» Any classic built (but not necessarily registered) before January 1, 1973 is entitled to free road tax. Other running costs to think about include insurance (get a quote before buying), fuel bills and both parts and servicing costs.

»What to look for

Bodywork and trim

Overhauling engines and gearboxes is usually the cheapest and easiest part of any restoration; it's the bodywork that will get you...

Fixing bodywork properly takes time and skill; it may be worth getting a professional to do some of the trickier bits as it'll take them a lot less time than it'll take you. Also bear in mind that a complete restoration project is often easier (but more costly and time-consuming) than a quick patch up, because it's easier to get to everything once a car is stripped down.

1 If a car has been badly pranged it can be difficult to attain proper alignment of everything, so make sure all panels line up properly. Check for rippled inner wings and shutlines that are all over the place – sorting these can be very costly, if not impossible. Unless you've got specialist bodywork skills, you're best avoiding any car that's been in a major shunt because you'll never get everything to line up.

2 Reshelling is common, as it's often more economical to source a decent used bodyshell than to patch up a badly damaged one. Although the legality of this is sometimes questionable, it's usually safe – unlike the cut 'n' shut. This is likely to affect only recent classics – but still ensure the car doesn't consist of two cars welded together across the middle. Don't even consider a cut 'n' shut, but a properly reshelled classic makes a great buy.

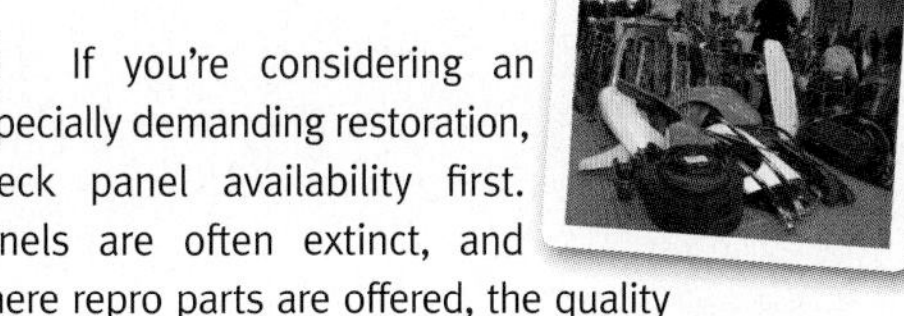

3 If you're considering an especially demanding restoration, check panel availability first. Panels are often extinct, and where repro parts are offered, the quality is variable. Often you'll need to create your own panels; for hidden items such as inner wings that may be fine, but outer panels can be very demanding because of their subtle contours. Unless you're a whizz on the wheeling machine, you might need an easier project.

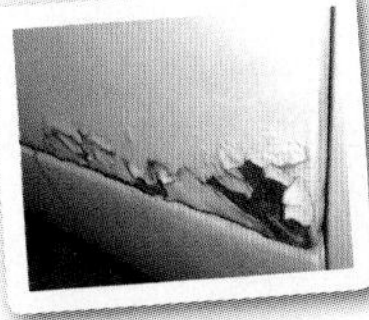

4 Rust is the most common issue, so check every nook and cranny for paint damage, microblistering or bubbling. Common rust traps include the sills and wheelarches, so run a magnet over them to check for filler. Seams and brightwork also frequently harbour rot, as do rain gutters. Cosmetic rust needn't be a problem, but structural rot could be, depending on your metal-bashing skills. Structural areas include the sills, bulkheads and any floorpan crossmembers.

5 Other areas to check include the door bottoms plus the front and rear valances, which often rot from the inside out. Also look at the leading edge of the bonnet and trailing edge of the bootlid; these start to corrode, get left, then dissolve. These areas aren't structural, but can be tricky to repair without specialist skills. Also ensure the rubber seals are intact; they perish then let water into the cabin.

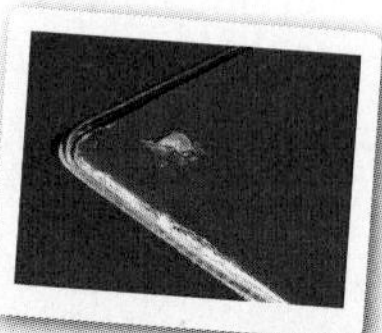

6 If the car has a sunroof, make sure it's not leaking and that its surround hasn't corroded. Lift the bonnet and see what state the inner wings and battery are in, and look closely at the bulkhead. If this has corroded it'll mean an engine bay strip down (and possibly dashboard removal) to effect proper repairs – extremely time-consuming, but not usually that difficult. If the car has MacPherson strut front suspension, look at the strut tops for corrosion.

7 Check the floorpans from underneath (including the spare wheel well) and lift any trim for a view from inside. Repairs to these areas can be time-consuming, as you may have to remove fuel and brake pipes and mechanical parts such as brake or suspension systems – but once stripped, repairs are usually straightforward. Finish by checking the doors aren't dropping because of rotten A-posts or worn hinges; the former is often very difficult because of poor accessibility.

8 Any car with a separate chassis needs careful inspection, as effecting proper repairs can mean removing the bodyshell – and you can't skimp, because a chassis gives a car most of its strength. Check the entire chassis for corrosion, along with stress cracks where sections meet – especially around suspension mountings. Repairs are usually easy, but it's common to have to remove fuel and brake lines or mechanical parts such as the suspension, before work can begin.

9 Exterior trim can cause headaches, with some model ranges having many different trim specifications. Light units get broken while chrome trim gets pitted, and replating mazak isn't usually possible so you need to find new parts. A lot of repro stuff is badly made and original bits are often unavailable or overpriced – so check all the exterior trim parts are present and in good nick or get costs for replacements.

10 Ensure door panels, carpets and seat covers are in good nick. Also make sure the wood trim, headlining and hood (if it's a convertible) are sound as these often need professional help to revive. Newton Commercial remanufactures trim for some classics; otherwise it's a case of scouring autojumbles or buying from fellow club members.

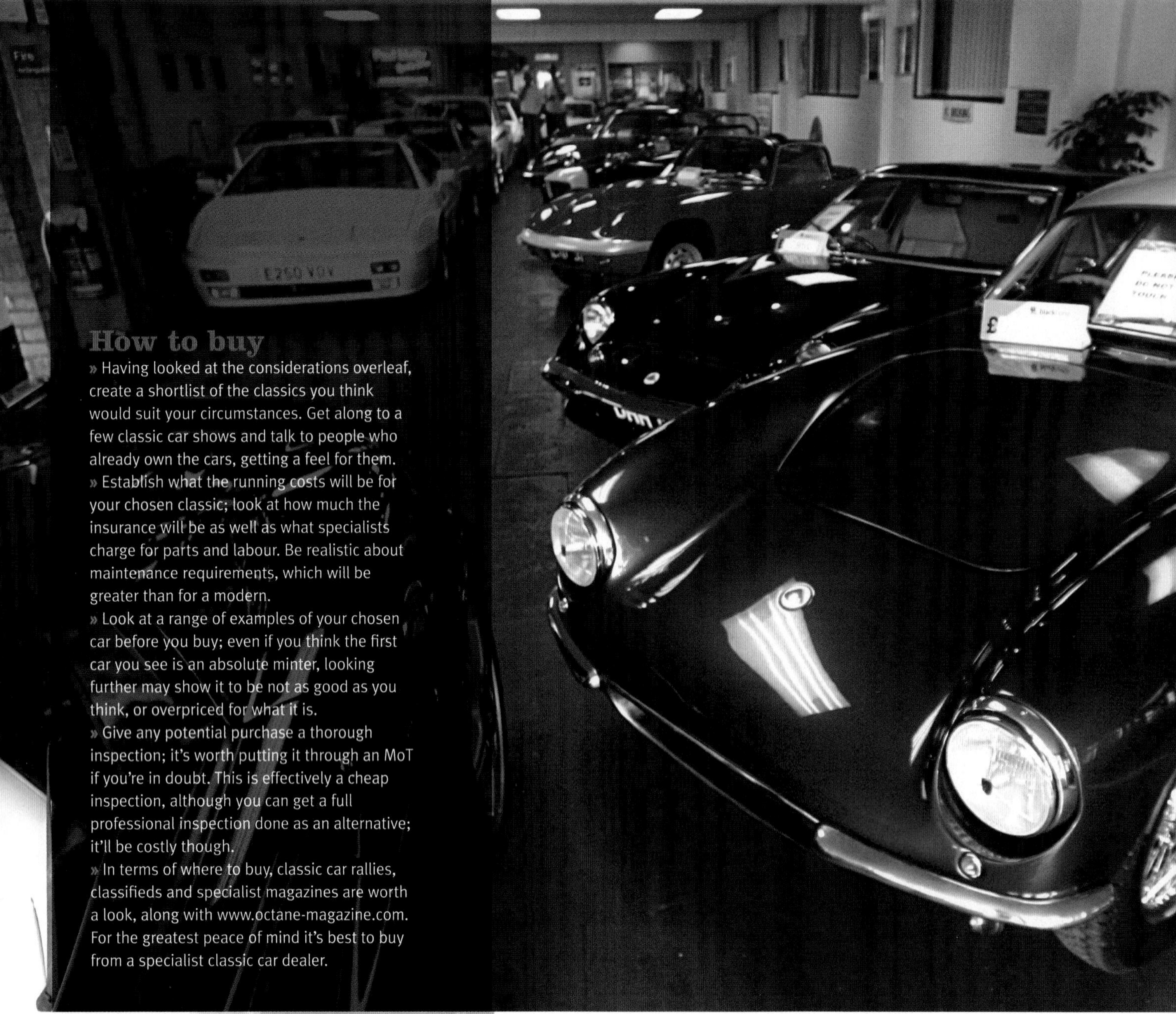

How to buy

» Having looked at the considerations overleaf, create a shortlist of the classics you think would suit your circumstances. Get along to a few classic car shows and talk to people who already own the cars, getting a feel for them.

» Establish what the running costs will be for your chosen classic; look at how much the insurance will be as well as what specialists charge for parts and labour. Be realistic about maintenance requirements, which will be greater than for a modern.

» Look at a range of examples of your chosen car before you buy; even if you think the first car you see is an absolute minter, looking further may show it to be not as good as you think, or overpriced for what it is.

» Give any potential purchase a thorough inspection; it's worth putting it through an MoT if you're in doubt. This is effectively a cheap inspection, although you can get a full professional inspection done as an alternative; it'll be costly though.

» In terms of where to buy, classic car rallies, classifieds and specialist magazines are worth a look, along with www.octane-magazine.com. For the greatest peace of mind it's best to buy from a specialist classic car dealer.

How to run

» Joining an owners' club will enable you to home in on the best specialists for your car. Also, you should find it easier to track down parts as well as solve problems if they crop up.

» As a general rule, the older the car the greater its servicing requirements. However, most classics were simply engineered, so DIY maintenance isn't as daunting as you might think. Buy a manual and you could save a fortune in maintenance costs.

» Make sure you insure the car on a specialist classic policy. Doing this will ensure that you get what the car is worth in the event of a total loss, as its value is agreed when you take out the cover.

» Even if you don't do many miles each year, give the car a service before you put it away for the winter, including an oil change. Refreshing the lubricant and filter annually is the best thing you can do to preserve the engine.

» When winter comes round, make sure the car is stored properly if you're not going to use it. Fit a battery conditioner and get the engine up to temperature once a month to make sure you don't have problems with bits seizing up.

What to look for

Mechanical parts

Most classics are like big Meccano kits; if you treat items such as the engine, gearbox and back axle as sealed units, you can just swap bits over with relatively little hassle. The cost of rebuilding these items can be very high, so get an idea of replacement costs before you inspect your potential purchase. At least brakes, steering and suspension are usually cheap and easy to sort – but not always!

1 Don't start the engine until you've inspected the bodywork and interior, giving it time to cool down if the owner has run it up to temperature before your arrival. Look for bad oil leaks and suspect out-of-balance carburettors if the engine runs unevenly. A worn engine will usually smoke badly, but even the most knackered powerplant can be rebuilt – although costs can be very high if it's something exotic or rare.

2 Knocking sounds on start up indicate bearing wear, caused by oil starvation, high mileage or hard use. Continuous rumbling signals worn main bearings while clattering from the top of the engine means the valve clearances need adjusting or something (probably the camshaft) has worn. Only the latter means a top-end rebuild; the others mean the bottom half needs reviving – and that's usually costly unless you just fit a used powerplant.

3 Make sure no water has collected at the bottom of the radiator, signalling leaks; a recore is usually £100+. Get the engine hot (to ensure the thermostat hasn't been removed) and if there's an electric fan, make sure it cuts in at the required temperature. Then switch off the engine and try to restart it a few seconds later; hot starting problems can be hard to sort out.

4 On the test drive, if the car has a manual gearbox, change up and down through the gears quickly, to reveal any synchromesh weaknesses. While doing this listen out for any whining from the gearbox and diff; rebuilding these is usually £250+ apiece, although first gear whine is normal on many classics. Check the overdrive works, if fitted; most (but not all) problems are electrical and easy to fix.

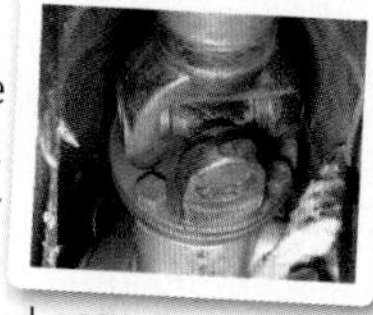

5 Clonks as you release the clutch signal that the universal joints on the propshaft and/or the driveshafts have worn out. Replacement is usually cheap and easy, but if there's a vibration at a certain speed it's because the propshaft is out of balance; a replacement is normally £100-£150. Also ensure the clutch isn't slipping; replacement parts are usually cheap but labour charges can increase the cost considerably.

6 Sourcing replacement steering boxes is often tricky, but originals tend to be durable with the possibility of adjusting out wear in most cases – if this has already been done, there might be stiff spots as a result. Steering racks are usually easier to source; they wear through use or because the rubber gaiters on each end have split, allowing dirt in, accelerating wear. Rebuilt racks are £40+; power assistance quadruples this cost.

7 The dampers are shot if you press down sharply at each corner and the car doesn't settle quickly. Leaf and coil springs wear out or break; the latter should be obvious from underneath, but wear isn't so easy to detect. Look at the ride height; if the car is sitting low at one end or the other it's time for new springs. Replacement dampers and springs are normally cheap, and they're easy to renew.

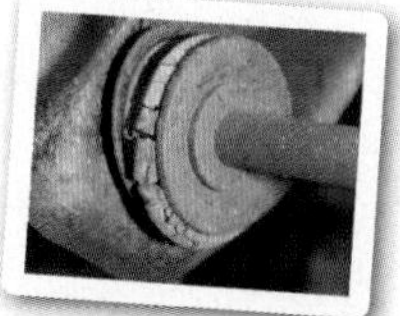

8 Uneven tyre tread wear may show that the tracking is out or it could show more serious problems such as misaligned suspension – especially if the car has been rebuilt. It could also be that the suspension bushes are worn. If the latter is the case, a visual inspection should suffice, but vague steering can also be the result. Also listen for worn wheelbearings; they rumble as you corner.

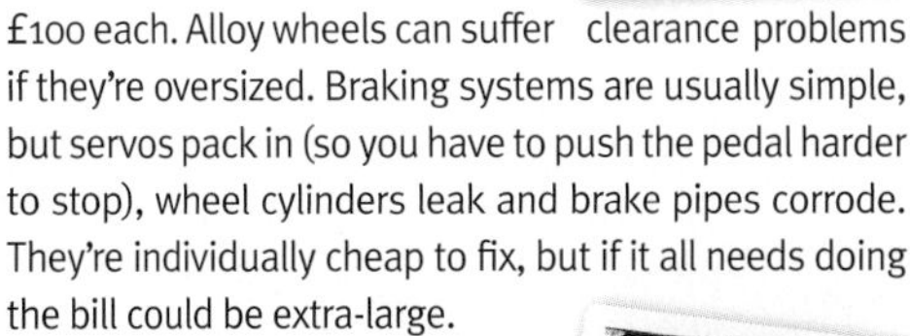

9 Pressed steel wheels rust, while wires suffer from worn splines and damaged spokes – replacements are around £60-£100 each. Alloy wheels can suffer clearance problems if they're oversized. Braking systems are usually simple, but servos pack in (so you have to push the pedal harder to stop), wheel cylinders leak and brake pipes corrode. They're individually cheap to fix, but if it all needs doing the bill could be extra-large.

10 Most classics have simple electrics, but problems can arise from poor earths, dodgy connections and brittle looms. Looms are cheap but fitting is tricky, while sourcing components such as switchgear and instrumentation can be impossible. If any upgrades have been carried out (such as an alternator conversion or extra spotlights etc), make sure the work has been done properly. Also check there's no chafing anywhere; electrical shorts could lead to a conflagration.

HOW TO BUY AT AUCTION

You coud pick up a bargain at a classic car auction. Or you could get carried away and bid away too much... Here's how to get it right

Words: David Lillywhite

Choose your sale
The big-name sales aren't generally the places to buy common-or-garden classics, they're all about big cars for big money. But if one does sneak in, you might find it tacked on the end, when the big guns have headed home. Time for a bargain? Generally, though, the provincial sales are bargain territory.

Decide what you're after
Don't be too random about your buying target because you must do your homework before a sale. You need to know the model's potential weak points – don't be embarrassed to take crib notes.

Get a catalogue
Order an auction catalogue as early as possible, to give yourself plenty of time for your research. Mark off a selection of cars that appeal, but don't set your heart on them.

Decide how much to pay
Set yourself a limit. And stick to it! Do not get carried away!

Give yourself plenty of time
Find out the viewing times and get there early to check out the cars in peace, before the hoards arrive.

Remember to register
Classic mistake. You spot the car you want, you try to bid, but you haven't regsitered with the auction house. You'll need to give bank details and show proof of identity (passport or driving licence).

Check the car's documents
The auction staff will hold all the documentation for the cars. If you're lucky there might be contact details for an old owner – ring them! You want lots of history, receipts, MoTs, etc.

Question the auction staff
The staff will know more about the history. Some might have driven the car you're interested in.

Be sneaky
Don't be polite – listen in on the conversations of other potential buyers to see if they mention any faults or let drop how much they're willing to pay. When you're bidding, postion yourself where you can see the other bidders.

Don't bid first!
And if no-one bids, seek out the auctioneer after the sale.

Be ready to walk away
There will always be another one!

Don't leave early though
If you stay to the bitter end, the casual buyers will have left or tired of the action and you might just pick up a bargain.

Don't assume the sale is over
Sometimes it's not clear to a novice whether or not a car has sold. If the auctioneer hasn't declared a sale then it's not sold – find him afterwards for a deal.

Plan ahead
Think about how you'll get a car home if you are successful. You'll need insurance or transportation, for example. Good luck!

ABARTH
Fiat 750 Zagato

Carlo Abarth's 750 Zagato GT first appeared at the Geneva Motor Show in 1956 and immediately caused a storm. The pretty little coupe and roadster was based on the Fiat 500's running gear, but was powered by a tuned version of the Abarth 747cc engine in high-compression form, delivering 47bhp. Later versions were available with a twin-cam head which was enough to take the featherweight sports car to a top speed of 118mph and on to success in motorsport, including a class win at Mille Miglia in 1957.

SPECIFICATIONS

Years produced:	1957-1961
Performance:	0-60mph: 15.8 secs (Top speed: 95mph)
Power & torque:	44bhp / 44lb/ft
Engine:	Normally aspirated 747cc in-line four, petrol, carburettor, eight valves
Drivetrain:	Rear-engine RWD
Suspension:	(F) Independent, trailing arms; (R) Independent, coil springs
Bodyframe:	Chassis and separate body
Transmission:	Four-speed manual
Weight:	535kgs
	PRICE GUIDE
Launch price:	£2248
Excellent:	£37,500
Good:	£32,500
Average:	£20,000
Project:	£12,500

ABARTH
595/595SS/695SS

Carlo Abarth cut his performance car teeth on the rear-engined Fiat 500, producing some of Italy's finest pocket rockets. Although based on one of the slowest cars you could buy, the Abarth was every inch a Mini Cooper rival during the 1960s, with the bored-out 695 version packing a 40bhp punch. Abarths feature extrovert styling and, on the right road, will give much more powerful cars a real run for their money. Very rare and relatively valuable in the UK, and well worth seeking out if you like your thrills served on the raw side.

SPECIFICATIONS

Years produced:	1963-1971
Performance:	0-60mph: N/A (Top speed: N/A)
Power & torque:	30bhp / 33lb/ft
Engine:	Normally aspirated 593cc, petrol, carburettor, four valves
Drivetrain:	Rear-engine RWD
Suspension:	(F) Independent, transverse leaf spring; (R) Independent, coil spring
Bodyframe:	Chassis and separate body
Transmission:	Four-speed manual
Weight:	500kgs
	PRICE GUIDE
Launch price:	Not known
Excellent:	£9500
Good:	£7500
Average:	£5000
Project:	£2500

AC
2-litre

After the war ended, AC resumed the building of low-volume quality cars with this gently sporting 2-litre saloon. A four-door was added to the range for 1953, by which time the already ageing triple-carb AC engine's output had risen from 74bhp to 85bhp. Bodies are aluminium over a wood frame and steel chassis; suspension also harks back to days past with solid axles and transverse leaf springs at each end of the car. At least the dampers are hydraulic: an AC first. Cable rear brakes are fitted to early cars, with an all-hydraulic system from 1951.

SPECIFICATIONS

Years produced:	1947-1958 (1284 in total)
Performance:	0-60mph: 19.9 secs (Top speed: 80mph)
Power & torque:	74bhp / 105lb/ft
Engine:	Normally aspirated 1991cc in-line six, petrol, carburettor, 12 valves
Drivetrain:	Front-engine RWD
Suspension:	(F) Beam axle, semi-elliptic leaf spring; (R) Beam axle, semi-elliptic leaf spring
Bodyframe:	Chassis and separate body
Transmission:	Four-speed manual
Weight:	1222kgs
	PRICE GUIDE
Launch price:	£1277
Excellent:	£12,000
Good:	£10,000
Average:	£4500
Project:	£2000

AC
2-Litre DHC/Buckland

Straightforward drophead version of the saloon was only in production a year, so few were built and all went for export – though most were still right-hand drive. You are more likely to come across one of the Buckland tourers, whose bodies were built by a coachbuilder of that name. These were a lot prettier, with more rounded lines and a fold-flat windscreen. Later examples also got cutaway doors for an even more sporting look, though mechanically they were identical to the saloons. Quite hard to find, but not usually that expensive when you do.

SPECIFICATIONS

Years produced:	1949-1956
Performance:	0-60mph: 19.9 secs (Top speed: 80mph)
Power & torque:	74bhp / 100lb/ft
Engine:	Normally aspirated 1991cc in-line six, petrol, carburettor, 12 valves
Drivetrain:	Front-engine RWD
Suspension:	(F) Beam axle, semi-elliptic leaf springs; (R) Beam axle, semi-elliptic leaf springs
Bodyframe:	Chassis and separate body
Transmission:	Four-speed manual
Weight:	1320kgs
	PRICE GUIDE
Launch price:	Not known
Excellent:	£22,500
Good:	£17,500
Average:	£12,000
Project:	£6000

AC
Ace (AC engine)

Designed to raise AC's post-war profile, and to tap into America's new-found enthusiasm for Brit sports cars. The simple but pretty aluminium body clothed a tube-frame chassis with all-independent suspension that gave excellent handling and stole a march over rivals like Jaguar – even if it was by transverse leaf springs. Finned aluminium drum brakes gradually gave way to discs around 1958. Only the engine disappointed. It was AC's own, but had been in production since the 1920s; output grew from 85bhp to 105bhp, but the car needed more.

SPECIFICATIONS

Years produced:	1951-1962 (223 in total)
Performance:	0-60mph: 9.5 secs (Top speed: 112mph)
Power & torque:	85bhp / 110lb/ft
Engine:	Normally aspirated 1991cc in-line six, petrol, carburettor, 12 valves
Drivetrain:	Front-engine RWD
Suspension:	(F) Independent, transverse leaf spring; (R) Independent, transverse leaf spring
Bodyframe:	Chassis and separate body
Transmission:	Four-speed manual
Weight:	762kgs
	PRICE GUIDE
Launch price:	£1439
Excellent:	£85,000
Good:	£70,000
Average:	£50,000
Project:	£27,500

AC
Aceca-AC

Introduced for 1955, the Aceca was a grand touring coupé version of the Ace, offering more luxury than the roadster that fully justified its extra cost. The basic chassis followed the lines of the Ace, but with heavier-duty main rails, an extra crossmember and rubber mountings for the differential to reduce the amount of road noise transmitted to the cabin. For similar reasons, glassfibre front and rear bulkheads were used. Rather than the tubes of the Ace, doors and tailgate were wood-framed in the traditional manner. Only 151 examples were built.

SPECIFICATIONS

Years produced: 1954-1963 (151 in total)
Performance: 0-60mph: 13.4 secs (Top speed: 102mph)
Power & torque: 85bhp / 110lb/ft
Engine: Normally aspirated 1991cc in-line six, petrol, carburettor, 12 valves
Drivetrain: Front-engine RWD
Suspension: (F) Independent, transverse leaf spring; (R) Independent, transverse leaf spring
Bodyframe: Chassis and separate body
Transmission: Four-speed manual
Weight: 890kgs

PRICE GUIDE

Launch price: £1439
Excellent: £50,000
Good: £40,000
Average: £22,500
Project: £15,000

AC
Ace-Bristol

From 1956, all those who had criticised the Ace for its lack of power got an answer (though it was to be the first of many): Bristol's six-cylinder unit of similar capacity was bought in. A slightly newer but more sophisticated design, most were supplied in 128bhp spec, though a few were delivered with 125 or even 105bhp. The better Bristol gearbox was also used, with overdrive a popular option. They were sold at a price premium alongside other Aces and one was driven to the 1959 Le Mans 24 Hours, winning the 2-litre class and finishing seventh overall.

SPECIFICATIONS

Years produced: 1956-1962 (463 in total)
Performance: 0-60mph: 9.1 secs (Top speed: 118mph)
Power & torque: 125bhp / 123lb/ft
Engine: Normally aspirated 1971cc in-line six, petrol, carburettor, 12 valves
Drivetrain: Front-engine RWD
Suspension: (F) Independent, transverse leaf spring; (R) Independent, transverse leaf spring
Bodyframe: Chassis and separate body
Transmission: Four-speed manual
Weight: 894kgs

PRICE GUIDE

Launch price: £2011
Excellent: £100,000
Good: £85,000
Average: £65,000
Project: £35,000

AC
Aceca-Bristol

In line with the Ace, a Bristol-engined version of the Aceca was added from 1956. Though markedly more expensive than the AC-engined car, it was a much better performer and outsold the lesser car, with 169 leaving the factory. As with all Acecas, you get details like two rows of four louvres in the bonnet, burr walnut instrument surrounds and glovebox lid and hinged rear side windows to aid ventilation. Though the car was directly related to the Ace, and had a similar nose and grill, no body panels are the same on both cars.

SPECIFICATIONS

Years produced: 1956-1963 (169 in total)
Performance: 0-60mph: 10.3 secs (Top speed: 115mph)
Power & torque: 105bhp / 123lb/ft
Engine: Normally aspirated 1971cc in-line six, petrol, carburettor, 12 valves
Drivetrain: Front-engine RWD
Suspension: (F) Independent, transverse leaf spring; (R) Independent, transverse leaf spring
Bodyframe: Chassis and separate body
Transmission: Four-speed manual
Weight: 895kgs

PRICE GUIDE

Launch price: £1722
Excellent: £55,000
Good: £45,000
Average: £25,000
Project: £17,500

AC
Greyhound

This stylish and dignified four-seater big brother to the Aceca was also panelled in aluminium and came with all the same engine choices, though in reality most ordered used the Bristol straight-six, either in 2-litre or 2.2 form. No more than three are thought to have got the Zephyr 2.6. Despite a change to coil springs for independent suspension, handling isn't a match for the Aceca, and though only a quarter as many were built as the smaller car, they have never set the market alight in the same way and can be bought for about half as much.

SPECIFICATIONS

Years produced: 1959-1963 (83 in total)
Performance: 0-60mph: 12.7 secs (Top speed: 104mph)
Power & torque: 125bhp / 132lb/ft
Engine: Normally aspirated 1971cc in-line six, petrol, carburettor, 12 valves
Drivetrain: Front-engine RWD
Suspension: (F) Independent, wishbone, coil spring; (R) ndependent, semi-trailing link
Bodyframe: Chassis and separate body
Transmission: Four-speed manual
Weight: 991kgs

PRICE GUIDE

Launch price: £2891
Excellent: £25,000
Good: £20,000
Average: £12,500
Project: £7000

AC
Ace RS 2.6

Introduced in 1961 and originally a Ruddspeed conversion – hence the 'RS' – this used the cheap and cheerful 2.6-litre six-cylinder engine from a MkII Ford Zephyr. Depending on which state of tune the customer ordered, output could be up to 170bhp (Stage 3, with aluminium head and triple Webers). Even in that most potent form it was still cheaper then the Bristol-engined Ace. Now the most valuable Ace, only 37 were built and are recognised by a new nose and grille that would soon adorn Cobras – along with a further eight Aceca coupés.

SPECIFICATIONS

Years produced: 1961-1963 (37 in total)
Performance: 0-60mph: N/A (Top speed: 120mph)
Power & torque: 100bhp / 133lb/ft
Engine: Normally aspirated 2553cc in-line six, petrol, carburettor, 12 valves
Drivetrain: Front-engine RWD
Suspension: (F) Independent, transverse leaf spring; (R) Independent, transverse leaf spring
Bodyframe: Monocoque
Transmission: Four-speed manual
Weight: 813kgs

PRICE GUIDE

Launch price: Not known
Excellent: £110,000
Good: £95,000
Average: £70,000
Project: £40,000

AC
Cobra 289

Carroll Shelby's big idea outsold the Ace it was based on, with most going to the US and none to the UK until 1964. The first 75 used 4.2-litre Ford V8s, and these and the next 51 4.7 versions had cam-and-peg steering; after that it was much improved rack-and-pinion. Ace chassis is beefed up to cope, but with all that power, handling can be entertaining. Cobra 289s are distinguished by the flat faces to their flared arches, though there were 27 AC 289s (no Cobra in name) built from mid-1966 with the big-arched Cobra 427 bodyshell and coil-sprung chassis.

SPECIFICATIONS
Years produced: 1961-1965 (673 in total)
Performance: 0-60mph: 5.5 secs (Top speed: 138mph)
Power & torque: 260bhp / 269lb/ft
Engine: Normally aspirated 4261cc V8, petrol, carburettor, 16 valves
Drivetrain: Front-engine RWD
Suspension: (F) Independent, transverse leaf-spring; (R) Independent, transverse leaf-spring
Bodyframe: Chassis and glassfibre body
Transmission: Four-speed manual
Weight: 952kgs
PRICE GUIDE
Launch price: £2454
Excellent: £300,000
Good: £250,000
Average: £185,000
Project: £150,000

AC
Cobra 427

A complete reworking of the Cobra's chassis was required for the installation of Ford's 'big block' 7-litre V8s, most of which were 427ci in various states of tune, though some were sold with smaller-bore/longer-stroke 428ci engines. Chassis tubes were larger, with more crossmembers, and suspension was unequal-length wishbones with coil springs. The body changed, with bulging rear wings to cover much larger tyres and aggressive flares on the front wings. The 31 427 S/C (Semi Competition) models are particularly sought after and valuable.

SPECIFICATIONS
Years produced: 1965-1967 (413 in total)
Performance: 0-60mph: 4.2 secs (Top speed: 165mph)
Power & torque: 410bhp / 480lb/ft
Engine: Normally aspirated 6997cc V8, petrol, carburettor, 16 valves
Drivetrain: Front-engine RWD
Suspension: (F) Independent, wishbone, coil spring; (R) Independent, wishbone, coil spring
Bodyframe: Chassis and separate body
Transmission: Five-speed manual
Weight: 1147kgs
PRICE GUIDE
Launch price: Not known
Excellent: £375,000
Good: £300,000
Average: £225,000
Project: £175,000

AC
428

Heavy-hitter from Thames Ditton uses a six-inch-extended Cobra chassis clothed in bodywork – steel this time – by Frua from Turin. Passing resemblance to Frua's Maserati Mistral, but only handles and door-glass frames are shared. Engine is the 7-litre Ford Galaxie V8 used in some Cobras, but the 428 was still no bargain. The cost of the bodies and shipping chassis to and from Italy meant prices were 20% higher than for Astons and Jensen Interceptors. The AC simply wasn't special enough to justify that and only 51 coupés were sold in six years.

SPECIFICATIONS
Years produced: 1967-1973 (51 in total)
Performance: 0-60mph: 5.4 secs (Top speed: 145mph)
Power & torque: 345bhp / 462lb/ft
Engine: Normally aspirated 7010cc V8, petrol, carburettor, 16 valves
Drivetrain: Front-engine RWD
Suspension: (F) Independent, wishbone, coil spring; (R) Independent, wishbone, coil spring
Bodyframe: Chassis and separate body
Transmission: Three-speed automatic
Weight: 1483kgs
PRICE GUIDE
Launch price: £4250
Excellent: £35,000
Good: £30.000
Average: £17,500
Project: £11,000

AC
428 Convertible

Soft-top version of the Frua-styled Mistral lookalike is even rarer than the coupé with just 29 of them finding homes between 1969 and '73. A phenomenal performer, with sub-six-second 0-60 times, even in more popular auto form, they somehow manage to feel lazy and laid-back at the same time. Excellent chassis makes sure it is more than a dragster, with neutral handling, almost too much feedback from the rack-and-pinion steering, plus great stopping power from Girling discs and twin servos. Only the rather bland interior is likely to disappoint.

SPECIFICATIONS
Years produced: 1967-1973 (29 in total)
Performance: 0-60mph: 5.9 secs (Top speed: 145mph)
Power & torque: 345bhp / 462lb/ft
Engine: Normally aspirated 7010cc V8, petrol, carburettor, 16 valves
Drivetrain: Front-engine RWD
Suspension: (F) Ind. coil spring, double wishbone; (R) Ind. coil spring, double wishbone
Bodyframe: Chassis and separate body
Transmission: Three-speed automatic
Weight: 1483kgs
PRICE GUIDE
Launch price: £4250
Excellent: £55,000
Good: £45,000
Average: £27,500
Project: £17,500

AC
3000ME

An attempt to lift sales by building something more affordable saw AC mid-mounting a Ford V6 transversely over a custom-made transmission. That was one problem: the engine's heavy weight and less-than-sporting output meant only 120mph. Delays in getting it into production saw the 3000ME pitched against the similarly-priced Lotus Esprit. Those volume sales never materialised, with only around 100 built, including a short-lived revival in 1984-85 when licenced to a Scottish factory. Good survival rate and those cars have a keen following.

SPECIFICATIONS
Years produced: 1979-1984 (100 approx in total)
Performance: 0-60mph: 8.5 secs (Top speed: 120mph)
Power & torque: 138bhp / 192lb/ft
Engine: Normally aspirated 2994cc V6, petrol, carburettor, 12 valves
Drivetrain: Mid-engine RWD
Suspension: (F) Independent, wishbone, coil spring; (R) Independent, wishbone, coil spring
Bodyframe: Chassis and glassfibre body
Transmission: Five-speed manual
Weight: 1128kgs
PRICE GUIDE
Launch price: £12,432
Excellent: £10,500
Good: £9000
Average: £6500
Project: £4250

AC
Cobra MkIV

Cobra purists tend to look down their noses at the MkIV, claiming that they're not the real thing at all, but merely a very nice kit car. And it's true – these steel-bodied Cobras don't have originality on their side, having been treated to a programme of improvements. If anything, that makes these a much more appealing proposition if you want to actually go out and use your Cobra. Relatively speaking, these are civilised cars with much better build quality than their 1960s forebears and, at current values, that makes them a bargain.

SPECIFICATIONS

Years produced: 1983-1989
Performance: 0-60mph: 5.3 secs (Top speed: 134mph)
Power & torque: 320bhp / 385lb/ft
Engine: Supercharged 4942cc V8, petrol, electronic fuel injection, 16 valves
Drivetrain: Front-engine RWD
Suspension: (F) Independent, double wishbone; (R) Independent, double wishbone
Bodyframe: Spaceframe
Transmission: Five-speed manual
Weight: N/A

PRICE GUIDE

Launch price: £25,000
Excellent: £60,000
Good: £50,000
Average: £35,000
Project: £27,500

ALFA ROMEO
Giulietta Sprint

Unusually, it was the coupé version of the Giulietta line that appeared on the market first. The floorpan would prove adaptable, as the sheer number of variations that subsequently appear bears testimony to, but for many, this remains the most desirable of the mainstream factory cars. From the beginning of its run, the Bertone-styled coupe was treated to a range of exciting twin-cams; even the original 1290cc version packed a respectable 65bhp, and enjoyed revving away. The later Veloce and SS versions boasted anything up to 100bhp.

SPECIFICATIONS

Years produced: 1954-1962 (27,142 in total)
Performance: 0-60mph: 13.0 secs (Top speed: 101mph)
Power & torque: 80bhp / 72lb/ft
Engine: Normally aspirated 1290cc in-line four, petrol, carburettor, eight valves
Drivetrain: Front-engine RWD
Suspension: (F) Independent wheels, transverse arms, coil springs, anti-roll bar. (R) Beam axle, trailing arm, central A-arm
Bodyframe: Monocoque
Trans/weight: Four-speed manual/860kgs

PRICE GUIDE

Launch price: £2261
Excellent: £15,000
Good: £12,000
Average: £6500
Project: £3000

ALFA ROMEO
Giulietta Spider

Like its coupé sister, the Spider's body was styled by Bertone, and was an object lesson in Italian style and understatement. Great to drive in all forms, and still in demand today. As with the rest of the family, rust was (and is) a serious factor in its survival rate, and the condition of the bodywork and chassis are of paramount importance. There are problems with the engine, too (such as head gasket issues), but as just about all of the mechanical bits are still readily available off-the-shelf, fixing the oily bits should be easy in comparison.

SPECIFICATIONS

Years produced: 1955-1962 (17,096 in total)
Performance: 0-60mph: 11.8 secs (Top speed: 113mph)
Power & torque: 80bhp / 72lb/ft
Engine: Normally aspirated 1290cc in-line four, petrol, carburettor, 16 valves
Drivetrain: Front-engine RWD
Suspension: (F) Independent, coil spring. (R) Beam axle, coil spring
Bodyframe: Monocoque
Transmission Four-speed manual
Weight: 860kgs

PRICE GUIDE

Launch price: £2116
Excellent: £22,500
Good: £18,500
Average: £9500
Project: £4500

ALFA ROMEO
Giulietta Berlina

These saloons might have hit the market during the mid-1950s, but they enjoyed an advanced specification and were built with the sporting driver in mind. In typical Alfa style, the Berlina started out powered by a modest engine, but with each new season, or so it seemed, a more powerful variation was shoehorned in. The pick of the crop ended up being the 75bhp Ti version, which ticked all of the important sporting saloon boxes. Sadly, the survival rate is very low, with the main culprits being damp climates and rabid rust.

SPECIFICATIONS

Years produced: 1955-1963 (39,057 in total)
Performance: 0-60mph: 17.7 secs (Top speed: 98mph)
Power & torque: 63bhp / 69lb/ft
Engine: Normally aspirated 1290cc in-line four, petrol, carburettor, eight valves
Drivetrain: Front-engine RWD
Suspension: (F) Independent, transverse arms, coil spring, anti-roll bar. (R) Rigid axle, trailing arm, central A-arm, coil spring
Bodyframe: Monocoque
Trans/weight: Four-speed manual/870kgs

PRICE GUIDE

Launch price: £1726
Excellent: £6500
Good: £5000
Average: £3000
Project: £800

ALFA ROMEO
Giulietta/Giulia Sprint Speciale

The Series 101 Giulietta was the first Alfa to be made available in Sprint Speciale form, but when the 105-Series Giulia followed on in 1962, these SS series Alfas really came into their own. Now powered by a 1570cc twin-cam, performance from these coupes and convertibles was something rather special. The most easily identifiable part of the SS was its bonnet bulge, to clear the slightly taller engine. Today, these are the Giulias that everyone wants, a fact reflected in their very strong values.

SPECIFICATIONS

Years produced: 1957-1962 (1366/1400 in total)
Performance: 0-60mph: 11.2 secs (Top speed: 122mph)
Power & torque: 106bhp / 83lb/ft
Engine: Normally aspirated 1290cc in-line four, petrol, carburettor, eight valves
Drivetrain: Front-engine RWD
Suspension: (F) Independent wheels, transverse arms, coil spring, anti-roll bar. (R) Rigid axle, trailing arm, central A-arm
Bodyframe: Monocoque
Trans/weight: Five-speed manual/785kgs

PRICE GUIDE

Launch price: £2721
Excellent: £25,000
Good: £20,000
Average: £11,000
Project: £6000

ALFA ROMEO
2000/2600 Spider

Although there's a strong family resemblance with the Giulietta, the in-line six-cylinder 2000/2600 harks back to the previous generation Alfa Romeo 1900. The elegant styling was by Touring and reflected its role as the grand tourer that sat at the top of the range – and its high price was justified by its 2+2 seating layout, detachable hardtop and five-speed gearbox. Performance was seriously improved with the arrival of the 2600cc version in 1962, with the top speed now a seriously impressive 125mph. Rare and expensive, too.

SPECIFICATIONS	
Years produced:	1958-1965 (2255 in total)
Performance:	0-60mph: 10.9 secs (Top speed: 124mph)
Power & torque:	145bhp / 156lb/ft
Engine:	Normally aspirated 2584cc in-line six, petrol, carburettor, 12 valves
Drivetrain:	Front-engine RWD
Suspension:	(F) Independent wheels, transverse arms, coil spring, anti-roll bar. (R) Rigid axle, trailing beams, central A-arm
Bodyframe:	Monocoque
Trans/weight:	Five-speed manual/1257kgs
PRICE GUIDE	
Launch price:	£2979
Excellent:	£25,000
Good:	£20,000
Average:	£10,000
Project:	£5000

ALFA ROMEO
Giulia Spider

The Spider is an anomaly in the classic car world. Not because there's anything wrong with it, or because it was a commercial failure, but simply because despite its good looks and excellent performance it lags behind its tin-top sister in terms of values. That's good news if you're looking for a Touring-bodied open-topped Alfa Giulia, even if its rarity today means your search will be long. Rust is a serious issue with these cars, and they suffer from it far more readily than the coupes and saloons. All versions are good to drive.

SPECIFICATIONS	
Years produced:	1962-1965 (10,341 in total)
Performance:	0-60mph: 11.8 secs (Top speed: 106mph)
Power & torque:	91bhp / 80lb/ft
Engine:	Normally aspirated 1570cc in-line four, petrol, carburettor, eight valves
Drivetrain:	Front-engine RWD
Suspension:	(F) Independent, transverse arms, coil spring, anti-roll bar. (R) Rigid axle, trailing arm, central A-arm
Bodyframe:	Monocoque
Trans/weight:	Five-speed manual/960kgs
PRICE GUIDE	
Launch price:	£1729
Excellent:	£25,000
Good:	£20,000
Average:	£10,000
Project:	£4500

ALFA ROMEO
2600 Sprint

The 2600 Sprint was the ultimate incarnation of the twin-cam in-line six. Still considered very much a grand tourer, the coupe lacked the agility of its smaller cousins, despite its sports car looks. The torquey straight-six made this a car for covering continents – despite its prodigious straight-line pace. Significant because, along with the Gordon-Keeble GK1, this was one of Giorgetto Giugiaro's first designs, laying the foundations for a significant career ahead. Unlike the more mainstream Alfas, parts are not so readily available.

SPECIFICATIONS	
Years produced:	1962-1966 (700/6999 in total)
Performance:	11.7 secs (Top speed: 117mph)
Power & torque:	145bhp / 156lb/ft
Engine:	Normally aspirated 2584cc in-line six, petrol, carburettor, 12 valves
Drivetrain:	Front-engine RWD
Suspension:	(F) Independent wheels, transverse arms, coil spring, anti-roll bar. (R) Rigid axle, trailing beams, central A-arm
Bodyframe:	Monocoque
Transmission:	Five-speed Manual/1361kgs
PRICE GUIDE	
Launch price:	£2806
Excellent:	£12,000
Good:	£9500
Average:	£4500
Project:	£2250

ALFA ROMEO
Giulia Sprint

A hot little number right now, these 'Step front' Giulia coupes are very much in demand because of their good looks, driving experience and ease of tuning. Values have increased significantly in recent years, bolstered by the desirability of the GTA. When launched, the twin-cam 1600cc versions were quick from the box, but subsequent versions (1750cc and 2000cc) added even more excitement to the mix. Offered in a bewildering array of models, the advice is to go for the example with the best body you can find and worry about the mechanicals after that.

SPECIFICATIONS	
Years produced:	1962-1966 (21,850 in total)
Performance:	0-60mph: 11.2 secs (Top speed: 107mph)
Power & torque:	92bhp / 87lb/ft
Engine:	Normally aspirated 1570cc in-line four, petrol, carburettor, eight valves
Drivetrain:	Front-engine RWD
Suspension:	(F) Independent, wishbone, coil spring, anti-roll bar. (R) Radius arms, trailing arms, coil spring, anti-roll bar
Bodyframe:	Monocoque
Trans/weight:	Five-speed manual/905kgs
PRICE GUIDE	
Launch price:	£1650
Excellent:	£14,000
Good:	£11,000
Average:	£6500
Project:	£2750

ALFA ROMEO
Giulia 1300/1600 Ti/Super

The boxy 105-Series Giulia might not look like the most exciting saloon on the planet, but underneath that plain-Jane exterior beats the heart of a truly sporting saloon. Given the lusty twin-cams, five-speed gearbox and well set-up chassis it's easy to see why Alfa Romeo was so annoyed by the way their cars were depicted being outrun by the Mini Coopers in *The Italian Job.* Despite its rarity today, the Giulia was a massive success when new, with much of that founded on being so good to drive. Well worth seeking out.

SPECIFICATIONS	
Years produced:	1962-1971 (836,323 in total)
Performance:	0-60mph: 11.8 secs (Top speed: 117mph)
Power & torque:	92bhp / 108lb/ft
Engine:	Normally aspirated 1570cc in-line four, petrol, carburettor, eight valves
Drivetrain:	Front-engine RWD
Suspension:	(f) Independent, transverse arm, oblique beam, coil springs, anti-roll bar. (R) Rigid axle, trailing arms
Bodyframe:	Monocoque
Trans/weight:	Five-speed manual/1016kgs
PRICE GUIDE	
Launch price:	£1659
Excellent:	£8250
Good:	£6500
Average:	£3250
Project:	£1250

ALFA ROMEO
Giulia Sprint GTA

The GTA might look like your standard Sprint GT, but it makes extensive use of aluminium body panels. The reason for this was simple – the GTA was built for racing and wherever possible weight saving was applied. The A in its name means Alleggerita, Italian for lightened, and even the sump, camshaft cover, timing cover and clutch housing were replaced by featherweight magnesium alloy items, just to save a few extra kilos. For additional performance, the engine gained a new twin-plug cylinder head. Today, it's considered a legend.

SPECIFICATIONS

Years produced: 1965-1969
Performance: 0-60mph: N/A (Top speed: 115mph)
Power & torque: 115bhp / 105lb/ft
Engine: Normally aspirated 1570cc in-line four, petrol, carburettor, eight valves
Drivetrain: Front-engine RWD
Suspension: (F) Independent wheels, transverse arms, oblique beam, coil spring, anti-roll bar (R) Rigid axle, trailing arm
Bodyframe: Monocoque
Trans/weight: Five-speed manual/820kgs

PRICE GUIDE

Launch price: £2128
Excellent: £40,000
Good: £35,000
Average: £25,000
Project: £14,000

ALFA ROMEO
Spider 1600 Duetto

Forever associated with Dustin Hoffman in *The Graduate*, the stylish little Duetto didn't hang around for too long at all. In 1966 the pretty little Pininfarina-styled roadster appeared as the final genuinely new variation of the 105-Series platform and was marked out by its enclosed headlamps and boat-tail rear end. Powered by the 1570cc twin-cam it was a gem to drive with great handling, sharp steering and excellent stopping from its all-round discs. It was also quicker than an MGB, although considerably more expensive in the UK.

SPECIFICATIONS

Years produced: 1966-1968 (6325 in total)
Performance: 0-60mph: 13.2 secs (Top speed: 102mph)
Power & torque: 110bhp / 101lb/ft
Engine: Normally aspirated 1570cc in-line four, petrol, carburettor, eight valves
Drivetrain: Front-engine RWD
Suspension: (F) Independent wheels, transverse arms, oblique beams, coil spring, anti-roll bar. (R) Rigid axle, trailing arm
Bodyframe: Monocoque
Trans/weight Five-speed manual/990kgs

PRICE GUIDE

Launch price: £1749
Excellent: £11,000
Good: £9250
Average: £6500
Project: £2750

ALFA ROMEO
Giulia GT Junior 1300/1600

Due to the complexity of the 105-Series Giulia range the easiest way of relating to the GT Junior is to think of it as the entry-level model. That means it initially came with a 1300cc engine and simplified interior, and gave sporting Italians the chance to own a Giulia Sprint GT lookalike without the fiscal implications. Over time it was developed in parallel with the larger engined cars, and in 1970 it lost its characteristic step-front. After that, in 1972, a 1600cc Junior was introduced to close the gap in the range to the 2000cc GTV.

SPECIFICATIONS

Years produced: 1966-1977 (92,053 in total)
Performance: 11.1 secs (Top speed: 109mph)
Power & torque: 103bhp / 104lb/ft
Engine: Normally aspirated 1290cc in-line four, petrol, carburettor, eight valves
Drivetrain: Front-engine RWD
Suspension: (F) Independent wheels, transverse arms, oblique beam, coil spring, anti-roll bar. (R) Rigid axle, trailing arm
Bodyframe: Monocoque
Trans/weight: Five-speed manual/990kgs

PRICE GUIDE

Launch price: £1749
Excellent: £9250
Good: £7250
Average: £3750
Project: £1650

ALFA ROMEO
1750/2000 GTV

To ally itself with the launch of the 1750 Berlina, the Giulia Sprint was facelifted to become the 1750 GTV coupe. It retained the original GT1300/GT Junior 1.6 bodyshell but gained a quad-headlight front end and cleaner external trim details (as well as losing the 'step front'). The revised interior was an ergonomic improvement, although purists prefer the older design. The 1779cc four cylinder was now the base power unit for the non-Junior line, meaning lusty performance. These later models are considered to be the easiest cars to live.

SPECIFICATIONS

Years produced: 1967-1969 (44,269/37,459 in total)
Performance: 0-60mph: 11.2 secs (Top speed: 118mph)
Power & torque: 122bhp / 137lb/ft
Engine: Normally aspirated 1779cc in-line four, petrol, carburettor, eight valves
Drivetrain: Front-engine RWD
Suspension: (F) Independent wheels, transverse arms, oblique beam, coil spring, anti-roll bar. (R) Rigid axle, trailing arm
Bodyframe: Monocoque
Trans/weight: Five-speed manual/1040kgs

PRICE GUIDE

Launch price: £2248
Excellent: £11,000
Good: £9000
Average: £4500
Project: £2000

ALFA ROMEO
Spider 1750 Veloce

After a mere 18 months in production, the gorgeous little Duetto was discontinued to make way for the 1750 Spider Veloce. The newer car wasn't a radical change and really just heralded the arrival of the more potent twin-carb engine and uprated suspension and braking set-up. Also revised for the new car were the wheels and tyres, which makes this one a bit of a spotter's favourite. Although the appealing Duetto name had been dropped, it was very much a case of more of the same. The bigger changes would follow later.

SPECIFICATIONS

Years produced: 1967-1971 (8701 in total)
Performance: 9.2 secs (Top speed: 114mph)
Power & torque: 114bhp / 137lb/ft
Engine: Normally aspirated 1779cc in-line four, petrol, carburettor, eight valves
Drivetrain: Front-engine RWD
Suspension: (F) Independent wheels, transverse arms, oblique beams, coil spring, anti-roll bar. (R) Rigid axle, trailing arm
Bodyframe: Monocoque
Trans/weight: Five-speed manual/1040kgs

PRICE GUIDE

Launch price: £2199
Excellent: £11,000
Good: £9000
Average: £6500
Project: £2500

ALFA ROMEO
1750/2000 Berlina

With Alfa Romeo's new model development concentrated on the 'Sud and Alfetta, the mid-range Giulia saloon was treated to a front and rear makeover and relaunched to become the 1750/2000 Berlina. Although the styling (by Pininfarina) was considered unimaginative, it retained the outgoing car's roomy interior and boot, as well as its driver's car credentials that made the original so appealing. An updated interior and dashboard brought the car usefully up to date. The top of the range 2000cc version with 132bhp was a genuine sports saloon.

SPECIFICATIONS

Years produced: 1967-1977 (101,883 in total)
Performance: 0-60mph: 10.8 secs (Top speed: 116mph)
Power & torque: 122bhp / 139lb/ft
Engine: Normally aspirated 1779cc in-line four, petrol, carburettor, eight valves
Drivetrain: Front-engine RWD
Suspension: (F) Ind. trans. arms, oblique beam, coil springs, anti-roll bar. (R) Rigid axle, trailing arms, T-stabiliser, coil springs
Bodyframe: Monocoque
Trans/weight: Five-speed manual/1110kgs

PRICE GUIDE

Launch price: £1898
Excellent: £5000
Good: £4000
Average: £1850
Project: £800

ALFA ROMEO
Spider 2000 S1/S2

Alfa Romeo couldn't leave its cars alone during the 1960s and '70s, and after just three years in production, revised the 1750 Spider Veloce to become the 2000 Spider. Unlike last time, when the beautiful Pininfarina styling was largely left alone, the 1970 restyle came at the price of an exterior upgrade, as well as the fitment of the lustier 2000cc twin-cam. The boat-tail gave way to a much longer Kamm tail, while the front end saw the removal of the plastic headlamp covers. The overall effect conspired to make the Spider look less streamlined.

SPECIFICATIONS

Years produced: 1969-1982 (22,059 in total)
Performance: 0-60mph: 8.8 secs (Top speed: 123mph)
Power & torque: 131bhp / 134lb/ft
Engine: Normally aspirated 1962cc in-line four, petrol, carburettor, eight valves
Drivetrain: Front-engine RWD
Suspension: (F) Ind. trans. arms, oblique beams, coil springs, anti-roll bar. (R) Rigid axle, trailing arm, T-shaped stabiliser
Bodyframe: Monocoque
Transmission: Five-speed manual/1040kgs

PRICE GUIDE

Launch price: £2439
Excellent: £8750
Good: £7250
Average: £4000
Project: £2000

ALFA ROMEO
1300/1600 Junior Z

An appealing Italian 'bitza' that somehow transcends the sum of its parts. Created by Zagato using the chassis from the Spider and the five-speed gearbox from the Giulietta, the Junior Zagato was an arresting-looking coupe that added real variety to the Alfa Romeo line-up. The sloping front and kamm tail were certainly a world apart from the well-crafted classicism of the rest of the Giulia-derived cars, but no less appealing for it. As it was lighter and more aerodynamic than the standard cars it was usefully quicker.

SPECIFICATIONS

Years produced: 1970-1975 (1108/402 in total)
Performance: 0-60mph: 11.5 secs (Top speed: 118mph)
Power & torque: 125bhp / 115lb/ft
Engine: Normally aspirated 1570cc in-line four, petrol, carburettor, eight valves
Drivetrain: Drivetrain: front-engine RWD
Suspension: (F) Ind. trans. arms, oblique beam, coil springs, anti-roll bar. (R) Rigid axle, trailing arm, T-stabiliser, coil spring
Bodyframe: Monocoque
Trans/weight: Five-speed manual/950kgs

PRICE GUIDE

Launch price: Not known
Excellent: £15,000
Good: £12,000
Average: £7500
Project: £3000

ALFA ROMEO
Montreal

Conceived as a junior league supercar, the Montreal proved to be a commercial failure for Alfa Romeo. It originally appeared at Expo '67 in Montreal (hence the name) as a concept car, and proved so popular the company decided to turn it into a production reality. The small V8, based on the Type 33 race car engine, wasn't really potent enough and although the performance was reasonable it did not match its price rivals. It remained in production throughout the worst of the 1970s, and today is viewed as a seriously desirable classic car.

SPECIFICATIONS

Years produced: 1970-1977 (3925 in total)
Performance: 7.6 secs (Top speed: 137mph)
Power & torque: 200bhp / 173lb/ft
Engine: Normally aspirated 2593cc V8, petrol, carburettor, 16 valves
Drivetrain: Front-engine RWD
Suspension: (F) Ind. trans. arms, oblique beam, long'l. torsion bar, anti-roll bar, coil springs. (R) Beam axle, trail. arm, coil springs
Bodyframe: Monocoque
Trans/weight: Five-speed manual/1267kgs

PRICE GUIDE

Launch price: £5077
Excellent: £16,000
Good: £12,500
Average: £8000
Project: £4000

ALFA ROMEO
Alfasud

When launched in 1972, the Alfasud took the world by surprise. Given that Alfa Romeo had no experience of small, front-driven cars, the sheer dynamic excellence of the flat-four powered 'Sud came as a shock. However, Alfasud was also a government-led experiment in the redistribution of manufacturing (a new factory was built near Naples, where the workforce was hardly skilled in car making). Customers found their new 'Suds would rust, or fall to pieces, overshadowing the great work done by the engineers. A flawed gem.

SPECIFICATIONS

Years produced: 1972-1983 (906,734 in total)
Performance: 0-60mph: 11.8 secs (Top speed: 103mph)
Power & torque: 93bhp / 96lb/ft
Engine: Normally aspirated 1490cc flat four, petrol, carburettor, eight valves
Drivetrain: Front-engine FWD
Suspension: (F) Ind. MacPherson strut, transverse arm, trailing beam, coils, anti-roll bar. (R) Rigid axle, Panhard rod, coil spring
Bodyframe: Monocoque
Trans./weight: Five-speed manual/ 885kgs

PRICE GUIDE

Launch price: £1399
Excellent: £3250
Good: £2500
Average: £1250
Project: £250

ALFA ROMEO
Alfetta GT 1.8/GTV 2000

It was left to Bertone to create a suitably handsome coupe from Alfetta underpinnings. Unsurprisingly, the Italian coachbuilders delivered the goods yet again, allowing buyers a taste of the exotic for a relatively modest outlay. Originally launched as the Alfetta GT in 1779cc twin-cam form, the concept truly came alive when re-engined with the lusty two-litre. Thanks to that transaxle and sophisticated suspension set-up, road manners were impeccable, and remain so today. As always, rust and flimsy build quality are the main enemy.

SPECIFICATIONS

Years produced: 1973-1980 (31,267 in total)
Performance: 0-60mph: 9.3 secs (Top speed: 120mph)
Power & torque: 122bhp / 129lb/ft
Engine: Normally aspirated 1962cc in-line four, petrol, carburettor, eight valves
Drivetrain: Front-engine RWD
Suspension: (F) Ind. trans. arms, oblique beam, long'l. torsion bar, anti-roll bar. (R) Rigid axle, de Dion, oblique arm
Bodyframe: Monocoque
Trans/weight: Five-speed manual/1080kgs

PRICE GUIDE

Launch price: £4799
Excellent: £4000
Good: £3000
Average: £1250
Project: £300

ALFA ROMEO
Alfasud Sprint

The Italians have always been great at turning humdrum family saloons into great sporting coupes. So, when Alfa Romeo turned the rather good 'Sud into a useable small sporting car, the results were predictably sparkling. Styling was handled by Giugiaro, and to many the Sprint successfully eclipsed the already desirable GTV. In twin-carb Veloce form the Sprint was very rapid indeed, but any example will reward the enthusiastic driver. An iffy 1980s facelift did it no favours, though, and fans prefer the crisp original.

SPECIFICATIONS

Years produced: 1976-1990 (96,450 in total)
Performance: 0-60mph: 10.0 secs (Top speed: 105mph)
Power & torque: 84bhp / 89lb/ft
Engine: Normally aspirated 1490cc flat four, petrol, carburettor, eight valves
Drivetrain: Front-engine FWD
Suspension: (F) Ind. MacPherson strut, trans. arm, trailing beam, coil, anti-roll bar. (R) Rigid axle, Panhard rod, coil spring
Bodyframe: Monocoque
Trans/weight: Five-speed manual/915kgs

PRICE GUIDE

Launch price: £3999
Excellent: £3000
Good: £2250
Average: £1100
Project: £275

ALFA ROMEO
Alfetta GTV6

As big Alfa saloons go the Six was not a huge success, but we do owe the existence of one of the best-sounding Alfa Romeos to the failed executive saloon as it donated its wonderful V6 engine to the Alfetta GTV. Running a new Bosch fuel injection system, the V6's power was up to 160bhp, giving the GTV6 a very useful power hike, as well as one of the most sublime soundtracks in motoring history. Like the Alfetta GT and GTV before it the GTV6 was a phenomenally good car in the bends and Alfa's coupe finally had the power to exploit it.

SPECIFICATIONS

Years produced: 1980-1987 (279,821 in total)
Performance: 0-60mph: 8.8 secs (Top speed: 130mph)
Power & torque: 160bhp / 157lb/ft
Engine: Normally aspirated 2492cc V6, petrol, electronic fuel injection, 12 valves
Drivetrain: Front-engine RWD
Suspension: (F) Ind. trans. arms, oblique beam, long'l torsion bar, anti-roll bar. (R) Rigid axle, de Dion, oblique arm, coil
Bodyframe: Monocoque
Trans/weight: Five-speed manual/1210kgs

PRICE GUIDE

Launch price: £9495
Excellent: £4750
Good: £3750
Average: £2000
Project: £450

ALFA ROMEO
Spider 2000 S3/S4

The final restyle of the Spider took place at the beginning of 1990 and it was Pininfarina who had the honour of preparing the Spider for its final days, the car being rounded off with smoother bumpers and slimmer rear light clusters. By this point in time the Spider was almost 30 years old, but the new fuel-injected engines, along with power assisted steering prolonged its life for a further three years. US sales of the S4 Spider remained strong right to the end, with more than 75 per cent of the production run ending up in North America.

SPECIFICATIONS

Years produced: 1982-1993 (18,456 in total)
Performance: 0-60mph: 9.2 secs (Top speed: 119mph)
Power & torque: 120bhp /117lb/ft
Engine: Normally aspirated 1962cc in-line four, petrol, electronic fuel injection, eight valves
Drivetrain: Front-engine RWD
Suspension: (F) Ind. trans. arms, oblique beam, coil spring, anti-roll bar; (R) Rigid axle, trailing arm, T-stabiliser, coil spring
Bodyframe: Monocoque
Trans/weight: Five-speed manual/1110kgs

PRICE GUIDE

Launch price: £15,950
Excellent: £7250
Good: £6000
Average: £3000
Project: £1500

ALFA ROMEO
75 V6

Launched on Alfa Romeo's 75th anniversary, the 75 was a mixture of Giulietta and Alfa 90. Alfa engineered the car to use a transaxle and this gave it almost perfect 50/50 weight distribution. When this was coupled with the melodic V6 engine the 75 became one of the most desirable sporting saloons of the 1980s. The styling was done in-house, following on from the Alfa 33, which had a similar square headlamp and grille arrangement. The 75 also came with a reasonable amount of equipment as standard, but power-steering was extra.

SPECIFICATIONS

Years produced: 1985-1992
Performance: 0-60mph: 9.0 secs (Top speed: 127mph)
Power & torque: 153bhp / 152lb/ft
Engine: Normally aspirated 2492cc V6, petrol, electronic fuel injection, 12 valves
Drivetrain: Front-engine RWD
Suspension: (F) Ind. dbl. wishbone, torsion bar, anti-roll bar; (R) de Dion, Watt linkage, coil springs
Bodyframe: Monocoque
Transmission: Five-speed manual
Weight: 1160kgs

PRICE GUIDE

Launch price: £11,649
Excellent: £2400
Good: £1800
Average: £850
Project: £350

ALFA ROMEO
164 3.0 V6

The 'Type Four' Project resulted in four cars from Alfa Romeo, Lancia, Fiat and Saab all sharing the same floorpan. Alfa Romeo was the only manufacturer to use a different set of doors, all the others shared the pressings to cut costs. The sharp Pininfarina styling also helped to differentiate the Alfa from its cousins, and the V6 could be ordered with a Veloce bodykit. Although not loved by everyone, the Veloce package did make the car stand out, and when it was facelifted in 1991, numerous changes improved the build quality.

SPECIFICATIONS

Years produced: 1988-1993 (3723 in total)
Performance: 0-60mph: 7.7 secs (Top speed: 152mph)
Power & torque: 228bhp / 207lb/ft
Engine: Normally aspirated 2959cc V6, petrol, electronic fuel injection, 24 valves
Drivetrain: Front-engine FWD
Suspension: (F) Ind. MacPherson strut, trans. arm, coil, anti-roll bar. (R) Ind. trans. arms, trailing beam, coil spring, anti-roll bar
Bodyframe: Monocoque
Transmission: Five-speed manual/1530kgs

PRICE GUIDE

Launch price: £20,250
Excellent: £3500
Good: £2500
Average: £850
Project: £250

ALFA ROMEO
SZ/RZ

First conceived as a design study in 1987, the Sprint Zagato looked so good that by 1989 Alfa had the car ready for launch at the Geneva Motor Show. Based on a heavily-modified 75, the SZ had the performance (and sound) to back up its sporty yet unconventional looks. It was the car's ability to hang on in the bends which really made the SZ special and with 1.1G of cornering force you can see why. The RZ (Roadster Zagato) was produced from 1992-end 1993. Only 284 were made, making it highly sought after – not to mention more expensive than the SZ.

SPECIFICATIONS

Years produced: 1989-1994 (998 in total)
Performance: 0-60mph: 6.9 secs (Top speed: 153mph)
Power & torque: 210bhp /181lb/ft
Engine: Normally aspirated 2959cc V6, petrol, electronic fuel injection, 24 valves
Drivetrain: Front-engine RWD
Suspension: (F) Ind. trans. arms, oblique beam, coil springs, anti-roll bar. (R) Rigid axle, de Dion, oblique arm, Watt linkage, coils
Bodyframe: Monocoque
Trans/weight: Five-speed manual/1260kgs

PRICE GUIDE

Launch price: £40,000
Excellent: £21,000
Good: £18,000
Average: £14,500
Project: £12,000

ALFA ROMEO
GTV 2.0i Twin Spark

Eye-watering Italian tax laws for cars over 2-litres meant that the GTV Twin Spark was always going to be the big seller. The 2.0 16-valve engine provided a healthy 150bhp but it did have 'Variable Valve Timing' and 'Variable Inlet Control' to help boost power. The Twin Spark head didn't actually give the GTV any more power, but it increased efficiency. The GTV could hit 60mph in a reasonable eight seconds, but could also manage 35mpg on a gentle run. Dynamically, the lighter front-end of the 2.0 really helped the overall balance.

SPECIFICATIONS

Years produced: 1995-2000
Performance: 0-60mph: 8.0 secs (Top speed: 130mph)
Power & torque: 150bhp / 137lb/ft
Engine: Normally aspirated 1970cc in-line four, petrol, electronic fuel injection, 16 valves
Drivetrain: Front-engine FWD
Suspension: (F) Ind. coil, MacPherson strut, trans. arm, anti-roll bar; (R) Ind. trans. arm, trail. arm, oblique arm, coil spring
Bodyframe: Monocoque
Trans/weight: Five-speed manual,1370kgs

PRICE GUIDE

Launch price: £19,950
Excellent: £5750
Good: £4500
Average: £2750
Project: £1000

ALFA ROMEO
Spider 2.0i Twin Spark

Phased in as a replacement for the Duetto Spider, which dated back to 1966, the new Spider was basically a topless version of the GTV Coupe. The 2.0 Twin Spark engine consisted of a cast iron block and a lightweight 16-valve, alloy head. The idea behind having two spark plugs per cylinder wasn't new, but Alfa Romeo saw the added benefits to overall efficiency with the addition of the smaller, secondary spark plug and developed the new 16-valve engine for the GTV/Spider which was used later in the Alfa 156.

SPECIFICATIONS

Years produced: 1995-2003
Performance: 0-60mph: 9.4 secs (Top speed: 122mph)
Power & torque: 150bhp / 137lb/ft
Engine: Normally aspirated 1970cc in-line four, petrol, electronic fuel injection, 16 valves
Drivetrain: Front-engine FWD
Suspension: (F) Ind. coil, MacPherson strut, trans. arm, anti-roll bar; (R) Ind. trans. arm, trail. arm, oblique arm, coil spring
Bodyframe: Monocoque
Trans/weight: Five-speed manual/1353kgs

PRICE GUIDE

Launch price: £19.950
Excellent: £6250
Good: £5000
Average: £3500
Project: £1750

ALFA ROMEO
GTV 3.0 V6

Although it looked entirely new the GTV was actually based on the Fiat Tempra; the ageing platform was thoroughly updated and improved by Alfa with a clever rear suspension set-up that added a touch of passive rear-steer to the car. All the chassis development in the world couldn't improve the weight distribution though and with the huge V6 up front the GTV tended to understeer. As with all Alfa Romeo V6s, the GTV was putting out healthy performance figures and was surprisingly frugal. Pininfarina was responsible for the design.

SPECIFICATIONS

Years produced: 1997-2000 (5021 in total)
Performance: 6.6 secs (Top speed: 155mph)
Power & torque: 220bhp / 199lb/ft
Engine: Normally aspirated 2959cc V6, petrol, electronic fuel injection, 24 valves
Drivetrain: Front-engine FWD
Suspension: (F) Ind. coil, MacPherson strut, transverse arm, anti-roll bar. (R) Ind. trans. arm, trail. arm, oblique arm, coil spring
Bodyframe: Monocoque
Trans/weight: Six-speed manual/1415kgs

PRICE GUIDE

Launch price: £26,590
Excellent: £7000
Good: £5500
Average: £3500
Project: £2000

ALLARD
L/M

If you enjoy your Allard-shaped kicks with the kids in the back seats then the Allard L and M are just the ticket. Effectively just a K1 with a six-inch wheelbase stretch (to 112in) and a pair of occasional seats in the rear, the additional model in the Allard line-up proved surprisingly popular. The M added some civilities such as coil-sprung suspension and a column gear change. Although most UK cars were fitted with Ford Pilot engines, many were shipped overseas without a powertrain, leaving the owner to chose a more suitable local engine.

SPECIFICATIONS

Years produced: 1946-1950 (191/500 in total)
Performance: 0-60mph: 15.2 secs (Top speed: 82mph)
Power & torque: 85bhp / N/A
Engine: Normally aspirated 3622cc V8, petrol, carburettor, 16 valves
Drivetrain: Front-engine RWD
Suspension: (F) Transverse leaf spring, beam axle. (R) Beam axle, leaf springs
Bodyframe: Chassis and separate body
Transmission: Three-speed manual
Weight: 1396kgs

PRICE GUIDE

Launch price: £1151
Excellent: £37,500
Good: £30,000
Average: £20,000
Project: £11,000

ALLARD
K1/K2

Allard's first post-war sports car was a leap forward. Although it looked ungainly (a subsequent family trait) it was a great car to drive, proving very effective in competition. The technical make-up might have been simple with a box section frame, transverse leaves front and rear and a steel body atop, but careful chassis development was the key. The fitment of a powerful V8 engine (from the Ford Pilot) delivered plenty of effortless performance. The end result was a charismatic English sports car that has a loyal following to this day.

SPECIFICATIONS

Years produced: 1946-1951 (151/119 in total)
Performance: 0-60mph: 13.6 secs (Top speed: 102mph)
Power & torque: 85bhp / 150lb/ft
Engine: Normally aspirated 3622cc V8, petrol, carburettor, 16 valves
Drivetrain: Front-engine RWD
Suspension: (F) Independent, coil springs; (R) Beam axle, transverse leaf spring
Bodyframe: Chassis and separate body
Transmission: Three-speed manual
Weight: 1118kgs

PRICE GUIDE

Launch price: £1277
Excellent: £47,500
Good: £40,000
Average: £25,000
Project: £15,000

ALLARD
P1

Derived from the M 'drophead coupe', the Allard P1 was a hard-topped two-door saloon that broke with tradition for the marque. Although marketed as something of a gentleman's carriage, the Allard P1 couldn't disguise its competition roots, making it an appealing proposition for enthusiastic drivers. Sydney Allard drove one to victory in the 1952 Monte Carlo Rally, making him the only person in the history of the event to win the event in a car bearing his own name. Today, the Allard P commands enviable market values.

SPECIFICATIONS

Years produced: 1949-1951 (559 in total)
Performance: 0-60mph: 15.2 secs (Top speed: 85mph)
Power & torque: 85bhp / 150lb/ft
Engine: Normally aspirated 3622cc V8, petrol, carburettor, 16 valves
Drivetrain: Front-engine RWD
Suspension: (F) Independent, coil springs. (R) Beam axle, transverse leaf springs
Bodyframe: Chassis and separate body
Transmission: Three-speed manual
Weight: 1372kgs

PRICE GUIDE

Launch price: £1277
Excellent: £14,000
Good: £12,000
Average: £8500
Project: £3500

ALLARD
J2/J2X

The most famous of all the Allard racers, and despite their rarity (just 83 were produced) the most likely to come onto the market. It was the J2X that introduced the new method of construction, which employed small chassis tubes and parallel side members attached together to create the chassis frame. It sounds rudimentary, but the results speak for themselves, with the J2 having a particularly successful racing career on both sides of the Atlantic. Suspension was more sophisticated than the earlier cars, ensuring excellent handling.

SPECIFICATIONS

Years produced: 1950-1951 (173 total – 90 J2, 83 J2X)
Performance: 0-60mph: 7.4 secs (Top speed: 111mph)
Power & torque: 120bhp / 221lb/ft
Engine: Normally aspirated 4375cc V8, petrol, carburettor, 16 valves
Drivetrain: Front-engine RWD
Suspension: (F) Independent, coil springs. (R) de Dion, coil springs
Bodyframe: Chassis and separate body
Transmission: Three-speed manual
Weight: 914kgs

PRICE GUIDE

Launch price: £1277
Excellent: £175,000
Good: £150,000
Average: £100,000
Project: £75,000

ALLARD
K3

Altogether more sophisticated than its earlier relatives, the K3 was Allard's attempt at appealing to more sophisticated buyers as it came with luxuries such as a one-piece bonnet and wide bench seat that was supposed to accommodate the entire family. Given that Americans were the target, and it was supposedly a softer option, this was a little strange as Stateside buyers were looking for the exact opposite in their English sports cars. But it was a pretty car and its market failure was disappointing nonetheless.

SPECIFICATIONS

Years produced:	1952-1955 (62 in total)
Performance:	0-60mph: N/A (Top speed: 85mph)
Power & torque:	85bhp / 150lb/ft
Engine:	Normally aspirated 3622cc V8, petrol, carburettor, 16 valves
Drivetrain:	Front-engine RWD
Suspension:	(F) Independent, coil springs; (R) De Dion axle, coil springs
Bodyframe:	Chassis and separate body
Transmission:	Three-speed manual
Weight:	1181kgs
PRICE GUIDE	
Launch price:	£1713
Excellent:	£70,000
Good:	£55,000
Average:	£32,500
Project:	£22,500

ALPINE
A110

Rally driver and dealer Jean Rédèle branched out into producing competition-style cars based on Renault running gear in 1956 with the Alpine A106. The car proved so effective (winning its class in the 1956 Mille Miglia), that production blossomed as keen drivers clamoured to get hold of their own versions. By the time the A110 hit the market in 1962 the formula was pretty much perfected with a glassfibre body fixed to Renault 8 Gordini running gear making for a seriously effective, and good-looking, rally weapon.

SPECIFICATIONS

Years produced:	1965-1973
Performance:	0-60mph: 6.3 secs (Top speed: 132mph)
Power & torque:	138bhp / 117lb/ft
Engine:	Normally aspirated 1565cc in-line four, petrol, carburettor, eight valves
Drivetrain:	Rear-engine RWD
Suspension:	(F) Ind. wishbones, coils, tele. dampers, anti-roll bar. (R)Ind. swing axles, coils and telescopic dampers
Bodyframe:	Chassis and glassfibre body
Trans/weight:	Five-speed manual/ 625kgs
PRICE GUIDE	
Launch price:	Not known
Excellent:	£22,500
Good:	£17,500
Average:	£10,000
Project:	£7000

ALPINE
A310

Bringing the Alpine family firmly into the 1970s, the A310 was developed from the rear engined A110 GT4, but civilised to such an extent that it could be taken seriously as a day-to-day road car. The wedge-shaped styling was certainly striking, but keeping with tradition the glassfibre body was light and aerodynamic. Powered by the Renault 17TS high output 1605cc engine it could easily top 125mph. Although never officially imported into the UK many examples have crossed the Channel but they are expensive compared with rivals.

SPECIFICATIONS

Years produced:	1971-1976 (40,386 in total)
Performance:	0-60mph: 8.1 secs (Top speed: 131mph)
Power & torque:	127bhp / 108lb/ft
Engine:	Normally aspirated 1606cc in-line four, petrol, carburettor, eight valves
Drivetrain:	Rear-engine RWD
Suspension:	(F) Ind. wishbone, coil, anti-roll bar. (R) Ind. wishbone, coil spring, anti-roll bar
Bodyframe:	Chassis and glassfibre body
Transmission:	Five-speed manual
Weight:	940kgs
PRICE GUIDE	
Launch price:	Not known
Excellent:	£7000
Good:	£5500
Average:	£3000
Project:	£1750

ALPINE
A310 V6

Alpine was rapidly moving upmarket and the scale of its ambition was reflected in the A310 V6. Introduced in 1976 it slotted in the range above the four-cylinder car, before replacing it shortly afterwards. Powered by the 2664cc Douvrin engine, co-developed by Renault and Peugeot, the latest Alpine developed 150bhp in the rortiest fashion possible. However, despite the excellent soundtrack, and the company's assertion that it was a credible Porsche 911 alternative, the car wasn't fast enough nor did it have the right badge.

SPECIFICATIONS

Years produced:	1976-1980 (5970 in total)
Performance:	0-60mph: 7.6 secs (Top speed: 137mph)
Power & torque:	150bhp / 150lb/ft
Engine:	Normally aspirated 2664cc V6, petrol, carburettor, 12 valves
Drivetrain:	Rear-engine RWD
Suspension:	(F) Ind. wishbone, coil spring, anti-roll bar. (R) Ind. wishbone, coil spring
Bodyframe:	Chassis and glassfibre body
Transmission:	Five-speed manual
Weight:	1016kgs
PRICE GUIDE	
Launch price:	£4300
Excellent:	£9250
Good:	£7500
Average:	£5000
Project:	£3000

ALPINE
GTA V6

Known as the Alpine A610 in Europe the GTA was a very effective update of the A310 V6. Although the basic layout was shared with the older car, the slippery new glassfibre body and expanded PRV V6 engine gave the standard model (which boasted 160bhp) a top speed of nearly 140mph. However, the GTA's main forte was its handling, which despite the overhung rear engine had huge amounts of lateral grip and near-flat cornering. Sales in the UK were pitiful and as a marketing exercise for Renault it was a huge failure. Buy one today and enjoy the attention.

SPECIFICATIONS

Years produced:	1986-1991
Performance:	0-60mph: 7.5 secs (Top speed: 139mph)
Power & torque:	157bhp / 163lb/ft
Engine:	Normally aspirated 2849cc V6, petrol, carburettor, 12 valves
Drivetrain:	Mid-engine RWD
Suspension:	(F) Ind. wishbones, coil, damper onto upper wish. anti-roll bar. (R) Ind. wishbones, coil, anti-roll bar
Bodyframe:	Chassis and glassfibre body
Trans/weight	Five-speed manual/1140kgs
PRICE GUIDE	
Launch price:	£19,040
Excellent:	£7000
Good:	£5500
Average:	£3750
Project:	£2000

ALPINE
GTA V6 Turbo

When launched, the GTA Turbo became France's fastest-ever production car. With a power output of 200bhp from its 1.5-litre V6 engine, shared with the Renault 25, its top speed pushed 150mph. Pricing in the UK was ambitious and the GTA went head-to-head with the Porsche 911 and Lotus Esprit. These more established cars continued to overshadow the French upstart, outselling it comfortably. Few original RHD cars remain in the UK (less than 40) but in recent years a number of left-hookers have been imported.

SPECIFICATIONS

Years produced: 1986-1991
Performance: 0-60mph: 6.3 secs (Top speed: 149mph)
Power & torque: 197bhp / 214lb/ft
Engine: Turbocharged 2458cc V6, petrol, elec. fuel injection, 12 valves
Drivetrain: Rear-engine RWD
Suspension: (F) Ind. wishbones, coil, damper onto upper wish. anti-roll bar. (R) Ind. wishbones, coil, anti-roll bar
Bodyframe: Chassis and glassfibre body
Trans/weight: Five-speed manual/ 1180kgs

PRICE GUIDE

Launch price: £23,635
Excellent: £8250
Good: £7000
Average: £4250
Project: £2500

ALVIS
4.3-litre Tourer

Using the earlier 3½-litre engine as a starting point, Alvis increased its capacity to 4387cc for its range-topping Tourer. Power was uprated to 137bhp giving the 4.3 a top speed of just over 100mph. No chassis modifications were needed to house the new 4.3 unit, which helped to keep the development costs down. Unlike its forerunner, the 4.3 was sold with a standard body, produced by the Coventry-based coachbuilder Charlesworth. The Vanden Plas-bodied 4.3 was the fastest British car at the time, thanks in part to its short, light weight chassis.

SPECIFICATIONS

Years produced: 1936-1940 (166 in total)
Performance: 0-60mph: N/A (Top speed: 103mph)
Power & torque: 137bhp / N/A
Engine: Normally aspirated 4387cc in-line six, petrol, carburettor, 12 valves
Drivetrain: Front-engine RWD
Suspension: (F) Independent, transverse leaf springs. (R) Beam axle, semi-elliptic leaf springs
Bodyframe: Chassis and separate body
Transmission: Four-speed manual
Weight: 1881kgs

PRICE GUIDE

Launch price: £995
Excellent: £300,000
Good: £230,000
Average: £170,000
Project: £150,000

ALVIS
Speed 20

The Speed 20 was the first British car to be fitted with an all-synchromesh gearbox, although fitted only to the later SB, SC and SD variants. The engine was a development of the 20hp unit found in the older Silver Eagle cars, but the triple Weber carburettor set-up and other modifications gave 87bhp, an additional 15bhp. The heavier chassis, along with a new luggage compartment, dulled performance considerably, although the top speed of 89mph was more than competitive. The Speed 20 cemented Alvis' reputation for comfortable cruising.

SPECIFICATIONS

Years produced: 1932-1936 (1164 in total)
Performance: 0-60mph: N/A (Top speed: 89mph)
Power & torque: 87bhp / N/A
Engine: Normally aspirated 2762cc in-line six, petrol, carburettor, 12 valves
Drivetrain: Front-engine RWD
Suspension: (F) Independent, transverse leaf springs. (R) Beam axle, semi-elliptic leaf springs
Bodyframe: Chassis and separate body
Transmission: Four-speed manual
Weight: 1576kgs

PRICE GUIDE

Launch price: £700
Excellent: £100,000
Good: £80,000
Average: £60,000
Project: £30,000

ALVIS
Speed 25

When the Alvis range was realigned in 1936, the 3½-litre became the 4.3-litre, while the Speed 20 became the Speed 25. With the opposition closing in on the Speed 20, Alvis took the 3½-litre's engine and married it to the Speed 20's chassis. Chassis-wise, the Speed 25 received new springs and dampers in an attempt to help control the new, and substantially more powerful, car. The body frame was redesigned by Cross and Ellis, and the result was a sleek and highly-desirable Alvis that found favour with a wide range of enthusiastic new buyers.

SPECIFICATIONS

Years produced: 1936-1940 (391 in total)
Performance: 0-60mph: N/A (Top speed: 92mph)
Power & torque: 115bhp / N/A
Engine: Normally aspirated 3571cc in-line six, petrol, carburettor, 12 valves
Drivetrain: Front-engine RWD
Suspension: (F) Independent, transverse leaf springs. (R) Beam axle, semi-elliptic leaf springs
Bodyframe: Chassis and separate body
Transmission: Four-speed manual
Weight: 1831kgs

PRICE GUIDE

Launch price: £700
Excellent: £140,000
Good: £100,000
Average: £75,000
Project: £30,000

ALVIS
TA14

Despite the fact that the TA14 was merely a mildly-modified version of the 1938 12/70 it was Alvis's post-war best-seller – which explains the traditional styling. It also means cart springs and mechanically-operated brakes, though you do get a slightly wider track and longer wheelbase. The engine was bored out by an extra 50cc, but extra weight means this high-quality car can make only 75mph. There were quite a few special bodies about, and it's these – particularly the Tickford and Carbodies dropheads – that are most sought after.

SPECIFICATIONS

Years produced: 1946-1950 (3311 in total)
Performance: 0-60mph: 22.2 secs (Top speed: 74mph)
Power & torque: 65bhp / 95lb/ft
Engine: Normally aspirated 1892cc in-line four, petrol, carburettor, eight valves
Drivetrain: Front-engine RWD
Suspension: (F) Beam axle, semi-elliptic leaf spring; (R) Beam axle, semi-elliptic leaf spring
Bodyframe: Chassis and separate body
Transmission: Four-speed manual
Weight: 1422kgs

PRICE GUIDE

Launch price: £893
Excellent: £13,500
Good: £11,000
Average: £5250
Project: £2500

ALVIS
TA21/TC21

The cabin was carried over from the TA14, but rounded wings with rear wheel covers and faired-in headlamps helped add a hint of modernity. Brakes are now hydraulic and there's independent coil-sprung front suspension, but the big change is under the bonnet. Alvis's all-new 3-litre engine – with twin carbs on all but the first few – is tough and torquey as well as smooth and quiet. By the time the TA evolved into the TC21/100 'Grey Lady' in 1953, with wire wheels and hidden hinges, higher compression meant 100bhp... and just about 100mph.

SPECIFICATIONS	
Years produced:	1950-1955 (2074 in total)
Performance:	0-60mph: 16.5 secs (Top speed: 86mph)
Power & torque:	90bhp / 147lb/ft
Engine:	Normally aspirated 2993cc in-line six, petrol, carburettor, 12 valves
Drivetrain:	Front-engine RWD
Suspension:	(F) Independent, coil springs. (R) Beam axle, semi-elliptic leaf spring
Bodyframe:	Chassis and separate body
Transmission:	Four-speed manual
Weight:	1518kgs
PRICE GUIDE	
Launch price:	£1598
Excellent:	£25,000
Good:	£20,000
Average:	£12,000
Project:	£7000

ALVIS
TA21/TC21 Cabriolet

Even though it looked distinctly pre-war, the TA21 was the first post-war Alvis to feature a brand new chassis. The coachwork was by Tickford, and it was heavily-influenced by the earlier TA14 Cabriolet. The new chassis and 90bhp engine gave the car hugely improved dynamics and driveability. The updated TC21 was unveiled in 1953 and the addition of twin SUs boosted the existing 2993cc engine to 100bhp. Both the TA21 and TC21 featured independent front suspension, which was a massive step forward, and remained unchanged for years to come.

SPECIFICATIONS	
Years produced:	1950-1955
Performance:	0-60mph: 16.5 secs (Top speed: 86mph)
Power & torque:	90bhp / 147lb/ft
Engine:	Normally aspirated 2993cc in-line six, petrol, carburettor, 12 valves
Drivetrain:	Front-engine RWD
Suspension:	(F) Independent, coil springs. (R) Beam axle, semi-elliptic leaf spring
Bodyframe:	Chassis and separate body
Transmission:	Four-speed manual
Weight:	1448kgs
PRICE GUIDE	
Launch price:	£1822
Excellent:	£50,000
Good:	£35,000
Average:	£20,000
Project:	£10,000

ALVIS
TA14 Cabriolet

With a design that originated in the '30s, the TA14 was never intended to be break new ground, merely re-start Alvis production following the war. The Cabriolet was introduced alongside the saloon, and two drophead bodies were offered from the start – one by Tickford and the other by Carbodies. All versions featured the same front-end treatment, and the interior had high quality leather seats and a wooden dashboard. The single-carburettor, pushrod engine, wasn't powerful, but it was smooth, and suited the touring-car nature of the TA14.

SPECIFICATIONS	
Years produced:	1946-1950
Performance:	0-60mph: 22.2 secs (Top speed: 74mph)
Power & torque:	65bhp / 95lb/ft
Engine:	Normally aspirated 1892cc in-line four, petrol, carburettor, eight valves
Drivetrain:	Front-engine RWD
Suspension:	(F) Beam axle, semi-elliptic leaf spring; (R) Beam axle, semi-elliptic leaf spring
Bodyframe:	Chassis and separate body
Transmission:	Four-speed manual
Weight:	1447kgs
PRICE GUIDE	
Launch price:	£893
Excellent:	£25,000
Good:	£20,000
Average:	£15,000
Project:	£7000

ALVIS
TB21

Alvis launched the TB21 to replace the TB14, which had been a huge commercial failure, but – unlike the TB14 – the new model had a much more conventional grille and was widely lauded as a great-looking sports car. The TB21 used the same chassis as the TA21, and AP Metalcraft modified its TB14 bodyshell to fit the upgraded chassis. The new car was also fitted with the TA21's 90bhp engine, giving it sprightly performance. However, it was expensive, being pitched at £1598. The result: a mere 31 cars were produced.

SPECIFICATIONS	
Years produced:	1952 (31 in total)
Performance:	0-60mph: N/A (Top speed: 95mph)
Power & torque:	90bhp / 150 lb/ft
Engine:	Normally aspirated 2993cc in-line six, petrol, carburettor, 12 valves
Drivetrain:	Front-engine RWD
Suspension:	(F) Independent, coil springs. (R) Beam axle, semi-elliptic leaf springs
Bodyframe:	Chassis and separate body
Transmission:	Four-speed manual
Weight:	1283kgs
PRICE GUIDE	
Launch price:	£1598
Excellent:	£50,000
Good:	£35,000
Average:	£20,000
Project:	£10,000

RED TRIANGLE
'The home of Alvis Cars'
ALVIS
Alvis car sales
Service and restoration
Authorised supplier of Alvis parts
For further details please contact:
Red Triangle
Common Lane, Kenilworth,
Warwickshire CV8 2EL England.
Telephone:
Car Sales: 01926 864867
Service & Restoration 01926 864867
Parts 01926 857303
Fax: 01926 857305
www.redtriangle.co.uk
e-mail: enquiries@redtriangle.co.uk
ALVIS

ALVIS
TD21

A completely new body was designed by Park Ward – based loosely on the 16 TC21s (designated TC108G) styled by Swiss coachbuilder Graber and built in Loughborough by bus maker Willowbrook from 1956-57. The TD, however, is larger and offers a lot more space for passengers and luggage. Front brakes are now discs, and all but the first few TDs got an uprated 120bhp engine. On the downside, a cheaper Austin-Healey gearbox was used, but these cars got better during production. The Series II, from October '62, has all-wheel disc brakes and a ZF five-speed box.

SPECIFICATIONS

Years produced:	1956-1963 (1070 in total)
Performance:	0-60mph: 13.9 secs (Top speed: 104mph)
Power & torque:	115bhp / 152lb/ft
Engine:	Normally aspirated 2993cc in-line six, petrol, carburettor, 12 valves
Drivetrain:	Front-engine RWD
Suspension:	(F) Independent, coil springs. (R) Beam axle, semi-elliptic leaf springs
Bodyframe:	Chassis and separate body
Transmission:	Four-speed manual
Weight:	1495kgs

PRICE GUIDE

Launch price:	£2766
Excellent:	£22,500
Good:	£18,500
Average:	£10,000
Project:	£4500

ALVIS
TE/TF21

Easily distinguished from its TD predecessor by those stacked twin headlamps that were fashionable for ten minutes in the early 1960s, the TE gains a new cylinder head that lifts power output to 130bhp. Once again both saloon and drophead are available, and it's the latter that make serious money today. Power-steering becomes a desirable option from 1965, but Alvis saved the best for last. Just 106 TFs were built, but they come with a triple-carb 150bhp engine, improved gearbox and uprated suspension. After 1967 Alvis concentrated on armoured vehicles.

SPECIFICATIONS

Years produced:	1963-1967
Performance:	0-60mph: 12.5 secs (Top speed: 112mph)
Power & torque:	130bhp / 172lb/ft
Engine:	Normally aspirated 2993cc in-line six, petrol, carburettor, 12 valves
Drivetrain:	Front-engine RWD
Suspension:	(F) Independent, wishbone, coil springs; (R) Beam axle, semi-elliptic leaf spring
Bodyframe:	Chassis and separate body
Transmission:	Four-speed manual
Weight:	1473kgs

PRICE GUIDE

Launch price:	£2775
Excellent:	£26,000
Good:	£22,000
Average:	£12,000
Project:	£5000

ARMSTRONG SIDDELEY
Hurricane DHC

As part of a two-pronged attack on the world's car markets, Armstrong Siddeley introduced this stylish two-door drophead. Using the same chassis and running gear as the Lancaster, it might have been a little stodgy to drive, but the styling set it apart from its pre-war counterparts: flush-fitting headlights and faired in front wings (from the Lancaster) were up to the minute. The 70bhp 1991cc overhead valve engine was carried over from the pre-war 16hp, but was rugged and torquey, offering easy 50mph cruising in those restrained times.

SPECIFICATIONS

Years produced:	1946-1949 (2606 in total)
Performance:	0-60mph: 29.9 secs (Top speed: 75mph)
Power & torque:	75bhp / 107lb/ft
Engine:	Normally aspirated 2309cc in-line six, petrol, carburettor, 12 valves
Drivetrain:	Front-engine RWD
Suspension:	(F) Independent, transverse leaf springs; (R) Live axle
Bodyframe:	Chassis and separate body
Transmission:	Four-speed manual
Weight:	1412kgs

PRICE GUIDE

Launch price:	£1151
Excellent:	£14,000
Good:	£11,000
Average:	£7500
Project:	£3250

ARMSTRONG SIDDELEY
Lancaster

It might have been the company's first post-war car, but underneath the Lancaster's skin beat the heart of a pre-war car. Despite that, it can justifiably be described as Britain's first all-new post-war car, appearing on the market the same week hostilities ceased in Europe. A two-litre saloon might not have been groundbreaking, but with torsion bar suspension, hydromechanical brakes and a four-speed all-synchromesh gearbox it was comfortable and easy to drive. Dignified and refined it might have been, but it suffered badly from rust.

SPECIFICATIONS

Years produced:	1946-1952 (3597 in total)
Performance:	0-60mph: 29.7 secs (Top speed: 75mph)
Power & torque:	70bhp / N/A
Engine:	Normally aspirated 1991cc in-line six, petrol, carburettor, 12 valves
Drivetrain:	Front-engine RWD
Suspension:	(F) Independent, torsion bar. (R) Live axle, semi-elliptic leaf springs
Bodyframe:	Chassis and separate body
Transmission:	Four-speed manual
Weight:	1527kgs

PRICE GUIDE

Launch price:	£1151
Excellent:	£10,000
Good:	£7500
Average:	£4500
Project:	£2250

ARMSTRONG SIDDELEY
Typhoon Coupé

The Typhoon might well have been an entry-level version of the Hurricane, but that doesn't stop it having an appeal all of its own. Just like its Hurricane/Lancaster brethren it features a suspension set-up of surprising sophistication: independent up-front with longitudinal torsion bars along with a more traditional rear set-up of a live rear axle and leaf springs. The driving experience is stately and dignified, befitting of its upright styling. The steel and aluminium bodywork is corrosion prone and tough to restore.

SPECIFICATIONS

Years produced:	1946-1953 (1701 in total)
Performance:	0-60mph: 29.7 secs (Top speed: 78mph)
Power & torque:	70bhp / 109lb/ft
Engine:	Normally aspirated 1991cc in-line six, petrol, carburettor, 12 valves
Drivetrain:	Front-engine RWD
Suspension:	(F) Independent, transverse leaf springs; (R) Live rear axle
Bodyframe:	Chassis and separate body
Transmission:	Four-speed manual
Weight:	1351kgs

PRICE GUIDE

Launch price:	£1214
Excellent:	£11,000
Good:	£8500
Average:	£5750
Project:	£2750

ARMSTRONG SIDDELEY
Whitley

Once the great export drive got underway, Armstrong Siddeley was in there building a car that it considered more than suitable for the Colonies. More imposing styling was the key to its appeal, with an updated nose and roofline distancing it from the Lancaster. It wasn't the new recipe that the British car industry needed, although it did prove a big seller. Underneath, it was a familiar story, powered by the familiar 2.3-litre in-line-six that saw service in the last-of-the-line previous generation of models; and it was big and comfortable.

SPECIFICATIONS

Years produced: 1950-1954 (2582 in total)
Performance: 0-60mph: 19.0 secs (Top speed: 80mph)
Power & torque: 75bhp / 107lb/ft
Engine: Normally aspirated 2309cc in-line six, petrol, carburettor, 12 valves
Drivetrain: Front-engine RWD
Suspension: (F) Independent, torsion bar. (R) Live axle, semi-elliptic leaf springs
Bodyframe: Chassis and separate body
Transmission: Four-speed manual
Weight: 1430kgs

PRICE GUIDE

Launch price: £1247
Excellent: £10,000
Good: £7500
Average: £4000
Project: £1750

ARMSTRONG SIDDELEY
Sapphire 346

When it appeared, it could have been easy to conclude that the 346 was just another rebody of the pre-war models, such was the timidity of its design. However, it was entirely new underneath, featuring a fresh suspension set-up comprised of coil springs at the front and leaves at the back. It received a new engine, too – a lusty 3.4-litre six that was powerful enough to push the the 346 to 95mph, a significant step forward. But compared with the opposition, it was too unwieldy for mass appeal, and a downturn in Armstrong Siddeley's fortunes quickly followed.

SPECIFICATIONS

Years produced: 1952-1958 (8187 in total)
Performance: 0-60mph: 13 secs (Top speed: 100mph)
Power & torque: 150bhp / 185lb/ft
Engine: Normally aspirated 3435cc in-line six, petrol, carburettor, 12 valves
Drivetrain: Front-engine RWD
Suspension: (F) Independent, coil spring, wishbone; (R) Live axle, semi-elliptic leaf spring
Bodyframe: Chassis and separate body
Transmission: Four-speed manual
Weight: 1575kgs

PRICE GUIDE

Launch price: £1728
Excellent: £12,000
Good: £9000
Average: £4750
Project: £1750

ARMSTRONG SIDDELEY
Sapphire 234/236

Despite sharing the same name with the bigger 346, the Sapphire 234/236 were less appealing thanks to (the latter) being powered by 2.3-litre engines previously seen on the Whitley and Lancaster/ Hurricane and (the former), a smaller version of the 346's power unit. Both cars failed to make an impression on the market, selling disastrously and you'll be hard-pressed to find one now, thanks to their relative lack of appeal compared with the 346 and the Star Sapphire. Most well known for being a contributing factor in Armstrong Siddeley's closure.

SPECIFICATIONS

Years produced: 1955-1958 (803/603 in total)
Performance: 0-60mph: 15.5 secs (Top speed: 97mph)
Power & torque: 120bhp / 139lb/ft
Engine: Normally aspirated 2290cc in-line four, petrol, carburettor, eight valves
Drivetrain: Front-engine RWD
Suspension: (F) Independent, coil spring. (R) Live axle, semi-elliptic leaf spring
Bodyframe: Chassis and separate body
Transmission: Four-speed manual
Weight: 1360kgs

PRICE GUIDE

Launch price: £1599
Excellent: £10,000
Good: £7000
Average: £3750
Project: £1500

ARMSTRONG SIDDELEY
Star Sapphire

Star by name, star by nature. Although it looked rather similar to the Sapphire 346, the Star Sapphire was in an entirely different league as far as driving pleasure was concerned. It received a lusty 4-litre straight-six that could deliver genuine 100mph performance – and finally, the four-speed all-synchromesh gearbox was joined by the option of a Rolls-Royce Hydramatic automatic transmission that made driving this swift saloon genuinely easy. Even today, a well-sorted Star Sapphire will surprise other people on the road.

SPECIFICATIONS

Years produced: 1958-1960 (980 in total)
Performance: 0-60mph: 15.7 secs (Top speed: 100mph)
Power & torque: 145bhp / 230lb/ft
Engine: Normally aspirated 3990cc in-line six, petrol, carburettor, 12 valves
Drivetrain: Front-engine RWD
Suspension: (F) Independent, wishbone, coil spring; (R) Live axle, semi-elliptic leaf spring
Bodyframe: Chassis and separate body
Transmission: Four-speed manual
Weight: 1778kgs

PRICE GUIDE

Launch price: £2646
Excellent: £13,000
Good: £10,000
Average: £5500
Project: £2500

ASTON MARTIN
DB2

While the 2-Litre of 1948 has become retrospectively known as the DB1, the DB2 of 1950 was the first to officially wear the initials of Aston owner David Brown. The chassis was largely the same as for the 2-Litre, but the curvaceous fastback body with an imposingly long bonnet was fresh and graceful, and would inspire Aston's styling for two decades. The 2.6-litre twin-cam engine was a WO Bentley design for Lagonda and initially proved temperamental. It eventually settled down to give the DB2 impressive performance, especially in 121mph Vantage form from 1951.

SPECIFICATIONS

Years produced: 1950-1953 (411 in total)
Performance: 0-60mph: 11.2 secs (Top speed: 116mph)
Power & torque: 105bhp / 125lb/ft
Engine: Normally aspirated 2580cc in-line six, petrol, carburettor, 12 valves
Drivetrain: Front-engine RWD
Suspension: (F) Independent, coil spring; (R) Live axle, coil spring
Bodyframe: Chassis and Superleggera
Transmission: Four-speed manual
Weight: 1207kgs

PRICE GUIDE

Launch price: £1920
Excellent: £92,500
Good: £80,000
Average: £50,000
Project: £30,000

ASTON MARTIN
DB2 & 2/4 Convertible

A peculiar quirk of Aston is that it refers to its fixed-head coupés as saloons. No such confusion with the drophead coupés though. The DB2 appeared soon after the 'saloon' and, like its tin-top sibling, could be specified with three-abreast seating if a column shift was fitted. Only 102 were built. Open-top DB 2/4s were slightly more plentiful, at 132. However, most exclusive were the Spiders built by Bertone. Alfred Hitchcock featured a drophead coupé in *The Birds* – an early brush with fame for a marque that would soon become a cinema celebrity.

SPECIFICATIONS

Years produced: 1951-1957
Performance: 0-60mph: 11.2 secs (Top speed: 116mph)
Power & torque: 105bhp / 125lb/ft
Engine: Normally aspirated 2580cc in-line six, petrol, carburettor, 12 valves
Drivetrain: Front-engine RWD
Suspension: (F) Independent, coil spring; (R) Live axle, coil spring
Bodyframe: Chassis and Superleggera
Transmission: Four-speed manual
Weight: 1207kgs

PRICE GUIDE
Launch price: £2621
Excellent: £125,000
Good: £110,000
Average: £75,000
Project: £50,000

ASTON MARTIN
DB2/4

The four tacked onto the DB2's title denoted that this reworking of the theme could now fit four people... at a squeeze. The 2+2 seating was made more habitable by a higher roofline and opening rear screen – perhaps so those in the back could escape easily if it became too tight! However, the extra weight affected performance, so a boost to three litres in 1954 took power to 140bhp. The Mk2 of 1955 incorporated a rear-end restyle and a tougher back axle, and also introduced the incredibly rare notchback hardtop version, of which just 34 were made.

SPECIFICATIONS

Years produced: 1953-1957 (764 in total)
Performance: 0-60mph: 10.5 secs (Top speed: 119mph)
Power & torque: 125bhp / 139lb/ft
Engine: Normally aspirated 2580cc in-line six, petrol, carburettor, 12 valves
Drivetrain: Front-engine RWD
Suspension: (F) Independent, coil springs; (R) Live axle, coil springs
Bodyframe: Chassis and Superleggera
Transmission: Four-speed manual
Weight: 1257kgs

PRICE GUIDE
Launch price: £2622
Excellent: £90,000
Good: £75,000
Average: £47,500
Project: £27,500

ASTON MARTIN
DB MkIII Coupé

It may have been the third series of DB2/4, but Aston dropped the 2/4 nomenclature for its 1957 to 1959 range of saloons and dropheads. The most noticeable change was a more tapering front end topped off by a neater grille, but vertical rear lights were also fitted and the body tidied up. Mechanically, the engine rose marginally in capacity but was made a lot stronger and more powerful at 162bhp. Aston claimed 214bhp was possible with the competition-tuned triple-carb version, but this was probably exaggerated. Front discs standard from late 1957.

SPECIFICATIONS

Years produced: 1957-1959 (551 in total)
Performance: 0-60mph: 9.3 secs (Top speed: 119mph)
Power & torque: 162bhp / 180lb/ft
Engine: Normally aspirated 2922cc in-line six, petrol, carburettor, 12 valves
Drivetrain: Front-engine RWD
Suspension: (F) Independent, coil springs; (R) Live axle, coil springs
Bodyframe: Chassis and Superleggera
Transmission: Four-speed manual
Weight: 1270kgs

PRICE GUIDE
Launch price: £3076
Excellent: £95,000
Good: £80,000
Average: £50,000
Project: £30,000

ASTON MARTIN
DB4

The definitive and most-loved Aston Martin shape was born with the DB4 of 1958. It was massively over-engineered with a hefty chassis and new all-alloy 240bhp dohc engine of three litres (but capable of being expanded well beyond this level if needed). But what really grabbed the headlines was the Superleggera body. Designed by Italian coachbuilder Tourer, its stunning lines were formed of aluminium panels laid over a frame of steel tubes, making the car strong but also lightweight. From 1958 to 1962, there were five series of DB4s.

SPECIFICATIONS

Years produced: 1958-1963 (1113 in total)
Performance: 0-60mph: 8.5 secs (Top speed: 141mph)
Power & torque: 240bhp / 240lb/ft
Engine: Normally aspirated 3670cc in-line six, petrol, carburettor, 12 valves
Drivetrain: Front-engine RWD
Suspension: (F) Independent coil springs; (R) Beam axle, coil springs
Bodyframe: Chassis and Superleggera
Transmission: Four-speed manual with overdrive/auto
Weight: 1361kgs

PRICE GUIDE
Launch price: £3980
Excellent: £140,000
Good: £120,000
Average: £90,000
Project: £60,000

ASTON MARTIN
DB4 GT

For some, the standard DB4 just wasn't enough... and thus was the DB4 GT created. With its wheelbase shortened by five inches, it became one of the great racers of its era. Less length meant less weight and the twin-plug engine meant more power (302bhp), so it was a fast machine. Later versions had faired-in headlamps, adopted as standard on the succeeding DB5. Zagato built 19 versions with an even sleeker, sexier body and 314bhp, 0-60mph in 6.1 seconds and a top speed of over 150mph. Very exhilarating – but one will cost you three times the GT price.

SPECIFICATIONS

Years produced: 1959-1961 (81 in total)
Performance: 0-60mph: 6.4 secs (Top speed: 152mph)
Power & torque: 302bhp / 278lb/ft
Engine: Normally aspirated 3670cc in-line six, petrol, carburettor, 12 valves
Drivetrain: Front-engine RWD
Suspension: (F) Ind. coil and wishbone, anti-roll bar, tele dampers. (R) Live axle, coils, trailing links, Watt linkage, lever-arm dampers
Bodyframe: Chassis and Superleggera
Trans/weight: Four-speed manual/1277kgs

PRICE GUIDE
Launch price: £4534
Excellent: £1,000,000
Good: £850,000
Average: £600,000
Project: £400,000

ASTON MARTIN
DB4 drophead

While DB4 saloons are special enough, even more prized are the scarce and beautiful drophead coupés. Production didn't begin until 1961, three years after the enclosed cars arrived. Just 70 emerged, of which 38 had the standard 240bhp engine and 32 were endowed with the 266bhp of the Vantage engine. In addition to the hood, a hard-top was available; when fitted, it made the British car look very like a Maserati 3500 coupé from behind. It's not surprising that Touring of Milan was responsible for the look of both vehicles...

SPECIFICATIONS

Years produced: 1961-1963 (70 in total)
Performance: 0-60mph: 8.5 secs (Top speed: 141mph)
Power & torque: 240bhp / 240lb/ft
Engine: Normally aspirated 3670cc in-line six, petrol, carburettor, 12 valves
Drivetrain: Front-engine RWD
Suspension: (F) Independent, coil springs; (R) Beam axle, coil springs
Bodyframe: Chassis and Superleggera
Transmission: Four-speed manual
Weight: 1352kgs

PRICE GUIDE

Launch price: £3980
Excellent: £200,000
Good: £160,000
Average: £110,000
Project: £85,000

ASTON MARTIN
DB5

Had not a certain James Bond turned the DB5 into the most famous car in the world, this DB4 evolution might have gone largely unnoticed; originally, it was just going to be called the DB4 Series 6. However, *Goldfinger* and *Thunderball* made stars of both the car and its maker. Four litres of potent power – 282bhp as standard, 314bhp for the Vantage – and long, lean looks meant that the legend was largely justified though. Disc brakes were now on each wheel, and all but the very earliest cars had five gears. Less entertaining were the autos. Licenced to thrill.

SPECIFICATIONS

Years produced: 1963-1965 (1063 in total)
Performance: 0-60mph: 8.1 secs (Top speed: 141mph)
Power & torque: 282bhp / 288lb/ft
Engine: Normally aspirated 3995cc in-line six, petrol, carburettor, 12 valves
Drivetrain: Front-engine RWD
Suspension: (F) Independent coil springs; (R) Beam axle coil springs
Bodyframe: Chassis and Superleggera
Transmission: Five-speed manual
Weight: 1346kgs

PRICE GUIDE

Launch price: £4249
Excellent: £190,000
Good: £160,000
Average: £110,000
Project: £80,000

ASTON MARTIN
DB5 Volante

As well as the rare Radford DB5 'shooting brake' estates, those seeking an out-of-the-ordinary DB5 could plump for the drophead coupé. Extra bracing compensated for the lack of a roof, although the huge chassis meant the DB5 could cope well with some of its original strength removed. Production of the saloon finished in 1965 but 37 convertibles were built afterwards. Aston would subsequently use the Volante name to describe all its soft-tops. While the styling was that of the DB6, the Superleggera construction rooted it firmly in the DB5 mould.

SPECIFICATIONS

Years produced: 1963-1966 (123 in total)
Performance: 0-60mph: 8.1 secs (Top speed: 141mph)
Power & torque: 282bhp / 288lb/ft
Engine: Normally aspirated 3995cc in-line six, petrol, carburettor, 12 valves
Drivetrain: Front-engine RWD
Suspension: (F) Independent, coil springs; (R) Beam axle, coil springs
Bodyframe: Chassis and Superleggera
Transmission: Five-speed manual
Weight: 1465kgs

PRICE GUIDE

Launch price: £4249
Excellent: £265,000
Good: £220,000
Average: £160,000
Project: £110,000

ASTON MARTIN
DB6

The 'proper' DB series reached a graceful end with the DB6. A longer wheelbase meant it could seat four people, although only the two up front would have any real comfort. The higher roofline, split bumpers and more aerodynamic Kamm tail were the main identifying points. Extra civilisation was offered in the form of power-steering, air-con and a limited-slip diff and, as was the Aston way, there was a more powerful Vantage version boasting 325bhp. In 1969, the Mk2 appeared, characterised by flared arches and fuel-injection system as an option.

SPECIFICATIONS

Years produced: 1965-1970 (1567 in total)
Performance: 0-60mph: 6.5 secs (Top speed: 148mph)
Power & torque: 325bhp / 290lb/ft
Engine: Normally aspirated 3995cc in-line six, petrol, carburettor, 12 valves
Drivetrain: Front-engine RWD
Suspension: (F) Independent coil springs; (R) Beam axle coil springs
Bodyframe: Spaceframe
Transmission: Five-speed manual/automatic
Weight: 1474kgs

PRICE GUIDE

Launch price: £4998
Excellent: £100,000
Good: £80,000
Average: £55,000
Project: £35,000

ASTON MARTIN
DB6 Volante

Although the first 37 Volantes – Aston speak for convertibles – were built on the shorter DB5 chassis, genuine DB6s started to appear from October 1966. The time-consuming Superleggera construction was dropped; although aluminium was still used for the panels, the steel tubing underneath was replaced by folded metal. 140 Mk1 Volantes were constructed up until the debut of the Mk2 in July 1969: its much shorter run meant that only 38 of this variant could be fitted in before the DB6 Volante reached the end of its road in November 1970.

SPECIFICATIONS

Years produced: 1965-1970 (215 in total)
Performance: 0-60mph: 6.5 secs (Top speed: 140mph)
Power & torque: 282bhp / 288lb/ft
Engine: Normally aspirated 3995cc in-line six, petrol, carburettor, 12 valves
Drivetrain: Front-engine RWD
Suspension: (F) Independent coil springs; (R) Beam axle coil springs
Bodyframe: Spaceframe
Transmission: Five-speed manual
Weight: 1466kgs

PRICE GUIDE

Launch price: £4998
Excellent: £250,000
Good: £200,000
Average: £150,000
Project: £100,000

ASTON MARTIN DBS

A new stylist – William Towns – meant a completely new look for Aston, with the DBS shifting focus from Italy to America with its arresting muscle-car stance. The four-passenger DBS was designed for a V8, but Aston's eight-pot wasn't ready in time so the car used the DB6's 4-litre engine with an uprated Vantage option. However, all that extra weight knocked performance back; a DBS could offer only the same kind of speeds as a DB4. Although the V8 model was available from 1969, the six-cylinder continued until 1973 as the entry-level Aston.

SPECIFICATIONS

Years produced: 1967-1973 (899 in total)
Performance: 0-60mph: 7.8 secs (Top speed: 140mph)
Power & torque: 282bhp / 288lb/ft
Engine: Normally aspirated 3995cc in-line six, petrol, carburettor, 12 valves
Drivetrain: Front-engine RWD
Suspension: (F) Independent coil springs; (R) de Dion, coil springs
Bodyframe: Monocoque
Transmission: Five-speed manual/automatic
Weight: 1705kgs

PRICE GUIDE

Launch price: £5500
Excellent: £27,500
Good: £20,000
Average: £11,500
Project: £7000

ASTON MARTIN DBS-V8

Two years after the 1967 launch of the DBS, the car finally gained the engine it had always been destined for; Tadek Marek's sparkling new quad-cam fuel-injected 5340cc V8. However, the model's size and weight made it more grand tourer than out-and-out sportscar. Externally, there was little difference to the DBS save for the alloy wheels – where the DBS had wires – and a front air dam. The Hillman Hunter rear lights remained the same, though, proving that even the most prestigious machines have some touches of the real world about them.

SPECIFICATIONS

Years produced: 1969-1972 (402 in total)
Performance: 0-60mph: 6.0 secs (Top speed: 162mph)
Power & torque: 315bhp / 400lb/ft
Engine: Normally aspirated 5340cc V8, petrol, fuel injection, 16 valves
Drivetrain: Front-engine RWD
Suspension: (F) Independent coil springs; (R) de Dion, coil springs
Bodyframe: Monocoque
Transmission: Five-speed manual/automatic
Weight: 1724kgs

PRICE GUIDE

Launch price: £6897
Excellent: £30,000
Good: £22,500
Average: £12,500
Project: £7000

ASTON MARTIN V8

If the 1960s was Aston's golden era, the 1970s saw the glow fade. David Brown sold the firm in 1972, resulting in the DB initials being dropped and the V8's front end being restyled with single lights, a smaller grille and a few more curves. The engine's troublesome fuel injection was soon dropped in favour of four Weber carbs, plus a gaping bonnet scoop to clear them. A lack of cash meant the V8 would have a long existence; with many detail changes and updates, it survived until 1990, an unprecedented lifespan for a top-flight luxury sportscar.

SPECIFICATIONS

Years produced: 1972-1990 (2012 in total)
Performance: 0-60mph: 7.2 secs (Top speed: 146mph)
Power & torque: 320bhp / 360lb/ft
Engine: Normally aspirated 5340cc V8, petrol, carburettor, 16 valves
Drivetrain: Front-engine RWD
Suspension: (F) Independent, double wishbone, coil spring, anti-roll bar. (R) de Dion axle, Watt linkage, coil spring
Bodyframe: Monocoque
Trans/weight: Five-spd man/three-spd auto/ 1814kgs

PRICE GUIDE

Launch price: N/A
Excellent: £35,000
Good: £28,500
Average: £15,000
Project: £8000

ASTON MARTIN V8 Vantage

With 1977 the Queen's Silver Jubilee year, Britain seemed keen to celebrate all that was best about itself... so what better time for the V8 Vantage to be launched? Hailed as 'Britain's first supercar,' its 5.3-litre V8 unleashed an incredible 438bhp. The dash to 60mph took just 5.4 seconds; top speed was 170mph. Visually, the car could be distinguished by a blanked-off grille and bonnet scoop. 1978's Oscar India variant adopted a small boot spoiler and a smoother bonnet, with the car continuing in this form until 1990. The rich person's Ford Capri!

SPECIFICATIONS

Years produced: 1977-1989 (313 in total)
Performance: 0-60mph: 5.4 secs (Top speed: 168mph)
Power & torque: 438bhp / 400lb/ft
Engine: Normally aspirated 5340cc V8, petrol, fuel injection, 16 valves
Drivetrain: Front-engine RWD
Suspension: (F) Independent, double wishbone, coil spring, anti-roll bar. (R) de Dion axle, Watt linkage, coil spring
Bodyframe: Monocoque
Trans/weight: Five-speed manual/1818kgs

PRICE GUIDE

Launch price: £20,000
Excellent: £60,000
Good: £50,000
Average: £30,000
Project: £17,500

ASTON MARTIN Lagonda

Even Aston Martin wasn't immune to the craziness of the 1970s: behold the strangely glorious Lagonda, launched in 1977. Outside, the car – on a stretched V8 chassis – was an uncompromising razor-edged wedge shape by William Towns, inside it was a technological tour de force of touch-sensitive switches, digital displays and futuristic gizmos. These proved its Achilles' heel, for the Lagonda soon became known for its unreliability. Simplification followed... allowing the wedge to stay in production until 1990. Utterly mad, yet endearingly British.

SPECIFICATIONS

Years produced: 1977-1990 (645 in total)
Performance: 0-60mph: 8.8 secs (Top speed: 143mph)
Power & torque: 280bhp / 302lb/ft
Engine: Normally aspirated 5340cc V8, petrol, fuel injection, 16 valves
Drivetrain: Front-engine RWD
Suspension: (F) Independent, coil springs; (R) de Dion, coil springs
Bodyframe: Monocoque
Transmission: Automatic
Weight: 2023kgs

PRICE GUIDE

Launch price: £24,570
Excellent: £25,000
Good: £17,500
Average: £10,000
Project: £7000

ASTON MARTIN
V8 Volante

Aston held out until June 1978 to slice the roof off its V8, a surprising length of time (as the saloon could trace its origins back to 1967) for a car with so much sales potential. But the firm's more optimistic outlook of the late-1970s finally gave rise to the marriage of open-top enjoyment with V8 performance. A fully-lined, power hood, together with a new burr walnut dash and door cappings, cosseted the occupants. Up until 1981, every Volante was exported to North America; the rest of the world had to wait until March of that year to see what all the fuss was about.

SPECIFICATIONS

Years produced:	1978-1990 (562 in total)
Performance:	0-60mph: 7.7 secs (Top speed: 140mph)
Power & torque:	N/A / N/A
Engine:	Normally aspirated 5340cc V8, petrol, fuel injection, 16 valves
Drivetrain:	Front-engine RWD
Suspension:	(F) Independent, coil springs; (R) de Dion, coil springs
Bodyframe:	Monocoque
Transmission:	Five-speed manual/automatic
Weight:	1794kgs
PRICE GUIDE	
Launch price:	£33,864
Excellent:	£52,500
Good:	£39,500
Average:	£20,000
Project:	£12,000

ASTON MARTIN
V8 Vantage Volante

Alongside the Vantage saloon, 'Britain's first supercar' could be had as a steroid-enhanced convertible. It came with the same luxuries as the 'ordinary' Volante, but also trumpeted the 5.3-litre Vantage-spec engine. The USA was desperate for a new high-performance drophead coupé – Aston hadn't built one since 1970 – so this breeze machine was keenly received there. That's where the vast majority ended up, making them a rare sight in Europe and their homeland... although James Bond managed to get hold of one for 1987's *The Living Daylights*.

SPECIFICATIONS

Years produced:	1986-1989 (116 in total)
Performance:	0-60mph: 5.4 secs (Top speed: 165mph)
Power & torque:	438bhp / 400lb/ft
Engine:	Normally aspirated 5340cc V8, petrol, fuel injection, 16 valves
Drivetrain:	Front-engine RWD
Suspension:	(F) Independent coil springs; (R) de Dion coil springs
Bodyframe:	Monocoque
Transmission:	Five-speed manual/automatic
Weight:	1650kgs
PRICE GUIDE	
Launch price:	£87,000
Excellent:	£100,000
Good:	£85,000
Average:	£60,000
Project:	£35,000

ASTON MARTIN
V8 Zagato

Looking to reignite a successful past relationship, Aston asked Italian coachbuilder Zagato to think up an exotic body which could be fitted to a lightened, shortened chassis. But the result divided opinion; gone were the luscious curves of Zagato's Aston revamps of the 1960s and in their place were brutal straight lines and angled edges, with an extensive use of flush-fitting glass. Critics found it hard to get over the resemblance to contemporary Japanese sports coupés but, with only 83 ever built, they are surprisingly valuable today.

SPECIFICATIONS

Years produced:	1986-1989 (83 in total)
Performance:	0-60mph: 5.0 secs (Top speed: 186mph)
Power & torque:	432bhp / 395lb/ft
Engine:	Normally aspirated 5340cc V8, petrol, fuel injection, 16 valves
Drivetrain:	Front-engine RWD
Suspension:	(F) Independent coil springs; (R) de Dion coil springs
Bodyframe:	Monocoque
Transmission:	Five-speed manual
Weight:	1650kgs
PRICE GUIDE	
Launch price:	£87,000
Excellent:	£72,500
Good:	£60,000
Average:	£40,000
Project:	£22,500

ASTON MARTIN
Virage

After 20 years of the V8 saloon, even Aston was forced to concede that it was time for a change – the Virage, the final blast of the original V8 concept. A bold and imposing new body was designed by Royal College of Art tutors John Hefferman and Ken Greenley, and slotted over the existing V8 chassis. Despite the old-fashioned underpinnings, the car still looked sufficiently sleek and modern to revitalise Aston Martin for the 1990s. From 1992, Aston Martin introduced a service to convert the Virage engine to a 500bhp 6.3-litre.

SPECIFICATIONS

Years produced:	1989-1995 (365 in total)
Performance:	0-60mph: 6.8 secs (Top speed: 157mph)
Power & torque:	330bhp / 350lb/ft
Engine:	Normally aspirated 5340cc V8, petrol, electronic fuel injection, 32 valves
Drivetrain:	Front-engine RWD
Suspension:	(F) Independent coil springs; (R) de Dion coil springs
Bodyframe:	Monocoque
Transmission:	Five-speed/automatic
Weight:	1948kgs
PRICE GUIDE	
Launch price:	£120,000
Excellent:	£32,000
Good:	£27,000
Average:	£20,000
Project:	£13,000

ASTON MARTIN
Virage Volante

With the success of the Virage saloon – in terms of both styling and sales – Aston felt confident enough to bring out variations on its theme. The logical next step was to remove the roof to create a Volante, and this the firm did in 1992. Fortunately, the Virage's shape was one that looked especially handsome in open form. The launch car was a strict two-seater, but the production models were a more practical proposition with 2+2 seating instead. Between 224 and 233 – estimates differ – were built up to the end of the line in 1996.

SPECIFICATIONS

Years produced:	1992-1996 (233 in total)
Performance:	0-60mph: 6.1 secs (Top speed: 174mph)
Power & torque:	330bhp / 350lb/ft
Engine:	Normally aspirated 5340cc V8, petrol, electronic fuel injection, 32 valves
Drivetrain:	Front-engine RWD
Suspension:	(F) Independent coil springs; (R) de Dion coil springs
Bodyframe:	Monocoque
Transmission:	Five-speed manual/automatic
Weight:	1935kgs
PRICE GUIDE	
Launch price:	£184,000
Excellent:	£40,000
Good:	£35,000
Average:	£30,000
Project:	£25,000

ASTON MARTIN
DB7

Ford's outright purchase of Aston brought fresh optimism and security. Nothing symbolised this new hope more than the DB7. Designed using Blue Oval resources, its chassis evolved from the Jaguar XJ6's, but the many changes and stunning body meant it was much more than a reskinned Jag – although the close resemblance of the later XK8 did steal some of its glory. The 335bbhp 3.2-litre six-cylinder was also new, the first six-pot to appear in an Aston since the DBS. 'DB' also harkened back to the past, a tribute to honorary life president David Brown.

SPECIFICATIONS

Years produced: 1993-1999 (7000 in total)
Performance: 5.8 secs (Top speed: 165mph)
Power & torque: 335bhp / 361lb/ft
Engine: Supercharged 3239cc in-line six, petrol, electronic fuel injection, 24 valves
Drivetrain: Front-engine RWD
Suspension: (F) Independent coil springs; (R) de Dion coil springs
Bodyframe: Monocoque
Transmission: Five-speed manual/automatic
Weight: 1750kgs

PRICE GUIDE

Launch price: £78,500
Excellent: £27,500
Good: £24,000
Average: £21,000
Project: £16,000

ASTON MARTIN
Vantage

As with previous Astons, the temptation to tweak the Virage formula for even higher performance was strong, and the Vantage name was applied in 1993. The body was reworked so only the doors and roof were the same as before, giving a more purposeful and powerful stance. Naturally, though, the best changes were kept for under the bonnet, where bolted-on twin superchargers gave a huge 550bhp. That was enough to propel this two tons of British beef to 186mph, with 60 coming up 4.2 seconds. Later ones were even more blistering with 600bhp.

SPECIFICATIONS

Years produced: 1993-1999 (1050 in total)
Performance: 0-60mph: 4.6 secs (Top speed: 186 mph)
Power & torque: 550bhp / 550lb/ft
Engine: Twin supercharged 5340cc V8, petrol, electronic fuel injection, 32 valves
Drivetrain: Front-engine RWD
Suspension: (F) Independent coil springs; (R) de Dion coil springs
Bodyframe: Monocoque
Transmission: Six-speed manual
Weight: 1981kgs

PRICE GUIDE

Launch price: £177,600
Excellent: £85,000
Good: £75,000
Average: £55,000
Project: £40,000

ASTON MARTIN
DB7 Volante

After waiting to see the world liked the DB7 saloon, a Volante was a welcome inevitability. Launched two years after the enclosed car, it lost a little of its elegance with the roof removed, but made up for it with its posing value. The USA was its natural environment, which is why it was launched at the 1996 Detroit Motor Show rather than a European venue. The same supercharged 335bhp straight-six engine as seen on the saloon also featured on the Volante... but something even bigger and much better was only a few years away.

SPECIFICATIONS

Years produced: 1996-1999
Performance: 0-60mph: 6.5 secs (Top speed: 152mph)
Power & torque: 335bhp / 360lb/ft
Engine: Supercharged 3239cc in-line six, petrol, electronic fuel injection, 24 valves
Drivetrain: Front-engine RWD
Suspension: (F) Ind. double wishbone, coil, anti-roll bar. (R) Ind. double wishbone, coil
Bodyframe: Monocoque
Transmission: Five-speed manual
Weight: 1650kgs

PRICE GUIDE

Launch price: £92,500
Excellent: £30,000
Good: £26,500
Average: £23,000
Project: £19,500

ASTON MARTIN
V8 Coupé

By 1996, the V8 Vantage was Aston's flagship while the DB7 was the more user-friendly model designed to attract new customers. With the assurance of Ford backing – it had started buying shares from 1987 – there was room to expand the range and so the little-known V8 Coupé was launched. A Virage in all but name, it had less aggressive styling than the Vantage and a softer 349bhp output. Its looks and performance were less extreme, and so was its price, slotting in neatly between the DB7 and the Vantage. It passed into history in 1999 along with its V8 sibling.

SPECIFICATIONS

Years produced: 1996-1999
Performance: 0-60mph: 5.9 secs (Top speed: N/A)
Power & torque: 349bhp / 369lb/ft
Engine: Normally aspirated 5340cc V8, petrol, electronic fuel injection, 32 valves
Drivetrain: Front-engine RWD
Suspension: (F) Ind. double wishbone, coil spring, anti-roll bar. (R) de Dion axle, radius arms, coil spring, Watts linkage
Bodyframe: Monocoque
Trans/weight: Four-speed automatic/1950kgs

PRICE GUIDE

Launch price: £149,500
Excellent: £42,500
Good: £37,500
Average: £32,500
Project: £27,500

ASTON MARTIN
DB7 Vantage

Previous Vantages had usually just increased the output of a type's existing engine; 1999's DB7 version went a radical step further... it had an entirely new motor dropped in. And what a powerhouse; a 6-litre 48-valve V12 of 420bhp, making the Vantage more than a match for any European supercar rival. Unfortunately, sales of the six-cylinder DB7 promptly dried up, forcing it to be dropped. A 2002 offshoot was the V12 GT (or GTA when sporting an automatic transmission) which offered 435bhp and other performance and cosmetic tweaks.

SPECIFICATIONS

Years produced: 1999-2003
Performance: 0-60mph: 5.0 secs (Top speed: 185mph)
Power & torque: 420bhp / 400lb/ft
Engine: Normally aspirated 5935cc V12, petrol, electronic fuel injection, 48 valves
Drivetrain: Front-engine RWD
Suspension: (F) Ind. double wishbone, coil spring, anti-roll bar. (R) Ind. double wishbone, coil spring, anti-roll bar
Bodyframe: Monocoque
Trans/weight: Six-speed manual/1780kgs

PRICE GUIDE

Launch price: £92,500
Excellent: £37,000
Good: £33,000
Average: £28,000
Project: £23,000

ASTON MARTIN
DB7 Vantage Volante

Just as with the six-cylinder DB7, the V12 was also complimented by an open-top Volante. There were no real mechanical differences from the saloon, although attempting to hit the potential 185mph of this fresh-air grand tourer with the hood back might have been a little hairy even without the scuttle shake this Volante was criticised for. An intriguing derivative was the DB AR1, a roadster sold only in America ('AR1' standing for American Roadster 1). Only 100 were produced, costing $226,000. Yet, for all that money, you didn't even get a soft-top!

SPECIFICATIONS

Years produced: 1999-2003
Performance: 0-60mph: 5.0 secs (Top speed: 185mph)
Power & torque: 420bhp / 400lb/ft
Engine: Normally aspirated 5935cc V12, petrol, electronic fuel injection, 48 valves
Drivetrain: Front-engine RWD
Suspension: (F) Ind. double wishbone, coil spring, anti-roll bar. (R) Ind. double wishbone, coil spring
Bodyframe: Monocoque
Transmission: Six-speed manual
Weight: 1860kgs

PRICE GUIDE

Launch price: £99,950
Excellent: £42,000
Good: £37,500
Average: £30,000
Project: £25,000

AUDI
60-90

Here's where the modern Audi phenomenon began. Based on the DKW F-102, this tidy hemi-headed saloon might not have set the world alight when it was launched, but its solid engineering and neat road manners soon won it lots of friends. If anything it was under-engined and so performance wasn't exactly sparkling. But the concept would soon be expanded once the Audi marque had been successfully re-established. Today few remain, but well worth seeking out if you fancy an inexpensive slice of Teutonic efficiency.

SPECIFICATIONS

Years produced: 1965-1972
Performance: 0-60mph: 18.0 secs (Top speed: 86mph)
Power & torque: 55bhp / 47lb/ft
Engine: Normally aspirated 1499cc in-line four, petrol, carburettor, eight valves
Drivetrain: Front-engine FWD
Suspension: (F) Ind. coil springs, wishbones. (R) Dead axle, trailing arms, Panhard rod
Bodyframe: Monocoque
Transmission: Four-speed manual
Weight: 1040kgs

PRICE GUIDE

Launch price: £1068
Excellent: £2250
Good: £1600
Average: £850
Project: £250

AUDI
100 (C1)

If the 60, 75 and 90 had done much to firmly establish Audi in the middle-market pecking order, it was down to the 100 to convince buyers further up the price scale that the Ingolstadt manufacturer was an alternative to Mercedes-Benz. Its powerful two-litre 'four' and front-wheel drive delivered a sound driving experience, while excellent quality and reliability were a nice contrast to the Rover and Triumph opposition. However, despite the upsides Audi was still seen by many as the new kid on the block.

SPECIFICATIONS

Years produced: 1968-1976
Performance: 0-60mph: 11.8 secs (Top speed: 107mph)
Power & torque: 100bhp / 111lb/ft
Engine: Normally aspirated 1760cc in-line four, petrol, carburettor, eight valves
Drivetrain: Front-engine FWD
Suspension: (F) Ind. wishbone, anti-roll bar. (R) Dead axle, trailing arms, torsion bar
Bodyframe: Monocoque
Transmission: Four-speed manual
Weight: 1090kgs

PRICE GUIDE

Launch price: £1475
Excellent: £2500
Good: £1900
Average: £900
Project: £300

AUDI
100 Coupé S

The 100 saloon was a bit like the school swat; useful to know but ultimately quite dull to be around. However, when shorn of its sensible suit and clothed in an Aston DBS-like coupe bodyshell, it suddenly starts to look a little more interesting. Although never a massive seller when new, the 100S Coupe is one of those cars that has become more desirable with the passage of time, as classic car enthusiasts warm to its love-me styling combined with thorough German engineering. That's turned it into something of a cult car.

SPECIFICATIONS

Years produced: 1970-1976 (30,687 in total)
Performance: 0-60mph: 10.8 secs (Top speed: 118mph)
Power & torque: 112bhp / 118lb/ft
Engine: Normally aspirated 1871cc in-line four, petrol, carburettor, eight valves
Drivetrain: Front-engine RWD
Suspension: (F) Independent, coil spring. (R) Live axle, torsion bar
Bodyframe: Monocoque
Transmission: Four-speed manual
Weight: 1082kgs

PRICE GUIDE

Launch price: £2418
Excellent: £3500
Good: £2750
Average: £1400
Project: £500

AUDI
quattro

Developed as a low-volume homologation special for the rallying stage, no one could have predicted just how big an impact the quattro would have on the motoring industry. With four-wheel drive and 200bhp of turbocharged power, the new coupe from Audi took the world by storm, and the rest of the industry struggled to catch up. But despite being a competition-bred machine, the quattro was always civilised on the road. These early cars are now the rarest and are easily identifiable thanks to their chrome rimmed quad headlamps.

SPECIFICATIONS

Years produced: 1980-1983
Performance: 0-60mph: 7.1 secs (Top speed: 137mph)
Power & torque: 200bhp / 210lb/ft
Engine: Turbocharged 2144cc in-line five, petrol, electronic fuel injection, 10 valves
Drivetrain: Front-engine AWD
Suspension: (F) Ind. struts, coils, tele. dampers, anti-roll bar. (R) Ind. struts, coils, lower wishbones,tele. dampers, anti-roll bar
Bodyframe: Monocoque
Trans/weight: Five-speed manual/ 1300kgs

PRICE GUIDE

Launch price: £14,500
Excellent: £10,000
Good: £8500
Average: £4500
Project: £2250

AUDI quattro

Not one to sit on its laurels, Audi continued to develop the quattro (which is now retrospectively known as the Ur-quattro). Big rectangular headlamps, RHD and a slightly larger engine came in 1983, with the controversial digital dashboard, an item you're either going to love or hate, arriving the following year. But despite that, the basic recipe remained the same throughout the 1980s and drivers continued to love the grippy handling and that warbling five-cylinder soundtrack. Thanks to the BBC's *Ashes to Ashes* values have soared.

SPECIFICATIONS

Years produced: 1983-1989
Performance: 0-60mph: 7.3 secs (Top speed: 137mph)
Power & torque: 200bhp / 210lb/ft
Engine: Turbocharged 2226cc in-line five, petrol, mechanical fuel injection, 10 valves
Drivetrain: Front-engine AWD
Suspension: (F) Ind. struts, coils, lower wishbone, anti-roll bar. (R) Independent, struts, coils, lower wishbone, anti-roll bar
Bodyframe: Monocoque
Trans/weight: Five-speed manual/1290kgs

PRICE GUIDE

Launch price: £29,445
Excellent: £10,000
Good: £9500
Average: £5250
Project: £2500

AUDI quattro 20v

The Audi quattro was supposed to fade quietly out of production in 1988. However massive demand – especially from the UK – ensured that the old favourite remained in production long after the 80/90/Coupe that it was derived from had disappeared from the scene. To celebrate its stay of execution, Audi shoehorned in the 20-valve five cylinder engine from the Audi 200 and upped the output to a more than useful 220bhp. Of all the quattros, these last of line 20Vs are by far the best to drive, and quickest to boot.

SPECIFICATIONS

Years produced: 1989-1991 (931 in total)
Performance: 0-60mph: 6.3 secs (Top speed: 141mph)
Power & torque: 220bhp / 228lb/ft
Engine: Turbocharged 2226cc in-line five, petrol, electronic fuel injection, 20 valves
Drivetrain: Front-engine AWD
Suspension: (F) Independent, struts, coils, tele. dampers, anti-roll bar. (R) Ind. struts, coils, lower wishbones, tele. dampers,
Bodyframe: Monocoque
Trans/weight: Five-speed manual/1300kgs

PRICE GUIDE

Launch price: £32,995
Excellent: £12,000
Good: £10,000
Average: £6000
Project: £3000

AUSTIN Seven

It's hard to believe just how this modest little car changed the face of motoring in the UK. Allegedly blueprinted on Herbert Austin's billiards table, the Austin Seven emerged as an economical, fun to drive and cheap alternative to the motorcycle and sidecar combination that ruled Britain's roads between the wars. And the more it sold the cheaper the price became: from £225 at launch in 1922 to £145 just four years later. Its influence spread to BMW in Germany the American Austin company in the USA.

SPECIFICATIONS

Years produced: 1923-1939
Performance: 0-60mph: N/A (Top speed: 40mph)
Power & torque: 10.5bhp / N/A
Engine: Normally aspirated 747cc in-line four, petrol, carburettor, side valves
Drivetrain: Front-engine RWD
Suspension: (F) Beam axle. (R) Beam axle
Bodyframe: Separate body/chassis
Transmission: Three-speed manual
Weight: 363kgs

PRICE GUIDE

Launch price: £225
Excellent: £6000
Good: £4750
Average: £2750
Project: £1200

AUSTIN A40 Devon/Dorset

Austin's first step into the brave new world of flush-mounted headlamps and front-hinged doors was a raging success with over a quarter of a million built. It's also notable for first using what would come to be known as the BMC B-series engine, here in its smallest capacity. There's still a separate chassis with hydromechanical brakes, but independent front suspension makes it a decent drive. Dorset is merely a two-door version of the Devon, nearly all of which went for export. More hot-rodded than standard examples survive in the UK.

SPECIFICATIONS

Years produced: 1947-1952 (289,897 in total)
Performance: 0-60mph: 34.8 secs (Top speed: 67mph)
Power & torque: 40bhp / 57lb/ft
Engine: Normally aspirated 1200cc in-line four, petrol, carburettor, eight valves
Drivetrain: Front-engine RWD
Suspension: (F) Independent, coil spring. (R) Live axle, semi-elliptic leaf spring
Bodyframe: Chassis and separate body
Transmission: Four-speed manual
Weight: 965kgs

PRICE GUIDE

Launch price: £403
Excellent: £4000
Good: £3200
Average: £1600
Project: £600

AUSTIN A125/A135

The Sheerline was Austin's first post-war flagship car, even if its design dated back to the 1930s. The first model, designated A110, was powered by a 3.5-litre straight-six, but this was soon upgraded to four litres to become the A125 – the iconic luxury car without the price. Offered in both saloon and limousine versions these big bruisers became synonymous with the undertaking world, as well as a mainstay on mayoral fleets. Not sophisticated, nor good to drive, but effective and surprisingly popular on the classic car scene.

SPECIFICATIONS

Years produced: 1947-1956 (9000/1910 in total)
Performance: 0-60mph: 19.4 secs (Top speed: 81mph)
Power & torque: 125bhp / N/A
Engine: Normally aspirated 3990cc in-line six, petrol, carburettor, 12 valves
Drivetrain: Front-engine RWD
Suspension: (F) Independent, coil springs. (R) Live axle, semi-elliptic leaf spring
Bodyframe: Chassis and separate body
Transmission: Four-speed manual
Weight: 2000kgs

PRICE GUIDE

Launch price: £1277
Excellent: £7750
Good: £6500
Average: £4000
Project: £1750

AUSTIN
A70 Hampshire

Just like an Austin Devon only larger (the easiest way to tell them apart is the Hampshire's rear 'skirts'). It's a tall car, designed for people who wore hats, and you can seat three abreast on the front and rear seats, making it just the thing for those extended family trips to Goodwood. The 2.2-litre engine is an overhead-valve unit carried over from the Austin 16, strong on torque but short on gearing, so they fly up hills but run out of steam above 60mph. Probably as well – the steering's not great and half-mechanical brakes need careful setting up.

SPECIFICATIONS

Years produced:	1948-1950 (35,261 in total)
Performance:	0-60mph: 21.5 secs (Top speed: 82mph)
Power & torque:	64bhp / 96lb/ft
Engine:	Normally aspirated 2199cc in-line four, petrol, carburettor, eight valves
Drivetrain:	Front-engine RWD
Suspension:	(F) Independent, coil spring. (R) Live axle, semi-elliptic leaf spring
Bodyframe:	Chassis and separate body
Transmission:	4-speed manual
Weight:	1270kgs
	PRICE GUIDE
Launch price:	£608
Excellent:	£5000
Good:	£4200
Average:	£2250
Project:	£750

AUSTIN
A90 Atlantic

Quirky styling that looks more interesting now than it did to Americans in 1948. That was the car's target market but the US had cheaper options with bigger engines and a row of chrome strips down the bonnet fooled nobody into thinking it was a Pontiac. At least the Atlantic's big four-pot found fame a little later in the Austin-Healey 100. Convertible version (add 60% for their values) was launched before fabric-topped coupé, but only stayed in production for two years. By the end in 1952 Austin had managed to shift slightly less than 8000 of them.

SPECIFICATIONS

Years produced:	1948-1952 (7981 in total)
Performance:	0-60mph: 16.6 secs (Top speed: 91mph)
Power & torque:	88bhp / 140lb/ft
Engine:	Normally aspirated 2660cc in-line four, petrol, carburettor, 8 valves
Drivetrain:	front-engine RWD
Suspension:	(F) Independent, coil spring. (R) Live axle, semi-elliptic leaf spring
Bodyframe:	Chassis and separate body
Transmission:	4-speed manual
Weight:	1359kgs
	PRICE GUIDE
Launch price:	£953
Excellent:	£9500
Good:	£7500
Average:	£4000
Project:	£1500

AUSTIN
A40 Sports

The aluminium body is by Jensen and mounted to an Austin Devon chassis. Fun as these soft-tops are 'Sports' is maybe pushing the idea a little too far. Still, with the help of twin carbs and larger inlet valves the Devon engine's power was raised from 40bhp to 46bhp, so a genuine 80mph was possible. Also, to lend credibility one was driven to victory in the 1956 RAC Rally Ladies' Cup, beating various Fords and an MGA in the process. Column-shift gearchange from 1952 is less desirable and despite low build numbers there are still quite a few about.

SPECIFICATIONS

Years produced:	1950-1953 (4011 in total)
Performance:	0-60mph: 25.6 secs (Top speed: 78mph)
Power & torque:	46bhp / 61lb/ft
Engine:	Normally aspirated 1200cc in-line four, petrol, carburettor, 8 valves
Drivetrain:	Front-engine RWD
Suspension:	(F) Independent, coil spring. (R) Live axle, semi-elliptic leaf spring
Bodyframe:	Chassis and separate body
Transmission:	4-speed manual
Weight:	695kgs
	PRICE GUIDE
Launch price:	£818
Excellent:	£7500
Good:	£6000
Average:	£3500
Project:	£1750

AUSTIN
A70 Hereford

This was the Hampshire's replacement and in keeping with Austin's styling policy it's very much an inflated Somerset. Indeed it can be difficult to tell those two cars apart when they're not side-by-side. They even share the same doors and rear wings. For at-a-glance recognition look out for the raised pressing around the front wheelarches and the full-width 'whiskers' below the grille. There's an improvement in power, but 68bhp is still disappointing from 2.2 litres. They are also quite thirsty and you don't buy one for its handling.

SPECIFICATIONS

Years produced:	1950-1954 (50,421 in total)
Performance:	0-60mph: 21.4 secs (Top speed: 81mph)
Power & torque:	68bhp / 116lb/ft
Engine:	Normally aspirated 2199cc in-line four, petrol, carburettor, 8 valves
Drivetrain:	Front-engine RWD
Suspension:	(F) Independent, coil spring. (R) Live axle, semi-elliptic leaf spring
Bodyframe:	Chassis and separate body
Transmission:	4-speed manual
Weight:	1280kgs
	PRICE GUIDE
Launch price:	£687
Excellent:	£4800
Good:	£3900
Average:	£2200
Project:	£700

AUSTIN
A30/A35

Austin's answer to the Morris Minor was lighter and more compact, but with a steering box and part-hydraulic, part-rod brakes, it doesn't feel as advanced. At first A30s came with an 803cc engine and four-doors. A two-door was added in late-1953. The more usable A35 replaced it in 1956, armed with more power from the 948cc A-series engine. Visually the changes included a painted grille and a much larger rear window. Saloon production ceased in 1959 but the van went on as late as 1968, with 1098cc, then 848cc engines.

SPECIFICATIONS

Years produced:	1951-1968 (527,000 in total)
Performance:	0-60mph: 30.1 secs (Top speed: 72mph)
Power & torque:	34bhp / 50lb/ft
Engine:	Normally aspirated 948cc in-line four, petrol, carburettor, 8 valves
Drivetrain:	Front-engine RWD
Suspension:	(F) Independent, coil spring. (R) Live axle, semi-elliptic leaf spring
Bodyframe:	Metal monocoque
Transmission:	4-speed manual
Weight:	685kgs
	PRICE GUIDE
Launch price:	£507
Excellent:	£3500
Good:	£2500
Average:	£1350
Project:	£500

AUSTIN
A40 Somerset

The successor to the Devon ensured Austin kept on churning out large numbers of quality saloons for the masses. The styling's more bulbous, but the separate chassis is much the same as before, though this time the brakes are low maintenance hydraulics. There's another couple of bhp from the 1200cc engine, though they still won't quite hit the national speed limit. Not particularly collectible, except for the convertible version. Rare in any condition, the good ones keep commanding ever-higher prices - currently double those of saloons.

SPECIFICATIONS

Years produced:	1952-1954 (173,306 in total)
Performance:	0-60mph: 31.6 secs (Top speed: 69mph)
Power & torque:	42bhp / 62lb/ft
Engine:	Normally aspirated 1200cc in-line four, petrol, carburettor, 8 valves
Drivetrain:	Front-engine RWD
Suspension:	(F) Independent, coil spring. (R) Live axle, semi-elliptic leaf spring
Bodyframe:	Chassis and separate body
Transmission:	4-speed manual
Weight:	1000kgs

PRICE GUIDE

Launch price:	£728
Excellent:	£3750
Good:	£2900
Average:	£1400
Project:	£500

AUSTIN
A40/A50/A55 Cambridge

Austin took a big step forward with its 1954 Cambridge saloons, finally adopting monocoque construction for its mid-sized cars. Bottom of the pile was the A40 which used the 1200cc 42bhp engine from the Somerset, while the A50 had the newly-enlarged 1489cc B-series unit and 50bhp. Customers spending the extra money for the Deluxe version were treated to extra chrome and leather. The A55 succeeded both types in 1957, with a bigger boot, fledgling fins and a larger back window. In van and pick-up form, these models lasted until 1971.

SPECIFICATIONS

Years produced:	1954-1958 (299,500 in total)
Performance:	0-60mph: 28.8 secs (Top speed: 74mph)
Power & torque:	50bhp / 74lb/ft
Engine:	Normally aspirated 1489cc in-line four, petrol, carburettor, 8 valves
Drivetrain:	Front-engine, RWD
Suspension:	(F) Independent, coil spring. (R) Live axle, semi-elliptic leaf spring
Bodyframe:	Metal monocoque
Transmission:	4-speed manual
Weight:	1118kgs

PRICE GUIDE

Launch price:	£650
Excellent:	£3250
Good:	£2500
Average:	£1000
Project:	£300

AUSTIN
A90/A95/A105 Westminister

Although it looked like a glammed-up version of the Cambridge it only shared the same doors as its smaller sibling. The 2.6-litre C-series put out a mere 85bhp meaning performance was leisurely. This was addressed with the A95 and A105 of 1956, the former getting 92bhp, the latter getting 102bhp. Together with its lower suspension, standard overdrive and two-tone paint, the A105 was almost sporty with a top speed approaching 100mph. For the ultimate in Westminster appeal, there was a Vanden Plas version, dripping with leather.

SPECIFICATIONS

Years produced:	1954-1959 (60,367 in total)
Performance:	0-60mph: 19.8 secs (Top speed: 90mph)
Power & torque:	92bhp / 130lb/ft
Engine:	Normally aspirated 2639cc in-line six, petrol, carburettor, 12 valves
Drivetrain:	Front-engine RWD
Suspension:	(F) Independent, coil spring. (R) Live axle, semi-elliptic leaf spring
Bodyframe:	Metal monocoque
Transmission:	4-speed manual
Weight:	1100kgs

PRICE GUIDE

Launch price:	£792
Excellent:	£4000
Good:	£3000
Average:	£1350
Project:	£500

AUSTIN
Metropolitan

Never actually badged an Austin, the Metropolitan was originally made solely for Nash in America, who wanted a small car but had no experience of building one. Which explains the bumper car-like American styling. On sale here from 1957 the car had by then been given the 1489cc B-series in place of the original 1200. One strange quirk is the three-speed gearbox, which is actually an A50 four-speed with the slot for first blanked off. Both hardtop and convertible versions were made and surviving numbers of each are about equal in the UK.

SPECIFICATIONS

Years produced:	1954-1956
Performance:	0-60mph: 22.4 secs (Top speed: 70mph)
Power & torque:	42bhp / 58lb/ft
Engine:	Normally aspirated 1240cc in-line four, petrol, carburettor, 8 valves
Drivetrain:	Front-engine RWD
Suspension:	(F) Independent, coil spring, wishbone. (R) Live axle, semi-elliptic leaf spring
Bodyframe:	Metal monocoque
Transmission:	3-speed manual
Weight:	810kgs

PRICE GUIDE

Launch price:	N/A
Excellent:	£6500
Good:	£5000
Average:	£2500
Project:	£750

AUSTIN
A30/35 Countryman

Introduced in September 1954 - so you won't find many A30 versions - the Countryman is a tiny estate created by fitting rear seats, a full headlining and two-piece sliding rear side windows to the A30 van. Many vans have since been converted to look like a Countryman (an okay alternative, but don't pay the Countryman premium for one of these). As a giveaway, many conversions use fixed side windows and fail to remove the van's vent roof. Also, only the A30 and early A35 versions have van-style indent pressings in the doors.

SPECIFICATIONS

Years produced:	1954-1962
Performance:	0-60mph: 31.0 secs (Top speed: 73mph)
Power & torque:	34bhp / 50lb/ft
Engine:	Normally aspirated 948cc in-line four, petrol, carburettor, 8 valves
Drivetrain:	Front-engine RWD
Suspension:	(F) Independent, coil spring. (R) Live axle, semi-elliptic leaf spring
Bodyframe:	Metal monocoque
Transmission:	4-speed manual
Weight:	749kgs

PRICE GUIDE

Launch price:	£541
Excellent:	£4000
Good:	£3000
Average:	£1500
Project:	£700

AUSTIN A40 Farina

The unassuming Austin A40 Farina is one of the most significant Austins ever. Why? Well it was the first Pininfarina-styled BMC car, the first 'two box' design and, in Countryman estate form with a split tailgate, has a claim to fame as one of the first hatchbacks. The 1958 Austin that would inform so many future models was mainly Austin A35 underneath its Italian suit, even down to the inferior hydro-mechanical brakes. Fortunately, these were changed to hydraulic on the 1961 MkII, while 1962 saw a 1098cc A-series slotted in.

SPECIFICATIONS

Years produced:	1958-1967 (364,064 in total)
Performance:	0-60mph: 27.1 secs (Top speed: 82mph)
Power & torque:	48bhp / 60lb/ft
Engine:	Normally aspirated 948cc in-line four, petrol, carburettor, 8 valves
Drivetrain:	Front-engine RWD
Suspension:	(F) Independent, coil spring. (R) Live axle, semi-elliptic leaf spring
Bodyframe:	Metal monocoque
Transmission:	4-speed manual
Weight:	761kgs
PRICE GUIDE	
Launch price:	£639
Excellent:	£2900
Good:	£2200
Average:	£1000
Project:	£350

AUSTIN A99/A110 Westminister

Pininfarina's finest BMC moment was the 1959-68 Westminster series; the larger canvas suited the angular lines and resulted in a suitably prestigious machine. A twin-carb C-series engine pumped up to 3-litres coupled with a three-speed transmission allowed stately progress with reasonable haste if pushed. Servo-assisted front disc brakes added to the enjoyment. 1961's A110 was even better but the ultimate Westminster was the MkII of 1964, which gained four gears for the model's final four years of production.

SPECIFICATIONS

Years produced:	1959-1968 (41,250 in total)
Performance:	0-60mph: 14.4 secs (Top speed: 98mph)
Power & torque:	103bhp / 165lb/ft
Engine:	Normally aspirated 2912cc in-line six, petrol, carburettor, 12 valves
Drivetrain:	Front-engine RWD
Suspension:	(F) Independent, coil spring. (R) Live axle, semi-elliptic leaf spring
Bodyframe:	Metal monocoque
Transmission:	4-speed manual/3-speed automatic
Weight:	1530kgs
PRICE GUIDE	
Launch price:	£1149
Excellent:	£4200
Good:	£3300
Average:	£1400
Project:	£550

AUSTIN A55/A60 Cambridge (Farina)

Pininfarina styled Austin's Cambridges for the 1960s and turned in a smart job. As fins were in, the A55 Cambridge had them but its underpinnings were much the same as with the previous series of Cambridges. The 1489cc engines struggled to shift these heavy cars so, in 1961, engine size was increased to 1622cc and the car renamed the A60. Other changes were an increased wheelbase and cropped fins as fashion was turning against flash styling. BMC badge engineering resulted in Morris, Wolseley, Riley and MG versions, too.

SPECIFICATIONS

Years produced:	1959-1969 (426,500 in total)
Performance:	0-60mph: 23.0 secs (Top speed: 78mph)
Power & torque:	52bhp / 82lb/ft
Engine:	Normally aspirated 1489cc in-line four, petrol, carburettor, 8 valves
Drivetrain:	Front-engine RWD
Suspension:	(F) Independent, coil spring. (R) Live axle, semi-elliptic leaf spring
Bodyframe:	Monocoque
Transmission:	4-speed manual
Weight:	1118kgs
PRICE GUIDE	
Launch price:	£802
Excellent:	£3000
Good:	£2200
Average:	£1000
Project:	£300

AUSTIN 1100/1300

BMC badge-engineering ran rampant with the 1100/1300 range, Alec Issigonis' extension of his Mini concept. The 1963 Austin variant was the best-seller thanks to front-wheel-drive, front disc brakes, interconnected Hydrolastic fluid suspension and a TARDIS-like interior. Performance was lively thanks to the A-series engines, in 1098cc and, from 1967, 1275cc sizes and handling came close to Mini standards. Much cleverer than their Ford, Vauxhall and Rootes rivals these cars consistently topped British sales charts but rust ferociously.

SPECIFICATIONS

Years produced:	1963-1974 (1,119,800 in total)
Performance:	0-60mph: 17.3 secs (Top speed: 87mph)
Power & torque:	60bhp / 69lb/ft
Engine:	Normally aspirated 1275cc in-line four, petrol, carburettor, 8 valves
Drivetrain:	Front-engine FWD
Suspension:	(F) Independent, wishbone, Hydrolastic unit. (R) Independent, Hydrolastic unit, rubber-cone spring, torsion bar
Bodyframe:	Metal monocoque
Trans/weight:	4-speed manual/776kgs
PRICE GUIDE	
Launch price:	£593
Excellent:	£2000
Good:	£1500
Average:	£750
Project:	£200

AUSTIN 1300GT

British Leyland's attempt at injecting some entertainment and passion into the 1300 was quite successful. Imagine a Mini-Cooper grown plump on pies, and you have some idea of what this racy 1300 was like. The twin carb engine was tuned to MG/Riley spec and lairy colours such as orange and yellow were offered, complemented by that essential black vinyl roof. 58bhp was the norm for an Austin 1300, the GT had 70bhp and a thoroughly entertaining 93mph capability. A cult following these days is proof that Minis don't have all the fun!

SPECIFICATIONS

Years produced:	1969-1974 (52,107 in total)
Performance:	0-60mph: 15.6 secs (Top speed: 92mph)
Power & torque:	70bhp / 74lb/ft
Engine:	Normally aspirated 1275cc in-line four, petrol, carburettor, 8 valves
Drivetrain:	Front-engine FWD
Suspension:	(F) Independent, wishbone, Hydrolastic unit. (R) Independent, Hydrolastic unit, rubber-cone spring, torsion bar
Bodyframe:	Metal monocoque
Trans/weight:	4-speed manual/855kgs
PRICE GUIDE	
Launch price:	£910
Excellent:	£3000
Good:	£2250
Average:	£1100
Project:	£450

AUSTIN
1800/2200 Landcrab

After the Mini and 1100/1300 range, the 1800/2200 models were expected to complete Alec Issigonis' successful hat-trick of BMC front-wheel-drive cars. But they didn't. Despite the 1800 winning the Car of the Year award in 1964 sales were disappointing. Although over-engineered and with Hydrolastic suspension the ungainly looks and austere interior counted against the models. For 1972 a six-cylinder 2.2-litre engine was fitted to create the 2200; more power and better to drive, but it was too late to make any real impact.

SPECIFICATIONS

Years produced:	1964-1975 (210,000 in total)
Performance:	0-60mph: 17.1 secs (Top speed: 90mph)
Power & torque:	85bhp / 90lb/ft
Engine:	Normally aspirated 1799cc in-line four, petrol, carburettor, 8 valves
Drivetrain:	Front-engine FWD
Suspension:	(F) Independent, Hydrolastic. (R) Independent, Hydrolastic, trailing arm
Bodyframe:	Metal monocoque
Transmission:	4-speed manual
Weight:	1200kgs
	PRICE GUIDE
Launch price:	£769
Excellent:	£2200
Good:	£1600
Average:	£800
Project:	£200

AUSTIN
3-Litre

After the handsome Westminster saloon, the 3-Litre - its 1967 replacement - was a big disappointment. Big was the operative word but being saddled with the centre section of the 1800/2200 with a long bonnet and boot tacked on either end did not make it attractive. The cabin was massive, but at the expense of much of the usual luxury and traditional design that buyers expected in a car of this class. Rear-wheel-drive and a 2.9-litre engine shared with the MGC gave reasonable performance, but prestige was lacking and, thus, so were sales.

SPECIFICATIONS

Years produced:	1967-1971 (9992 in total)
Performance:	0-60mph: 15.7 secs (Top speed: 100mph)
Power & torque:	124bhp / 163lb/ft
Engine:	Normally aspirated 2912cc in-line six, petrol, carburettor, 12 valves
Drivetrain:	Front-engine RWD
Suspension:	(F) Independent, Hydrolastic. (R) Independent, Hydrolastic, trailing arm
Bodyframe:	Metal monocoque
Transmission:	4-speed manual
Weight:	1524kgs
	PRICE GUIDE
Launch price:	£1418
Excellent:	£2600
Good:	£2000
Average:	£1000
Project:	£350

AUSTIN
Maxi

BMC became British Leyland in 1968, and one of its first products was the Austin Maxi. It was essentially a good car with some innovative ideas, but it was the finer details and lack of quality that let the Maxi down, traits that would come to characterise BL. Britain's first real hatchback had much space and seats that folded down into a double bed, but taking the centre section from the 1800/2200 range meant looks were bland. Hydrolastic (and later Hyrdagas) suspension and five gears were its good points, but the gearchange itself wasn't that great.

SPECIFICATIONS

Years produced:	1969-1981 (472,098 in total)
Performance:	0-60mph: 13.2 secs (Top speed: 97mph)
Power & torque:	91bhp / 104lb/ft
Engine:	Normally aspirated 1485cc in-line four, petrol, carburettor, 8 valves
Drivetrain:	Front-engine FWD
Suspension:	(F) Independent, Hydrolastic. (R) Independent, Hydrolastic
Bodyframe:	Metal monocoque
Transmission:	5-speed manual
Weight:	979kgs
	PRICE GUIDE
Launch price:	£979
Excellent:	£1500
Good:	£1000
Average:	£500
Project:	£100

AUSTIN
Allegro

The Allegro stood as the foremost icon of all that was wrong with Britain's car industry in the 1970s. Strange looks, lack of quality, reliability issues and that infamous rectangular 'Quartic' steering wheel meant that what good touches it did have (a wide choice of engines from 1-litre through to 1750cc, compliant Hydragas suspension, five gears and a distinctive character) were overlooked. 1975's estate version looked like a shrunken hearse, which didn't help matters. However, Allegros have cult appeal nowadays.

SPECIFICATIONS

Years produced:	1973-1982 (642,340 in total)
Performance:	0-60mph: 11.0 secs (Top speed: 100mph)
Power & torque:	80bhp / 100lb/ft
Engine:	Normally aspirated 1747cc in-line four, petrol, carburettor, 8 valves
Drivetrain:	Front-engine FWD
Suspension:	(F) Independent, Hydragas. (R) Independent, Hydragas
Bodyframe:	Metal monocoque
Transmission:	Five-speed manual
Weight:	838kgs
	PRICE GUIDE
Launch price:	£974
Excellent:	£1250
Good:	£900
Average:	£550
Project:	£100

AUSTIN
Princess/Ambassador

The Princess couldn't have looked more different from the 1800/2200 series it replaced, even though it kept the same four- and six-cylinder engines and front-wheel-drive. Originally badged as Austins, Morrises and Wolseleys, the individual marques were soon dropped and all types became collectively known as Princess. Quality and reliability let down what was an innovative design, although if a hatchback had been incorporated right from the start it might well have done better. More appreciated now than when current.

SPECIFICATIONS

Years produced:	1975-1984 (224,942 in total)
Performance:	0-60mph: 13.1 secs (Top speed: 99mph)
Power & torque:	93bhp / 112lb/ft
Engine:	Normally aspirated 1994cc in-line four, petrol, carburettor, 8 valves
Drivetrain:	Front-engine FWD
Suspension:	(F) Independent, Hydragas unit. (R) Independent, Hydragas unit
Bodyframe:	Metal monocoque
Transmission:	Five-speed manual
Weight:	1089kgs
	PRICE GUIDE
Launch price:	£2237
Excellent:	£1400
Good:	£950
Average:	£450
Project:	£100

AUSTIN-HEALEY
100-4

What was originally the Healey 100 became the Austin-Healey 100 overnight when Leonard Lord of BMC saw it at the 1952 London Motor Show and liked it enough to offer to build it. The brusque, low-slung looks hid running gear plucked from the Austin parts bin, including the four-cylinder 2660cc engine from the A90 Atlantic. The USA took the 100 to its heart and it was an instant success there. Racing improved the breed, leading to the legendary 100S of 1954, with light aluminium panels and a higher output engine.

SPECIFICATIONS

Years produced:	1953-1956 (14,634 in total)
Performance:	0-60mph: 10.3 secs (Top speed: 103mph)
Power & torque:	90bhp / 144lb/ft
Engine:	Normally aspirated 2660cc in-line four, petrol, carburettor, 8 valves
Drivetrain:	Front-engine RWD
Suspension:	(F) Independent, coil spring, wishbone, anti-roll bar. (R) Panhard rod
Bodyframe:	Chassis and separate body
Transmission:	3-speed with overdrive
Weight:	975kgs
	PRICE GUIDE
Launch price:	£1064
Excellent:	£27,500
Good:	£22,500
Average:	£15,000
Project:	£9000

AUSTIN-HEALEY
100S

Created so the marque could be seen motor racing more widely than the works cars could cover, 50 examples of the 100S were built, though only six stayed in the UK. The 'S' actually refers to the Sebring 12-hour race in Florida where a prototype finished a surprise third in 1954. Based on the 100, the 100S had a stiffer chassis but more aluminium body panels. Brakes were discs front and rear. The engines had the same capacity but a different block casting and aluminium Weslake head. Larger SU carburettors were fitted and the result was 132bhp.

SPECIFICATIONS

Years produced:	1954-1955 (50 in total)
Performance:	0-60mph: 7.8 secs (Top speed: 119mph)
Power & torque:	132bhp / 168lb/ft
Engine:	Normally aspirated 2660cc in-line four, petrol, carburettor, 8 valves
Drivetrain:	Front-engine RWD
Suspension:	(F) Independent, coil spring, wishbone, anti-roll bar. (R) Panhard rod
Bodyframe:	Chassis and separate body
Transmission:	4-speed manual
Weight:	873kgs
	PRICE GUIDE
Launch price:	£Special order only
Excellent:	£250,000
Good:	£200,000
Average:	£150,000
Project:	£100,000

AUSTIN-HEALEY
100M

The potent abilities of the 100 meant that many owners wanted to take their cars racing, so the factory put together an upgrade kit which could either be retro-fitted or specified from new. If the latter option was chosen, the car became known as the 100M, the letter standing for 'Modified.' In 1955, the 100M became a model in its own right. Its engine - tuned to Le Mans specification - boasted 110bhp, the strapped-down bonnet had louvres in it to help keep it cool, and there was stiffer suspension and an anti-roll bar. 1159 were made.

SPECIFICATIONS

Years produced:	1955-1956 (1159 in total)
Performance:	0-60mph: 10.3 secs (Top speed: 103mph)
Power & torque:	110bhp / 144lb/ft
Engine:	Normally aspirated 2660cc in-line four, petrol, carburettor, 8 valves
Drivetrain:	Front-engine RWD
Suspension:	(F) Independent, coil spring, wishbone, anti-roll bar. (R) Panhard rod
Bodyframe:	Chassis and separate body
Transmission:	4-speed manual with overdrive
Weight:	1041kgs
	PRICE GUIDE
Launch price:	£Special order only
Excellent:	£40,000
Good:	£32,000
Average:	£20,000
Project:	£13,000

AUSTIN-HEALEY
100-6

The runaway success of the 100 convinced BMC it had a bright future, but its Austin four-cylinder engine was due to cease manufacture in 1956. No problem, the Westminster's six-cylinder 2639cc unit took its place. Actually, this didn't automatically make it a better car as the heavier engine sapped performance until a new cylinder head and manifolds boosted power to 117bhp. Other changes included an oval grille and 2+2 seating, although the latter was a needless alteration that was dispensed with after just two years.

SPECIFICATIONS

Years produced:	1956-1959 (58,370 in total)
Performance:	0-60mph: 12.9 secs (Top speed: 103mph)
Power & torque:	102bhp / 142lb/ft
Engine:	Normally aspirated 2639cc in-line six, petrol, carburettor, 12 valves
Drivetrain:	Front-engine RWD
Suspension:	(F) Independent, coil spring, wishbone, anti-roll bar. (R) Panhard rod
Bodyframe:	Chassis and separate body
Transmission:	4-speed with overdrive
Weight:	1105kgs
	PRICE GUIDE
Launch price:	£1144
Excellent:	£26,500
Good:	£22,000
Average:	£13,500
Project:	£8000

AUSTIN-HEALEY
3000 MkI

The first generation of the 'Big Healey' arrived in 1959, when the C-series engine from the 100-Six was upgraded to three litres, for use in the new Westminster saloons. Although there was no change of styling (except new badges), the mechanical alterations – more power, a better gearbox and disc brakes on the front – were thought significant enough to merit the change of model designation. And there was the return of a 2+2 format, available alongside the two-seater roadster. The MkI continued without change until 1961.

SPECIFICATIONS

Years produced:	1959-1961 (58,370 in total)
Performance:	0-60mph: 11.2 secs (Top speed: 111mph)
Power & torque:	117bhp / 149lb/ft
Engine:	Normally aspirated 2639cc in-line six, petrol, carburettor, 8 valves
Drivetrain:	Front-engine RWD
Suspension:	(F) Independent, coil spring, wishbone, anti-roll bar. (R) Panhard rod
Bodyframe:	Chassis and separate body
Transmission:	4-speed manual with overdrive
Weight:	1143kgs
	PRICE GUIDE
Launch price:	£11,159
Excellent:	£28,000
Good:	£23,000
Average:	£13,500
Project:	£8000

AUSTIN-HEALEY Sprite MkI

The original Sprite was a cheap and cheerful mass-produced sporting convertible that was also tremendous fun. Cheeky looks - those 'frogeye' headlamps were initially planned to be retractable until it was realised that would put the price up - distracted from the fact that underneath the skin it was mainly a blend of Austin A35 and Morris Minor. However, that still meant entertaining performance. Prices today are out of all proportion to the budget origins; these are now dear machines in more ways than one.

SPECIFICATIONS

Years produced:	1958-1961 (48,987 in total)
Performance:	0-60mph: 20.5 secs (Top speed: 86mph)
Power & torque:	43bhp / 52lb/ft
Engine:	Normally aspirated 948cc in-line four, petrol, carburettor, 8 valves
Drivetrain:	Front-engine RWD
Suspension:	(F) Independent, coil spring. (R) Live axle, semi-elliptic leaf spring
Bodyframe:	Metal monocoque
Transmission:	4-speed manual
Weight:	602kgs

PRICE GUIDE

Launch price:	£669
Excellent:	£9500
Good:	£8250
Average:	£4500
Project:	£2250

AUSTIN-HEALEY 3000 MkII

In theory the move to triple carburettors for the 3000 MkII was a good one. In practice the set-up proved difficult to keep in tune resulting in probably the least popular of the Big Healeys. Many owners found themselves spending more time fiddling with the engine rather than driving the car. The arrangement was dropped after a year when the 3000 MkIIa Convertible went back to just two carburettors plus featured a curved front windscreen, wind-up windows, more user-friendly hood and 2+2 seating as standard.

SPECIFICATIONS

Years produced:	1961-1962 (11,564 in total)
Performance:	0-60mph: 11.5 secs (Top speed: 112mph)
Power & torque:	132bhp / 167lb/ft
Engine:	Normally aspirated 2912cc in-line six, petrol, carburettor, 12 valves
Drivetrain:	Front-engine RWD
Suspension:	(F) Independent, coil spring, wishbone, anti-roll bar. (R) Panhard rod
Bodyframe:	Chassis and separate body
Transmission:	4-speed manual with overdrive
Weight:	1158kgs

PRICE GUIDE

Launch price:	£1159
Excellent:	£30,000
Good:	£24,000
Average:	£15,000
Project:	£9000

AUSTIN-HEALEY Sprite MkII/III

The 1961 MkII was an effort to modernise the Sprite and make it more practical. Unfortunately, it also took away much of its character and novelty. However, it was still affordable and enjoyable and at least passengers now had an opening bootlid to put a limited amount of luggage in. Gone were the upright headlamps, the light units now sitting conventionally either side of the grille. From 1962, there was a bigger 1098cc engine plus front disc brakes, but buyers had to wait until the MkIII of 1964 for door handles and winding windows.

SPECIFICATIONS

Years produced:	1961-1966 (20,450 in total)
Performance:	0-60mph: 20.0 secs (Top speed: 85mph)
Power & torque:	46bhp / 53lb/ft
Engine:	Normally aspirated 948cc in-line four, petrol, carburettor, 8 valves
Drivetrain:	Front-engine RWD
Suspension:	(F) Independent, coil spring, wishbone. (R) Live axle, quarter-elliptic leaf spring
Bodyframe:	Metal monocoque
Transmission:	4-speed manual
Weight:	700kgs

PRICE GUIDE

Launch price:	£670
Excellent:	£5000
Good:	£4000
Average:	£2250
Project:	£950

AUSTIN-HEALEY 3000 MkIII

The final genesis of the 'Big Healey' appeared in 1964. Although the looks remained largely the same this was the most powerful Austin-Healey ever, its 148bhp output making for a top speed of 121mph. The Phase 2 versions had revised rear suspension which improved handling. However, the end was nigh for the Healey and the final car was built in March 1968. Many mourned its passing, and its replacement, the MGC, failed to impress buyers in the same way. MkIIIs fetch the best Big Healey money these days.

SPECIFICATIONS

Years produced:	1964-1968 (17,712 in total)
Performance:	0-60mph: 9.8 secs (Top speed: 121mph)
Power & torque:	148bhp / 165lb/ft
Engine:	Normally aspirated 2912cc in-line six, petrol, carburettor, 12 valves
Drivetrain:	Front-engine RWD
Suspension:	(F) Independent, coil spring, wishbone, anti-roll bar. (R) Live axle
Bodyframe:	Chassis and separate body
Transmission:	4-speed manual with overdrive
Weight:	1180kgs

PRICE GUIDE

Launch price:	£1108
Excellent:	£33,000
Good:	£27,500
Average:	£17,000
Project:	£10,000

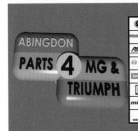

AUSTIN-HEALEY
Sprite MkIV

In 1966 BMC upped the Sprite's game with the MkIV. Improvements included a 1275cc engine giving 65bhp and near-100mph potential. A proper hood improved things still further. The 1969 styling update saw the introduction of rather fetching black sills and Rostyle wheels, but the Sprite was sadly not long for this world: the end of BMC's arrangement with Healey in 1971 saw the final few cars badged Austin Sprite. However, its sibling, the MG Midget, soldiered on until 1979, so at least the type endured if not the name.

SPECIFICATIONS
Years produced: 1966-1971 (21,768 in total)
Performance: 0-60mph: 14.6 secs (Top speed: 94mph)
Power & torque: 64bhp / 72lb/ft
Engine: Normally aspirated 1275cc in-line four, petrol, carburettor, 8 valves
Drivetrain: Front-engine RWD
Suspension: (F) Independent, coil spring, wishbone. (R) Live axle, quarter-elliptic leaf spring
Bodyframe: Metal monocoque
Transmission: 4-speed manual
Weight: 714kgs
PRICE GUIDE
Launch price: £672
Excellent: £5000
Good: £4000
Average: £2500
Project: £1000

BENTLEY
MkVI

The first of the postwar Bentleys was also the first with a steel body as standard, although many buyers still took the coachbuilding route. The chassis was quite advanced for its time with independent front suspension, servo brakes, a four-speed gearbox and the very useful centralised chassis lubrication system. The 4257cc (4566cc from 1951) six-cylinder engine gained a reputation for sturdiness; not so the standard body which, despite its painstaking handbuilt construction, showed an unfortunate tendency to rust.

SPECIFICATIONS
Years produced: 1946-1955 (5201 in total)
Performance: 0-60mph: 15.2 secs (Top speed: 100mph)
Power & torque: N/Q / N/Q
Engine: Normally aspirated 4526cc in-line six, petrol, carburettor, 12 valves
Drivetrain: Front-engine RWD
Suspension: (F) Independent, coils spring. (R) Live axle, semi-elliptic leaf spring
Bodyframe: Chassis and separate body
Transmission: 4-speed manual
Weight: 1816kgs
PRICE GUIDE
Launch price: £2997
Excellent: £25,000
Good: £19,000
Average: £10,000
Project: £5500

BENTLEY
R-Type

With the standard steel body fitted, the 1952-1955 R-type looked a lot like the MkVI, something the marque's traditional customers no doubt approved of. However, there was extra grace to the design thanks to the more flowing lines and a capacious boot. The same 4566cc six-cylinder engine as on the MkVI continued but with the option of a four-speed automatic transmission from 1952. For 1953 there was a dashboard revamp but the most exciting developments with the R-type were saved for the Continental models.

SPECIFICATIONS
Years produced: 1952-1955 (2320 in total)
Performance: 0-60mph: 15.0 secs (Top speed: 101mph)
Power & torque: N/Q / N/Q
Engine: Normally aspirated 4556cc in-line six, petrol, carburettor, 12 valves
Drivetrain: Front-engine RWD
Suspension: (F) Independent, coils spring. (R) Live axle, semi-elliptic leaf spring
Bodyframe: Chassis and separate body
Transmission: 4-speed manual or 4-speed automatic
Weight: 1816kgs
PRICE GUIDE
Launch price: £4474
Excellent: £27,500
Good: £20,000
Average: £11,000
Project: £6500

BENTLEY
R-Type Continental

HJ Mulliner's Bentley Continental variant of the R-type was pure automotive art. Looking far more modern than its 1952 origins the sublime fastback shape, with the rear wheels concealed by the curvaceous rear wings, was constructed from light alloy. This allowed a top speed of nigh-on 120mph; far faster than the saloon versions but the streamlined shape also helped the performance considerably, as did the 4887cc engine that found its way into the final cars. Hugely expensive now but every penny is worth it.

SPECIFICATIONS
Years produced: 1952-1955 (208 in total)
Performance: 0-60mph: 13.8 secs (Top speed: 117mph)
Power & torque: N/Q / N/Q
Engine: Normally aspirated 4566cc in-line six, petrol, carburettor, 12 valves
Drivetrain: Front-engine RWD
Suspension: (F) Independent, coils spring. (R) Live axle, semi-elliptic leaf spring
Bodyframe: Chassis and separate body
Transmission: 4-speed manual or 4-speed automatic
Weight: 1651kgs
PRICE GUIDE
Launch price: £7608
Excellent: £250,000
Good: £200,000
Average: £140,000
Project: £80,000

BENTLEY
S1 Saloon

As striking as the S1 certainly was, it was also the Rolls-Royce Silver Cloud with different badges. However, gone were the traditional pre-war looks as in came a very sleek integrated body built out of alloy. The six-cylinder engine was now enlarged to 4887cc and improved brakes and front suspension were adopted, followed by a power steering option from 1956. Bentleys outsold their Rolls-Royce counterparts, so these more numerous winged-B models are generally cheaper than their Spirit of Ecstasy counterparts.

SPECIFICATIONS
Years produced: 1955-1959 (3072 in total)
Performance: 0-60mph: 14.2 secs (Top speed: 101mph)
Power & torque: N/Q / N/Q
Engine: Normally aspirated 4887cc in-line six, petrol, carburettor, 8 valves
Drivetrain: Front-engine RWD
Suspension: (F) Independent, coil spring. (R) Live axle, semi-elliptic leaf spring
Bodyframe: Chassis and separate body
Transmission: 4-speed manual or 3-speed automatic
Weight: 1880kgs
PRICE GUIDE
Launch price: £4669
Excellent: £29,500
Good: £22,000
Average: £11,000
Project: £6500

BENTLEY
S1 Continental

While there was nothing that scaled the heights of the R the Continental S-types, constructed by a variety of different builders, were almost universally elegant. Park Ward constructed a significant proportion of the 431 cars and most were two-door, although HJ Mulliner and James Young weighed in with four-door versions. Special permission needed to be obtained from Rolls-Royce for these four-door Continentals to be built. The most innovative S1s were made by Hooper. A small number of dropheads accompanied the coupés.

SPECIFICATIONS

Years produced:	1955-1959 (431 in total)
Performance:	0-60mph: 12.9 secs (Top speed: 119mph)
Power & torque:	N/Q / N/Q
Engine:	Normally aspirated 4887cc in-line six, petrol, carburettor, 12 valves
Drivetrain:	Front-engine RWD
Suspension:	(F) Independent, coil spring. (R) Live axle, semi-elliptic leaf spring
Bodyframe:	Chassis and separate body
Transmission:	4-speed manual or 4-speed automatic
Weight:	1930kgs

PRICE GUIDE

Launch price:	£6127
Excellent:	£100,000
Good:	£80,000
Average:	£55,000
Project:	£35,000

BENTLEY
S2 Saloon

By 1959 it was time to replace the Rolls-Royce/Bentley six-cylinder inlet-over-exhaust valve engines and what better than a chunky V8 for a company with its eyes on the American market? The 6230cc unit installed in the S2 was smoothly powerful and transformed the Bentley into a silky Grand Tourer that could waft around all day. Power steering and automatic transmission were standard fitments, but there was very little to distinguish an S2 from an S1 visually. Drophead coupé and Continental versions were also built.

SPECIFICATIONS

Years produced:	1959-1962 (1863 in total)
Performance:	0-60mph: 11.5 secs (Top speed: 113mph)
Power & torque:	N/Q / N/Q
Engine:	Normally aspirated 6230cc V8, petrol, carburettor, 16 valves
Drivetrain:	Front-engine RWD
Suspension:	(F) Independent, coil spring. (R) Live axle, semi-elliptic leaf spring
Bodyframe:	Chassis and separate body
Transmission:	4-speed manual or 3-speed automatic
Weight:	1981kgs

PRICE GUIDE

Launch price:	£5661
Excellent:	£30,000
Good:	£22,500
Average:	£11,500
Project:	£6500

BENTLEY
S2/S3 Flying Spur

Continental chassis were intended just for two-door Bentleys but, in 1957, HJ Mulliner was given special dispensation to build variations with four doors. These graceful cars were christened Flying Spurs and featured bigger boots than their more racy-looking two-door counterparts. The same changes made to the S2 and S3 saloons were also applied to the Flying Spur, so in 1959 there came the 6230cc V8 engine and, for 1962, twin headlamps were adopted. These final cars were considered the most handsome of the bunch.

SPECIFICATIONS

Years produced:	1959-1965
Performance:	0-60mph: 12.3 secs (Top speed: 120mph)
Power & torque:	N/Q / N/Q
Engine:	Normally aspirated 6230cc V8, petrol, carburettor, 16 valves
Drivetrain:	Front-engine RWD
Suspension:	(F) Independent, wishbone, coil spring. (R) Live axle, semi-elliptic leaf spring
Bodyframe:	Chassis and separate body
Transmission:	4-speed automatic
Weight:	1981kgs

PRICE GUIDE

Launch price:	£6127
Excellent:	£90,000
Good:	£70,000
Average:	£45,000
Project:	£25,000

BENTLEY
S3 Saloon

Hullabaloo surrounded the Bentley S3 of 1962-65 because of its twin headlamps. There were other, less revolutionary touches as well in the form of restyled front wings, a lower bonnet line and improved appointments inside. Mechanically some of the criticisms were answered with a higher compression V8 engine and more effective power steering. Alongside the saloons were the usual long-wheelbase version, a drophead coupé and some startling Continental creations which made intriguing use of the double light units.

SPECIFICATIONS

Years produced:	1962-1965 (1286 in total)
Performance:	11.5 secs (Top speed: 113mph)
Power & torque:	N/Q / N/Q
Engine:	Normally aspirated 6230cc V8, petrol, carburettor, 16 valves
Drivetrain:	Front-engine RWD
Suspension:	(F) Independent, wishbone, coil spring. (R) Live axle, semi-elliptic leaf spring
Bodyframe:	Chassis and separate body
Transmission:	4-speed automatic
Weight:	2077kgs

PRICE GUIDE

Launch price:	£6127
Excellent:	£32,500
Good:	£25,000
Average:	£13,000
Project:	£7000

BENTLEY
T1/T2

1965's T-series was another badge engineering exercise in that the Bentleys were exactly the same as the Rolls-Royce Silver Shadows save for some minute details. This was the first of the marque to have unitary construction, which made it more difficult for coachbuilders to magic up alternative versions. Disc brakes featured on all wheels as did self-levelling suspension. The V8 engine increased to 6750cc in 1970, while the T2 of 1977 had rubber bumpers, a revised dashboard and sharper rack-and-pinion steering.

SPECIFICATIONS

Years produced:	1965-1980 (1712 in total)
Performance:	0-60mph: 10.9 secs (Top speed: 115mph)
Power & torque:	N/Q / N/Q
Engine:	Normally aspirated 6230cc V8, petrol, carburettor, 16 valves
Drivetrain:	Front-engine RWD
Suspension:	(F) Independent, coil spring. (R) Independent, coil spring
Bodyframe:	Metal monocoque
Transmission:	3-speed automatic
Weight:	2113kgs

PRICE GUIDE

Launch price:	£6496
Excellent:	£15,000
Good:	£12,500
Average:	£6500
Project:	£2250

BENTLEY
Mulsanne/Eight Saloon

Rolls-Royce continued to build Bentleys as badge-engineered models with the Mulsanne of 1980. Named after the famous Le Mans straight, the alterations to the Silver Spirit included a black radiator insert and sports seats. The Eight, of 1984, departed further from the Rolls' appearance though. The single rectangular headlamps were replaced by twin circular ones, a mesh radiator grille was fitted along with a front spoiler. It was enough to set the car apart from the Rolls-Royce and help kick-start a revival of interest in Bentley.

SPECIFICATIONS

Years produced:	1980-1992 (2039 in total)
Performance:	0-60mph: 9.6 secs (Top speed: 119mph)
Power & torque:	N/Q / N/Q
Engine:	Normally aspirated 6750cc V8, petrol, carburettor, 16 valves
Drivetrain:	Front-engine RWD
Suspension:	(F) Independent, coil spring. (R) Independent, coil spring
Bodyframe:	Metal monocoque
Transmission:	3-speed automatic
Weight:	2226kgs
	PRICE GUIDE
Launch price:	£49,629
Excellent:	£14,500
Good:	£12,000
Average:	£7000
Project:	£4000

BENTLEY
Mulsanne Turbo

Sales of Bentleys had fallen so low during the T-series era that Rolls-Royce considered axing the marque. Fortunately, the decision was taken to make the Winged B cars stand out instead. The renaissance started with the Mulsanne Turbo of 1982. While the looks didn't differ much from the equivalent Rolls, attached to the 6750cc V8 engine was a Garrett AirResearch turbocharger which increased power by 50%. Being Rolls-Royce of course, what this figure was wasn't actually announced officially.

SPECIFICATIONS

Years produced:	1983-1986
Performance:	0-60mph: 7.0 secs (Top speed: 135mph)
Power & torque:	298bhp / 450lb/ft
Engine:	Turbocharged 6750cc V8, petrol, electronic fuel injection, 16 valves
Drivetrain:	Front-engine RWD
Suspension:	(F) Independent, coil spring. (R) Independent, coil spring
Bodyframe:	Metal monocoque
Transmission:	3-speed automatic
Weight:	2250kgs
	PRICE GUIDE
Launch price:	£58,613
Excellent:	£15,500
Good:	£13,000
Average:	£7500
Project:	£4250

BENTLEY
Turbo R Saloon

In 1985, the Mulsanne Turbo theme was made more extreme with the Turbo R. The new Blower Bentley used the turbocharger and V8 engine of its previous incarnation but complemented it with a Bosch MK-Motronic fuel injection. This put power up to 328bhp, not that the discreet Rolls-Royce would ever admit to that, and gave a top speed of 135mph; this velocity had to be electronically limited because of concerns that the tyres wouldn't cope with the weight of the car. Untethered, 170mph was rumoured to be obtainable.

SPECIFICATIONS

Years produced:	1985-1995 (4815 in total)
Performance:	0-60mph: 6.7 secs (Top speed: 135mph)
Power & torque:	328bhp / 350lb/ft
Engine:	Turbocharged 6750cc V8, petrol, carburettor, overhead valves
Drivetrain:	Front-engine RWD
Suspension:	(F) Independent, coil, spring. (R) Independent, coil, spring
Bodyframe:	Metal monocoque
Transmission:	4-speed automatic
Weight:	2234kgs
	PRICE GUIDE
Launch price:	£79,397
Excellent:	£17,500
Good:	£14,000
Average:	£8500
Project:	£5000

BENTLEY
Continental R Coupé

In a nod to the most beautiful Bentley of them all, the first Continental since 1966 used the R suffix to recall memories of the R-type. The name wasn't taken in vain for this was also the first individually-styled Bentley since the Sixties. Launched in 1991, the glossy coupé looks were substantially more streamlined than the contemporary Bentley saloons and the usual V8 engine was boosted in power. Offshoots were the higher performance Continental S, Continental R Mulliner, Continental T and Continental T Mulliner.

SPECIFICATIONS

Years produced:	1991-2003
Performance:	0-60mph: 6.1 secs (Top speed: 151mph)
Power & torque:	385bhp / 553lb/ft
Engine:	Turbocharged 6750cc V8, petrol, electronic fuel injection, 16 valves
Drivetrain:	Front-engine RWD
Suspension:	(F) Independent, coil spring. (R) Independent, coil spring
Bodyframe:	Metal monocoque
Transmission:	4-speed automatic
Weight:	2450kgs
	PRICE GUIDE
Launch price:	£175,000
Excellent:	£52,000
Good:	£45,000
Average:	£36,000
Project:	£26,000

BERKELEY
SA322/SE328

Sporting cars don't come much more minimalist than this – an Anzani two-cylinder engine powered this glassfibre-bodied two-seater to a top speed of 65mph. Not fast, but certainly fun, and surprisingly popular during the boomtime 1950s. When seen away from other cars, the 322 and 328 look well-proportioned and ahead of their time, but the tiny size makes them a singular choice for the adventurous fans in real life. Cheap to fuel, cheap to buy, and easy to work on, these Berkeleys make great sense, and have a real following today.

SPECIFICATIONS

Years produced:	1956-1958 (146/1272 in total)
Performance:	0-60mph: 38.3 secs (Top speed: 65mph)
Power & torque:	15bhp / 16lb/ft
Engine:	Normally aspirated 322cc twin cylinder, petrol, carburettor, 4 valves
Drivetrain:	Front-engine FWD
Suspension:	(F) Independent, coil spring. (R) Independent, coil spring
Bodyframe:	Glassfibre monocoque
Transmission:	3-speed manual
Weight:	280kgs
	PRICE GUIDE
Launch price:	£575
Excellent:	£5000
Good:	£4000
Average:	£2200
Project:	£1100

BERKELEY
Sport SE492

First real update to the series saw power boosted by the fitment of a three-cylinder Excelsior motorcycle engine. The car was now considerably quicker, topping out at 80mph, a feat proved in motor sport, when Giovanni Lurani found success running a team of three (with his own design of hardtop) in the Italian 750cc GT class of racing. The pinnacle of Berkeley's success was when Lorenzo Bandini scored a win in the 1958 Monza-12 hour race. A Foursome four-seater was also introduced, proving the flexibility of Laurie Bond's original design.

SPECIFICATIONS

Years produced: 1957-1959 (666 in total)
Performance: 0-60mph: 21.8 secs (Top speed: 80mph)
Power & torque: 30bhp / 36lb/ft
Engine: Normally aspirated 492cc in-line three, petrol, carburettor, 6 valves
Drivetrain: Front-engine FWD
Suspension: (F) Independent, coil spring. (R) Independent, coil spring
Bodyframe: Glassfibre monocoque
Transmission: 4-speed manual
Weight: 318kgs

PRICE GUIDE

Launch price: £650
Excellent: £5500
Good: £4500
Average: £2400
Project: £1250

BERKELEY
T60

Lop a wheel off the 322/328 and you're left with the T60 – a three-seater microcar that is just as much fun to drive as its four-wheel counterparts. Designed by Lawrie Bond, who went on to build cars under his own name, the three-wheeler lightweight was incredibly fun to drive in the right circumstances, and remains so to this day. Berkeley even managed to squeeze in a rear seat to some of the last models off the line, and had it not been for the collapse of the parent company, many more than 1830 might have been built.

SPECIFICATIONS

Years produced: 1959-1960 (1830 in total)
Performance: 0-60mph: N/A (Top speed: 60mph)
Power & torque: 18bhp / 22lb/ft
Engine: Normally aspirated 328cc twin cylinder, petrol, carburettor, 4 valves
Drivetrain: Front-engine FWD
Suspension: (F) Independent, coil spring. (R) Independent, coil spring
Bodyframe: Glassfibre monocoque
Transmission: 4-speed manual
Weight: 280kgs

PRICE GUIDE

Launch price: £400
Excellent: £4000
Good: £3000
Average: £1750
Project: £1000

BERKELEY
B95/B105

The evolution of the Berkeley was rapid, and unabated, with the B95 and B105 the ultimate examples of the breed. Power was from a high-compression Royal Enfield Constellation parallel-twin, putting out 50bhp and pushing the car to a top speed of more than 100mph on the 105 model. Roadholding was excellent, as the chassis was easily capable of handling the extra power. However, as sound as the concept was, the Berkeley twins lost out in the market compared with the Austin-Healey Sprite and ended up selling disappointingly.

SPECIFICATIONS

Years produced: 1959-1961 (200 in total)
Performance: 0-60mph: 17.2 secs (Top speed: 105mph)
Power & torque: 50bhp / 45lb/ft
Engine: Normally aspirated 692cc parallel twin, petrol, carburettor, 4 valves
Drivetrain: Front-engine FWD
Suspension: (F) Independent, coil spring. (R) Independent, coil spring
Bodyframe: Glassfibre monocoque
Transmission: 4-speed manual
Weight: 363kgs

PRICE GUIDE

Launch price: £628
Excellent: £5750
Good: £4750
Average: £2500
Project: £1350

BMW
501 V8/502

Starting from near enough the ground up, BMW worked quickly to design, develop and launch the brand new 501 from its new factory in Munich. But what an impressive new beginning – the six cylinder saloon and roadsters were impressively styled (hence the nickname 'Baroque Angel'), refined, expensive and luxurious. Considering Germany was recovering from the effects of WW2, it was probably a case of too much, too soon, but these grand cars put BMW firmly on the map.

SPECIFICATIONS

Years produced: 1952-1961 (12,896 in total)
Performance: 0-60mph: 15.2 secs (Top speed: 103mph)
Power & torque: 105bhp / 95lb/ft
Engine: Normally aspirated 2581cc V8, petrol, carburettor, 16 valves
Drivetrain: Front-engine RWD
Suspension: (F) Independent, torsion bar, wishbone. (R) Live axle, torsion bar
Bodyframe: Chassis and separate body
Transmission: 4-speed manual
Weight: 1334kgs

PRICE GUIDE

Launch price: £2458
Excellent: £16,000
Good: £12,500
Average: £7500
Project: £2500

BMW
507

When it was launched alongside the 503 Coupe in 1956, the 507 was possibly the most beautiful convertible in the world. Whereas its hard-topped sister was slightly awkward to look at from some angles, the 507 came close to perfection. The aluminium-bodied roadster was built on a shortened 502 chassis and powered by the same V8 engine, which produced 150bhp and gave the 507 a fair turn of speed. Despite its beauty, high price and lack of an established image hampered sales – a mere 252 were made, at a significant loss.

SPECIFICATIONS

Years produced: 1956-1959 (252 in total)
Performance: 0-60mph: 9.5 secs (Top speed: 124mph)
Power & torque: 150bhp / 174lb/ft
Engine: Normally aspirated 3168cc V8, petrol, carburettor, 16 valves
Drivetrain: Front-engine RWD
Suspension: (F) Independent, torsion bar. (R) Live axle, torsion bar
Bodyframe: Chassis and separate body
Transmission: 4-speed manual
Weight: 1330kgs

PRICE GUIDE

Launch price: £4201
Excellent: £220,000
Good: £195,000
Average: £140,000
Project: £100,000

BMW Isetta 250/300

Although universally admired, BMW's luxury cars were selling slowly. So, the decision to acquire the licence to build the Isetta proved to be an inspired piece of lateral thinking by BMW management. The Isetta was just what was needed, and as the effects of the Suez Crisis started to hit, and petrol became a rare commodity, suddenly the motorcycle engine car that could achieve 50mpg all day long made a great deal of sense. Front-hinged door and three wheeled handling were questionable, but buyers loved them...for a while.

SPECIFICATIONS

Years produced:	1955-1965 (161,728 in total)
Performance:	0-60mph: N/A (Top speed: 60mph)
Power & torque:	13bhp / 11lb/ft
Engine:	Normally aspirated 297cc flat twin, petrol, carburettor, 2 valves
Drivetrain:	Rear-engine RWD
Suspension:	(F) Independent, coil spring. (R) Live axle, quarter-elliptic leaf spring
Bodyframe:	Chassis and separate body
Transmission:	4-speed manual
Weight:	350kgs
	PRICE GUIDE
Launch price:	£415
Excellent:	£7500
Good:	£6000
Average:	£3000
Project:	£1600

BMW 503 Coupé

Based on the impressive 501, BMW's 503 Coupé sported an exciting new body style penned by Albrecht Goertz. It introduced a new era of modernism for BMW, but at a hefty price that few could afford. It drove as well as it looked, too, with a top speed of nearly 120mph. The 503 Coupé was designed primarily for the American market, but sadly, it was far too expensive to take off, and a mere 412 were built. The outcome was disastrous for BMW, which teetered on the edge of bankruptcy by the end of the 1950s.

SPECIFICATIONS

Years produced:	1956-1959 (412 in total)
Performance:	0-60mph: 10 secs (Top speed: 118mph)
Power & torque:	162bhp / 163lb/ft
Engine:	Normally aspirated 3169cc V8, petrol, carburettor, 16 valves
Drivetrain:	Front-engine RWD
Suspension:	(F) Independent, torsion bar. (R) Live axle, torsion bar
Bodyframe:	Chassis and separate body
Transmission:	4-speed manual
Weight:	1501kgs
	PRICE GUIDE
Launch price:	£4801
Excellent:	£100,000
Good:	£75,000
Average:	£50,000
Project:	£25,000

BMW 600

Following on from the original Isetta, the BMW 600 was a logical upward extension of the theme to capture buyers who'd grown out of their original bubble cars. The front-opening door remained in place, but the new car was larger, with an extra side door for rear seat passengers, a more powerful 600cc BMW flat-twin motorcycle engine and – most importantly – four wheels. It was usefully quicker than the original Isetta but still crude for the price tag, being only marginally cheaper than a Beetle. Sales were unimpressive.

SPECIFICATIONS

Years produced:	1957-1959 (34,813 in total)
Performance:	0-60mph: N/A (Top speed: 63mph)
Power & torque:	19.5bhp / 29lb/ft
Engine:	Normally aspirated 585cc flat twin, petrol, carburettor, 4 valves
Drivetrain:	Rear-engine RWD
Suspension:	(F) Independent, coil spring. (R) Independent, coil spring
Bodyframe:	Chassis and separate body
Transmission:	4-speed manual
Weight:	510kgs
	PRICE GUIDE
Launch price:	£676
Excellent:	£5500
Good:	£4500
Average:	£2650
Project:	£1000

BMW 700

Perhaps the most important car in BMW's history, and certainly the one that saved the company. The BMW 700 may have been based upon the quirky 600, but elegant Michelotti styling and an uprated engine resulted in a budget car that looked good and was great to drive. Grown-up styling and features (four-speed floor-mounted gear selector was a major advance over the 600) and improved suspension that was now fully independent, made the car so much more appealing than its economy car rivals. Coupé version is much in demand today.

SPECIFICATIONS

Years produced:	1959-1965 (188,121 in total)
Performance:	0-60mph: 33.7 secs (Top speed: 75mph)
Power & torque:	32bhp / 37lb/ft
Engine:	Normally aspirated 697cc Flat 2, petrol, carburettor, 4 valves
Drivetrain:	Rear-engine RWD
Suspension:	(F) Independent, coil spring. (R) Independent, coil spring
Bodyframe:	Metal monocoque
Transmission:	4-speed manual
Weight:	640 kgs
	PRICE GUIDE
Launch price:	£894
Excellent:	£4500
Good:	£3500
Average:	£2000
Project:	£950

BMW 2000C/CS

BMW's 'Neue Klasse' range had proved an instant and substantial hit in Germany; and just like the Rover and Triumph 2000s in the UK had revolutionised the executive class here, the BMW equivalent changed the face of the market there. Easily the most appealing was the CS version, a pillarless coupé by Wilhelm Hofmeister. The Karmann-built bodies were pretty, but weren't immune to rust, and have now almost disappeared from the scene. Find a nice one and cherish it – BMW's future success was mapped out here.

SPECIFICATIONS

Years produced:	1966-1969 (11,720 in total)
Performance:	0-60mph: 12.0 secs (Top speed: 110mph)
Power & torque:	120bhp / 123lb/ft
Engine:	Normally aspirated 1991cc in-line four, petrol, carburettor, 8 valves
Drivetrain:	Front-engine RWD
Suspension:	(F) Independent, MacPherson strut, coil spring, anti-roll bar. (R) Independent, semi-trailing arm, coil spring
Bodyframe:	Metal monocoque
Transmission:	4-speed manual
Weight:	1150 kgs
	PRICE GUIDE
Launch price:	£2950
Excellent:	£7500
Good:	£6000
Average:	£3500
Project:	£1650

BMW
2000 Saloon

The 2000 was the ultimate evolution of the 1500/1800cc saloon car line. The medium-sized saloon seemed its most appealing with the bored-out in-line-four under the bonnet, especially in fuel injected tii form, which packed a useful 135bhp. Interesting to drive and a bit of a handful in the wet, the 2000 set the tone for the next generations of BMW's mid-sized saloons – sporting and satisfying. Survival rate in the UK is low, although still fairly commonplace in Germany, and that would be your first place to look when buying.

SPECIFICATIONS

Years produced: 1966-1972 (113,074 in total)
Performance: 0-60mph: 12.4 secs (Top speed: 104mph)
Power & torque: 100bhp / 116lb/ft
Engine: Normally aspirated 1990cc in-line four, petrol, carburettor, 8 valves
Drivetrain: Front-engine RWD
Suspension: (F) Independent, MacPherson strut, coil spring. (R) Independent, semi-trailing arm, coil spring
Bodyframe: Metal monocoque
Transmission: 4-speed manual
Weight: 1130kgs

PRICE GUIDE

Launch price: £1777
Excellent: £4000
Good: £3250
Average: £1800
Project: £600

BMW
1600/1602/1502

With the 'Neue Klasse' doing the business in the executive market, BMW repeated the trick in the small saloon sector with its '02 series models. Despite their relatively high prices the smaller-engined cars in the '02 range were popular entry level models, turning on a generation of drivers to BMW ownership – and today, these cars still enjoy a healthy following. Overshadowed somewhat by the pocket rocket 2002, in many ways, the 1502/1602 are better balanced and more satisfying to own – if you can find one.

SPECIFICATIONS

Years produced: 1966-1977 (324,320 in total)
Performance: 0-60mph: 14.5 secs (Top speed: 96mph)
Power & torque: 85bhp / 91lb/ft
Engine: Normally aspirated 1574cc in-line four, petrol, carburettor, 8 valves
Drivetrain: Front-engine RWD
Suspension: (F) Independent, MacPherson strut, coil spring. (R) Independent, semi-trailing arm, coil spring
Bodyframe: Metal monocoque
Transmission: 4-speed manual
Weight: 920kgs

PRICE GUIDE

Launch price: £1298
Excellent: £3500
Good: £2750
Average: £1600
Project: £500

BMW
2800 CS/CSA

With a straight-six under the bonnet and tidied up front-end styling, the BMW CS Coupé had finally come of age. The 2.8-litre engine developed 150bhp and that was enough to give the handsome CS a maximum speed of 120mph. But speed wasn't this car's major trick, and neither was its elegant styling – the firm and well-controlled suspension settings blessed the car with first-rate handling and long-distance comfort. Mercedes-Benz had met its match, and BMW was now considered a key player in the luxury car market.

SPECIFICATIONS

Years produced: 1968-1975 (9399 in total)
Performance: 0-60mph: 8.3 secs (Top speed: 124mph)
Power & torque: 168bhp / 173lb/ft
Engine: Normally aspirated 2788cc in-line six, petrol, carburettor, 12 valves
Drivetrain: Front-engine RWD
Suspension: (F) Independent, coil spring. (R) Independent, coil spring
Bodyframe: Metal monocoque
Transmission: 4-speed manual
Weight: 1290kgs

PRICE GUIDE

Launch price: £4997
Excellent: £7000
Good: £6000
Average: £3000
Project: £800

BMW
2500/2800/3.0/3.3

With the compact and executive saloon car markets now cornered, BMW turned its attention to the luxury car market and came up with the 2500. It looked like an upscaled version of the '02 Series, but that was no bad thing considering the strong identity, Wilhelm Hofmeister had carved out for the niche. On the road, the 2500 and its larger-engined derivatives were also true to the marque, with all the power and poise you could need in a full-sized saloon. Despite huge sales (relatively speaking), few survive, thanks to widespread corrosion.

SPECIFICATIONS

Years produced: 1968-1977 (217,635 in total)
Performance: 0-60mph: 9.0 secs (Top speed: 127mph)
Power & torque: 180bhp / 255lb/ft
Engine: Normally aspirated 2494cc in-line six, petrol, carburettor, 12 valves
Drivetrain: Front-engine RWD
Suspension: (F) Ind. coil spring, MacPherson strut, lower wishbone. (R) Ind. coil spring, semi-trailing arm
Bodyframe: Metal monocoque
Transmission: 4-speed manual
Weight: 1295kgs

PRICE GUIDE

Launch price: £2197
Excellent: £4000
Good: £3000
Average: £1500
Project: £350

BMW
2002 Saloon/Cabriolet

The 2002 was introduced a couple of years after the 1502/1602 and ended up cementing the series' reputation as the car to beat in the sporting saloon sector. The 2-litre engine was essentially a bored out version of the old 1.8-litre unit, producing 100bhp in standard form. The twin- carburettor TI version, with 120bhp was far more exciting, proving a real handful on challenging roads. The Baur-bodied cabriolet version had no rivals when it was launched, but failed to sell well – perhaps because of its high price and lack of body rigidity.

SPECIFICATIONS

Years produced: 1971-1975 (2517 in total)
Performance: 0-60mph: 12.0 secs (Top speed: 107mph)
Power & torque: 100bhp / 116lb/ft
Engine: Normally aspirated 1990cc in-line four, petrol, carburettor, 8 valves
Drivetrain: Front-engine RWD
Suspension: (F) Independent, MacPherson strut, coil spring. (R) Independent, semi-trailing arm, coil spring
Bodyframe: Metal monocoque
Transmission: 4-speed manual
Weight: 1040kgs

PRICE GUIDE (Cabriolets are worth double)

Launch price: £1948
Excellent: £4500
Good: £3750
Average: £1850
Project: £650

BMW 2002tii

One of Europe's finest Q-cars of its era, the fuel injected 2002tii could crack 120mph on the Autobahn and drive sideways on the merest whiff of throttle. Retaining all the strengths of the rest of the '02 series cars, the tii has justifiably gone on to become something of a legend. However, like all '02s, it can suffer from extensive corrosion, which undermines the quality and ruggedness of the rest of the package. Cult following means these cars are in demand and command a healthy premium over their less-glamorous counterparts.

SPECIFICATIONS

Years produced: 1971-1975 (38,701 in total)
Performance: 0-60mph: 10.0 secs (Top speed: 119mph)
Power & torque: 130bhp / 131lb/ft
Engine: Normally aspirated 1990cc in-line four, petrol, mechanical fuel injection, 8 valves
Drivetrain: Front-engine RWD
Suspension: (F) Ind. MacPherson strut, coil spring. (R) Ind. trailing arm, coil spring
Bodyframe: Metal monocoque
Transmission: 4-speed manual; 5-speed optional
Weight: 1010kgs

PRICE GUIDE

Launch price: £2299
Excellent: £7500
Good: £6000
Average: £3000
Project: £1200

BMW 3.0 CS/CSi

Although outwardly similar to the outgoing 2800, the 1971 3.0CS was a major step forwards thanks to an uprated chassis and braking set-up first seen in the saloon range. The excellent roadholding of the former model was easily surpassed, and unlike the smaller cars in the range, snap-oversteer was rare. The fuel injected CSi passed the 200bhp mark, making it a paid-up member of the performance car elite, with a top speed of 135mph and 0-60mph time of less than eight seconds. Still considered by many to be the most desirable BMW coupé of them all.

SPECIFICATIONS

Years produced: 1971-1975 (19,207 in total)
Performance: 0-60mph: 7.5 secs (Top speed: 139mph)
Power & torque: 200bhp / 200lb/ft
Engine: Normally aspirated 2986cc in-line six, petrol, electronic fuel injection, 12 valves
Drivetrain: Front-engine RWD
Suspension: (F) Independent, MacPherson strut, anti-roll bars. (R) Ind. semi-trailing arms, coil spring, telescopic damper
Bodyframe: Metal monocoque
Transmission: 4-speed manual
Weight: 1270kgs

PRICE GUIDE

Launch price: £6199
Excellent: £15,000
Good: £10,000
Average: £5000
Project: £1500

BMW 3.0 CSL

As homologation specials go, the BMW CSL is perhaps the most memorable. Featuring lightweight aluminium panels, a stripped out interior and plexiglasss side windows, the CSL was as effective on the track as its vanilla brother was on the road. UK models retained the luxury interior of the standard cars, taking away some of the raw appeal – but buyers loved them. The most famous of all, the Batmobile, of which only 39 were made, sported extraordinary aerodynamic appendages, and are now worth serious money for a BMW of this era.

SPECIFICATIONS

Years produced: 1972-1975 (1096 in total)
Performance: 0-60mph: 7.5 secs (Top speed: 138mph)
Power & torque: 206bhp / 195lb/ft
Engine: Normally aspirated 3153cc in-line six, petrol, mechanical fuel injection, 12 valves
Drivetrain: Front-engine RWD
Suspension: (F) Independent, MacPherson strut, anti- roll bar. (R) Ind. semi-trailing arm, coil spring, telescopic damper
Bodyframe: Metal monocoque
Transmission: 4-speed manual
Weight: 1270kgs

PRICE GUIDE

Launch price: £6399
Excellent: £25,000
Good: £20,000
Average: £12,000
Project: £5000

BMW 2002 Turbo

For those thrill-seekers who wanted real excitement in their lives, and who could afford one, the BMW 2002 Turbo really was the ultimate driving machine. It was Europe's first turbocharged production car, and like all the earliest cars to sport a blower, the 2002 Turbo was prodigiously powerful and suffered from massive turbo lag. But keep the revs up, and anticipate when the turbo would start spinning, and there were few saloons in the world that could keep up. Only 1672 were built, making them rare and expensive today – but what a laugh for the money...

SPECIFICATIONS

Years produced: 1973-1974 (1672 in total)
Performance: 0-60mph: 8.0 secs (Top speed: 130mph)
Power & torque: 170bhp / 177lb/ft
Engine: Turbocharged 1990cc in-line four, petrol, mechanical fuel injection, 8 valves
Drivetrain: Front-engine RWD
Suspension: (F) Ind, MacPherson strut, coil spring. (R) Ind. semi-trailing arm, coil spring
Bodyframe: Metal monocoque
Transmission: 4-speed manual
Weight: 1080kgs

PRICE GUIDE

Launch price: £2433
Excellent: £17,500
Good: £15,000
Average: £8500
Project: £4250

BMW 633/628 CSi

Like the CS before it, the 6-Series coupé was closely related to the luxury saloon in the BMW range. The key BMW selling points of sharp steering, keen dynamics and strong performance were all intact, but many customers bemoaned the styling of the new car, which is far less pretty. Conceived as more of a grand tourer than the CS, the 6-Series was easier to live with – and as a classic car, it makes far more sense thanks to its commodious interior and improved reliability and rust resistance.

SPECIFICATIONS

Years produced: 1976-1987 (29,382 in total)
Performance: 0-60mph: 8.5 secs (Top speed: 134mph)
Power & torque: 197bhp / 210lb/ft
Engine: Normally aspirated 3210cc in-line six, petrol, electronic fuel injection, 12 valves
Drivetrain: Front-engine RWD
Suspension: (F) Ind. MacPherson strut, anti-roll bar. (R) Ind. semi-trailing arm
Bodyframe: Metal monocoque
Transmission: 4-speed manual
Weight: 1495kgs

PRICE GUIDE

Launch price: £13,980
Excellent: £5000
Good: £4000
Average: £2000
Project: £700

BMW
M1

The original M car, and easily the most exciting. The M1 was created for Group Five racing, but thanks to delays during development which lead to BMW taking control of body production (when partner, Lamborghini, couldn't deliver its side of the bargain), it arrived late and never fulfilled its obvious racing potential. The styling by Giugiaro was spot on, as was its chassis and race bred 24-valve engine, and BMW was justifiably proud of its new supercar. But after a run of 456, production of the era's most drivable supercar came to a halt. Revered today.

SPECIFICATIONS

Years produced:	1979-1980 (456 in total)
Performance:	0-60mph: 6.5 secs (Top speed: 163mph)
Power & torque:	277bhp / 243lb/ft
Engine:	Normally aspirated 3453cc in-line six, petrol, mechanical fuel injection, 24 valves
Drivetrain:	Mid-engine RWD
Suspension:	(F) Ind. double wishbone, coil spring. (R) Ind. double wishbone, coil spring
Bodyframe:	Spaceframe
Transmission:	5-speed manual
Weight:	1300kgs
	PRICE GUIDE
Launch price:	£37,570
Excellent:	£95,000
Good:	£80,000
Average:	£65,000
Project:	£50,000

BMW
635CSi

The earliest 6-Series cars never seemed quite as satisfying as they should have. The heavier body stunted performance, and the big coupé just didn't seem quite as sporting as it once did. But the 635CSi went a long way to redressing the balance thanks to its crisp new engine and altered chassis settings. Throughout its life, the CSi continued to be improved, thanks to further running changes. When it was replaced by the 850 in 1989, commentators bemoaned the fact the new car wasn't as instantly appealing as the old – sound familiar?

SPECIFICATIONS

Years produced:	1978-1989
Performance:	0-60mph: 8.0 secs (Top speed: 138mph)
Power & torque:	218bhp / 228lb/ft
Engine:	Normally aspirated 3453cc in-line six, petrol, electronic fuel injection, 12 valves
Drivetrain:	Front-engine RWD
Suspension:	(F) Independent, MacPherson strut, anti-roll bar, (R) Independent, semi-trailing arm, coil spring, anti-roll bar
Bodyframe:	Metal monocoque
Transmission:	5-speed manual
Weight:	1475kgs
	PRICE GUIDE
Launch price:	£16,499
Excellent:	£7000
Good:	£5500
Average:	£2750
Project:	£800

BMW
3-series Baur Cabriolet

The BMW 3-Series was another landmark car for BMW – as it took the best bits of the '02 Series and refined them for the 1970s. Huge sales success followed, while the numbers 325 become something of a legend. The Baur cabriolet, introduced in 1979 further extended the appeal of the range, even if its bulky roll-over bar marred the open air feel. But there were positive benefits – it felt solid, and had ample crash protection. Sales were slow, though, no doubt because of the high price. Rare today, after many examples fell prey to the effects of rust.

SPECIFICATIONS

Years produced:	1979-1982
Performance:	0-60mph: 9.5 secs (Top speed: 116mph)
Power & torque:	123bhp / 125lb/ft
Engine:	Normally aspirated 1991cc in-line six, petrol, electronic fuel injection, 12 valves
Drivetrain:	front-engine RWD
Suspension:	(F) Independent, MacPherson struts, anti-roll bar. (R) Independent, semi-trailing arm, coil spring, anti-roll bar
Bodyframe:	Metal monocoque
Transmission:	5-speed manual
Weight:	1104kgs
	PRICE GUIDE
Launch price:	Not sold in UK
Excellent:	£5500
Good:	£4500
Average:	£2250
Project:	£650

BMW
M5 (E28)

The first M-Sport 5-Series was another case of following the formula to stuff a powerful engine under the bonnet of the well-proportioned 5-Series. This time around, the full-fat 286bhp M1 engine created a super-saloon par excellence, and unlike the first car, which looked every bit the road car racer, the M5 was discrete to the point of anonymity. Canny owners debadged their cars and went supercar baiting. After years in the doldrums, the E28 is beginning to gain recognition as an '80s icon, and values are beginning to rise sharply.

SPECIFICATIONS

Years produced:	1984-1987 (2145 in total)
Performance:	0-60mph: 7.0 secs (Top speed: 156mph)
Power & torque:	282bhp / 251lb/ft
Engine:	Normally aspirated 3452cc in-line six, petrol, electronic fuel injection, 24 valves
Drivetrain:	Front-engine RWD
Suspension:	(F) Independent, MacPherson strut, lower wishbone. (R) Independent, coil spring, semi-trailing arm
Bodyframe:	Metal monocoque
Transmission:	5-speed manual
Weight:	1250kgs
	PRICE GUIDE
Launch price:	£21,805
Excellent:	£9500
Good:	£8000
Average:	£6000
Project:	£3000

BMW
M535i

The first in a long line of hot 5-Series variants, the E12 generation M535i was something special when it first appeared in 1979. Created by installing the 218bhp 635CSi engine into the 5-Series body, the M535i emerged as an astounding Q-car. Deep front spoiler and cross-spoke ally wheels were an immediate give away, but treats for the driver included a ZF gearbox, Recaro seats and a limited slip differential. Most have rusted away (or ended up going off the road backwards), and the remaining cars are cheap considering their all-round ability.

SPECIFICATIONS

Years produced:	1984-1987 (45,655 in total)
Performance:	0-60mph: 6.9 secs (Top speed: 143mph)
Power & torque:	218bhp / 224lb/ft
Engine:	Normally aspirated 3430cc in-line six, petrol, electronic fuel injection, 12 valves
Drivetrain:	Front-engine RWD
Suspension:	(F) Independent, MacPherson strut. (R) Independent, semi-trailing arm, coil spring
Bodyframe:	Metal monocoque
Transmission:	5-speed manual
Weight:	1391kgs
	PRICE GUIDE
Launch price:	£13,745
Excellent:	£4250
Good:	£3250
Average:	£1500
Project:	£650

BMW
M635CSi

A 1980s sporting classic was created in 1984 when BMW hit on the bright idea of fitting the 286bhp M-Power engine from the mid-engined M1 into the 635CSi body. With stiffened suspension, improved damping as well as standard limited slip differential the full-sized coupé became a sublime package, with masses of all-round ability. Values remain significantly higher than non M-Sport coupes. Keep an eye out for fakes, and remember that the M-Sport engine costs significantly more to fix when it goes wrong.

SPECIFICATIONS

Years produced:	1985-1989 (5803 in total)
Performance:	0-60mph: 6.5 secs (Top speed: 158mph)
Power & torque:	282bhp / 246lb/ft
Engine:	Normally aspirated 3453cc in-line six, petrol, electronic fuel injection, 24 valves
Drivetrain:	Front-engine RWD
Suspension:	(F) Independent, MacPherson strut, anti-roll bar. (R) Independent, semi-trailing arm, coil spring, anti-roll bar
Bodyframe:	Metal monocoque
Transmission:	5-speed manual
Weight:	1505kgs
PRICE GUIDE	
Launch price:	£32,195
Excellent:	£12,000
Good:	£9500
Average:	£5750
Project:	£2500

BMW
3-series convertible E30

After the Baur convertibles with their bulky roll-over structures, the in-house 3-Series convertible, which made do with a strengthened windscreen surround instead, looked an incredibly clean design. And in a marketplace dominated by cluttered convertible designs, the E30 convertible did very well indeed. Available with a variety of engine options, the 318i version was the most popular in the UK, although the 325i came a close second. Rapidly disappearing from the UK's roads, grab a good one now – values are bound to be on the up soon.

SPECIFICATIONS

Years produced:	1985-1993 (143,425 in total)
Performance:	0-60mph: 8.4 secs (Top speed: 135mph)
Power & torque:	169bhp / 167lb/ft
Engine:	Normally aspirated 2494cc in-line six, petrol, electronic fuel injection, 12 valves
Drivetrain:	Front-engine RWD
Suspension:	(F) Independent, MacPherson strut. (R) Ind. semi-trailing arm, coil spring
Bodyframe:	Metal monocoque
Transmission:	5-speed manual
Weight:	1090kgs
PRICE GUIDE	
Launch price:	£11,590
Excellent:	£5250
Good:	£4000
Average:	£2000
Project:	£700

BMW
M3 E30

The M3 was conceived to compete in Group A Touring Cars, and was one of a rare breed of BMW homologation specials, as most M-Sport cars were designed solely for the road. The 2.3-litre S14 engine was loosely based on the venerable M10 four-cylinder and it produced 192bhp straight from the box. However, it was developed through its life, and late Evo and Sport versions were pushing out 235bhp, a remarkable figure considering the lack of forced induction. In short, a brilliant sports saloon.

SPECIFICATIONS

Years produced:	1986-1990 (17,184 in total)
Performance:	0-60mph: 6.5 secs (Top speed: 154mph)
Power & torque:	238bhp / 177lb/ft
Engine:	Normally aspirated 2467cc in-line four, petrol, electronic fuel injection, 16 valves
Drivetrain:	Front-engine RWD
Suspension:	(F) Independent, MacPherson strut, anti-roll bar. (R) Independent, semi-trailing arm, coil spring, anti-roll bar
Bodyframe:	Metal monocoque
Transmission:	5-speed manual
Weight:	1200kgs
PRICE GUIDE	
Launch price:	£22,750
Excellent:	£14,000
Good:	£11,500
Average:	£8000
Project:	£5000

BMW
Z1

The Z1 was initially a concept at the 1987 Frankfurt Motor Show, but buyers were soon clamouring to buy one, leaving BMW to rush to get the innovative little roadster into production. Most notable for its doors, which drop into the sills, the Z1 bristled with advanced design features and weight-saving touches. Powered by the same engine as the 325i, it was no ball of fire considering its high price. Rapidly diminishing interest from buyers saw BMW halt production after 8000 were built. Not an official UK import but plenty have been shipped in.

SPECIFICATIONS

Years produced:	1988-1991 (8000 in total)
Performance:	0-60mph: 9.0 secs (Top speed: 136mph)
Power & torque:	170bhp / 164lb/ft
Engine:	Normally aspirated 2494cc in-line six, petrol, electronic fuel injection, 12 valves
Drivetrain:	Front-engine RWD
Suspension:	(F) Independent, MacPherson strut, anti-roll bar. (R) Independent, trailing arm, diagonal link, coil spring
Bodyframe:	Metal monocoque
Transmission:	5-speed manual
Weight:	1290kgs
PRICE GUIDE	
Launch price:	£36,925
Excellent:	£17,500
Good:	£15,000
Average:	£11,000
Project:	£8000

BMW
M5 (E34)

The E34 generation took the M5 squarely into the 1990s, thanks to substantially-modernised styling, and a smooth new interior. The fabulous in-line six received various modifications to boost power to 315bhp, pushing the top speed to a limited 155mph. King of the hill from the moment it was launched, rivals struggled to match the M5's intimacy, balance and pace. Further improved in 1994, when the 3.5-litre engine's output was raised to 340bhp, although top speed remained the same, unless the owner removed the limiter.

SPECIFICATIONS

Years produced:	1988-1995 (11,098 in total)
Performance:	0-60mph: 6.5 secs (Top speed: 155mph)
Power & torque:	315bhp / 265lb/ft
Engine:	Normally aspirated 3535cc in-line six, petrol, electronic fuel injection, 24 valves
Drivetrain:	Front-engine RWD
Suspension:	(F) Ind. MacPherson strut. (R) Ind. Semi-trailing arm, coil spring and damper unit, hydropneumatic self levelling
Bodyframe:	Metal monocoque
Transmission:	5-speed manual
Weight:	1720kgs
PRICE GUIDE	
Launch price:	£31,295
Excellent:	£8500
Good:	£7000
Average:	£4500
Project:	£2000

BMW
325i Sport E30

The E30 is another '80s icon, regarded as a yuppie's plaything at the time, but now seen as the ultimate evolution of Hofmeister's seminal designs of the '60s. The small saloon lent itself well to every engine installed, but the ultimate 2.5-litre straight-six offered the biggest dose of thrills. The Sport model may have worn a slightly out-of-place bodykit, lessening its Q-car appeal, but that wailing engine, controllable rear-biased handling and all-round quality made this the sports saloon to beat. Today, it's seen as an inexpensive road to RWD fun, and shabby examples are still cheap.

SPECIFICATIONS

Years produced: 1989-1991
Performance: 0-60mph: 7.5 secs (Top speed: 140mph)
Power & torque: 195bhp / 195lb/ft
Engine: Normally aspirated 2693cc in-line six, petrol, electronic fuel injection, 12 valves
Drivetrain: Front-engine RWD
Suspension: (F) Independent, MacPherson strut. (R) Independent, coil spring, semi-trailing arm, anti-roll bar
Bodyframe: Metal monocoque
Transmission: 5-speed manual
Weight: 1147kgs

PRICE GUIDE

Launch price: £17,250
Excellent: £6000
Good: £4500
Average: £2500
Project: £1250

BMW
840/850 CSi

A push upmarket for BMW, the 850i was a true measure of the company's confidence by the late '80s. Powered by BMW's first V12 engine, it was quick and effortless, and its sleek styling was a big departure from its last coupé, the 6-Series. However, sales were slow during the recession of the early '90s so BMW introduced lower-priced V8 versions under the CSi banner. However, when production ended, the company chose not to replace the 8-Series, deciding instead to abandon that sector of the market.

SPECIFICATIONS

Years produced: 1991-1999 (22,776 in total)
Performance: 0-60mph: 6.0 secs (Top speed: 155mph)
Power & torque: 381bhp / 406lb/ft
Engine: Normally aspirated 5576cc V12, petrol, electronic fuel injection, 24 valves
Drivetrain: Front-engine RWD
Suspension: (F) Ind. MacPherson struts. (R) Ind. multi-link axle, coil spring, self levelling, electronic damper control
Bodyframe: Metal monocoque
Transmission: 6-speed manual
Weight: 1780kgs

PRICE GUIDE

Launch price: £54,490
Excellent: £11,500
Good: £9500
Average: £5500
Project: £2750

BMW
Z8

Everyone was into retro design during the late '90s, and when BMW unveiled its Z07 concept at the 1997 Tokyo Motor Show, it was clear that a production version would follow. Deliberately styled – and detailed – to recall the gorgeous 507, the production version, known as the Z8, aroused considerable interest, even starring in the James Bond film, *The World is Not Enough*. Powered by the M5's V8 engine, pushing out 400bhp, the Z8 was very quick, but it failed to sell. A handful were made, though, and it's sure to be collectable in future years.

SPECIFICATIONS

Years produced: 2000-2003 (5703 in total)
Performance: 0-60mph: 4.7 secs (Top speed: 155mph)
Power & torque: 394bhp / 369lb/ft
Engine: Normally aspirated 4941cc V8, petrol, electronic fuel injection, 32 valves
Drivetrain: Front-engine RWD
Suspension: (F) Ind, MacPherson strut. (R) Multi-link axle with trailing arm, twin transverse upper link, coil spring
Bodyframe: Spaceframe
Transmission: 6-speed manual
Weight: 1583kgs

PRICE GUIDE

Launch price: £80,000
Excellent: £65,000
Good: £55,000
Average: £46,000
Project: £37,000

BOND
Minicar 3-wheeler

At the end of the war cars were at a premium so engineer Lawrie Bond came up with a budget three-wheeler Britain could afford. The Bond Minicar was poverty motoring in the extreme: no roof, no doors, brakes only at the rear and precious little suspension. The 1-cylinder two-stroke 122cc motorcycle engine started life with just 5bhp but gave 40mph and a claimed 104mpg. Minicars gradually became more refined and powerful until production ended in 1966. The final Mark G had a roof, doors and hydraulic brakes.

SPECIFICATIONS

Years produced: 1948-1965 (24,484 in total)
Performance: 0-60mph: N/A (Top speed: 50mph)
Power & torque: 5-12bhp / N/A
Engine: Normally aspirated 122cc, single cylinder two-stroke, petrol, carburettor
Drivetrain: Front-engine FWD
Suspension: (F) Independent, coil spring. (R) None then independent, rubber or coil spring
Bodyframe: Monocoque then separate chassis
Transmission: Chain drive
Weight: 140kgs

PRICE GUIDE

Launch price: £199
Excellent: £3750
Good: £3000
Average: £1500
Project: £700

BOND
GT 2+2/GT4S

In 1963 Bond expanded into the world of specialist sportscars – with four wheels. But the full quotient of wheels still didn't fulfil Bond's claims that this was 'the most beautiful car in the world' although this glassfibre coupé on a Triumph Herald chassis was a neat enough effort. Initially the engine was the 1147cc from the Triumph Spitfire, which rose to 1296cc in 1967 when the Spitfire expanded. The improved GT4S of 1964 had four headlamps, a boot that actually opened and greater headroom that helped to up the comfort level.

SPECIFICATIONS

Years produced: 1963-1970 (2949 in total)
Performance: 0-60mph: 20.0 secs (Top speed: 91mph)
Power & torque: 67bhp / 67lb/ft
Engine: Normally aspirated 1147cc in-line four, petrol, carburettor, 8 valves
Drivetrain: Front-engine RWD
Suspension: (F) Independent, wishbone, coil spring. (R) Independent, transverse leaf spring
Bodyframe: Chassis and separate glassfibre body
Transmission: 4-speed manual
Weight: 737kgs

PRICE GUIDE

Launch price: £822
Excellent: £2800
Good: £2200
Average: £1400
Project: £400

BOND
875

Bond three-wheelers grew up in 1965 with the advent of the 875. Fabricated from glassfibre the designation came from the 875cc Hillman Imp engine installed in the rear. Despite it being detuned to 34bhp the Bond was still disconcertingly fast and also rather precarious on corners. A MkII version in 1967 saw the front end remodelled with rectangular headlamps. Like the Minicar, the 875 would probably have enjoyed a long life had not Reliant taken over Bond in 1969 and brought production of this Regal rival to an end.

	SPECIFICATIONS
Years produced:	1965-1970 (3431 in total)
Performance:	0-60mph: 17.4 secs (Top speed: 81mph)
Power & torque:	34bhp / 49lb/ft
Engine:	Normally aspirated 875cc in-line four, petrol, carburettor, 8 valves
Drivetrain:	Rear-engine RWD
Suspension:	(F) Independent, coil spring. (R) Independent, coil spring
Bodyframe:	Chassis and separate glassfibre body
Transmission:	4-speed manual
Weight:	362kgs
	PRICE GUIDE
Launch price:	£495
Excellent:	£1850
Good:	£1400
Average:	£650
Project:	£200

BOND
Equipe 2-litre

Having built a Herald-based sports coupe, it was only logical that Bond would try something similar with the Vitesse chassis. The result, in 1967, was the Equipe GT, also known as the 2-Litre. The styling of the glassfibre/steel-panelled vehicle was completely different to Bond's previous Equipe; more square-rigged and heavier. However, the extra weight didn't matter too much as the additional power of the Triumph six-pot (95bhp at first, 104bhp from 1968) gave this specialist sportscar adequate performance, with 100mph easily obtainable.

	SPECIFICATIONS
Years produced:	1967-1970 (1432 in total)
Performance:	0-60mph: 10.7 secs (Top speed: 102mph)
Power & torque:	95bhp / 117lb/ft
Engine:	Normally aspirated 1998cc in-line six, petrol, carburettor, 12 valves
Drivetrain:	Front-engine RWD
Suspension:	(F) Ind. wishbone, coil spring, anti-roll bar. (R) Ind. transverse leaf spring
Bodyframe:	Chassis and separate glassfibre body
Transmission:	4-speed manual
Weight:	914kgs
	PRICE GUIDE
Launch price:	£1096
Excellent:	£3700
Good:	£2750
Average:	£1500
Project:	£450

BOND
Bug 700E

This funky and fun three-wheeler was built for pure entertainment purposes by Reliant, Bond's owner from 1969. A cheesy car for a cheesy decade, Ogle Design came up with the wedge shape where the two passengers gained access via the pull-forward canopy. The only official colour available was a very vibrant tangerine. The engines were Reliant: a 700cc unit offering 29bhp, and 31bhp on the ES model, followed by a 748cc offering 32bhp in 1973. Utterly mad but the classic car world is all the richer for bizarre cars such as these.

	SPECIFICATIONS
Years produced:	1970-1974 (2270 in total)
Performance:	0-60mph: 23.2 secs (Top speed: 76mph)
Power & torque:	29bhp / 35lb/ft
Engine:	Normally aspirated 700cc in-line four, petrol, carburettor, 8 valves
Drivetrain:	Front-engine RWD
Suspension:	(F) Independent, coil spring. (R) Independent, coil spring
Bodyframe:	Chassis and separate glassfibre body
Transmission:	4-speed manual
Weight:	394kgs
	PRICE GUIDE
Launch price:	£629
Excellent:	£4250
Good:	£3250
Average:	£1750
Project:	£1000

BORGWARD
Isabella TS saloon

A superbly-engineered car that was a revelation in its day. Alloy-head 1500 engine puts out an impressive 75bhp, which Ford only just surpassed eight years later with the Cortina GT, and no Cortina ever enjoyed the Isabella's independent rear suspension. Before he became a Vauxhall tuning guru, Bill Blydenstein successfully raced one in the Fifties. Brakes are another strong point and even the four-speed column-change is a delight to use. Thanks to a strong following in their native Germany, parts supply is almost total.

	SPECIFICATIONS
Years produced:	1954-1961 (202,862 in total)
Performance:	0-60mph: 16.0 secs (Top speed: 95mph)
Power & torque:	75bhp / 85lb/ft
Engine:	Normally aspirated 1493cc in-line four, petrol, carburettor, 8 valves
Drivetrain:	Front-engine RWD
Suspension:	(F) Independent, coil spring. (R) Independent,coil spring
Bodyframe:	Metal monocoque
Transmission:	4-speed manual
Weight:	1080kgs
	PRICE GUIDE
Launch price:	£1124
Excellent:	£7250
Good:	£6000
Average:	£3000
Project:	£1000

BORGWARD
Isabella Coupé

Generally considered to be Carl Borgward's masterpiece, the Isabella Coupé was initially conceived as an image booster for the firm. The 2+2 oozes class, has a decent turn of speed and handles tidily with its all-independent coil-sprung suspension and rear swing axles. The unburstable engines even run happily on unleaded fuel without any alteration. A cabriolet version was also built, but these are much rarer. However, they are very highly thought of in Germany, and can easily fetch twice the price of a Coupé.

	SPECIFICATIONS
Years produced:	1955-1961
Performance:	0-60mph: (Top speed: 81mph)
Power & torque:	60 bhp / 79lb/ft
Engine:	Normally aspirated 1493cc in-line four, petrol, carburettor, 8 valves
Drivetrain:	Front-engine RWD
Suspension:	(F) Independent, coil spring. (R) Independent coil spring
Bodyframe:	Metal monocoque
Transmission:	4-speed manual
Weight:	1080kgs
	PRICE GUIDE
Launch price:	£1874
Excellent:	£13,500
Good:	£10,000
Average:	£5500
Project:	£1750

BRISTOL 400

Bristol Cars was formed when the Bristol Aircraft Company joined forces with Frazer-Nash's parent company, AFN. Before the War, AFN was the concessionaire for BMW in the UK, so after Bristol took possession of BMW's designs, AFN was the natural choice for a build partner. The 400 was the first fruit of their efforts, and was clearly based on a mixture of the pre-war BMW 326 (chassis) and 327/80 (body). Many changes were made – and aircraft levels of build quality were a clear benefit.

SPECIFICATIONS

Years produced: 1947-1950 (700 in total)
Performance: 0-60mph: 14.7 secs (Top speed: 94mph)
Power & torque: 80bhp / 96lb/ft
Engine: Normally aspirated 1971cc in-line six, petrol, carburettor, 12 valves
Drivetrain: Front-engine RWD
Suspension: (F) Independent, transverse leaf spring. (R) Live axle, torsion bar
Bodyframe: Chassis and separate body
Transmission: 4-speed manual
Weight: 1118kgs

PRICE GUIDE

Launch price: £2374
Excellent: £24,000
Good: £20,000
Average: £9500
Project: £4750

BRISTOL 401/403

Putting right the 400's main failing, its ungainly body, the 401 was introduced initially for export markets only. Its handsome styling was the result of extensive wind tunnel work, after a basic design was submitted by Superleggera Touring. It was a design way ahead of its time, merely let down by a lack of power. This shortcoming was put right five years later, with the appearance of the 403 – and a welcome upgrade to 100bhp. Bristols were expensive and well crafted – the latter trait keeps them surprisingly usable today.

SPECIFICATIONS

Years produced: 1949-1955 (950 in total)
Performance: 0-60mph: 15.1 secs (Top speed: 97mph)
Power & torque: 85bhp / 107lb/ft
Engine: Normally aspirated 1971cc in-line six, petrol, carburettor, 12 valves
Drivetrain: Front-engine RWD
Suspension: (F) Independent, transverse leaf spring. (R) Live axle, torsion bar
Bodyframe: Chassis and separate body
Transmission: 4-speed manual
Weight: 1224kgs

PRICE GUIDE

Launch price: £3214
Excellent: £22,500
Good: £19,000
Average: £9500
Project: £4250

BRISTOL 404

Essentially, the 404 was a short-wheelbase Arnold-Bristol chassis married to an exquisitely styled two-door coupé bodyshell. But it was not without problems. There was the small issue of price (it cost twice as much as a Jaguar XK120) and a lack of ultimate power compared with its Coventry rival. There were problems with the construction, too. The aluminium body and a pitch pine chassis frame have caused problems with owners in later years. But for all its problems, the 404, in looks at least, allowed it to break away from its Teutonic forbears.

SPECIFICATIONS

Years produced: 1953-1955 (52 in total)
Performance: 0-60mph: N/A (Top speed: 110mph)
Power & torque: 105bhp / 123lb/ft
Engine: Normally aspirated 1971cc in-line six, petrol, carburettor, 12 valves
Drivetrain: Front-engine RWD
Suspension: (F) Independent, transverse leaf spring. (R) Live axle, torsion bar
Bodyframe: Chassis and separate body
Transmission: 4-speed manual
Weight: 1039kgs

PRICE GUIDE

Launch price: £3543
Excellent: £39,000
Good: £32,500
Average: £20,000
Project: £10,000

BRISTOL 405

This was effectively a long-wheelbase version of the 404 (the saloon had four doors). It went on to score significantly more commercial success and was the first car produced by Bristol to have an opening bootlid. Unlike the 404, which, through its extensive use of wood in its construction, has a low survival rate, the 405's done much better over the years, as what wood had been used in the body was above the waistline. A pretty four-door GT that was crying out for more power.

SPECIFICATIONS

Years produced: 1954-1956 (340 in total)
Performance: 0-60mph: N/A (Top speed: 110mph)
Power & torque: 105bhp / 123lb/ft
Engine: Normally aspirated 1971cc in-line six, petrol, carburettor, 12 valves
Drivetrain: Front-engine RWD
Suspension: (F) Ind transverse leaf spring. (R) Live axle, torsion bar
Bodyframe: Chassis and separate body
Transmission: 4-speed manual with overdrive
Weight: 1230kgs

PRICE GUIDE

Launch price: £3189
Excellent: £17,000 (Add £10,000 for convertible)
Good: £14,000
Average: £7000
Project: £3000

BRISTOL 406

The 406 ended up being the last Bristol to be powered by the BMW-derived straight-six; but the first of a long line of cars that would use essentially the same body, with a series of running updates. In terms of power, the 406 had no more than the 405, despite its engine being enlarged to 2.2-litres, and performance with this large body was predictably leisurely. The brakes were improved, though, featuring discs front and rear, and the rear suspension got a Watt's linkage . More would come with the arrival of the V8-powered cars.

SPECIFICATIONS

Years produced: 1958-1961 (292 in total)
Performance: 0-60mph: N/A (Top speed: 106mph)
Power & torque: 105bhp / 129lb/ft
Engine: Normally aspirated 2216cc in-line six, petrol, carburettor, 12 valves
Drivetrain: Front-engine RWD
Suspension: (F) Independent, transverse leaf spring. (R) Live axle, torsion bar
Bodyframe: Chassis and separate body
Transmission: 4-speed manual with overdrive
Weight: 1365kgs

PRICE GUIDE

Launch price: £4494
Excellent: £17,000
Good: £13,500
Average: £7500
Project: £3250

BRISTOL 407/408/409/410

Changes in the ownership of Bristol Cars meant that it was now a separate entity to the aeroplane manufacturer. Although that wouldn't make much difference to the high-quality cars produced, it marked the point when the Chrysler V8 was finally installed under the long bonnet of the 406, giving the elegant sporting saloon the performance to match its looks. With a top speed of over 125mph the Bristol became a credible alternative to Aston Martin and Jaguar. With American muscle under the bonnet, parts and support is also improved.

SPECIFICATIONS

Years produced: 1961-1969 (88/83/74/79 in total)
Performance: 0-60mph: 8.8 secs (Top speed: 130mph)
Power & torque: 250bhp / 340lb/ft
Engine: Normally aspirated 5211cc V8, petrol, carburettor, 16 valves
Drivetrain: Front-engine RWD
Suspension: (F) Independent coil springs. (R) Beam axle torsion bar
Bodyframe: Chassis and separate body
Transmission: 3-speed automatic
Weight: 1600kgs

PRICE GUIDE

Launch price: £4848
Excellent: £19,000
Good: £15,000
Average: £8500
Project: £3500

BRISTOL 411

Considered to be the best of the V8 powered 400-Series cars, the 411 appeared at the end of the 1960s, still looking understated and elegant. This version sported a 6.3-litre version of the Chrysler engine and could effortlessly top 140mph after sprinting to 60mph in seven seconds. It might not have been the ideal power unit during the oil crisis of the early '70s, but Bristol continued to sell cars while those around went under – and continue to do so against the odds.

SPECIFICATIONS

Years produced: 1969-1976 (600 in total)
Performance: 0-60mph: 7.0 secs (Top speed: 140mph)
Power & torque: 264bhp / 335lb/ft
Engine: Normally aspirated 6556cc V8, petrol, carburettor, 16 valves
Drivetrain: front-engine RWD
Suspension: (F) Independent, coil springs. (R) Beam axle, torsion bar
Bodyframe: Chassis and separate body
Transmission: 3-speed automatic
Weight: 1712kgs

PRICE GUIDE

Launch price: £8793
Excellent: £21,000
Good: £17,000
Average: £9500
Project: £4000

BRISTOL 412

Even maestros have a bad day. That could explain the square-looking Zagato styling of the 412. But despite being launched during the blackest days of the '70s with a gigantic V8 engine, the 412 continued to sell for Bristol, even building up a modest waiting list. The quality was as deep rooted as ever, and the chassis was straight from the tried-and-tested 411, although the targa roof panel was a genuine innovation for the company. The 6.6-litre V8 was downsized to 5.9-litres in the late '70s, but the grunt remained intact.

SPECIFICATIONS

Years produced: 1975-1980
Performance: 0-60mph: 7.4 secs (Top speed: 140mph)
Power & torque: 172bhp / N/A
Engine: Normally aspirated 6556cc V8, petrol, carburettor, 16 valves
Drivetrain: Front-engine RWD
Suspension: (F) Independent, coil springs. (R) Beam axle, torsion bar
Bodyframe: Chassis and separate body
Transmission: 3-speed automatic
Weight: 1715kgs

PRICE GUIDE

Launch price: £14,584
Excellent: £14,500
Good: £11,500
Average: £6000
Project: £2800

BRISTOL 603/Britannia

In the late-1970s, Bristol started offering a two-model range: the 412 for those looking for open-topped motoring; and the 603, an elegantly-styled fastback with saloon levels of interior accommodation. It was an interesting mix, and one that ensured the firm's survival into the '80s. Under that new aluminium body lay the same basic separate chassis found in the 412 (and its predecessors), and it was none the worse for it. By this time, Bristol was positively delighted with its image of exclusivity, and had a number of high profile fans, notably writer LJK Setright, in its ranks.

SPECIFICATIONS

Years produced: 1976-1982
Performance: 0-60mph: 8.6 secs (Top speed: 140mph)
Power & torque: 172bhp / 270lb/ft
Engine: Normally aspirated 5898cc V8, petrol, carburettor, 16 valves
Drivetrain: Front-engine RWD
Suspension: (F) Independent, coil springs. (R) Beam axle, torsion bar
Bodyframe: Chassis and separate body
Transmission: 3-speed automatic
Weight: 1783kgs

PRICE GUIDE

Launch price: £19,661
Excellent: £15,500
Good: £12,500
Average: £7000
Project: £3500

BRISTOL Beaufighter Convertible

An interesting one, this, as although it was yet another revision of the continuously-evolving model line, the Beaufighter had rather more (undisclosed) power than the 412 it was based upon. The secret was, of course, turbocharging, which by the time the Beaufighter appeared, everyone was getting in on. Although Bristol was coy about power figures, or lending out test cars, the performance had leapt forwards – 0-60mph in 5.9 seconds with a top speed of 150mph. But importantly, this fine car remains rather less obvious than a Bentley Turbo R.

SPECIFICATIONS

Years produced: 1980-1993
Performance: 0-60mph: 5.9 secs (Top speed: 150mph)
Power & torque: N/A / N/A
Engine: Turbocharged 5898cc V8, petrol, carburettor, 16 valves
Drivetrain: Front-engine RWD
Suspension: (F) ndependent, coil springs. (R) Beam axle, torsion bar
Bodyframe: Chassis and separate body
Transmission: 3-speed automatic
Weight: 1746kgs

PRICE GUIDE

Launch price: £37,999
Excellent: £17,000
Good: £14,000
Average: £7500
Project: £4000

BRISTOL
Brigand

It was inevitable the turbocharged version of the Chrysler V8 that was so praised by Beaufighter customers would find its way into the Britannia. And just as it did with the targa-topped car's upgrade, Bristol re-named its coupé, launching the newly-boosted Britannia as a brand new car. Considering the chassis and suspension set-up originated from the late-1940s – albeit with countless changes – it's remarkable it remained unchanged when given an additional 20% of power. Specialist help is readily available, most notably from Bristol itself.

SPECIFICATIONS

Years produced: 1982-1993
Performance: 0-60mph: 5.9 secs (Top speed: 150mph)
Power & torque: N/A / N/A
Engine: Turbocharged 5898cc V8, petrol, carburettor, 16 valves
Drivetrain: Front-engine RWD
Suspension: (F) Independent, coil springs. (R) Beam axle, torsion bar
Bodyframe: Chassis and separate body
Transmission: 3-speed automatic
Weight: 1746kgs

PRICE GUIDE

Launch price: £46,843
Excellent: £16,500
Good: £13,500
Average: £7500
Project: £3750

CATERHAM
Super Seven S3

You can thank Colin Chapman for the fact you can still buy the Seven today. Taking Lotus upmarket in the early 1970s, he sold the lucrative Seven to dealer Caterham Cars, who quickly put the sporting icon into production, never looking back. The tubular steel chassis, covered in aluminium, has remained almost unchanged since – only the engines have been updated to reflect improvements in technology. Prices depend on condition and specification rather than age and mileage, so decide how much performance you want before going shopping.

SPECIFICATIONS

Years produced: 1974-1995
Performance: 0-60mph: 7.7 secs (Top speed: 99mph)
Power & torque: 84bhp / 96lb/ft
Engine: Normally aspirated 1598cc in-line four, petrol, carburettor, 8 valves
Drivetrain: Front-engine RWD
Suspension: (F) Independent, coil springs. (R) Beam axle, coil springs
Bodyframe: Spaceframe
Transmission: 4-speed manual
Weight: 518kgs

PRICE GUIDE

Launch price: £2887
Excellent: £12,500
Good: £10,000
Average: £7000
Project: £4500

CHEVROLET
Corvette C1

Conceived as an image-builder, the Corvette was built in glassfibre because that was the quickest and cheapest way to get it into production. Only 300 were completed in 1953, all hand-built; these now command almost double the prices quoted here for '54/55 'Vettes. Most of this first series of Corvettes used a 3.8-litre straight-six and all but seven of the paltry 700 built in 1955 used a new 4.3-litre V8. The low numbers were because GM still had plenty of '54 Corvettes left to sell and nearly pulled the plug. Now, of course, these models are very collectible.

SPECIFICATIONS

Years produced: 1953-1955 (4640 in total)
Performance: 0-60mph: 11.0 secs (Top speed: 107mph)
Power & torque: 150bhp / 172lb/ft
Engine: Normally aspirated 3859cc in-line six, petrol, carburettor, 12 valves
Drivetrain: Front-engine RWD
Suspension: (F)Independent, short and long wishbones, coil springs, stabiliser bar. (R)Solid axle
Bodyframe: Chassis and glassfibre body
Transmission: 2-speed automatic
Weight: 1227kgs

PRICE GUIDE

Launch price: N/A
Excellent: £50,000
Good: £42,500
Average: £30,000
Project: £20,000

CHEVROLET
Bel Air Coupe

These are the cars that best encapsulate the optimistic era of '50s America, the dawn of rock 'n' roll, and any number of roadside diners. The Bel Air tag generically attached to them is actually the range-topping trim level – there was also the One-Fifty and Two-Ten. A radical departure from previous dull and dumpy Chevrolets, each year got a different body styling treatment, with ever-growing fins, and this was the car that introduced the small-block Chevy V8 engine, in 1955. Six-cylinder versions were also available.

SPECIFICATIONS

Years produced: 1955-1957
Performance: 0-60mph: 9.7 secs (Top speed: 105mph)
Power & torque: 180bhp / 260lb/ft
Engine: Normally aspirated 4344cc V8, petrol, carburettor, 16 valves
Drivetrain: Front-engine RWD
Suspension: (F) Independent, coil springs. (R) Live axle, semi-elliptic leaf spring
Bodyframe: Chassis and separate body
Transmission: 3-speed automatic
Weight: 1515kgs

PRICE GUIDE

Launch price: £2326
Excellent: £20,000
Good: £15,000
Average: £10,000
Project: £5000

CHEVROLET
Bel Air Convertible

As ever, it's the soft-top in the range that brings in the big money. Added to that, all the convertibles were sold in range-topping Bel Air trim. Out of the three years – which has led to devotees referring to these cars as 'Tri-Chevys' – the 1957 incarnation is the most popular, and therefore expensive. Not only do you get more chrome and bigger fins, but there was a larger capacity V8, with tuning options all the way up to fuel injection, as used in the Corvette. Though never officially marketed in the UK, plenty have found their way here over the years.

SPECIFICATIONS

Years produced: 1955-1957
Performance: 0-60mph: 9.7 secs (Top speed: 106mph)
Power & torque: 180bhp / 260lb/ft
Engine: Normally aspirated 3860cc V8, petrol, carburettor, 16 valves
Drivetrain: Front-engine RWD
Suspension: (F) Independent, coil springs. (R) Live axle, semi-elliptic leaf spring
Bodyframe: Chassis and separate body
Transmission: 3-speed automatic
Weight: 1550kgs

PRICE GUIDE

Launch price: N/A
Excellent: £30,000
Good: £25,000
Average: £18,000
Project: £10,000

CHEVROLET
Corvette C1

Evolved styling provides a more aggressive face, along with more efficient (and trendy) twin headlamps. Power rose again, with even base models getting 230bhp, though a golden rule for Corvettes (then and now) is the higher the quoted power output, the more you pay; to which might be added: and the more you wonder about the wisdom of trying to control up to 290bhp on 5.5in crossply tyres. The 1961 model brought new ducktail rear styling, and the following year engine saw capacity increased to 5.3 litres/327ci, with up to 360bhp.

SPECIFICATIONS

Years produced: 1958-1962 (54,569 in total)
Performance: 0-60mph: 5.9 secs (Top speed: 131mph)
Power & torque: 270bhp / 285lb/ft
Engine: Normally aspirated 4638cc V8, petrol, carburettor, 16 valves
Drivetrain: Front-engine RWD
Suspension: (F) Independent, short and long wishbones, coil springs, stabiliser bar. (R) Solid axle
Bodyframe: Chassis and glassfibre body
Transmission: 4-speed manual
Weight: 1397kgs

PRICE GUIDE

Launch price: N/A
Excellent: £42,500
Good: £36,500
Average: £20,000
Project: £12,500

CHEVROLET
Corvette C1

This is the version that started the Corvette legend, thanks to the input of two men. Bill Mitchell turned it from good-looking into gorgeous and Zora Arkus Duntov added power. By early '57 even the carburetted version (now 4.7 litres) was up from 195bhp to as high as 270bhp. In place of the old two-speed auto, a manual gearbox was now standard. Sales rose five-fold, just don't ask about the handling. The optional Rochester fuel-injected 'Fuelie' versions introduced in 1957 attract a 20-25% premium on the prices shown here.

SPECIFICATIONS

Years produced: 1955-1957 (9806 in total)
Performance: 0-60mph: N/A (Top speed: 119mph)
Power & torque: 195bhp / 260lb/ft
Engine: Normally aspirated 4344cc V8, petrol, carburettor, 16 valves
Drivetrain: Front-engine RWD
Suspension: (F) Independent, short and long wishbones, coil springs, stabiliser bar. (R) Solid axle
Bodyframe: Chassis and glassfibre body
Transmission: 4-speed manual
Weight: 1227kgs

PRICE GUIDE

Launch price: N/A
Excellent: £40,000
Good: £34,000
Average: £21,000
Project: £15,000

CHEVROLET
Corvette Sting Ray C2

Everything but the engine and gearbox were changed, independent rear suspension and power steering were useful advances and the Corvette now came as a coupé or convertible. More of the latter were sold, and prices are now roughly the same as for coupés. Sting Rays from 1964 are worth around 20% less than quoted, thanks to not having the '63 coupés' split rear window, or the later cars' disc brakes. From 1965 a 'big-block' 6.5-litre V8 was added to the range; these, and fuel-injected cars, attract 30-50% more than quoted.

SPECIFICATIONS

Years produced: 1963-1967 (117,966 in total)
Performance: 0-60mph: 6.2 secs (Top speed: 142mph)
Power & torque: 360bhp / 352lb/ft
Engine: Normally aspirated 5354cc V8, petrol, carburettor, 16 valves
Drivetrain: Front-engine RWD
Suspension: (F) Independent, coil springs, wishbones, anti-roll bar. (R) Independent, trailing arms, transverse leaf springs
Bodyframe: Chassis and separate body
Transmission: 3-speed manual
Weight: 1377kgs

PRICE GUIDE

Launch price: £3323
Excellent: £42,500
Good: £35,000
Average: £18,500
Project: £10,000

CHEVROLET
Camaro

The Camaro was General Motors' response to the success of the Ford Mustang, and a very good response it was too. The 'Coke bottle' styling of the coupé body for this first generation of Camaros was spot-on for the time, yet still looks good today, and this was the perfect home for exploiting Chevrolet's range of ever-more-powerful V8 engines. You'll need to pay more than quoted for any that come with an 'SS' performance upgrade package, and really big amounts for those with the initials 'Z/28' attached. They excite the serious collectors.

SPECIFICATIONS

Years produced: 1967-1969
Performance: 0-60mph: 9.1 secs (Top speed: 125mph)
Power & torque: 325bhp / 410lb/ft
Engine: Normally aspirated 6478cc V8, petrol, carburettor, 16 valves
Drivetrain: Front-engine RWD
Suspension: (F) Independent, coil spring, wishbone. (R) Live axle, transverse leaf spring
Bodyframe: Chassis and separate body
Transmission: 3-speed automatic
Weight: 1403kgs

PRICE GUIDE

Launch price: N/A
Excellent: £17,500
Good: £14,000
Average: £9000
Project: £5000

CHEVROLET
Corvette Stingray C3

Based on the Mako Shark concept, the Corvette's late-'60s makeover is largely defined by its long, pointed nose and fat tyres – at eight inches wide for 1969, the largest on any car at the time. Coupés started to outsell convertibles, so the latter are now worth around 25% more. Once again, engines come in a variety of big and small-block options, with outputs ranging from 300-435bhp. Our prices are for the former – expect double for the latter and fill the gap with anything in between. Emissions regulations put the squeeze on power from 1971.

SPECIFICATIONS

Years produced: 1968-1972 (133,449 in total)
Performance: 0-60mph: 7.2 secs (Top speed: 135mph)
Power & torque: 370bhp / 370lb/ft
Engine: Normally aspirated 5733cc V8, petrol, carburettor, 16 valves
Drivetrain: Front-engine RWD
Suspension: (F) Independent, coil spring, wishbone, anti-roll bar. (R) Independent, wishbone, coil springs, radius arms, anti-roll bar
Bodyframe: Chassis and separate body
Transmission: 3-speed manual
Weight: 1402kgs

PRICE GUIDE

Launch price: £3432
Excellent: £20,000
Good: £15,000
Average: £9500
Project: £5000

CHEVROLET
Corvette Stingray C3

Corvettes from this era might still look the part, but are more for your ageing rock star. By 1975 output of the base model's 5.7-litre V8 had fallen as low as 165bhp (though weight had gone up significantly) and the 7.5-litre big-block had been consigned to the dustbin. A year later the poor-selling convertible joined it. That of course means a big-block or convertible (or both) 'Vette from this era is worth more than a small-block coupé. Strangely, despite all this, sales of Corvettes continued to rise, which also contributes to their bargain prices now.

SPECIFICATIONS

Years produced: 1973-1977 (202,202 in total)
Performance: 0-60mph: 7.4 secs (Top speed: 124mph)
Power & torque: 250bhp / 285lb/ft
Engine: Normally aspirated 7440cc V8, petrol, carburettor, 16 valves
Drivetrain: Front-engine RWD
Suspension: (F) Independent, parallel A-arms, coil springs. (R) Independent, 3-link with transverse leaf spring
Bodyframe: Chassis and glassfibre body
Transmission: 4-speed manual
Weight: 1600kgs

PRICE GUIDE

Launch price: N/A
Excellent: £15,000
Good: £12,000
Average: £7000
Project: £3500

CHEVROLET
Corvette C3

The main change for the Corvette's 25th anniversary year was the adoption of fastback styling for the coupé – no convertibles were built in these years and the Stingray name was gone. The only engine size offered was Chevrolet's ubiquitous 350ci/5.7-litre small-block, though at least its output had risen over its predecessor. Base models from 1978-80 offer 185-195bhp, with the preferable L82 option ranging from 220-230bhp (also add 30-35% to the price tag). For 1981 and '82, only a single version was offered, with 190-200bhp.

SPECIFICATIONS

Years produced: 1978-1982 (182,219 in total)
Performance: 0-60mph: 7.7 secs (Top speed: 130mph)
Power & torque: 190bhp / 280lb/ft
Engine: Normally aspirated 5733cc V8, petrol, carburettor, 16 valves
Drivetrain: Front-engine RWD
Suspension: (F) Independent, coil spring, wishbone. (R) Independent, transverse leaf spring
Bodyframe: Chassis and glassfibre body
Transmission: 3-speed automatic
Weight: 1677kgs

PRICE GUIDE

Launch price: N/A
Excellent: £14,000
Good: £10,000
Average: £6000
Project: £2750

CHEVROLET
Corvette C4

After taking a year out to solve production problems, Chevrolet returned with an all-new and vastly improved Corvette in 1984. Sadly, the 'Vette's image was blunted by styling that – when compared with what had gone before – was clean and tidy rather than wild and rebellious. Fans welcomed the return of a convertible version in 1986, now worth around 40% more than a coupé, However, the real collectible arrived in 1990 in the shape of the ZR-1 coupé. Lotus were involved in developing the aluminium four-cam V8 and handling settings.

SPECIFICATIONS

Years produced: 1984-1996 (366,227 in total)
Performance: 0-60mph: 6.0 secs (Top speed: 155mph)
Power & torque: 245bhp / 340lb/ft
Engine: Normally aspirated 5733cc V8, petrol, electronic fuel injection, 16 valves
Drivetrain: Front-engine RWD
Suspension: (F) Independent via wishbones and transverse springs, telescopic dampers, anti-roll bars. (R) Live axle with five-link
Bodyframe: Chassis and glassfibre body
Transmission: 6-speed manual
Weight: 1523kgs

PRICE GUIDE

Launch price: £28,757
Excellent: £11,000
Good: £9000
Average: £6000
Project: £4000

CHEVROLET
Corvette C5

Better in every ways than the C4 it replaced, 1997's high-tech C5 brought back aggressive styling along with its associated aerodynamics. Squeaks and rattles are gone, and weight has been drastically reduced. The gearbox is now in unit with the rear axle for improved weight distribution and the engine is the all-new 5.7-litre LS1 small-block V8. From 1999 there's also a convertible option, then from 2001 the high performance Z06 is added, in hardtop form only. This also uses the LS1 engine, but tweaked for an extra 35bhp.

SPECIFICATIONS

Years produced: 1997-2004 (248,715 in total)
Performance: 0-60mph: 4.8 secs (Top speed: 172mph)
Power & torque: 345bhp / 350lb/ft
Engine: Normally aspirated 5666cc V8, petrol, electronic fuel injection, 16 valves
Drivetrain: Front-engine RWD
Suspension: (F & R) Double wishbones, transverse springs, telescopic dampers, anti-roll bars.
Bodyframe: Chassis and glassfibre body
Transmission: 6-speed manual
Weight: 1465kgs

PRICE GUIDE

Launch price: £36,525
Excellent: £19,000
Good: £15,000
Average: £12,000
Project: £9000

CITROËN
Traction Avant

Prior to the Traction Avant, Citroën were just another European manufacturer of worthy but dull cars. The Traction's arrival in 1934 changed all that. It was a revolutionary machine, the first front-wheel-drive car to be built by a major car firm. Unitary construction, independent suspension and some very sleek bodies were also part of its chic cocktail; there was simply nothing like it at the time and its rivals wouldn't catch up for years. Initial cars had 1303cc engines and the range gradually expanded to include the popular 1911cc.

SPECIFICATIONS

Years produced: 1934-1957 (760,000 in total)
Performance: 0-60mph: 23.4 secs (Top speed: 72mph)
Power & torque: 56bhp / 91lb/ft
Engine: Normally aspirated 1911cc in-line four, petrol, carburettor, 8 valves
Drivetrain: Front-engine FWD
Suspension: (F) Independent, wishbone, torsion bar. (R) Beam axle, Panhard rod
Bodyframe: Metal monocoque
Transmission: 4-speed manual
Weight: 1143kgs

PRICE GUIDE

Launch price: £573
Excellent: £12,500
Good: £9000
Average: £5000
Project: £2500

CITROËN 2CV

Envisaged as a car to motorise the French peasant population, the 2CV went on to become a true world car. The deceptively simple appearance belied a car that was very clever, with interconnected suspension and a tough air-cooled twin-cylinder engine. The simply-constructed body was considered ugly when the car was launched in 1948, leading to the nicknames of the Tin Snail and the Duck. But it was these endearing looks that helped win the 2CV a legion of followers, and it stayed in production for 42 years.

SPECIFICATIONS

Years produced:	1948-1960
Performance:	0-60mph: N/A (Top speed: 49mph)
Power & torque:	9bhp / 17lb/ft
Engine:	Normally aspirated 375cc flat 2, petrol, carburettor, 4 valves
Drivetrain:	Front-engine FWD
Suspension:	(F) Independent, leading arm, coil spring. (R) Independent, trailing arm, coil spring
Bodyframe:	Chassis and separate body
Transmission:	4-speed manual
Weight:	682kgs
	PRICE GUIDE
Launch price:	£565
Excellent:	£4500
Good:	£3500
Average:	£2000
Project:	£1000

CITROËN DS19/ID19

The Citroën DS is one of the most extraordinary cars ever created. Its 'Goddess' name – 'Deesse' in French – was entirely justified because it did seem to be from another world. The beautiful shape was like nothing else, while hydropneumatics controlled the self-levelling suspension, brakes, clutch and power steering, with the ride height adjustable from inside the car. Only the old 1911cc engine was carried over from the Traction Avant. The budget-conscious ID19 appeared a year after the DS19 and featured conventional brakes and steering.

SPECIFICATIONS

Years produced:	1955-1975
Performance:	0-60mph: 22.1 secs (Top speed: 88mph)
Power & torque:	75bhp / 101lb/ft
Engine:	Normally aspirated 1911cc in-line four, petrol, carburettor, 8 valves
Drivetrain:	Front-engine FWD
Suspension:	(F) Independent, hydropneumatic sphere. (R) Independent, hydropneumatic sphere
Bodyframe:	Metal monocoque
Transmission:	4-speed manual
Weight:	1237kgs
	PRICE GUIDE
Launch price:	£1486
Excellent:	£8250
Good:	£6750
Average:	£3000
Project:	£900

CITROËN DS Decapotable

While a few European coachbuilders decapitated DSs, it was the guillotine work of Henri Chapron that was considered the most stylish and elegant – so much so that Citroën added his cars to their catalogue in 1961. The mechanics and any improvements mirrored those of the saloons but the looks were far more eye-catching, with the open-top, two-door format and long, sloping tail giving an almost sports car look. However, at twice the price of the saloon, the DS cabriolet needed to be special. Only 1365 were officially built.

SPECIFICATIONS

Years produced:	1958-1973 (1365 in total)
Performance:	0-60mph: 15.5 secs (Top speed: 100mph)
Power & torque:	83bhp / 98lb/ft
Engine:	Normally aspirated 1911cc in-line four, petrol, carburettor, 8 valves
Drivetrain:	Front-engine FWD
Suspension:	(F & R) Hydropneumatic units, leading/trailing arms, anti-roll-bar.
Bodyframe:	Metal monocoque
Transmission:	4-speed manual
Weight:	1235kgs
	PRICE GUIDE
Launch price:	Special order only
Excellent:	£95,000
Good:	£80,000
Average:	£52,500
Project:	£35,000

CITROËN DS19 Safari

The Citroën DS Safari, introduced in 1958, was one of the most competent estate cars ever produced. As well as swallowing luggage it was also a seven-seater in ordinary form, but the Familiale version had three rows of seats and could accommodate eight. The hydropneumatic suspension came into its own on the load-lugging DS as, however much you packed in the back, the car would always stay level. Safaris followed IDs, but offered all engine options of the DS saloons and adopted the same shark-ish front end as its siblings in 1967.

SPECIFICATIONS

Years produced:	1959-1975
Performance:	0-60mph: 19.4 secs (Top speed: 88mph)
Power & torque:	66bhp / 98lb/ft
Engine:	Normally aspirated 1911cc in-line four, petrol, carburettor, 8 valves
Drivetrain:	Front-engine FWD
Suspension:	(F) Independent, hydropneumatic sphere. (R) Independent, hydropneumatic sphere
Bodyframe:	Metal monocoque
Transmission:	4-speed maual
Weight:	1260kgs
	PRICE GUIDE
Launch price:	£1745
Excellent:	£8500
Good:	£7000
Average:	£3250
Project:	£950

CITROËN Ami 6/8/Super

Citroën produced several 2CV-based cars, with the Ami being one of the more fascinating. The styling was strange even by French standards, especially the original 6 model which had a reverse-rake window emulating the Ford Anglia 105E. A 602cc 20bhp engine provided reasonable performance and the Ami was better appointed inside than the 2CV. A redesign in 1969 made the back window slope the conventional – and more boring – way, creating the Ami 8. The ultimate Ami was the Super of 1972 with the four-cylinder overhead cam engine from the GS.

SPECIFICATIONS

Years produced:	1961-1978 (1,840,159 in total)
Performance:	0-60mph: 17.1 secs (Top speed: 88mph)
Power & torque:	26bhp / 31lb/ft
Engine:	Normally aspirated 602cc Flat 2, petrol, carburettor, 4 valves
Drivetrain:	Front-engine FWD
Suspension:	(F) Independent, leading arm, coil spring. (R) Independent, trailing arm, coil spring
Bodyframe:	Chassis and separate body
Transmission:	4-speed manual
Weight:	673kgs
	PRICE GUIDE
Launch price:	£824
Excellent:	£2500
Good:	£1900
Average:	£900
Project:	£400

CITROËN DS 20/21/23

The DS deserved better engines than those which had been used in the Traction Avant before the war and, from 1965, it started to get them. In that year, the Citroën DS21 was launched with a 2175cc engine offering 109bhp. After a very successful restyle of the vehicle in 1967 – with swivelling headlamps and a shark-like nose – the DS19 was replaced by the DS20 (1985cc and 90bhp). But it was in the 1970s that the Goddess reached its ultimate evolution, with a 2347cc engine, to create the DS23. In fuel injected form, this pumped out 141bhp.

SPECIFICATIONS

Years produced: 1966-1974
Performance: 0-60mph: 10.4 secs (Top speed: 120mph)
Power & torque: 100bhp / 121lb/ft
Engine: Normally aspirated 2175cc in-line four, petrol, carburettor, 8 valves
Drivetrain: Front-engine FWD
Suspension: (F) Independent, hydropneumatic sphere. (R) Independent, hydropneumatic sphere
Bodyframe: Metal monocoque
Transmission: 4-speed manual
Weight: 1280kgs

PRICE GUIDE

Launch price: £1977
Excellent: £11,000
Good: £9000
Average: £4250
Project: £1200

CITROËN Dyane 4/6

The Dyane was intended to replace the 2CV... but the Tin Snail was too much of a survivor. So this upgraded and restyled 2CV went on sale alongside the model it was designed to supersede. The chassis was the same with a 425cc flat-twin engine on the 4 and a 602cc powerhouse on the 6, and the more angular looks were still closely 2CV-related, even down to the full-length canvas sunroof. It was clearly an update of the original design, with the addition of a hatchback. It was dropped five years before the car it was meant to oust.

SPECIFICATIONS

Years produced: 1967-1985 (1,443,583 in total)
Performance: 0-60mph: 30.8 secs (Top speed: 70mph)
Power & torque: 32bhp / 31lb/ft
Engine: Normally aspirated 602cc flat 2, petrol, carburettor, 4 valves
Drivetrain: Front-engine FWD
Suspension: (F) Independent, leading arm, coil spring. (R) Independent, trailing arm, coil spring
Bodyframe: Chassis and separate body
Transmission: 4-speed manual
Weight: 600kgs

PRICE GUIDE

Launch price: £549
Excellent: £2250
Good: £1750
Average: £800
Project: £300

CITROËN SM

The 1968 marriage of Citroën and Maserati led to the birth of a highly individualistic sports coupé. The SM took DS technology, threw in a Maserati V6 engine and finished it off with a brooding, angular body that was distinctively Citroën, but also looked very prestigious and expensive. Utterly original and technologically advanced, this idiosyncratic French supercar demanded careful care and developed a reputation for fragility which harmed sales. When Citroën was taken over by Peugeot in 1975 the SM was one of the first casualties.

SPECIFICATIONS

Years produced: 1970-1975 (12,920 in total)
Performance: 0-60mph: 7.5 secs (Top speed: 146mph)
Power & torque: 170bhp / 172lb/ft
Engine: Normally aspirated 2965cc V6, petrol, carburettor, 12 valves
Drivetrain: Front-engine FWD
Suspension: (F&R) Independent via self-levelling hydropneumatic spring and damper units, pressurised by engine-driven pump
Bodyframe: Metal monocoque
Transmission: 5-speed manual
Weight: 1450kgs

PRICE GUIDE

Launch price: £5480
Excellent: £18,000
Good: £15,000
Average: £8000
Project: £4000

CITROËN GS/GSA

Citroën brought its big car hydropneumatic technology to the small car market with 1970's GS. Looking like a scaled-down blend of DS and SM, motive power for this futuristic family saloon was, at first, a 1015cc air-cooled flat-four engine. The interior looked like it had borrowed its controls from a spaceship and, naturally, there was self-levelling suspension throughout. The car became a hatchback as the GSA in 1979, but far more intriguing was the GS Birotor of 1973, which showcased Citroën's Wankel rotary engine leanings.

SPECIFICATIONS

Years produced: 1970-1986 (2,473,150 in total)
Performance: 0-60mph: 16.2 secs (Top speed: 92mph)
Power & torque: 55bhp / 52lb/ft
Engine: Normally aspirated 1015cc flat 4, petrol, carburettor, 8 valves
Drivetrain: Front-engine FWD
Suspension: (F) Independent, double wishbone, hydropneumatic spheres. (R) Independent, hydropneumatic spheres
Bodyframe: Metal monocoque
Transmission: 4-speed manual
Weight: 880kgs

PRICE GUIDE

Launch price: £1001
Excellent: £2500
Good: £1850
Average: £850
Project: £250

CITROËN CX

Enthusiasts generally refer to 1975's CX as the last of the true Citroëns because it was the final model launched before Peugeot took over. A technological tour de force with typically innovative and individualistic sleek looks, the CX featured the usual hydraulics controlling many aspects of the car plus Vari-power self-centring steering, which took a little getting used to. The interior was simply mad, although from 1985, Series 2 cars had traditional instrumentation and colour-coded bumpers. Engines extended from 2-litre petrol to 2.5-litre diesel.

SPECIFICATIONS

Years produced: 1974-1989 (1,034,489 in total)
Performance: 0-60mph: 9.7 secs (Top speed: 114mph)
Power & torque: 115bhp / 131lb/ft
Engine: Normally aspirated 2165cc in-line four, petrol, carburettor, 8 valves
Drivetrain: Front-engine FWD
Suspension: (F) Independent, wishbone, hydropneumatic sphere. (R) Semi-trailing arms, hydropneumatic sphere
Bodyframe: Metal monocoque
Transmission: 5-speed manual
Weight: 1245kgs

PRICE GUIDE

Launch price: £3195
Excellent: £3600
Good: £2250
Average: £900
Project: £300

CITROËN 2CV6

Although probably the world's best minimalist car, the 2CV became increasingly luxurious. These terms are relative, of course, and additions to the car that motorised a generation of French farmers included improved interior trim and a slightly uprated flat-twin. The best features remained – the loping ride, the comfortable seats and pull back roof – and that helped maintain sales for what had become a cult car even during its production run. Finally laid to rest in 1990, the Citroën 2CV's place in society is assured, as are its values, which continue to rise.

SPECIFICATIONS

Years produced: 1978-1990
Performance: 0-60mph: 32.4 secs (Top speed: 71mph)
Power & torque: 26bhp / 29lb/ft
Engine: Normally aspirated 602cc flat 2, petrol, carburettor, 4 valves
Drivetrain: Front-engine FWD
Suspension: (F) Independent, leading arm, coil spring. (R) Independent, trailing arm, coil spring
Bodyframe: Chassis and separate body
Transmission: 4-speed manual
Weight: 560kgs

PRICE GUIDE

Launch price: £899
Excellent: £3750
Good: £2750
Average: £1000
Project: £350

CITROËN CX GTi/GTi Turbo

Finally matching high performance to dramatic looks, 1977's CX GTi was Citroën's return to grand touring after the demise of the SM. Using the DS23's fuel-injected 2347cc engine gave 128bhp and a 120mph top speed, while the cars could be identified by their special alloy wheels, blacked-out trim and more sports-orientated interiors. In 1984 Citroën made things even more frantic with the CX GTi Turbo, rated at168bhp. A long time in the shadow of the DS, the CX is now being recognised as one of the great Citroëns.

SPECIFICATIONS

Years produced: 1984-1989
Performance: 0-60mph: 8.2 secs (Top speed: 129mph)
Power & torque: 166bhp / 217lb/ft
Engine: Turbocharged 2500cc in-line four, petrol, electronic fuel injection, 8 valves
Drivetrain: Front-engine FWD
Suspension: (F) Independent, hydropneumatic sphere. (R) Independent, hydropneumatic sphere
Bodyframe: Metal monocoque
Transmission: 5-speed manual
Weight: 1490kgs

PRICE GUIDE

Launch price: £6530
Excellent: £4500
Good: £3600
Average: £1500
Project: £750

CLAN Crusader

So much more than a kit car, the Clan Crusader was an exercise in lightness and efficiency, while proving that the Hillman Imp's Coventry Climax engine really was something special. It was a classic '70s British sports car – fibreglass body, off-the-shelf engine and gearbox, all clothed in a wedge-shaped body. It was pricey, at 40% more than an MG Midget, but the Crusader was electric to drive, and the material choice for the bodywork means the survival rate is rather good. The engine is well-supported in the tuning community, too.

SPECIFICATIONS

Years produced: 1971-1974 (315 in total)
Performance: 0-60mph: 12.5 secs (Top speed: 100mph)
Power & torque: 51bhp / 52lb/ft
Engine: Normally aspirated 875cc in-line four, petrol, carburettor, 8 valves
Drivetrain: Rear-engine RWD
Suspension: (F) Independent, coil spring. (R) Independent, coil spring
Bodyframe: Chassis and glassfibre body
Transmission: 4-speed manual
Weight: 578kgs

PRICE GUIDE

Launch price: £1399
Excellent: £4250
Good: £3250
Average: £1650
Project: £650

DAF 55 Marathon

The 55 was a big step forward for the Dutch firm. It used a Renault inline four-cylinder water-cooled engine that offered a huge improvement in performance, even if the characteristic hum of the older model was gone. To celebrate its success in the London-Sydney Marathon, DAF introduced a Marathon upgrade kit, boosting power, handling and roadholding. It was an immediate success and soon became a fully-fledged production model. Renault parts commonality means that availability is good, and the club has excellent back-up.

SPECIFICATIONS

Years produced: 1968-1972
Performance: 19.4 secs (Top speed: 90mph)
Power & torque: 63bhp / 63lb/ft
Engine: Normally aspirated 1108cc in-line four, petrol, carburettor, 8 valves
Drivetrain: Front-engine RWD
Suspension: (F) Ind. torsion bar, lower wishbone, anti-roll bar. (R) Ind. semi-trailing arm
Bodyframe: Monocoque
Transmission: CVT
Weight: 810kgs

PRICE GUIDE

Launch price: £1050
Excellent: £2400
Good: £1650
Average: £750
Project: £300

DAIMLER DB18/Consort

Daimler started moving towards smaller, more sporty cars before World War 2, with its DB18 proving quite successful in rallies. World War Two caused a hiatus in production, but the car returned afterwards largely unchanged as a saloon or drophead coupé. A 2522cc six-cylinder engine gave 70bhp and reasonable performance. Things moved forward with the 1949 Consort, an update of the design with headlamps that merged into the wings, the grille and bumpers developed curves and hydromechanical brakes were fitted.

SPECIFICATIONS

Years produced: 1938-1953 (8223 in total)
Performance: 28.3 secs (Top speed: 72mph)
Power & torque: 70bhp / N/A
Engine: Normally aspirated 2522cc in-line six, petrol, carburettor, 12 valves
Drivetrain: Front-engine RWD
Suspension: (F) Independent, coil springs. (R) Live axle, leaf spring
Bodyframe: Chassis and separate body
Transmission: 4-speed manual
Weight: 1650kgs

PRICE GUIDE

Launch price: £1183
Excellent: £6750
Good: £5000
Average: £2500
Project: £700

DAIMLER
DB18 Sports Special

With the DB18 saloons and convertibles representing the sportier side of Daimler, the 1948 Sports Special version of the type was a step closer to the wild side. Twin carburettors helped squeeze 85bhp from the 2522cc six-cylinder engine. Barker were responsible for most of the bodies and its design featured a rear passenger seat facing sideways, thus making the car a three-seater. Hooper weighed in with the heavier 'Empress' saloon style, although alloy-on-ash construction for both machines helped keep performance up.

SPECIFICATIONS

Years produced: 1948-1953 (608 in total)
Performance: 0-60mph: 23.3 secs (Top speed: 84mph)
Power & torque: 85bhp / N/A
Engine: Normally aspirated 2522cc in-line six, petrol, carburettor, 12 valves
Drivetrain: Front-engine RWD
Suspension: (F) Independent, coil spring, (R) Beam axle, leaf springs
Bodyframe: Chassis and separate body
Transmission: 4-speed manual
Weight: 1650kgs

PRICE GUIDE

Launch price: £2560
Excellent: £20,000
Good: £16,500
Average: £9000
Project: £4000

DAIMLER
Regency

The Regency took the Consort chassis, fitted it with a new 3-litre engine and topped it all off with a larger, more flowing and graceful body. Introduced in 1951, just 50 were built before production stalled in 1952. Reincarnation came in 1954 with the Regency Mk2, this time with a longer, lower body and a more powerful 3.5-litre engine. Offshoots were the Hooper-built Empress saloon and the more exciting Sportsman, which had a 140bhp alloy-head engine and offered good performance for its size and the era.

SPECIFICATIONS

Years produced: 1951-1956 (452 in total)
Performance: 19.1 secs (Top speed: 83mph)
Power & torque: 90bhp / N/A
Engine: Normally aspirated 3468cc in-line six, petrol, carburettor, 12 valves
Drivetrain: Front-engine RWD
Suspension: (F) Independent, coil springs. (R) Beam axle, leaf springs
Bodyframe: Chassis and separate body
Transmission: 4-speed manual
Weight: 1721kgs

PRICE GUIDE

Launch price: £2335
Excellent: £7000
Good: £5250
Average: £3500
Project: £950

DAIMLER
Conquest Roadster

Daimler's first attempt at an out-and-out sportscar was the Conquest-based, aluminium-bodied Roadster of 1953. Much sleeker and lower than any previous car from the company it was a somewhat bizarre-looking creation; this was thanks to Daimler trying to retain the style of the big saloons, which didn't lend itself to the hunkered-down format. After 65 had been made from 1953 to 1955, it was dropped, but then came back from 1956 to 1957. Unfortunately, just 54 managed to find homes that time around.

SPECIFICATIONS

Years produced: 1953-1957 (119 in total)
Performance: 0-60mph: 14.5 secs (Top speed: 101mph)
Power & torque: 100bhp / N/A
Engine: Normally aspirated 2443cc in-line six, petrol, carburettor, 12 valves
Drivetrain: Front-engine RWD
Suspension: (F) Independent, torsion bar. (R) Live axle, leaf spring
Bodyframe: Chassis and separate body
Transmission: 4-speed manual
Weight: 1219kgs

PRICE GUIDE

Launch price: £1673
Excellent: £16,500
Good: £12,500
Average: £8000
Project: £3500

DAIMLER
Conquest/Century

The Consort gave way to the Conquest in 1953. Well, it actually gave way to Daimler's badge-engineered version of the Lanchester 14, which was what the Conquest actually was. The Dame was an improvement on its sister model though – thanks to a bigger engine with two extra cylinders – while its compact size gave it pleasing performance and handling. But for those who wanted a little more performance there was the Century drophead coupé, so called because of the 100bhp afforded by its alloy-head twin-carb engine.

SPECIFICATIONS

Years produced: 1953-1958 (9620 in total)
Performance: 0-60mph: 24.3 secs (Top speed: 82mph)
Power & torque: 75bhp / N/A
Engine: Normally aspirated 2433cc in-line six, petrol, carburettor, 12 valves
Drivetrain: Front-engine RWD
Suspension: (F) Independent, coil spring. (R) Live axle, leaf spring
Bodyframe: Chassis and separate body
Transmission: 4-speed manual
Weight: 1397kgs

PRICE GUIDE

Launch price: £1511
Excellent: £6250
Good: £4500
Average: £2200
Project: £700

DAIMLER
104/Majestic

Although the 1954 Daimler 104 looked very much like the Regency it replaced, the structure was bulked up, the brakes were improved and the 3468cc six-pot engine was granted more power. A special version was the Lady's Model, with a more 'feminine' interior including walnut veneer, satin chrome, picnic gear and, of all things, a gold-propelling pencil! 50 customers bought one. In 1958, the body put on considerable weight to become the Majestic. The bigger 3794cc engine pitched it directly against Jaguar.

SPECIFICATIONS

Years produced: 1955-1962 (1399 in total)
Performance: 0-60mph: 15.4 secs (Top speed: 100mph)
Power & torque: 137bhp / N/A
Engine: Normally aspirated 3468cc in-line six, petrol, carburettor, 12 valves
Drivetrain: Front-engine RWD
Suspension: (F) Independent, coil spring. (R) Live axle, leaf springs
Bodyframe: Chassis and separate body
Transmission: 4-speed manual
Weight: 1880kgs

PRICE GUIDE

Launch price: £2672
Excellent: £7500
Good: £5250
Average: £3000
Project: £750

DAIMLER SP250

The final all-new sports car to be offered by Daimler, and the most interesting of all. With its fibreglass body and 2.5-litre V8 engine, the SP250 was quick and agile. It was originally called 'Dart', but Chrysler forced Daimler to drop the name. There were problems – the fibreglass used to crack, and the handling wasn't as good as it should have been – and following Jaguar's takeover of Daimler, the appealing roadster was on borrowed time, as it was considered a rival to the E-type. Numbers are low, and that helps keep values up.

SPECIFICATIONS

Years produced: 1959-1964 (2650 in total)
Performance: 0-60mph: 10.2 secs (Top speed: 121mph)
Power & torque: 140bhp / 155lb/ft
Engine: Normally aspirated 2548cc V8, petrol, carburettor, 16 valves
Drivetrain: Front-engine RWD
Suspension: (F) Independent, coil springs. (R) Live axle, leaf springs
Bodyframe: Chassis and glassfibre body
Transmission: 4-speed manual
Weight: 940kgs

PRICE GUIDE

Launch price: £1395
Excellent: £15,000
Good: £11,000
Average: £8000
Project: £3000

DAIMLER Majestic Major

What was most majestic and major about 1960's Majestic Major was its engine... Daimler's new 4561cc V8 with hemispherical combustion heads, designed by Edward Turner. An impressive 220bhp gave a top speed of 120mph, making the Majestic Major a superb luxury express and one that was easy to drive thanks to the automatic transmission and power steering. The bodywork remained largely unchanged from the standard Majestic, save for a longer boot. For 1961 there was a two-ton limousine version, which was dubbed a '120mph funeral taxi'.

SPECIFICATIONS

Years produced: 1960-1968 (1180 in total)
Performance: 0-60mph: 10.3 secs (Top speed: 119mph)
Power & torque: 220bhp / 283lb/ft
Engine: Normally aspirated 4561cc V8, petrol, carburettor, 16 valves
Drivetrain: Front-engine RWD
Suspension: (F) Independent, coil springs. (R) Live axle, leaf springs
Bodyframe: Chassis and separate body
Transmission: 4-speed manual
Weight: 1778kgs

PRICE GUIDE

Launch price: £2995
Excellent: £9250
Good: £7250
Average: £3750
Project: £800

DAIMLER 2.5-litre/V8 250

1959's Mk2 was the archetypal Jaguar saloon of the Sixties; Daimler's version saw the 2548cc V8 from the SP250 roadster dropped under the bonnet. The two suited each other well with the handsome and refined curvy body complemented by the smooth and sophisticated power source. Arguably, the Daimler was a nicer car to drive than the Jaguar thanks to the engine's light weight and the eight cylinders endowing it with silky flexibility. Just imagine what it would have been like with the 4561cc version of the V8 as well...

SPECIFICATIONS

Years produced: 1962-1969 (17,620 in total)
Performance: 0-60mph: 13.8 secs (Top speed: 112mph)
Power & torque: 140bhp / N/A
Engine: Normally aspirated 2548cc V8, petrol, carburettor, 16 valves
Drivetrain: Front-engine RWD
Suspension: (F) Independent, coil spring. (R) Live axle, leaf spring
Bodyframe: Monocoque
Transmission: 4-speed manual
Weight: 1473kgs

PRICE GUIDE

Launch price: £1786
Excellent: £14,000
Good: £11,000
Average: £5250
Project: £2500

DAIMLER Sovereign

There was probably a very good case for the 1966-69 Sovereign – the badge-engineered version of Jaguar's big 420 – making use of the existing 4.5-litre Daimler V8 engine to power it. Unfortunately, Jaguar didn't hear it, and so the Sovereign came out with the same 4235cc six-cylinder XK engine as the 420. Not that this made it a bad car, but it did take away some Daimler distinctiveness as the only different touches were a fluted grille, the 'D' bonnet mascot, 'Daimler' on the cam cover and assorted badges.

SPECIFICATIONS

Years produced: 1966-1969 (5700 in total)
Performance: 0-60mph: 9.9 secs (Top speed: 123mph)
Power & torque: 245bhp / 283lb/ft
Engine: Normally aspirated 4235cc V8, petrol, carburettor, 16 valves
Drivetrain: Front-engine RWD
Suspension: (F) Independent, coil spring. (R) Independent, coil spring
Bodyframe: Monocoque
Transmission: 4-speed manual
Weight: 1575kgs

PRICE GUIDE

Launch price: £2121
Excellent: £10,000
Good: £8000
Average: £4000
Project: £1250

DAIMLER
Sovereign SI-SIII

The Sovereign name was re-used for the Daimler version of the XJ6, introduced in 1969. As with the original Sovereign, any 'Daimlerisations' were confined to the most minor of details; the traditional fluted grille and Daimler badges here, there and everywhere. The original engine options were either the 2.8-litre or 4.2-litre XK variant; by now Daimler's wonderful V8 engine – which might have suited the Sovereign so well – had ceased production. The Sovereign name continued through the Series 2 and 3 versions of the XJ until 1983.

SPECIFICATIONS

Years produced:	1969-1987 (55435 in total)
Performance:	0-60mph: 8.8 secs (Top speed: 124mph)
Power & torque:	173bhp / 227lb/ft
Engine:	Normally aspirated 2792cc in-line six, petrol, carburettor, Twin valves
Drivetrain:	Front-engine RWD
Suspension:	(F) Independent coil springs. (R) Independent coil springs
Bodyframe:	Monocoque
Transmission:	4-spd (+O/D)/Auto
Weight:	1537kgs
	PRICE GUIDE
Launch price:	£2356
Excellent:	£6500
Good:	£5000
Average:	£2200
Project:	£750

DAIMLER
Double Six SI-III saloon

Jaguar took its XJ saloon to new heights with its new and exciting V12 engine from 1972. The Daimler variant revived a title which had last been used from 1926 to 1938, that of the Double Six. This created one of the better luxury cruisers of the era, a worthy rival for BMW, Mercedes-Benz and even Rolls-Royce, although build quality was often patchy. The 5342cc V12 engine may have been terribly thirsty, but it was also terribly fast and refined too. Vanden Plas versions had even more opulence, including better interiors and a vinyl roof.

SPECIFICATIONS

Years produced:	1972-1979 (16,608 in total)
Performance:	0-60mph: 7.4 secs (Top speed: 146mph)
Power & torque:	265/285bhp / 304/350lb/ft
Engine:	Normally aspirated 5343cc V12, petrol, carburettor, overhead valves
Drivetrain:	Front-engine RWD
Suspension:	(F) Independent coil springs. (R) Independent coil springs
Bodyframe:	Monocoque
Transmission:	Auto
Weight:	1760kgs
	PRICE GUIDE
Launch price:	£3849
Excellent:	£8500
Good:	£6000
Average:	£2200
Project:	£1000

DAIMLER
4.2 Coupé

Announced in 1973, the Daimler Coupé – a short-wheelbase, pillarless variation on the XJ6/Sovereign saloon theme – seemed to have a lot going for it. The lines were even more handsome than those of the standard saloons and the truncated length added a sporty aura. However, when the Coupé finally made it into production in 1975, as a Series 2 model, it had a difficult life. Build quality was poor and the black vinyl roofs sported by each model were allegedly there to hide imperfections. Just 1598 were made before a halt was called in 1977.

SPECIFICATIONS

Years produced:	1975-1977 (399 in total)
Performance:	0-60mph: 8.8 secs (Top speed: 124mph)
Power & torque:	173/247bhp / 227/300lb/ft
Engine:	Normally aspirated 4235cc in-line six, petrol, carburettor, twin valves
Drivetrain:	Front-engine RWD
Suspension:	(F) Independent coil springs. (R) Independent coil springs
Bodyframe:	Monocoque
Transmission:	4-spd (+O/D)/Auto
Weight:	1689kgs
	PRICE GUIDE
Launch price:	£5590
Excellent:	£10,250
Good:	£8250
Average:	£4000
Project:	£1200

DAIMLER
Double Six Coupé

As with the Sovereign saloons, Jaguar's V12 engine also made its way into the Daimler-badged Coupés. One of the rarest of all Daimlers – just 407 were made from 1975 to 1977 – this 285bhp 5343cc pillarless and shortened sophisticate had wonderful looks with a top speed a whisker under 150mph. Unfortunately, all this couldn't quite make up for the supply and quality problems that bedevilled it during its short life. This was a model that deserved a fate better than befell it. Rarity makes them even more exclusive than the 1855 Jaguar versions made.

SPECIFICATIONS

Years produced:	1975-1977 (399 in total)
Performance:	0-60mph: 7.6 secs (Top speed: 148mph)
Power & torque:	285bhp / 301lb/ft
Engine:	Normally aspirated 5343cc V12, petrol, carburettor, 24 valves
Drivetrain:	Front-engine RWD
Suspension:	(F) Independent, coil spring. (R) Independent coil spring
Bodyframe:	Monocoque
Transmission:	3-speed automatic
Weight:	1835kgs
	PRICE GUIDE
Launch price:	£6959
Excellent:	£9250
Good:	£7000
Average:	£3250
Project:	£1200

DATSUN
240Z

Here's where it all began. The first in what has become the world's best sports car line, the Datsun 240Z had success written all over it from day one. The looks were spot on, thanks to styling input from Albrecht Goertz, and performance from its rorty straight-six was ample. Being a Datsun, reliability was a given, but the agile (if tail-happy) handling was a pleasant surprise. During its five year run, over 150,000 were produced, but survivors are now seriously appreciating. Rust has been its main enemy, so be careful when buying.

SPECIFICATIONS

Years produced:	1969-1978 (622,649 (inc 260Z) in total)
Performance:	0-60mph: 8.3 secs (Top speed: 125mph)
Power & torque:	161bhp / 198lb/ft
Engine:	Normally aspirated 2393cc in-line six, petrol, carburettor, 12 valves
Drivetrain:	Front-engine RWD
Suspension:	(F) Independent, coil springs. (R) Independent, coil springs
Bodyframe:	Monocoque
Transmission:	5-speed manual
Weight:	1025kgs
	PRICE GUIDE
Launch price:	£2288
Excellent:	£11,000
Good:	£9000
Average:	£5000
Project:	£2000

DATSUN
260Z

Despite adding power and equipment to the mix, the Datsun 260Z has always lived in the shadow of its older brother. Two-seat models looked as good as the original, but the introduction of the 2+2 with 12-inch longer wheelbase and reprofiled roofline diluted appeal despite being a lot more useful. Performance for the two-seater car is similar to the 240Z's, and because prices are lower, they are excellent value. Sold half as many as the first Z-car, and survival rate is shocking in the UK – mainly because like all '70s Datsuns, it rusts appallingly.

SPECIFICATIONS

Years produced: 1969-1978 (See 240Z in total)
Performance: 0-60mph: 10.1 secs (Top speed: 115mph)
Power & torque: 162bhp / 152lb/ft
Engine: Normally aspirated 2565cc in-line six, petrol, carburettor, valves
Drivetrain: Front-engine RWD
Suspension: (F) Independent, coil spring. (R) Independent, coil spring
Bodyframe: Monocoque
Transmission: 5-speed manual
Weight: 1164kgs

PRICE GUIDE

Launch price: £2896
Excellent: £9000
Good: £7000
Average: £3500
Project: £1500

DATSUN
280ZX

Symbolic of the Z-cars decent into middle-aged spread, the 280ZX was far less appealing than the car it replaced. Longer, wider, heavier and uglier, the new 2.8-litre car was very much a boulevardier rather than a full-blooded sports car. Equipment levels were lavish, and power steering, all-round disc brakes and semi-trailing arm rear suspension were further refinements that cast the Z-car very much in the luxury car sector. Despite being panned when new, it sold well in the USA and is still very much in demand as a modern, useable classic car.

SPECIFICATIONS

Years produced: 1978-1983 (414,358 in total)
Performance: 0-60mph: 8.3 secs (Top speed: 117mph)
Power & torque: 140bhp / 149lb/ft
Engine: Normally aspirated 2753cc in-line six, petrol, electronic fuel injection, 12 valves
Drivetrain: Front-engine RWD
Suspension: (F) Ind. MacPherson strut, coil spring. (R) Ind. semi-trailing arm, coil spring
Bodyframe: Monocoque
Transmission: 5-speed manual
Weight: 1272kgs

PRICE GUIDE

Launch price: £8103
Excellent: £4250
Good: £3000
Average: £1750
Project: £800

DE LOREAN
DMC-12

John DeLorean set out to build his own vision of a sportscar in the late 1970s and on paper it must have looked amazing. It featured a low-slung and pointy Giugiaro design, brushed steel outer skin, 'gullwing' doors and a fuel-injected 2849cc V6 engine mounted 911-style at the rear. Unfortunately, the 1981 reality turned out to be less stimulating. The car was so heavy that the V6 struggled to offer a sporty performance and the handling remained dodgy even after Lotus engineers had done their best. The company collapsed amid scandal in 1982.

SPECIFICATIONS

Years produced: 981-1982 (9200 in total)
Performance: 0-60mph: 9.6 secs (Top speed: 130mph)
Power & torque: 130bhp / 153lb/ft
Engine: Normally aspirated 2849cc V6, petrol, electronic fuel injection, 12 valves
Drivetrain: Rear-engine RWD
Suspension: (F) Independent, coil springs. (R) Independent, trailing arms, coils
Bodyframe: Chassis and separate body
Transmission: 5-speed manual
Weight: 1244kgs

PRICE GUIDE

Launch price: £10,674
Excellent: £21,000
Good: £17,000
Average: £12,000
Project: £8000

DE TOMASO
Mangusta

De Tomaso married the cancelled Ford 70P racing car programme with a rejected Iso design proposal by Giugiaro to create the Mangusta – the company's very first supercar. Essentially a racing car for the road with svelte styling, it ended up being too hard to handle on the road, and extremely difficult to live with. But that doesn't stop it being a great today – and although values seriously lag behind the supercar opposition, don't imagine that the Mangusta isn't a desirable car with prices that are bound to rise.

SPECIFICATIONS

Years produced: 1967-1972 (400 in total)
Performance: 0-60mph: 6.0 secs (Top speed: 155mph)
Power & torque: 305bhp / 392lb/ft
Engine: Normally aspirated 4727cc V8, petrol, carburettor, 16 valves
Drivetrain: Mid-engine RWD
Suspension: (F) Independent coil springs. (R) Independent coil springs
Bodyframe: Chassis and glassfibre body
Transmission: 5-speed manual
Weight: 1322kgs

PRICE GUIDE

Launch price: Special order only
Excellent: £55,000
Good: £45,000
Average: £30,000
Project: £17,500

DE TOMASO
Deauville

It seemed like a good idea at the time, and had there been any justice, more Deauvilles might have found their way into owners' hands. As it was, it was a big failure. De Tomaso set out to create its own XJ6, but without the complexity. So out went the XK, and in went the Pantera's Detroit V8, and had BL not been in dire straits itself, the company's lawyers may well have been knocking on the door over the matter of the Deauville's styling. Despite the market not wanting it then, it's an interesting classic today, and well worth a look, should the opportunity come up.

SPECIFICATIONS

Years produced: 1970-1989 (355 in total)
Performance: 0-60mph: 6.4 secs (Top speed: 143mph)
Power & torque: 330bhp / 325lb/ft
Engine: Normally aspirated 5763cc V8, petrol, carburettor, 16 valves
Drivetrain: Front-engine RWD
Suspension: (F & R) Independent telescopic dampers, coil springs
Bodyframe: Monocoque
Transmission: 5-speed manual/automatic
Weight: 1814kgs

PRICE GUIDE

Launch price: £8992
Excellent: £15,000
Good: £10,000
Average: £5000
Project: £2000

DE TOMASO
Pantera

De Tomaso learnt a lot of lessons from the Mangusta, so when it came to creating a new supercar for Ford to sell in the USA, it made sure it was a lot more habitable. The reworked chassis ensured there was a lot less rearward weight bias, and therefore, snap oversteer wasn't an inevitable consequence of bungled corner. The interior was roomier, and had standard air conditioning, too. However, quality and reliability was poor, and when Ford withdrew its support, De Tomaso had to go it alone when selling the Pantera.

SPECIFICATIONS

Years produced: 1971-1985
Performance: 0-60mph: 6.2 secs (Top speed: 159mph)
Power & torque: 330bhp / 325lb/ft
Engine: Normally aspirated 5763cc V8, petrol, carburettor, 16 valves
Drivetrain: Mid-engine RWD
Suspension: (F) Independent coil springs. (R) Independent coil springs
Bodyframe: Monocoque
Transmission: 5-speed manual
Weight: 1411kgs

PRICE GUIDE

Launch price: £6996
Excellent: £28,500
Good: £24,000
Average: £15,000
Project: £9000

DE TOMASO
Longchamps

Having failed with the Deauville, De Tomaso went and repeated the concept with its Longchamp. Again, it was a case of producing an Italian version of another manufacturer's car – this time, the Mercedes-Benz 450SLC – going down the same road to do so. Again, sales were non-existent, mainly because there was simply no demand, and the quality just wasn't there. Once De Tomaso took a controlling interest in Maserati, it tried again with the car, rebadging it the Kyalami, but was met with similar apathy from buyers.

SPECIFICATIONS

Years produced: 1972-1989 (409 in total)
Performance: 0-60mph: 6.4 secs (Top speed: 149mph)
Power & torque: 330bhp / 325lb/ft
Engine: Normally aspirated 5763cc V8, petrol, carburettor, 16 valves
Drivetrain: Front-engine RWD
Suspension: (F) Independent coil springs. (R) Independent coil springs
Bodyframe: Monocoque
Transmission: 5-speed manual/Automatic
Weight: 1814kgs

PRICE GUIDE

Launch price: £9945
Excellent: £16,500
Good: £12,500
Average: £6000
Project: £2500

DE TOMASO
Pantera GT5/GT5S

De Tomaso didn't give up on the Pantera. The firm toughened it up, offered a 300bhp entry model and rejigged the Tom Tjaarda styling with flared arches and wider wheels wearing Pirelli P7s to give it near-Countach levels of road presence. The days of big sales were gone, but somehow the Pantera survived like this into the 1990s by receiving a number of facelifts along the way. Its survival and subsequent appreciation are a credit to the original design, and testament to the effectiveness of an Italian supercar powered by Detroit muscle.

SPECIFICATIONS

Years produced: 1985-1991 (10,000 approx in total)
Performance: 0-60mph: 5.2 secs (Top speed: 146mph)
Power & torque: 350bhp / 330lb/ft
Engine: Normally aspirated 5763cc V8, petrol, carburettor, 16 valves
Drivetrain: Mid-engine RWD
Suspension: (F & R) Ind. wishbones, coils, telescopic dampers, anti-roll bars.
Bodyframe: Monocoque
Transmission: ZF 5-speed manual
Weight: 1491kgs

PRICE GUIDE

Launch price: £41,410
Excellent: £36,000
Good: £30,000
Average: £20,000
Project: £12,000

DELLOW
MkI-V

Produced in Alvechurch, Birmingham, these sporting roadsters were built for racing. Basically a Trial car that went through a series of evolutions which started out based on an Austin Seven special before moving to a bespoke lightweight A-frame chassis powered by a 1172cc Ford Ten engine. It proved a winning formula thanks to rearward weight bias, and to this day, Dellows still star in these events. Considering their simple, but clever, construction and the plug-in nature of their engines, the survival rate is high, and the fan base is huge.

SPECIFICATIONS

Years produced: 1949-1957 (500 approx in total)
Performance: 0-60mph: 20.3 secs (Top speed: 69mph)
Power & torque: 30/40bhp / N/A
Engine: Normally aspirated 1172cc in-line four, petrol, carburettor, side valves
Drivetrain: Front-engine RWD
Suspension: (F & R) Beam axles
Bodyframe: Chassis and separate aluminium body
Transmission: 3-speed manual
Weight: 610kgs

PRICE GUIDE

Launch price: £570
Excellent: £8500
Good: £7000
Average: £4500
Project: £2500

DODGE
Viper RT/10 Roadster

In 1992, there was nothing else like the Viper. Inspired by the AC Cobra, the Viper followed the same formula – a obscenely powerful lump of Detroit Iron (a V10 based on a truck engine) mounted in a simple chassis and body. Carroll Shelby was involved in the early stages of development, so that similarity had some resonance. With 400bhp and no electronics to rein it all in, the Viper was an exciting drive, and you're not encouraged to drive it in the rain due to there being no hood. Official imports into the UK means availability is straightforward.

SPECIFICATIONS

Years produced: 1992-1995
Performance: 0-60mph: 4.6 secs (Top speed: 180mph)
Power & torque: 400bhp / 450lb/ft
Engine: Normally aspirated 7997cc V10, petrol, electronic fuel injection, 20 valves
Drivetrain: Front-engine RWD
Suspension: (F) Independent coil spring. (R) Independent coil spring
Bodyframe: Spaceframe with glassfibre body
Transmission: 6-speed manual
Weight: 1588kgs

PRICE GUIDE

Launch price: £55,000
Excellent: £30,000
Good: £25,000
Average: £20,000
Project: £14,000

ELVA
Courier

Created by Frank Nichols for racing, the Courier was a quintessential English specialist car that married low weight, great handling and excellent performance in a low-cost package. However, Nichols sold the project to Trojan, who introduced an improved version of the Courier in 1962. In MkIII form, the Courier received a number of small changes to its chassis as well as a roomier cockpit. However, sales dried up following the Trojan takeover and after a final fling with a stylish coupé version, ceased production in 1968.

SPECIFICATIONS

Years produced:	1958-1961 (500 in total)
Performance:	0-60mph: 12.7 secs (Top speed: 98mph)
Power & torque:	72bhp / 77lb/ft
Engine:	Normally aspirated 1489cc in-line four, petrol, carburettor, 8 valves
Drivetrain:	Front-engine RWD
Suspension:	(F) Ind. double wishbone, coil spring. (R) Panhard rod, radius arms, coil spring
Bodyframe:	Chassis and glassfibre body
Transmission:	4-speed manual
Weight:	453kgs

PRICE GUIDE

Launch price:	£725
Excellent:	£9500
Good:	£8000
Average:	£5000
Project:	£2500

FACEL VEGA
FVS

Facel started out by building bodies for other manufacturers before going it alone in 1954 with a De Soto-engined car called the Vega. Once the car became established the company rebranded itself Facel Vega, and the car became the FVS. From the original 4.5-litre V8, the FVS moved to 5.4-litre Chrysler power – and the tubular-framed chassis car boasted 335bhp. To rein in all that power, a brake servo was fitted in 1957, and disc brakes were an option the following year. It was a simple recipe and the quality was there, as was the driving experience.

SPECIFICATIONS

Years produced:	1954-1958 (352 in total)
Performance:	0-60mph: 9.6 secs (Top speed: 134mph)
Power & torque:	325bhp / 430lb/ft
Engine:	Normally aspirated 5801cc V8, petrol, carburettor, 16 valves
Drivetrain:	Front-engine RWD
Suspension:	(F) Independent, coil springs. (R) Beam axle, semi-elliptic leaf spring
Bodyframe:	N/A
Transmission:	4-speed manual
Weight:	1863kgs

PRICE GUIDE

Launch price:	£4726
Excellent:	£30,000
Good:	£25,000
Average:	£15,000
Project:	£10,000

FACEL VEGA
HK500

The FVS was uprated in 1959 with a 360bhp 6.3-litre engine, making it one of the most powerful cars in Europe. Even with the power boost, the all-disc brake set-up was standard kit on the HK500 – not what you would necessarily want in a car with such prodigious amounts of straight line performance. Despite that, a perfect flagship for the French car industry, even if the overall dynamics of the HK500 lagged behind the styling and straight line performance. Chrysler power, steering and transmissions mean that parts supply is good. Rare, expensive and hard to find now.

SPECIFICATIONS

Years produced:	1958-1961 (490 in total)
Performance:	0-60mph: 9.7 secs (Top speed: 130mph)
Power & torque:	360bhp / 400lb/ft
Engine:	Normally aspirated 5901cc V8, petrol, carburettor, 16 valves
Drivetrain:	Front-engine RWD
Suspension:	(F) Independent, coil spring. (R) Beam axle, semi-elliptic leaf spring
Bodyframe:	Chassis and separate body
Transmission:	4-speed manual
Weight:	1829kgs

PRICE GUIDE

Launch price:	£4726
Excellent:	£37,500
Good:	£30,000
Average:	£20,000
Project:	£10,000

FACEL VEGA
Facellia

Facel Vega needed to up its production volumes to make up the shortfall in its third-party body supply business. As the 'affordable' second model, the Facellia was to help the firm expand while allowing it to continue producing V8-powered supercars. The 1.6-litre twin-cam engine had an impressive specification, but the 115bhp it made wasn't enough for anything other than average performance, and it wasn't exactly reliable either. A great concept, with gorgeous HK500-like styling, marred in the execution, but prized by enthusiasts today.

SPECIFICATIONS

Years produced:	1960-1964 (1767 in total)
Performance:	0-60mph: 11.9 secs (Top speed: 106mph)
Power & torque:	115bhp / 106lb/ft
Engine:	Normally aspirated 1647cc in-line four, petrol, carburettor, 8 valves
Drivetrain:	Front-engine RWD
Suspension:	(F) Independent, coil spring, (R) Beam axle, semi-elliptic leaf spring
Bodyframe:	Chassis and separate body
Transmission:	4-speed manual
Weight:	1153kgs

PRICE GUIDE

Launch price:	£2582
Excellent:	£17,500
Good:	£14,000
Average:	£8000
Project:	£3250

FACEL VEGA
Facel II

Continuing Facel Vega's policy of regular updates, the HK500 remained in production for a mere two years, moving over for the Facel II. The new car featured sharper styling and an even more powerful Chrysler V8, now boasting 390bhp and finally allowing the French supercar to top a genuine 150mph. However, the chassis and steering were simply not good enough to control all this power, marring what was an extremely appealing package. Despite all that, a very cool car today, especially as it's the last in the line of big V8 Facel Vegas.

SPECIFICATIONS

Years produced: 1961-1964 (183 in total)
Performance: 0-60mph: 8.4 secs (Top speed: 129mph)
Power & torque: 355bhp / 380lb/ft
Engine: Normally aspirated 6286cc V8, petrol, carburettor, 16 valves
Drivetrain: Front-engine RWD
Suspension: (F) Independent, coil spring. (R) Beam axle, semi-elliptic leaf spring
Bodyframe: Chassis and separate body
Transmission: 4-speed manual
Weight: 1842kgs

PRICE GUIDE

Launch price: £4879
Excellent: £45,000
Good: £37,500
Average: £23,000
Project: £12,000

FACEL VEGA
Facel III

Amazingly, when it came to replacing the Facel II, the idea of increasing power and opulence was thrown out of the window as the company adopted a clean sheet policy for its new car. The Facel III was powered by a 1780cc Volvo engine, and delivered the sort of performance that was ample for most drivers. It sold well too, as it managed to retain all the dignity and style of the V8 cars in a more manageable package. However, the company was already in trouble when it launched, and despite its relative success, it failed to halt the inevitable.

SPECIFICATIONS

Years produced: 1963-1964
Performance: 0-60mph: N/A (Top speed: N/A)
Power & torque: 108bhp / N/A
Engine: Normally aspirated 1780cc in-line four, petrol, carburettor, 8 valves
Drivetrain: Front-engine RWD
Suspension: (F) Independent, coil springs. (R) Live axle, semi-elliptic leaf springs
Bodyframe: Chassis and separate body
Transmission: 4-speed manual
Weight: 1089kgs

PRICE GUIDE

Launch price: N/A
Excellent: £20,000
Good: £16,000
Average: £9000
Project: £4000

FERRARI
250 GT Boano/Ellena

The strange name comes from the coachbuilding firm that bodied the cars for Ferrari. Although designed by Pininfarina, they were erecting a new plant and didn't have capacity to build them. The work was given to former employee Mario Boano, then after around 80 were built the contract was passed to his son-in-law Ezio Ellena who assembled another 50. Early cars put out 220bhp from their three-litre V12 engines, but this rose to 240bhp. Despite independent double wishbone front suspension the chassis is fairly crude.

SPECIFICATIONS

Years produced: 1956-1959 (130 in total)
Performance: 0-60mph: 7.1 secs (Top speed: 126mph)
Power & torque: 260bhp / 232lb/ft
Engine: Normally aspirated 2953cc V12, petrol, carburettor, 24 valves
Drivetrain: Front-engine RWD
Suspension: ((F) Independent, wishbone, coil spring. (R) Live axle, semi-elliptic leaf spring
Bodyframe: Chassis and separate body
Transmission: 4-speed manual
Weight: 1315kgs

PRICE GUIDE

Launch price: N/A
Excellent: £250,000
Good: £220,000
Average: £175,000
Project: £125,000

FERRARI
250 California Spyder

Largely built for the American market, California Spyders were that bit more sporting than the 250 GT Cabriolets they were based on. By 1960 just under 50 long wheelbase versions were built with 240bhp engines. Eight inches was then chopped from the middle of the car to create the short wheelbase version. Power went up to 280bhp and another 50 of these were sold over the next three years. They can be worth around 25% more than the LWB cars, but the rare alloy-bodied versions of either (just 12 built) can hit the £5m mark.

SPECIFICATIONS

Years produced: 1958-1962 (100 approx in total)
Performance: 0-60mph: 7.2 secs (Top speed: 137mph)
Power & torque: 240bhp / 181lb/ft
Engine: Normally aspirated 2953cc V12, petrol, carburettor, 24 valves
Drivetrain: Front-engine RWD
Suspension: (F) Independent, wishbone, coil spring. (R) Live axle, semi-elliptic leaf spring
Bodyframe: Chassis and separate body
Transmission: 4-speed manual
Weight: 1277kgs

PRICE GUIDE

Launch price: XXXXX
Excellent: £2,500,000
Good: £2,000,000
Average: £1,500,000
Project: £1,000,000

FERRARI
250 GT SWB

Seriously collectible Ferraris, not least due to the fact that only just over 150 were built and almost half were competition cars. The racers reigned supreme in the GT classes and one was even driven in period by Sir Stirling Moss; such exploits rub off on the desirability and value of road cars. History and provenance can have almost as much effect on an individual SWB's price as condition. All came with three-litre V12s and power can range from 220/240 in road cars to 280bhp from competition-specification engines.

SPECIFICATIONS

Years produced: 1959-1962 (167 in total)
Performance: 0-60mph: 6.4 secs (Top speed: 167mph)
Power & torque: 280bhp / 203lb/ft
Engine: Normally aspirated 2953cc V12, petrol, carburettor, 24 valves
Drivetrain: Front-engine RWD
Suspension: (F) Independent, wishbone, coil spring. (R) Live axle, semi-elliptic leaf spring
Bodyframe: Monocoque
Transmission: 4-speed manual
Weight: 1180kgs

PRICE GUIDE

Launch price: N/A
Excellent: £2,500,000
Good: £2,000,000
Average: £1,500,000
Project: £1,000,000

FERRARI
250 GT Cabrio S2

Well-appointed and suitably expensive in its day, the GT Cabriolet was very much an open version of the 250 Coupé – less sporting and more sober-looking than the Spyders they were sold alongside. The giveaway is that Cabriolets had small quarterlights in the doors; you'd have to see the cars side-by-side to see they also had a taller windscreen. Under the bonnet, however, you'll find the same engine as in the LWB Spyder, so with little performance difference between them the Cabriolet looks quite a bargain in comparison.

SPECIFICATIONS

Years produced:	1960-1962 (200 in total)
Performance:	0-60mph: 7.1 secs (Top speed: 161mph)
Power & torque:	240bhp / N/A
Engine:	Normally aspirated 2953cc V12, petrol, carburettor, 24 valves
Drivetrain:	Front-engine RWD
Suspension:	(F) Independent, double wishbones, coil springs, anti-roll bar. (R) Live axle
Bodyframe:	Chassis and separate body
Transmission:	4-speed manual
Weight:	1200kgs

PRICE GUIDE

Launch price:	N/A
Excellent:	£275,000
Good:	£225,000
Average:	£175,000
Project:	£135,000

FERRARI
250 GTE 2+2

Built with the clear intention of taking a slice of the premium four-seater market, this was Ferrari's first production 2+2. It was powered by the same three-litre V12 used in the 250 Coupés, but moved forward eight inches in the chassis to help create interior space without making the car look too long. The GTE's success is evident in the 955 examples sold over three years. The collectors' market, of course, doesn't appreciate big numbers like that – or Ferrari's with extra seats – so they are relatively cheap to buy, though hard to find in top condition.

SPECIFICATIONS

Years produced:	1960-1963 (955 in total)
Performance:	0-60mph: 8.0 secs (Top speed: 136mph)
Power & torque:	240bhp / 181lb/ft
Engine:	Normally aspirated 2953cc V12, petrol, carburettor, 24 valves
Drivetrain:	Front-engine RWD
Suspension:	(F) Independent, wishbone, coil spring. (R) Live axle, semi-elliptic leaf spring
Bodyframe:	Chassis and separate body
Transmission:	4-speed manual with overdrive
Weight:	1406kgs

PRICE GUIDE

Launch price:	£6326
Excellent:	£95,000
Good:	£80,000
Average:	£50,000
Project:	£35,000

FERRARI
400 Superamerica

The Ferrari tradition of naming their cars after the displacement of a single cylinder should have seen this called the 330, but it chose 400 instead, referring to the four-litre capacity, perhaps as the model was very much headed for the land where more is better. Aimed at the super-rich, numbers were low with just 47 built over four years. Most of these were 'Aerodynamica' coupés, but Pininfarina also built 11 quite exquisite and imposing cabriolets which fetch roughly 50% more than the coupé prices quoted here.

SPECIFICATIONS

Years produced:	1960-1964 (58 in total)
Performance:	0-60mph: 9.2 secs (Top speed: 160mph)
Power & torque:	340bhp / 235lb/ft
Engine:	Normally aspirated 3967cc V12, petrol, carburettor, 24 valves
Drivetrain:	Front-engine RWD
Suspension:	(F) Independent double wishbone, coil spring, anti-roll bar. (R) Live axle
Bodyframe:	Monocoque
Transmission:	5-speed manual
Weight:	1363kgs

PRICE GUIDE

Launch price:	XXXXX
Excellent:	£650,000
Good:	£550,000
Average:	£400,000
Project:	£300,000

FERRARI
250 GT Berlinetta Lusso

Last of the 250 GT line, the Lusso is also on many an aficionado's list of all-time best looking Ferraris. On a chassis derived from the 250 GTO, but with the engine moved forward to improve cabin space, the Lusso has a steel shell with all the opening panels, floor and firewall in aluminium – a fact that can add to the cost and complication of restoration. The engine is the familiar three-litre V12 with three twin-choke Webers and 250bhp. Bucket seats add to the sporting feel, though still manage to be comfortable.

SPECIFICATIONS

Years produced:	1962-1964 (350 in total)
Performance:	0-60mph: 8.0 secs (Top speed: 149mph)
Power & torque:	250bhp / 217lb/ft
Engine:	Normally aspirated 2953cc V12, petrol, carburettor, 24 valves
Drivetrain:	Front-engine RWD
Suspension:	(F) Independent, double wishbone, coil spring. (R) Live axle
Bodyframe:	Chassis and separate body
Transmission:	4-speed manual
Weight:	1020kgs

PRICE GUIDE

Launch price:	£5607
Excellent:	£375,000
Good:	£325,000
Average:	£250,000
Project:	£175,000

FERRARI
250 LM

The 'LM', if you haven't already worked it out, stands for Le Mans, the spiritual home of competition Ferraris and somewhere these cars did indeed race. They weren't the planned success, however, as the FIA wouldn't homologate them as a replacement for the 250 GTO in the GT class, so they had to compete against the more powerful Prototypes. That said, the 250 LM still stands as Ferrari's first series production mid-engined car and many of the 32 built racked up good competition careers in the hands of privateers.

SPECIFICATIONS

Years produced:	1964-1966 (32 in total)
Performance:	0-60mph: N/A (Top speed: 183mph)
Power & torque:	320bhp / 231lb/ft
Engine:	Normally aspirated 3285cc V12, petrol, carburettor, 24 valves
Drivetrain:	Mid-engine RWD
Suspension:	(F) Independent, coil spring, double wishbone. (R) Independent
Bodyframe:	Spaceframe
Transmission:	5-speed manual
Weight:	850kgs

PRICE GUIDE

Launch price:	N/A
Excellent:	£3,000,000
Good:	£2,500,000
Average:	£2,000,000
Project:	£1,500,000

FERRARI
275 GTS

The Spyder version shared the new 3.3-litre V12 and all the advances of its GTB brother, but this was far from just a soft-topped version of the coupé. Their bodies – though both styled by Pininfarina – were totally different, with the softer, less aggressive looking GTS staying much closer to the lines of previous 250 GTs. It is perhaps this factor that has resulted in the unusual situation of a convertible being worth less than its coupé equivalent, a fact that looks even more surprising when you consider twice as many coupés were sold.

SPECIFICATIONS

Years produced: 1964-1966 (200 in total)
Performance: 0-60mph: 7.2 secs (Top speed: 150mph)
Power & torque: 280bhp / 188lb/ft
Engine: Normally aspirated 3286cc V12, petrol, carburettor, 24 valves
Drivetrain: Front-engine RWD
Suspension: (F) Ind. double wishbones, coil springs, anti-roll bar. (R) Ind. double wishbones
Bodyframe: Chassis and separate body
Transmission: 5-speed manual
Weight: 1152kgs

PRICE GUIDE

Launch price: £5973
Excellent: £350,000
Good: £300,000
Average: £225,000
Project: £175,000

FERRARI
500 Superfast

Evolved from the 400 Superamerica, the 500 Superfast had a slightly longer wheelbase and only came in aerodynamic coupé form, with the 400's styling tidied up and improved upon. Surprisingly, the market says they're actually worth a lot less than those 400s, despite only 36 Superfasts being built. Some of that may be down to fear of the mighty five-litre V12 engine. Despite the low build numbers, much of its construction was unique to this model, so you wouldn't want to break one. Eight were built with right-hand-drive.

SPECIFICATIONS

Years produced: 1964-1966 (36 in total)
Performance: 0-60mph: 7.8 secs (Top speed: 174mph)
Power & torque: 400bhp / 350lb/ft
Engine: Normally aspirated 4963cc V12, petrol, carburettor, 24 valves
Drivetrain: Front-engine RWD
Suspension: (F) Ind. double wish. coil springs. (R) Live axle, semi-elliptic leaf springs
Bodyframe: Monocoque
Transmission: 5-speed manual
Weight: 1400kgs

PRICE GUIDE

Launch price: £11,519
Excellent: £400,000
Good: £350,000
Average: £250,000
Project: £175,000

FERRARI
330 GT 2+2

Taking over from the commercially very successful 250 GTE as Ferrari's four-seater option, the 330 GT came with a litre more engine capacity for vastly improved performance figures – top speed was raised by 10mph over the older car. Unfortunately the 330 GT also came with an awkward twin headlamp arrangement that, in polite terms, received mixed reviews. Thankfully the Series II, introduced halfway through production, reverted to a prettier single headlamp arrangement, and it's these the market prefers.

SPECIFICATIONS

Years produced: 1964-1967 (1075 in total)
Performance: 0-60mph: 6.3 secs (Top speed: 152mph)
Power & torque: 300bhp / 288lb/ft
Engine: Normally aspirated 3967cc V12, petrol, carburettor, 24 valves
Drivetrain: Front-engine RWD
Suspension: (F) Independent, upper and lower wishbones, anti-roll bar. (R) Live axle
Bodyframe: Chassis and separate body
Transmission: 5-speed manual
Weight: 1442kgs

PRICE GUIDE

Launch price: £6522
Excellent: £70,000
Good: £55,000
Average: £35,000
Project: £20,000

FERRARI
275 GTB/GTB4

Though the body was a gentle evolution from what had gone before, it was underneath where the 275 is special, and significant, as Ferrari finally introduced long-overdue advances in chassis technology. All-independent suspension, a disc brake at every corner, plus a five-speed transaxle to aid weight distribution. Bodies were built in both steel and alloy – with the latter being worth 25% more than the prices quoted. Power from the 3.3-litre V12 could be 250bhp, or 275bhp with the optional six-carb set-up. This was raised to 300bhp for the four-cam GTB/4.

SPECIFICATIONS

Years produced: 1964-1968 (730 in total)
Performance: 0-60mph: 6.0 secs (Top speed: 162mph)
Power & torque: 280bhp / 188lb/ft
Engine: Normally aspirated 3286cc V12, petrol, carburettor, 24 valves
Drivetrain: Front-engine RWD
Suspension: (F) Independent, double wishbone, coil spring. (R) Independent
Bodyframe: Monocoque
Transmission: 5-speed manual
Weight: 1098kgs

PRICE GUIDE

Launch price: £5973
Excellent: £475,000
Good: £400,000
Average: £300,000
Project: £250,000

FERRARI
330 GTC

Looking like a coupé version of the 275 GTS with the nose of a 500 Superfast, the 330 GTC lacks the styling purity of the coupés either side of it in the Ferrari family tree. It's a lot better from some angles than others and that is reflected in their values, though they are by no means cheap – even by Ferrari collectors' standards. They certainly suffer no shortfall in the performance department, the four-litre V12's 300bhp offering up genuine 150mph capability. Continued use of a five-speed rear transaxle ensures good handling and cruising.

SPECIFICATIONS

Years produced: 1966-1968 (600 in total)
Performance: 0-60mph: 6.8 secs (Top speed: 152mph)
Power & torque: 300bhp / 288lb/ft
Engine: Normally aspirated 3967cc V12, petrol, carburettor, 24 valves
Drivetrain: Front-engine RWD
Suspension: (F) Ind. double wishbones, coil springs, anti-roll bar. (R) Ind. double wishbones
Bodyframe: Chassis and separate body
Transmission: 5-speed manual
Weight: 1433kgs

PRICE GUIDE

Launch price: £6515
Excellent: £140,000
Good: £110,000
Average: £80,000
Project: £55,000

FERRARI
330 GTS

In something of a break with Ferrari tradition, the 330 Spyder was simply the coupé 330 GTC with the roof lopped off. Then again, given how much better the topless car looks, it's very likely that the Spyder was designed first and had the roof added. Buyers certainly value the Spyder significantly higher than the coupé, and that difference isn't all to do with the lack of roof and only 100 being built compared to six times as many GTCs. The GTS really is that far ahead in style and bragging rights. Remarkably friendly to drive despite its 300bhp.

SPECIFICATIONS

Years produced: 1966-1968 (100 in total)
Performance: 0-60mph: 6.9 secs (Top speed: 146mph)
Power & torque: 300bhp / 288lb/ft
Engine: Normally aspirated 3967cc V12, petrol, carburettor, 24 valves
Drivetrain: Front-engine RWD
Suspension: (F) Ind. double wishbones, coil springs, anti-roll bar. (R) Ind. double wishbones
Bodyframe: Chassis and separate body
Transmission: 5-speed manual
Weight: 1297kgs

PRICE GUIDE

Launch price: £6515
Excellent: £300,000
Good: £250,000
Average: £160,000
Project: £100,000

FERRARI
365 GTC/GTS

These were stop-gap models, little more than 330 GTC and GTSs with the V12 bored out by 400cc to 4.4 litres. Visually the only way to tell them apart is that the row of three outlet vents on each front wing has vanished, to be replaced by a pair of flush-fit grilles to the rear of the bonnet. Mechanically the cars were identical to their predecessors, with the exception of the braking system which was switched from Dunlop/Girling to ATE. The GTS was short-lived, being dropped after just a year with just 20 completed. GTCs numbered 150.

SPECIFICATIONS

Years produced: 1968-1970 (150/20 in total)
Performance: 0-60mph: 6.3 secs (Top speed: 152mph)
Power & torque: 320bhp / 268lb/ft
Engine: Normally aspirated 4390cc V12, petrol, carburettor, 24 valves
Drivetrain: Front-engine RWD
Suspension: (F) Ind. double wishbone, coil spring, anti-roll bar. (R) Ind. double wishbone
Bodyframe: Monocoque
Transmission: 5-speed manual
Weight: 1451kgs

PRICE GUIDE

Launch price: £7909
Excellent: £140,000
Good: £120,000
Average: £80,000
Project: £55,000

FERRARI
365 GT 2+2

Replacement for the 330 GT, the 365 was Ferrari's first 2+2 to have independent rear suspension – a Koni self-levelling system to boot. It's a big car, once dubbed 'the Queen Mother of Ferraris' by *Road & Track*, but the sleek lines are more successful than the 330's, especially at the front. With the V12 bored out to 4.4 litres it's not short of performance, grip is good and the standard power steering helps make it feel smaller from the driver's seat. 800 of them were built and it's never really caught on with collectors.

SPECIFICATIONS

Years produced: 1968-1970 (800 in total)
Performance: 0-60mph: 7.1 secs (Top speed: 125mph)
Power & torque: 320bhp / 268lb/ft
Engine: Normally aspirated 4390cc V12, petrol, carburettor, 24 valves
Drivetrain: Front-engine RWD
Suspension: (F) Independent, double wishbone, coil spring. (R) Independent, double wishbone
Bodyframe: Monocoque
Transmission: 5-speed manual
Weight: 1462kgs

PRICE GUIDE

Launch price: £7500
Excellent: £60,000
Good: £50,000
Average: £35,000
Project: £20,000

FERRARI
365 GTB/4 Daytona

One of the legendary Ferraris, not least because it held the title of World's Fastest Production Car for some time at 174mph. That was all made possible by the quad-cam 4.4-litre V12 with its bank of six twin-choke Weber carbs – good for 352bhp in street trim. And though built as a road car, privateers were still racing them successfully as late as 1979. Headlamps were initially fixed behind a Perspex nose, but after complaints they were changed for pop-up lights in 1970. Nearly 1400 were built – a lot for a top-end Ferrari.

SPECIFICATIONS

Years produced: 1968-1973 (1284 in total)
Performance: 0-60mph: 5.9 secs (Top speed: 174mph)
Power & torque: 352bhp / 318lb/ft
Engine: Normally aspirated 4390cc V12, petrol, carburettor, 24 valves
Drivetrain: Front-engine RWD
Suspension: (F) Independent, double wishbone, coil spring. (R) Independent, double wishbone
Bodyframe: Monocoque
Transmission: 5-speed manual
Weight: 1197kgs

PRICE GUIDE

Launch price: £8750
Excellent: £200,000
Good: £175,000
Average: £140,000
Project: £95,000

FERRARI
Dino 206/246 GT

Undeniably pretty, and with a mid-mounted V6 in an alloy body, but two litres weren't quite enough for Ferrari's move into a more volume market and only around 150 206 GTs were built before it was replaced by the real deal 246 GT. OK, these were built in steel, with an iron rather than alloy engine block, but the four-cam 2.4-litre V6 would take it all the way to 150mph. The public snapped them up and they continue to feature on many an enthusiast's wish list. Estimates vary, but between 1868 and 2609 were built.

SPECIFICATIONS

Years produced: 1969-1974 (206/1868 in total)
Performance: 0-60mph: 7.1 secs (Top speed: 145mph)
Power & torque: 195bhp / 167lb/ft
Engine: Normally aspirated 2418cc V6, petrol, carburettor, 12 valves
Drivetrain: Mid-engine RWD
Suspension: (F) Independent, double wishbone, coil spring. (R) Independent, double wishbone
Bodyframe: Chassis and separate body
Transmission: 5-speed manual
Weight: 1077kgs

PRICE GUIDE

Launch price: £5486
Excellent: £100,000
Good: £80,000
Average: £55,000
Project: £35,000

FERRARI
365 GTC/4

Sharing its four-cam V12, though in a slightly lower state of tune and with six side, rather than downdraft, Webers, the GTC/4 was sold alongside the Daytona – notching up 500 sales in 18 short months. It sports a similar profile to the Daytona too, though there's just about room to squeeze two kids into the back of the GTC/4. It compares favourably to the Daytona in two ways: with its power steering, softer suspension and hydraulic clutch the GTC/4 is nice to drive. It also happens to cost about a third of what you need for a Daytona.

SPECIFICATIONS

Years produced: 1971-1972 (500 in total)
Performance: 0-60mph: 6.2 secs (Top speed: 163mph)
Power & torque: 340bhp / 312lb/ft
Engine: Normally aspirated 4390cc V12, petrol, carburettor, 24 valves
Drivetrain: Front-engine RWD
Suspension: (F) Independent, wishbone, coil spring, anti-roll bar. (R) Independent, wishbone
Bodyframe: Monocoque
Transmission: 5-speed manual
Weight: 1450kgs

PRICE GUIDE

Launch price: £10,251
Excellent: £62,500
Good: £52,500
Average: £35,000
Project: £20,000

FERRARI
Dino 246 GTS

The Targa-roofed spin on the Dino theme arrived in 1972, setting a trend for the fresh air option in mid-engined Ferraris that soon became the norm. As well as the lift-out roof panels, the other big change was deletion of the rear side windows. Not a big deal to many, but it is felt by some to detract ever so slightly from the fine balance of the original design. It's still one of the most beautiful cars ever built and would surely cost a lot more if Ferrari hadn't managed to sell so many. Figures for the GTS are lower than for the GT.

SPECIFICATIONS

Years produced: 1972-1974 (1274 in total)
Performance: 0-60mph: 7.1 secs (Top speed: 146mph)
Power & torque: 195bhp / 166lb/ft
Engine: Normally aspirated 2419cc V6, petrol, carburettor, 12 valves
Drivetrain: Mid-engine RWD
Suspension: (F) Independent, double wishbone, coil spring. (R) Independent, double wishbone
Bodyframe: Spaceframe
Transmission: 5-speed manual
Weight: 1100kgs

PRICE GUIDE

Launch price: £5486
Excellent: £110,000
Good: £90,000
Average: £65,000
Project: £42,500

FERRARI
365 GT4 2+2/400/412i

Aimed at the family man of style and substance. Allow for number changes around the same bodyshell and this is the longest-running Ferrari of all time at 17 years. The 365s started with a 4.4-litre V12, but this grew to 4.8 litres (400) and finally five litres (412i) by 1986. Quick and fine-handling despite their size, the penalty comes at the pumps, where you can expect 10-12mpg. Prices quoted are for the 412i; 365s are a little more and 400s cost a little less. Most came with a General Motors-sourced four-speed automatic gearbox.

SPECIFICATIONS

Years produced: 1972-1989 (525/1810/576 in total)
Performance: 0-60mph: 6.7 secs (Top speed: 147mph)
Power & torque: 340bhp / 333lb/ft
Engine: Normally aspirated 4390cc V12, petrol, carburettor, 24 valves
Drivetrain: Front-engine RWD
Suspension: (F) Independent, wishbone, coil spring. (R) Independent, wishbone, coil spring
Bodyframe: Monocoque
Transmission: 5-speed manual
Weight: 1884kgs

PRICE GUIDE

Launch price: £12,783
Excellent: £25,000
Good: £17,500
Average: £13.500
Project: £9000

FERRARI
365 BB Boxer

Having experimented with a small, mid-engined road car in the shape of the Dino, Ferrari went the whole hog with the Daytona's replacement – the Berlinetta Boxer. The Boxer bit refers to the new engine's flat-12 layout; all it shared with the outgoing V12 was its 4.4-litre capacity. Keeping with its race car image the whole tail section lifts to reveal the bare bones of the chassis and the engine, which, thanks to its low profile, sits above the transmission. For the first time in a road-going Ferrari the camshafts were belt driven.

SPECIFICATIONS

Years produced: 1973-1976 (387 in total)
Performance: 0-60mph: 6.5 secs (Top speed: 176mph)
Power & torque: 380bhp / 302lb/ft
Engine: Normally aspirated 4390cc V12, petrol, carburettor, 24 valves
Drivetrain: Mid-engine RWD
Suspension: (F) Independent, double wishbone, coil spring. (R) Independent, double wishbone
Bodyframe: Monocoque
Transmission: 5-speed manual
Weight: 1235kgs

PRICE GUIDE

Launch price: £15,492
Excellent: £80,000
Good: £65,000
Average: £45,000
Project: £30,000

FERRARI
Dino 308 GT4

The 308 GT4 has the rare distinction of being designed by Bertone, making it the first Ferrari for nearly 20 years that wasn't styled by Pininfarina. It also contained the company's first production V8 engine, and was its first mid-engined 2+2. None of those facts have helped endear it to latter-day Ferrari buyers, though it stayed in production for seven years and racked up almost 3000 sales. The engine is effectively two-thirds of a 365's V12. A competent and quick car; find a good one and it makes a fine first Ferrari.

SPECIFICATIONS

Years produced: 1974-1980 (2826 in total)
Performance: 0-60mph: 6.7 secs (Top speed: 147mph)
Power & torque: 255bhp / 209lb/ft
Engine: Normally aspirated 2927cc V8, petrol, carburettor, 16 valves
Drivetrain: Mid-engine RWD
Suspension: (F) Ind. wish. anti-roll bar, coil springs, tele. dampers. (R) Ind. wish. anti-roll bar
Bodyframe: Spaceframe
Transmission: 5-speed manual
Weight: 1265kgs

PRICE GUIDE

Launch price: £7699
Excellent: £18,500
Good: £15,000
Average: £10,000
Project: £5500

FERRARI
308 GTB (GRP)

Blessed with the V8 from the recently-launched 308 GT4, this was Ferrari's first ever glassfibre car, though that bold move fizzled out after less than two years and 712 examples. Quite simply it was cheaper and quicker to build in steel, and demand for the 308 was high. The steel cars were also heavier, and when you add that lot together, it makes the original GRP cars much more collectible and expensive than their successors. You have less rust issues to worry about as well, though only with regard to the outer panels.

SPECIFICATIONS

Years produced:	1975-1977 (712 in total)
Performance:	0-60mph: 6.7 secs (Top speed: 152mph)
Power & torque:	255bhp / 209lb/ft
Engine:	Normally aspirated 2927cc V8, petrol, carburettor, 16 valves
Drivetrain:	Mid-engine RWD
Suspension:	(F) Independent, double wishbone, coil spring. (R) Independent, double wishbone
Bodyframe:	Spaceframe with glassfibre body
Transmission:	5-speed manual
Weight:	1265kgs

PRICE GUIDE

Launch price:	£11,992
Excellent:	£40,000
Good:	£32,500
Average:	£22,500
Project:	£15,000

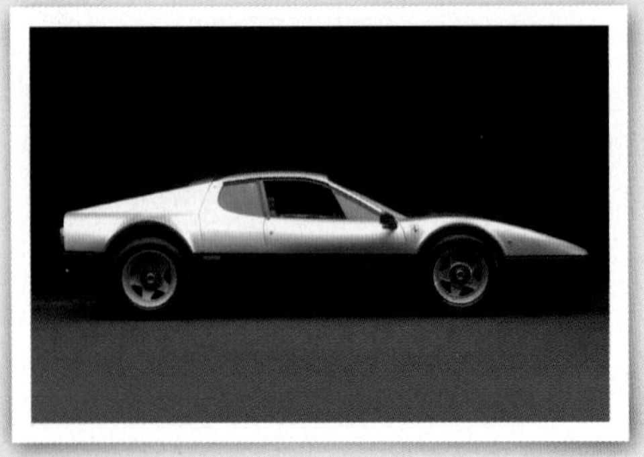

FERRARI
512 BB

Took over from the 365 BB as Ferrari's twelve-cylinder range-topper and stayed there for over a decade. Similar to its predecessor, little was changed apart from the lower nose with integrated spoiler to reduce front-end lift. The five-litre flat-12 was treated to Bosch fuel injection from 1981 which added another 20bhp and gave a little assistance to economy. Probably a better bet than a 365 BB, but the fact that four times as many 512 Berlinetta Boxers were built makes them a little cheaper to put in your garage.

SPECIFICATIONS

Years produced:	1976-1985 (1936 in total)
Performance:	0-60mph: 5.9 secs (Top speed: 188mph)
Power & torque:	360bhp / 332lb/ft
Engine:	Normally aspirated 4942cc V12, petrol, electronic fuel injection, 24 valves
Drivetrain:	Mid-engine RWD
Suspension:	(F) Independent, wishbone, coil spring. (R) Independent, wishbone
Bodyframe:	Monocoque
Transmission:	5-speed manual
Weight:	1515kgs

PRICE GUIDE

Launch price:	£26,000
Excellent:	£75,000
Good:	£60,000
Average:	£40,000
Project:	£27,500

FERRARI
308 GTB/GTS (steel)

One of the company's great success stories and still regarded as one of the best ways to introduce yourself to Ferrari ownership. Early cars are the most powerful, with the 1980-on Bosch fuel-injected models (signified by an 'i' suffix) losing 40bhp to emission controls. Much of this was restored two years later with the four-valves-per-cylinder qv models, identified by cooling slats in the front bonnet. Perhaps the best buys are those built after January 1984, thanks to corrosion-reducing Zincrox coating on the steel panels.

SPECIFICATIONS

Years produced:	1977-1985
Performance:	0-60mph: 7.3 secs (Top speed: 145mph)
Power & torque:	227bhp / 203lb/ft
Engine:	Normally aspirated 2926cc V8, petrol, carburettor, 32 valves
Drivetrain:	Mid-engine RWD
Suspension:	(F) Ind. coil springs, wishbones, anti-roll bar. (R) Ind. coil springs, wishbones
Bodyframe:	Spaceframe with separate body
Transmission:	5-speed manual
Weight:	1265kgs

PRICE GUIDE

Launch price:	£16,499
Excellent:	£26,500
Good:	£20,000
Average:	£14,000
Project:	£8500

FERRARI
Mondial

A cheaper four-seater alternative to Ferrari's 400i, the Mondial was built around 308 GTB running gear. As such, it shared that car's mechanical upgrades: four valves per cylinder from 1982, 3.2 litres from 1985, then 3.4 litres from a longitudinal engine and transverse gearbox for the Mondial t from 1989. Those four seats, along with less than striking looks (for a Ferrari at any rate), combine to make this the cheapest ticket to the Prancing Horse ball, though not all have been well cared for. A cabriolet version joined the coupé in 1984.

SPECIFICATIONS

Years produced:	1980-1994 (4274 in total)
Performance:	0-60mph: 7.1 secs (Top speed: 145mph)
Power & torque:	260bhp / 213lb/ft
Engine:	Normally aspirated 2927cc V8, petrol, electronic fuel injection, 16 valves
Drivetrain:	Mid-engine RWD
Suspension:	(F) Ind. double wishbone, coil spring, anti-roll bar. (R) Ind. double wishbone
Bodyframe:	Monocoque
Transmission:	5-speed manual
Weight:	1446kgs

PRICE GUIDE

Launch price:	£24,488
Excellent:	£18,000
Good:	£14,000
Average:	£9000
Project:	£4000

FERRARI
288 GTO

The revival of that legendary GTO badge on a car whose looks obviously derive from the ageing 308 GTB could easily have been a travesty. It wasn't. Let's start with the lightweight glassfibre and Kevlar bodyshell, on a revised chassis with four inches more wheelbase than the 308. That was done to accommodate longitudinal mounting of the twin-turbocharged 2.9-litre engine. The result is electrifying performance that helped make the GTO an almost instant collector's item. The low build number ensures superstar status and prices.

SPECIFICATIONS

Years produced:	1984-1987 (272 in total)
Performance:	0-60mph: 4.8 secs (Top speed: 190mph)
Power & torque:	400bhp / 366lb/ft
Engine:	Twin-turbocharged 2855cc V8, petrol, electronic fuel injection, 32 valves
Drivetrain:	Mid-engine RWD
Suspension:	(F) Independent, double wishbone, coil spring. (R) Independent
Bodyframe:	Spaceframe
Transmission:	5-speed manual
Weight:	1160kgs

PRICE GUIDE

Launch price:	Special order only
Excellent:	£275,000
Good:	£225,000
Average:	£175,000
Project:	£130,000

FERRARI
Testarossa

Perhaps the ultimate automotive status symbol to emerge from the 'greed is good' decade. The Testarossa's imposing size and in-your-face attitude tends to hide the fact that here we have a remarkably user-friendly supercar; mighty performance delivered in a smooth manner by a sweet and free-revving flat-12. It also has windows you can actually see out of. That Testarossas remain so comparatively cheap to buy is partly due to the stigma of Eighties excess, but mostly because of the vast numbers built.

SPECIFICATIONS

Years produced:	1984-1992 (7177 in total)
Performance:	0-60mph: 5.2 secs (Top speed: 180mph)
Power & torque:	390bhp / 361lb/ft
Engine:	Normally aspirated 4942cc flat 12, petrol, electronic fuel injection, 48 valves
Drivetrain:	Mid-engine RWD
Suspension:	(F) Ind. double wishbone, coil spring, anti-roll bar. (R) Ind. double wishbone
Bodyframe:	Monocoque
Transmission:	5-speed manual
Weight:	1506kgs
	PRICE GUIDE
Launch price:	£62,666
Excellent:	£40,000
Good:	£36,000
Average:	£25,000
Project:	£18,500

FERRARI
328 GTB/GTS

Not wanting to risk its golden goose, changes from the 308 were kept to a minimum and even then justified as improvements to aerodynamics and stability. Front and rear panels below bumper level were deepened, a larger grille fitted, and some lights changed. There's the same glorious howl from the mid-mounted quad-cam V8, but in the 328 it uses an extra 200cc to provide 30bhp more than its predecessor along with a lot more torque. The only downside is the interior, with Fiat-issue switchgear items.

SPECIFICATIONS

Years produced:	1985-1988 (1344/6068 in total)
Performance:	0-60mph: 6.0 secs (Top speed: 163mph)
Power & torque:	270bhp / 224lb/ft
Engine:	Normally aspirated 3186cc V8, petrol, electronic fuel injection, 32 valves
Drivetrain:	Mid-engine RWD
Suspension:	(F) Independent, wishbone, coil spring, anti-roll bar. (R) Independent, wishbone
Bodyframe:	Monocoque
Transmission:	5-speed manual
Weight:	1263kgs
	PRICE GUIDE
Launch price:	£32,220
Excellent:	£28,000
Good:	£25,000
Average:	£18,000
Project:	£11,000

FERRARI
F40

Built to celebrate Ferrari's 40th birthday, the F40 is just the car for anyone who finds the 288 GTO a bit on the tame side. The spec of the two cars carries a similarity too: twin-turbocharged V8 engine and a composite body mounted on a spaceframe chassis. The difference is that the F40 has an extra 78bhp from its slightly larger engine, and in the search for lightness it offers even less in the way of content – not even carpets or door panels. But buyers loved it and Ferrari built almost three times as many as originally intended.

SPECIFICATIONS

Years produced:	1987-1992 (1315 in total)
Performance:	0-60mph: 3.9 secs (Top speed: 201mph)
Power & torque:	478bhp / 426lb/ft
Engine:	Twin-turbocharged 2936cc V8, petrol, electronic fuel injection, 32 valves
Drivetrain:	Mid-engine RWD
Suspension:	(F) Independent, double wishbone, coil spring. (R) Independent, double wishbone
Bodyframe:	Monocoque
Transmission:	5-speed manual
Weight:	1100kgs
	PRICE GUIDE
Launch price:	£193,000
Excellent:	£250,000
Good:	£220,000
Average:	£170,000
Project:	£125,000

FERRARI
348 tb/ts

In many ways the 348 is more closely related to its big brother Testarossa than the 328 it replaced. The V8 engine is still there, but it's been much revised, upped to 3.4 litres with an extra 30bhp, and turned 90 degrees to be mounted longitudinally and set lower in the chassis. Only the gearbox is transverse this time. Great strides have been made with aerodynamics, and the side strakes and black grille over the tail-lights are straight out of the Testarossa design book, as is the relatively spacious cockpit. It is more nervous to drive than a 328 though.

SPECIFICATIONS

Years produced:	1989-1995 (8844 in total)
Performance:	0-60mph: 5.6 secs (Top speed: 170mph)
Power & torque:	300bhp / 237lb/ft
Engine:	Normally aspirated 3405cc V8, petrol, electronic fuel injection, 32 valves
Drivetrain:	Mid-engine RWD
Suspension:	(F) Ind. double wishbone, coil spring. (R) Ind. double wishbone, coil spring
Bodyframe:	Monocoque
Transmission:	5-speed manual
Weight:	1393kgs
	PRICE GUIDE
Launch price:	£67,499
Excellent:	£28,000
Good:	£25,000
Average:	£20,000
Project:	£15,000

FERRARI
512TR/F512M

The Testarossa's replacement returned to Ferrari's naming by numbers system. Visually the 512TR is little changed: only a more pouty mouth, cleaner rear end styling and 18in alloys give the game away. Power is up by 10% though, and the engine and transmission are repositioned to lower the centre of gravity. The clutch is lighter, too. In 1994 it morphed into the short-lived F512M. Less successful in the looks department, thanks largely to fixed headlamps under squares of glass rather than pop-ups, it does have a slightly more power.

SPECIFICATIONS

Years produced:	1991-1996 (2280/500 in total)
Performance:	0-60mph: 4.9 secs (Top speed: 195mph)
Power & torque:	428bhp / 360lb/ft
Engine:	Normally aspirated 4942cc flat 12, petrol, electronic fuel injection, 48 valves
Drivetrain:	Mid-engine RWD
Suspension:	(F) Ind. double wishbone, coil spring, anti-roll bar. (R) Ind. double wishbone
Bodyframe:	Monocoque
Transmission:	6-speed manual
Weight:	1471kgs
	PRICE GUIDE
Launch price:	£129,954
Excellent:	£55,000
Good:	£47,500
Average:	£35,000
Project:	£25,000

FERRARI
456

Only the layout is traditional in Ferrari's return to 'proper' GT production: the long bonnet hiding a front-mounted V12 engine. Everything else about the car is unashamedly high-tech, yet assembled with an uncharacteristic and almost Germanic build quality. With useable rear accommodation, at launch this was the world's most powerful production four-seater. Despite its bulk you get searing acceleration and almost completely roll-free cornering in a car that turns out to be surprisingly easy to drive.

SPECIFICATIONS

Years produced:	1992-1997 (1936 in total)
Performance:	0-60mph: 5.1 secs (Top speed: 186mph)
Power & torque:	442bhp / 406lb/ft
Engine:	Normally aspirated 5474cc V12, petrol, electronic fuel injection, 48 valves
Drivetrain:	Front-engine RWD
Suspension:	(F) Ind. double wishbone, coil spring, anti-roll bar. (R) Ind. double wishbone
Bodyframe:	Monocoque
Transmission:	6-speed manual/4-speed automatic
Weight:	1690kgs
	PRICE GUIDE
Launch price:	£145,999
Excellent:	£44,000
Good:	£35,000
Average:	£27,000
Project:	£22,000

FERRARI
F355

After the slightly disappointing 348, the 355 signalled a real return to form for Ferrari. It had to – Porsche had upped its game with the 911, and the success and useability of Honda's NSX was really applying pressure to sales and prestige. The response moved the junior Ferrari into the supercar league. The much-revised engine has five-valve heads and an 80bhp power increase. It's mated to a slick-shifting six-speed gearbox, with driveability vastly improved by electronic dampers. The cabin is a much nicer place to be and build quality is terrific.

SPECIFICATIONS

Years produced:	1994-1999 (5349 in total)
Performance:	0-60mph: 4.7 secs (Top speed: 183mph)
Power & torque:	380bhp / 268lb/ft
Engine:	Normally aspirated 3496cc V8, petrol, electronic fuel injection, 40 valves
Drivetrain:	Mid-engine RWD
Suspension:	(F) Independent, double wishbone, coil spring. (R) Independent, double wishbone
Bodyframe:	Monocoque
Transmission:	6-speed manual
Weight:	1350kgs
	PRICE GUIDE
Launch price:	£83,031
Excellent:	£47,000
Good:	£43,000
Average:	£35,000
Project:	£28,000

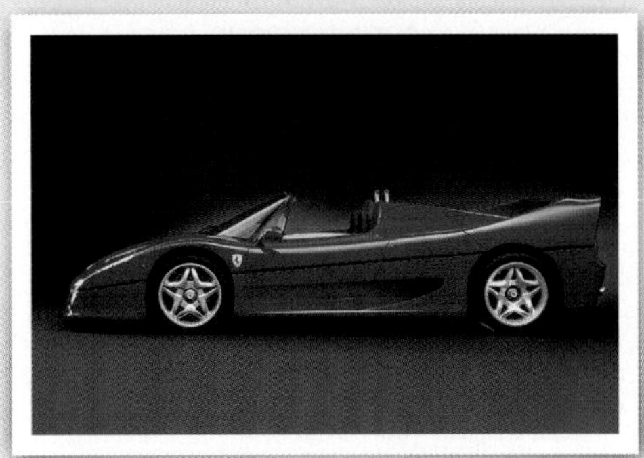

FERRARI
F50

Based heavily on F1 technology, the F50 was built to celebrate the company's 50th birthday – perhaps a little prematurely as it went on sale just seven years after the F40. This time the celebrations involved what to Ferrari cognoscenti is a proper engine, so there's a 4.7-ltre V12 mounted under the transparent engine cover. That engine pumped out enough power to make this the first open-top production car to top 200mph. This time there's no steel chassis, the whole car being constructed from composite panels around a carbon-fibre central tub.

SPECIFICATIONS

Years produced:	1995-1997 (349 in total)
Performance:	0-60mph: 3.7 secs (Top speed: 202mph)
Power & torque:	520bhp / 347lb/ft
Engine:	Normally aspirated 4698cc V12, petrol, electronic fuel injection, 60 valves
Drivetrain:	Mid-engine RWD
Suspension:	(F) Independent, double wishbone, coil spring. (R) Independent, double wishbone
Bodyframe:	Carbon/composite monocoque
Transmission:	6-speed manual
Weight:	1230kgs
	PRICE GUIDE
Launch price:	£329,000
Excellent:	£325,000
Good:	£310,000
Average:	£295,000
Project:	£285,000

FERRARI
F355 Spider

Building on the success of the Berlinetta and targa-topped models, after a year's production Ferrari decided to chop the roof off its 355 and create a proper Spider. But this was new Ferrari, remember, so the job had to be done right. The chassis was given extra reinforcement around the door openings and windscreen pillars to minimise torsional flex, so there's no rattle and squeak, and minimal extra weight. They even look good with the roof up. The final 100 Spiders were Serie Fiorana limited editions fitted with an F1 paddle-shift.

SPECIFICATIONS

Years produced:	1995-1999 (3741 in total)
Performance:	0-60mph: 4.6 secs (Top speed: 183mph)
Power & torque:	380bhp / 268lb/ft
Engine:	Normally aspirated 3496cc V8, petrol, electronic fuel injection, 40 valves
Drivetrain:	Mid-engine RWD
Suspension:	(F) Independent, double wishbone, coil spring. (R) Independent, double wishbone
Bodyframe:	Monocoque
Transmission:	6-speed manual/6-speed sequential
Weight:	1390kgs
	PRICE GUIDE
Launch price:	£83,031
Excellent:	£49,000
Good:	£45,000
Average:	£37,500
Project:	£30,000

FERRARI
550 Maranello

Though the successor to the mid-engined F512M, this was Ferrari's first front-engined two-seater GT since the Daytona ceased production 23 years earlier. The 5.5-litre V12 has been called the best production Ferrari engine by experts, and some may be pleased to hear that its vast power output is kept in check by traction control, so it looks after you and is generally very civilised for a near-200mph machine. A six-speed manual gearbox is standard, but some will have been sold with the optional four-speed auto.

SPECIFICATIONS

Years produced:	1996-2001
Performance:	0-60mph: 4.8 secs (Top speed: 199mph)
Power & torque:	485bhp / 360lb/ft
Engine:	Normally aspirated 5474cc V12, petrol, electronic fuel injection, 48 valves
Drivetrain:	Front-engine RWD
Suspension:	(F) Double wishbone, coil spring, anti-roll bar. (R) Ind. double wishbone, coil spring
Bodyframe:	Monocoque
Transmission:	6-speed manual
Weight:	1471kgs
	PRICE GUIDE
Launch price:	£143,684
Excellent:	£54,000
Good:	£48,000
Average:	£40,000
Project:	£30,000

FIAT
500 Topolino

The tiny two-seater Topolino was launched in 1936 but after the war it came back in restyled 500B and 500C form. This is the latter and the only post-war version that came to the UK, and even then imports didn't begin until 1954. Earlier cars have found their way here since though. Nearly all of the post-war series were roll-back cabriolets, but there is the odd estate version around and even a woodie. Expect to pay a premium for both. The little four-cylinder engines are quite perky but still very economical.

SPECIFICATIONS

Years produced:	1948-1955
Performance:	Top speed: 55mph
Power & torque:	13bhp / N/A
Engine:	Normally aspirated 569cc in-line four, petrol, carburettor, 8 valves
Drivetrain:	Front-engine RWD
Suspension:	(F) Independent, wishbone, transverse leaf spring. (R) Live axle, leaf spring
Bodyframe:	Separate body/chassis
Transmission:	4-speed manual
Weight:	740kgs
	PRICE GUIDE
Launch price:	£582
Excellent:	£7000
Good:	£5250
Average:	£2750
Project:	£1250

FIAT
600 Multipla

This is the version of the 600 that most classic car enthusiasts are more familiar with. It's also probably the world's smallest minibus, with six-seater capacity despite being under 12 feet long. A highly sought after collectible in its own right, recent price rises have made their restoration a more sensible proposition. They share the same engines as the 600, but their progress has never been more than sedate. However, if originality is not at issue, these engines were developed into the 903cc unit and used in the Fiat Cinquecento.

SPECIFICATIONS

Years produced:	1955-1960 (130,000 in total)
Performance:	Top speed: 59mph
Power & torque:	29bhp / 40lb/ft
Engine:	Normally aspirated 767cc in-line four, petrol, carburettor, 8 valves
Drivetrain:	Rear-engine RWD
Suspension:	(F) Independent, transverse leaf spring. (R) Independent, coil spring
Bodyframe:	Monocoque
Transmission:	4-speed manual
Weight:	700kgs
	PRICE GUIDE
Launch price:	£799
Excellent:	£9000
Good:	£7500
Average:	£4000
Project:	£2000

FIAT
600

No, this wasn't merely a big-engined version of the Fiat 500. Though they share a strong family resemblance, the 600 was launched first and has the benefit of a water-cooled four-cylinder engine. That started out at 633cc, but grew to 767cc for 1960's revamped Fiat 600D. Being a direct competitor to the Mini spoiled things for the 600 in the UK, but there's a school of thought that says it's a better bet than the smaller, less practical 500. And you may never tire of telling people that this was the best selling car of the 1960s... in Argentina.

SPECIFICATIONS

Years produced:	1955-1970 (891,107 in total)
Performance:	Top speed: 66mph
Power & torque:	29bhp / 40lb/ft
Engine:	Normally aspirated 767cc in-line four, petrol, carburettor, 8 valves
Drivetrain:	Rear-engine RWD
Suspension:	(F) Independent, transverse leaf springs. (R) Independent, coil spring
Bodyframe:	Monocoque
Transmission:	4-speed manual
Weight:	585kgs
	PRICE GUIDE
Launch price:	£585
Excellent:	£5000
Good:	£4000
Average:	£2000
Project:	£850

FIAT
500

Cheap to run, and with excellent spares support, the diminutive Fiat 500 makes the ideal classic for city dwellers. In fact darting around busy city streets is what it has always done best. Pre-1965 cars had suicide doors and never more than 17.5bhp except in the rare 500 Sport. The later 500F and 500L are a better bet, especially if you want to drive any distance, and have conventional front-hinged doors. Last model, the 500R has a detuned 594cc Fiat 126 engine; a point not lost on many Fiat 500 owners, who commonly fit the full strength 126 engine.

SPECIFICATIONS

Years produced:	1957-1975
Performance:	Top speed: 59mph
Power & torque:	22bhp / N/A
Engine:	Normally aspirated 500cc, petrol, carburettor, 4 valves
Drivetrain:	Rear-engine RWD
Suspension:	(F) Independent, transverse leaf spring. (R) Independent, coil spring
Bodyframe:	Separate body/chassis
Transmission:	4-speed manual
Weight:	500kgs
	PRICE GUIDE
Launch price:	£556
Excellent:	£7000
Good:	£5500
Average:	£3000
Project:	£1250

FIAT
1500 Cabriolet

Predecessor to the better known Fiat Spider, the 1500 cabriolet was also only available in left-hand drive. That and prices that were grossly inflated by import duty meant that few reached UK shores. No reason why you couldn't import from Europe though, where their numbers are much greater. Styling was by Pininfarina, which explains their passing resemblance to the Ferrari 275 GTS, only smaller, and much cheaper. Advanced for its time with a five-speed gearbox and disc brakes. Engines are tough and reliable.

SPECIFICATIONS

Years produced:	1960-1967
Performance:	0-60mph: 14.8 secs (Top speed: 100mph)
Power & torque:	72bhp / 82lb/ft
Engine:	Normally aspirated 1481cc in-line four, petrol, carburettor, 8 valves
Drivetrain:	Front-engine RWD
Suspension:	(F) Independent, coil spring. (R) Live axle, semi-elliptic leaf spring
Bodyframe:	Monocoque
Transmission:	5-speed manual
Weight:	970kgs
	PRICE GUIDE
Launch price:	£1197
Excellent:	£6000
Good:	£4750
Average:	£2500
Project:	£1000

FIAT
2300S Coupé

Fiat's large car efforts have tended to lack commercial success, and sometimes it is difficult to understand why. While the Dino and 130 had obvious failings, the 2300S Coupé looked like the right product for its time. Styled by Ghia's Tom Tjaarda, the 2300S Coupé was very much a grand tourer, even featuring electric windows. Its 2.3-litre six-cylinder engine delivered plenty of power and had been further boosted by twin carburettors. However, true to form, the 2300S wasn't a big seller, and remains one of the lost cousins of Fiat history.

SPECIFICATIONS

Years produced: 1961-1968
Performance: 0-60mph: 11.6 secs (Top speed: 121mph)
Power & torque: 136bhp / 145lb/ft
Engine: Normally aspirated 2279cc in-line six, petrol, carburettor, 12 valves
Drivetrain: Front-engine RWD
Suspension: (F) Independent, torsion bar, wishbone, (R) Live axle, semi-elliptic leaf spring
Bodyframe: Monocoque
Transmission: 4-speed manual
Weight: 1266kgs

PRICE GUIDE

Launch price: £2610
Excellent: £6500
Good: £5000
Average: £2750
Project: £1000

FIAT
850 Coupé

Based on the slightly dull and dumpy 850 saloon, the Coupé thankfully bore no resemblance to it, being more in the fashion of a scaled-down Dino. It had a perkier version of the saloon's 843cc engine too, which was upgraded to 903cc from 1968. Rear-mounted and water-cooled, it gives the baby coupé a decent turn of speed and its light weight contributes to the car's excellent handling abilities. It sold well in the UK, but our climate has wiped out most of them now. Survivors are reasonably priced, or you could sniff out a left-hooker to import.

SPECIFICATIONS

Years produced: 1965-1973 (342,873 in total)
Performance: 0-60mph: 15.6 secs (Top speed: 84mph)
Power & torque: 47bhp / 45lb/ft
Engine: Normally aspirated 843cc in-line four, petrol, carburettor, 8 valves
Drivetrain: Rear-engine RWD
Suspension: (F) Independent, leaf spring. (R) Independent, coil spring
Bodyframe: Monocoque
Transmission: 4-speed manual
Weight: 690kgs

PRICE GUIDE

Launch price: £850
Excellent: £3500
Good: £2500
Average: £1250
Project: £500

FIAT
850 Spider

A small, pretty and nippy but rust-prone roadster. We could be talking about a Midget, but this is an Italian job with styling beautifully executed by Bertone that includes a hood that neatly stows away beneath the rear deck. As with all the 850 range it's rear-engined, initially with 843cc, but receiving the more powerful and just as rev-happy 903cc unit in 1968. At the same time the original sloping headlamps were replaced by more efficient upright units. Most 850s went to America and once again none were built with right-hand-drive.

SPECIFICATIONS

Years produced: 1965-1973 (124,660 in total)
Performance: 0-60mph: 18.2 secs (Top speed: 87mph)
Power & torque: 47bhp / 45lb/ft
Engine: Normally aspirated 843cc in-line four, petrol, carburettor, 8 valves
Drivetrain: Rear-engine RWD
Suspension: (F) Independent, leaf spring (R) Independent, coil spring
Bodyframe: Monocoque
Transmission: 4-speed manual
Weight: 735kgs

PRICE GUIDE

Launch price: £1000
Excellent: £5500
Good: £4250
Average: £2200
Project: £1000

FIAT
124 Saloon

Advanced saloon that outshone and outsold the MkI Escort. With disc brakes all round and a rear axle well located on coil springs it's a capable driver. Has suffered in classic terms from the usual Fiat rust problems, but mostly by growing up to become the long-running heart of the Lada range. Revvy overhead-valve engines are even impressive in base 1200 form, but the Special T is the one to have. UK available from 1971, this used a 1438cc twin-cam engine, upgraded to 1600cc from 1973. You'll pay more than the prices shown here for one of those.

SPECIFICATIONS

Years produced: 1966-1974 (1,543,000 in total)
Performance: 0-60mph: 11.8 secs (Top speed: 102mph)
Power & torque: 80bhp / 80lb/ft
Engine: Normally aspirated 1438cc in-line four, petrol, carburettor, 8 valves
Drivetrain: Front-engine RWD
Suspension: (F) Independent, wishbone, anti-roll bar (R) Live axle, trailing arm
Bodyframe: Metal monocoque
Transmission: 4-speed manual
Weight: 950kgs

PRICE GUIDE

Launch price: £774
Excellent: £2400
Good: £1500
Average: £750
Project: £150

FIAT
124 Coupé

A thin-pillared beauty from Fiat's own design team, blessed with real ability thanks to twin-cam engines and all-wheel disc brakes. Favoured models are the 1967-69 'AC', which is prettier with its single headlamps and lower bonnet line, and lighter so it handles better. The 1974-75 final 'CC'models also get snapped up as their 1800cc engine is the most powerful offered. A small thumbs-down for the BC-series cars that arrived in 1970 with softer suspension and twin headlamps. Sadly all 124 Coupés suffered badly from corrosion.

SPECIFICATIONS

Years produced: 1966-1975 (279,672 in total)
Performance: 0-60mph: 10.5 secs (Top speed: 115mph)
Power & torque: 118bhp / 113lb/ft
Engine: Normally aspirated 1438cc in-line four, petrol, carburettor, 8 valves
Drivetrain: Front-engine RWD
Suspension: (F) Independent, coil spring, wishbone (R) Independent, coil spring, wishbone
Bodyframe: Monocoque
Transmission: 4-speed manual
Weight: 980kgs

PRICE GUIDE

Launch price: £1298
Excellent: £5000
Good: £4000
Average: £1750
Project: £500

FIAT
124 Spider

Pininfarina designed and built the bodies for these pretty sports cars, using any number of Ferrari styling cues and Fiat's excellent twin-cam engines. All are left-hand drive and around 85% of them were sold in America, although upwards of 1500 have since been imported to the UK. As with the 124 Coupé the first and last cars are most popular with collectors, pre-1975 cars having lower suspension and prettier slimline bumpers, 1979-on Spiders got Bosch fuel-injected two-litre engines. From 1982-85 complete production passed to Pininfarina.

SPECIFICATIONS

Years produced: 1966-1985 (178,439 in total)
Performance: 0-60mph: 10.9 secs (Top speed: 109mph)
Power & torque: 102bhp / 110lb/ft
Engine: Normally aspirated 1438cc in-line four, petrol, carburettor, 8 valves
Drivetrain: Front-engine RWD
Suspension: (F) Independent, wishbone, coil spring. (R) Independent, wishbone, coil spring
Bodyframe: Chassis and separate body
Transmission: 5-speed manual
Weight: 945kgs

PRICE GUIDE

Launch price: Special order
Excellent: £8750
Good: £6250
Average: £3000
Project: £1250

FIAT
Dino Spider

Fancy a cheap convertible Ferrari? This is about as close as you'll get without having the actual Prancing Horse badge on the nose. Styled by Pininfarina and using the same engines that powered the Dino GTs, they also have rarity on their side as far as collectibility goes. Early models had an all-alloy two-litre engine and a solid axle on leaf springs. In 1969 it was all change to an iron block 2.4-litre V6 with another 15bhp, and the rear axle was changed to an independent unit on coil springs. Mechanical and body parts still in good supply.

SPECIFICATIONS

Years produced: 1967-1973 (1583 in total)
Performance: 0-60mph: 8.0 secs (Top speed: 124mph)
Power & torque: 160bhp / 127lb/ft
Engine: Normally aspirated 1987cc V6, petrol, carburettor, 12 valves
Drivetrain: Front-engine RWD
Suspension: (F) Independent, coil spring, wishbone. (R) Live axle, semi-elliptic leaf spring
Bodyframe: Monocoque
Transmission: 5-speed manual
Weight: 1222kgs

PRICE GUIDE

Launch price: Special order
Excellent: £30,000
Good: £25,000
Average: £13,000
Project: £6500

FIAT
Dino Coupé 2000/2400

Though mechanically identical to the closely related Dino Spiders, the Coupé has a completely different body, designed by Bertone. The same changes were made in 1969, from 2.0 to a 2.4-litre quad-cam V6, along with a tougher ZF five-speed gearbox and the independent rear suspension swiped from underneath Fiat's 130 saloon. The 2000 and 2400 bodies look identical at first sight, but changes in grille, badge and vent arrangements mean that only the bootlid is a straight swap between cars. The 2400 was assembled at the Ferrari factory.

SPECIFICATIONS

Years produced: 1967-1973 (6068 in total)
Performance: 0-60mph: 8.1 secs (Top speed: 124mph)
Power & torque: 160bhp / 127lb/ft
Engine: Normally aspirated 1987cc V6, petrol, carburettor, 12 valves
Drivetrain: Front-engine RWD
Suspension: (F) Independent, coil spring, wishbone. (R) Live axle, semi-elliptic leaf spring
Bodyframe: Metal monocoque
Transmission: 5-speed manual
Weight: 1220kgs

PRICE GUIDE

Launch price: £3493
Excellent: £15,000
Good: £12,000
Average: £6500
Project: £3000

FIAT
130 Saloon

Fiat had no history of building big saloon cars before they surprised everyone with the technologically advanced, Mercedes-baiting, 130 so the world was bound to treat it with caution. But what a car. The styling may lack flair, but underneath we find full independent suspension, passive rear-steering and four disc brakes. Not bad for 1969. Capacity of the quad-cam V6 went up from 2.8 litres to 3.2 in 1971, and UK imports started in '72. Worth seeking out. After all, do you need any greater recommendation than the fact that Enzo Ferrari daily drove one?

SPECIFICATIONS

Years produced: 1969-1976 (15,000 in total)
Performance: 0-60mph: 11.4 secs (Top speed: 118mph)
Power & torque: 165bhp / 184lb/ft
Engine: 3235cc V6, petrol, carburettor, 12 valves
Drivetrain: Front-engine RWD
Suspension: (F) Ind. MacPherson struts, lower wish, anti-roll bar, torsion bar. (R) Ind. MacPherson strut, semi-trailing arm
Bodyframe: Monocoque
Transmission: 5-speed manual
Weight: 1615kgs

PRICE GUIDE

Launch price: £3818
Excellent: £4250
Good: £3000
Average: £1500
Project: £500

FIAT
124 Spider Abarth

Homologation special based on 1800-engined 124 Spider. There's extra power from twin Weber carbs and new exhaust manifold – the last ones even being offered with an optional 16-valve head – and the stiffened shell was fitted with lightweight glassfibre bonnet and boot and alloy door skins. All got a rollcage and permanent hardtop. Independent rear suspension improved handling and one won the 1972 European rally Championship. 1013 were built, but pure road-going ones are near-impossible to find.

SPECIFICATIONS

Years produced: 1972-1975 (1013 in total)
Performance: 0-60mph: 7.5 secs (Top speed: 118mph)
Power & torque: 128bhp / 117lb/ft
Engine: Normally aspirated 1756cc in-line four, petrol, carburettor, 8 valves
Drivetrain: Front-engine RWD
Suspension: (F) Independent, coil spring, wishbone (R) Independent, coil spring, wishbone
Bodyframe: Monocoque
Transmission: 5-speed manual
Weight: 939kgs

PRICE GUIDE

Launch price: Special order
Excellent: £16,500
Good: £13,000
Average: £8500
Project: £5000

FIAT
130 Coupé

With straight-edged styling from Pininfarina's Rolls Camargue/Lancia Gamma Coupé era, the 130 Coupé has a vast and elegant but almost intimidating presence. Arriving a couple of years later than the 130 saloon, the Coupés only ever came with the larger 3.2-litre four-cam V6, so there's plenty of performance to go with the tidy handling and thankfully this isn't spoilt by the light power steering. Many came with a three-speed auto, but enough were specified with the ZF five-speed manual.

SPECIFICATIONS

Years produced:	1972-1976 (4491 in total)
Performance:	0-60mph: 10.6 secs (Top speed: 123mph)
Power & torque:	165bhp / 184lb/ft
Engine:	3235cc V6, petrol, carburettor, 12 valves
Drivetrain:	Front-engine RWD
Suspension:	(F) Ind. lower wishbones, MacPherson strut. (R) Independent, MacPherson strut, semi-trailing arms
Bodyframe:	Monocoque
Transmission:	5-speed manual
Weight:	1559kgs
	PRICE GUIDE
Launch price:	£6165
Excellent:	£7000
Good:	£5500
Average:	£2650
Project:	£600

FIAT
X1/9

There's a lot to be said for a compact mid-engined two-seater with a Targa top, not least in the handling department. So it seems unfair that though the X1/9 was launched in Europe in 1972, the UK had to wait five years before right-hand drive examples became available. Those early cars had 1300 engines and four-speed gearboxes, though in 1978 this package was changed for a 1500 engine and five-speed transmission. Styled by Bertone from 1982 the cars were built by them too and badged Bertone X1/9s.

SPECIFICATIONS

Years produced:	1972-1982 (150,000 in total)
Performance:	0-60mph: 12.7 secs (Top speed: 99mph)
Power & torque:	75bhp / 72lb/ft
Engine:	Normally aspirated 1290cc in-line four, petrol, carburettor, 8 valves
Drivetrain:	Mid-engine RWD
Suspension:	(F) Independent, coil spring. (R) Independent, coil spring
Bodyframe:	Monocoque
Transmission:	4/5-speed manual
Weight:	912kgs
	PRICE GUIDE
Launch price:	£2997
Excellent:	£3500
Good:	£2500
Average:	£1000
Project:	£500

FIAT
128 3P Coupé

A car that lurks somewhere in that grey area between coupé and hatchback that was popularised by the VW Scirocco a year earlier. In fact the 3P part of the name stands for 'tre porte', Italian for three-door. With that cleared up, it's time to point out just how under-rated these cars are. Though they have long had a cult following, most in the UK have long since lost the battle against corrosion, though you can still find fair numbers in Italy and Greece. There's decent performance from the overhead-cam 1300, and entertaining handling too.

SPECIFICATIONS

Years produced:	1975-1978
Performance:	0-60mph: 11.7 secs (Top speed: 93mph)
Power & torque:	64bhp / 61lb/ft
Engine:	Normally aspirated, 1116cc in-line four, petrol, carburettor, 8 valves
Drivetrain:	Front-engine RWD
Suspension:	(F) Ind. MacPherson strut, coil spring. (R) Ind. wishbone, leaf spring
Bodyframe:	Monocoque
Transmission:	4-speed manual
Weight:	820kgs
	PRICE GUIDE
Launch price:	£1398
Excellent:	£5000
Good:	£4000
Average:	£2000
Project:	£500

FIAT
131 TC/Sport

Based on a two-door Mirafiori shell, the 131 Sport was in effect an Italian equivalent to the Escort RS2000 that was launched at the same time. Both have two-litre engines with the Fiat's twin-cam efficiency compensating for the 131 Sport's extra weight. Both were pure road cars being sold on the back of rally successes. These days, however, the Fiat is substantially cheaper to buy. They were only sold in black, orange, silver or grey and have plastic wheelarches and a spoiler built into the front bumper.

SPECIFICATIONS

Years produced:	1978-1984
Performance:	0-60mph: 10.1 secs (Top speed: 112mph)
Power & torque:	115bhp / 123lb/ft
Engine:	Normally aspirated, 1995cc in-line four, petrol, carburettor, 8 valves
Drivetrain:	Front-engine RWD
Suspension:	(F) Ind. MacPherson strut, coil springs. (R) Rigid axle, trailing arms, coil spring
Bodyframe:	Monocoque
Transmission:	5-speed manual
Weight:	1020kgs
	PRICE GUIDE
Launch price:	£4636
Excellent:	£4000
Good:	£3000
Average:	£1500
Project:	£500

FIAT
Strada Abarth 130TC

Built to bloody some noses in the escalating hot-hatch wars of the Eighties, the Abarth 130TC was a real drivers' car that posted better performance figures than even the omnipresent Golf GTI for a year or so. Surprisingly, in a world where fuel injection was now king, Fiat did it the old-fashioned way with a pair of Weber carburettors. Unfortunately the car found more friends among the motoring press than it did in showrooms, so they have always been quite exclusive. Also, many found their way onto race tracks.

SPECIFICATIONS

Years produced:	1984-1987
Performance:	0-60mph: 7.9 secs (Top speed: 122mph)
Power & torque:	128bhp / 130lb/ft
Engine:	1995cc in-line four, petrol, carb. 8 valves
Drivetrain:	Front-engine FWD
Suspension:	(F) Ind. MacPherson strut, coil spring, anti-roll bar. (R) Ind. MacPherson strut, lower wishbone
Bodyframe:	Monocoque
Transmission:	5-speed manual
Weight:	950kgs
	PRICE GUIDE
Launch price:	£7800
Excellent:	£3750
Good:	£2750
Average:	£1500
Project:	£600

FIAT Uno Turbo i.e.

In the mid-1980s the hot hatch ruled, and without one Fiat would have missed a great opportunity. Like Renault with the 5, they decided to go down the route of forced induction and the Uno Turbo i.e. was born. Fiat cleverly decided to price the Turbo to directly compete with the 205 GTi, but straight-line speed alone was not enough to take sales from the mighty lion, and the Uno lacked overall finesse in the chassis department when put up against its rivals. The car received a mild face-lift in 1989, when power was increased from 105 to 118bhp.

SPECIFICATIONS

Years produced: 1985-1989
Performance: 0-60mph: 8.3 secs (Top speed: 122mph)
Power & torque: 105bhp / 108lb/ft
Engine: Turbocharged 1299cc in-line four, petrol, mechanical fuel injection, 8 valves
Drivetrain: Front-engine FWD
Suspension: (F) Independent, MacPherson struts, (R) Independent, coil spring
Bodyframe: Monocoque
Transmission: 5-speed manual
Weight: 845kgs

PRICE GUIDE

Launch price: £6889
Excellent: £2000
Good: £1500
Average: £700
Project: £250

FIAT Coupé

When Fiat launched the Coupé in 1993, Chris Bangle's mixture of curves and razor sharp edges was a bit of a shock to the automotive world. This striking design along with the firepower of Fiat's 2.0 16v Turbo engine should have created a world-beating car, but it was always missing something. An extra cylinder to be precise! In 1996, Fiat unveiled the Coupé 20-valve Turbo. The 217bhp 5-pot pushed the car's front-wheel drive chassis to the limit, but a clever limited-slip differential helped the car immeasurably.

SPECIFICATIONS

Years produced: 1994-2000 (72,762 in total)
Performance: 0-60mph: 9.5 secs (Top speed: 124mph)
Power & torque: 142bhp / 135lb/ft
Engine: Normally aspirated 1995cc in-line four, petrol, electronic fuel injection, 16 valves
Drivetrain: Front-engine FWD
Suspension: (F) Independent, coil spring. (R) Independent, coil spring
Bodyframe: Monocoque
Transmission: 5-speed manual
Weight: 1244kgs

PRICE GUIDE

Launch price: £17,349
Excellent: £5500
Good: £4000
Average: £1750
Project: £600

FIAT Barchetta

Even though the Barchetta was front-wheel drive, there was still some serious fun to be had, and the 1.7 16-valve power plant provided sprightly performance. Production of the Barchetta stopped in 2002 when coachbuilder Maggiora – who built the assembled the Barchetta – went bankrupt. Fiat moved production to their Mirafiori plant in Turin, and thoroughly updated the car for its re-launch in 2004. The later cars can be easily identified by the third brake light located on the boot lid. A soulful option to the MX-5.

SPECIFICATIONS

Years produced: 1995-2005
Performance: 0-60mph: 8.7 secs (Top speed: 118mph)
Power & torque: 130bhp / 121lb/ft
Engine: Normally aspirated 1747cc in-line four, petrol, electronic fuel injection, 16 valves
Drivetrain: Front-engine FWD
Suspension: (F) Independent, coil spring. (R) Independent, coil spring
Bodyframe: Monocoque
Transmission: 5-speed manual
Weight: 1059kgs

PRICE GUIDE

Launch price: £13,995
Excellent: £5250
Good: £4250
Average: £2750
Project: £1750

FORD Prefect

When launched in 1938 the Prefect was the first Ford to have a name rather than a number/letter designation. However, despite this radical move the car was little more than a mechanical update of the previous 7W but with a bulkier body and rear-hinged bonnet. Updates were few – in 1948 the headlamps were incorporated into the front wings and a taller grille was adopted. The 31bhp 1172cc sidevalve engine persisted until the end of production in 1953, by which time the Prefect seemed old-fashioned compared with its competition.

SPECIFICATIONS

Years produced: 1938-1953 (350,236 in total)
Performance: Top speed: 60mph
Power & torque: 30bhp / 60lb/ft
Engine: Normally aspirated 1172cc in-line four, petrol, carburettor, 8 valves
Drivetrain: Front-engine RWD
Suspension: (F) Transverse leaf springs. (R) Transverse leaf springs
Bodyframe: Chassis and separate body
Transmission: 3-speed manual
Weight: 762kgs

PRICE GUIDE

Launch price: £352
Excellent: £3200
Good: £2500
Average: £1100
Project: £450

FORD Pilot V8

The V8 Pilot was the British Ford flagship immediately postwar. In essence it was an amalgam of the pre-war V8-62 model body with a new 2.5-litre engine. This proved not quite up to the task of propelling such a large lump of metal around, so the old and lazy 3622cc V8 that Ford used in so many wartime military vehicles came out of retirement. Despite the size of its engine, its power was just 85bhp, giving this lumbering but bulletproof beast a top speed of 83mph. Despite this, it proved popular as a police car.

SPECIFICATIONS

Years produced: 1947-1951 (21,487 in total)
Performance: 0-60mph: 20.5 secs (Top speed: 83mph)
Power & torque: 85bhp / 140lb/ft
Engine: Normally aspirated, 3622cc V8, petrol, carburettor, 16 valves
Drivetrain: Front-engine RWD
Suspension: (F) Transverse leaf springs, anti-roll bar. (R) Transverse leaf springs, anti-roll bar
Bodyframe: Chassis and separate body
Transmission: 3-speed manual
Weight: 1473kgs

PRICE GUIDE

Launch price: £585
Excellent: £11,000
Good: £9000
Average: £6000
Project: £3000

FORD
Consul MkI

Ford UK adopted unitary construction for their all-new Consul of 1950, the entry level model in the new EOTA range which also included the Zephyr and Zephyr Zodiac. The Consul 'made do' with a 1508cc 4-cylinder overhead valve engine of 48hp and three speed transmission, although its MacPherson strut front suspension and fully hydraulic brakes meant that what performance there was could be made the most of. The slab-sided styling was very American in appearance, but suited the convertibles very well.

SPECIFICATIONS

Years produced: 1950-1956 (231,481 in total)
Performance: 0-60mph: 27.7 secs (Top speed: 75mph)
Power & torque: 47bhp / 72lb/ft
Engine: Normally aspirated 1508cc in-line four, petrol, carburettor, 8 valves
Drivetrain: Front-engine RWD
Suspension: (F) Ind. MacPherson strut, coil spring. (R) Live rear axle, leaf springs
Bodyframe: Monocoque
Transmission: 3-speed manual
Weight: 1041kgs

PRICE GUIDE

Launch price: £544
Excellent: £3850
Good: £3000
Average: £1500
Project: £500

FORD
Zephyr/Zodiac Mk I

The next step up from the Mk I Consul was the Zephyr, distinguished by its different grille, longer wheelbase and 2262cc six-cylinder engine of 68bhp giving better, smoother performance. Unveiled in 1951, the range was further complemented by the Zephyr Zodiac of 1953, with a high compression (71bhp) engine, leather, fog lamps and, just so everybody knew it was special, two-tone paint and gold-plated badges. As well as the coachbuilt estates, there was the convertible with its power-operated hood.

SPECIFICATIONS

Years produced: 1950-1956 (152,677 in total)
Performance: 0-60mph: 20.1 secs (Top speed: 84mph)
Power & torque: 68bhp / 112lb/ft
Engine: Normally aspirated, 2262cc in-line six, petrol, carburettor 12 valves
Drivetrain: Front-engine RWD
Suspension: (F) Ind. MacPherson strut, coil spring. (R) Live rear axle, leaf springs
Bodyframe: Monocoque
Transmission: 3-speed manual
Weight: 1181kgs

PRICE GUIDE

Launch price: £684
Excellent: £5000
Good: £4000
Average: £1900
Project: £650

FORD
Consul MkII

The first of 'the Three Graces' – the advertising slogan Ford used for this MkII family – was the Consul. It was the cheapest of the bunch, with four cylinders rather than the six found in the Zephyr and Zodiac, and a lesser level of trim. Convertibles had manually operated hoods and estates were only available as special coachbuilt orders. Ford also introduced a future industry standard by having a combined key-operated ignition and starter. The Consul Deluxe of 1957 was equipped almost to Zodiac level and had two-tone paintwork.

SPECIFICATIONS

Years produced: 1956-1962 (290,951 in total)
Performance: 0-60mph: 23.2 secs (Top speed: 79mph)
Power & torque: 59bhp / 91lb/ft
Engine: Normally aspirated 1702cc in-line four, petrol, carburettor, 8 valves
Drivetrain: Front-engine RWD
Suspension: (F) Ind. MacPherson struts, anti-roll bar. (R) Live rear axle, half-elliptic springs
Bodyframe: Monocoque
Transmission: 3-speed manual
Weight: 1143kgs

PRICE GUIDE

Launch price: £520
Excellent: £4750
Good: £3750
Average: £1600
Project: £550

FORD
Prefect 107E

The exciting new Anglia 105E of 1959 brought a revolution to small Fords... but not, unfortunately, four doors. So, for those who wanted the practicality of a four-door car and the innovation of an overhead valve engine but weren't that bothered about fashion-conscious looks, there was the Prefect 107E. Effectively, this was the four-door 100E shape fitted with the 105E's overhead valve engine and four-speed transmission, plus some plusher touches than had been the case on previous 100Es. Two-tone paintwork was standard.

SPECIFICATIONS

Years produced: 1959-1961 (38,154 in total)
Performance: 0-60mph: 27.2 secs (Top speed: 73mph)
Power & torque: 39bhp / 52.5lb/ft
Engine: Normally aspirated 996cc in-line four, petrol, carburettor, 8 valves
Drivetrain: Front-engine RWD
Suspension: (F) Independent, MacPherson struts. (R) Live rear axle, half-elliptic leaf springs
Bodyframe: Monocoque
Transmission: 4-speed manual
Weight: 800kgs

PRICE GUIDE

Launch price: £622
Excellent: £2500
Good: £1900
Average: £950
Project: £350

FORD
Pop/Anglia/Prefect 100E

Unitary construction reached small Fords in 1953 with the 100E models. Looking like scaled-down Consuls and Zephyrs 100Es came in basic two-door Anglia form or as the higher-spec Prefect, with four doors. Sidevalve engine technology persisted even though the all new 1172cc engine just happened to be exactly the same capacity as that in the old Anglias and Prefects. When the 105E Anglia was launched in 1959 the 100E became the Popular, a no-nonsense, low budget machine intended to lure customers away from the Mini.

SPECIFICATIONS

Years produced: 1959-1962 (572,510 in total)
Performance: 0-60mph: 33.2 secs (Top speed: 68mph)
Power & torque: 36bhp / 52lb/ft
Engine: Normally aspirated 1172cc in-line four, petrol, carburettor, 8 valves
Drivetrain: Front-engine RWD
Suspension: (F) Ind. MacPherson strut, coil spring. (R) Live rear axle, telescopic dampers
Bodyframe: Monocoque
Transmission: 3-speed manual
Weight: 749kgs

PRICE GUIDE

Launch price: £348
Excellent: £2250
Good: £1750
Average: £800
Project: £300

FORD
Anglia 105E/123E

One of the most significant Fords ever, the Anglia 105E brought new levels of sophistication to small British Blue Ovals. At last, there was an eager overhead valve engine and nifty handling. These alone might have made the Anglia a family favourite, but allied to this was the eye-catching mini-Ford Thunderbird fins 'n' chrome styling and that infamous reverse-rake rear window, which was like nothing seen in Britain before. Estate versions arrived in 1961, closely followed by the 123E Super the following year.

SPECIFICATIONS

Years produced:	1959-1967 (1,083,960 in total)
Performance:	0-60mph: 26.9 secs (Top speed: 77mph)
Power & torque:	39bhp / 52lb/ft
Engine:	Normally aspirated, 997cc in-line four, petrol, carburettor, 8 valves
Drivetrain:	Front-engine RWD
Suspension:	(F) Ind. coil spring, MacPherson strut. (R) Live axle, semi-elliptic lever spring
Bodyframe:	Monocoque
Transmission:	4-speed manual
Weight:	786kgs

PRICE GUIDE

Launch price:	£610
Excellent:	£3500
Good:	£2750
Average:	£1400
Project:	£700

FORD
Consul Capri/GT

The Consul Classic was one of the prettier cars ever built by Ford in the UK. While the saloon just looked clumsy and fussy, the coupé was svelte and elegant. Unfortunately, performance didn't live up to the looks, although the Capri GT of 1963 managed to squeeze 78bhp out of its twin-carburettor 1498cc engine, meaning 95mph flat out. Out of the total production run of 18,716, a mere 2002 were GTs though. Ford would revive the Capri name in 1969, with much more successful results, but these original Capris are now much sought after.

SPECIFICATIONS

Years produced:	1961-1963 (18,716 in total)
Performance:	0-60mph: 14.1 secs (Top speed: 93.3mph)
Power & torque:	78bhp / 91lb/ft
Engine:	Normally aspirated 1499cc in-line four, petrol, carburettor, 8 valves
Drivetrain:	Front-engine RWD
Suspension:	(F) Ind. coil spring, MacPherson strut. (R) Live axle, semi-elliptic lever spring
Bodyframe:	Monocoque
Transmission:	4-speed manual
Weight:	950kgs

PRICE GUIDE

Launch price:	£916
Excellent:	£6750
Good:	£5000
Average:	£3000
Project:	£1000

FORD
Consul Classic

Seeking to repeat the success of the Anglia, Ford launched the similarly-styled Consul Classic in 1961. The reverse-rake window was back but the larger canvas gave Ford the opportunity to really go to town with the Transatlantic touches. But it proved a little too much for conservative British tastes, especially once the Cortina arrived to occupy a similar niche. The original 1340cc engine was replaced by a 1498cc unit in 1962. After only two years the car was dropped. The looks make it an interesting classic today though.

SPECIFICATIONS

Years produced:	1961-1963 (109,045 in total)
Performance:	0-60mph: 20.1 secs (Top speed: 80mph)
Power & torque:	59bhp / 79lb/ft
Engine:	1340cc in-line four, petrol, carb. 8 valves
Drivetrain:	Front-engine RWD
Suspension:	(F) Independent, MacPherson strut. (R) Live axle, semi-elliptic leaf spring, half-elliptic leaf springs
Bodyframe:	Monocoque
Transmission:	4-speed manual
Weight:	930kgs

PRICE GUIDE

Launch price:	£767
Excellent:	£3500
Good:	£2500
Average:	£1200
Project:	£500

FORD
Zephyr MkIII

For their 1962 MkIII incarnation Ford's Zephyrs put on considerable weight and adopted a razor sharp style with prominent fins framing the wide, capacious boot, and huge bonnets. As the Consul name was now being used elsewhere, the four-cylinder cars – using the same 1703cc engine as on the MkII, albeit giving an extra 5bhp to give 65bhp – became known as Zephyr 4s, those blessed with an additional two cylinders were dubbed Zephyr 6s. Externally the 6s had a different split grille plus other dashes of affluence.

SPECIFICATIONS

Years produced:	1962-1966 (229,450 in total)
Performance:	0-60mph: 17.5 secs (Top speed: 87mph)
Power & torque:	98bhp / 134lb/ft
Engine:	Normally aspirated, 2553cc in-line six, petrol, carburettor, 12 valves
Drivetrain:	Front-engine RWD
Suspension:	(F) Ind. coil spring, MacPherson strut. (R) Live axle, semi-elliptic lever spring
Bodyframe:	Monocoque
Transmission:	4-speed manual
Weight:	1242kgs

PRICE GUIDE

Launch price:	£772
Excellent:	£4000
Good:	£3200
Average:	£1750
Project:	£500

FORD
Zodiac MkIII

The Zodiac MkIII differed from its Zephyr counterparts in more than just engine size and trim level. Yes, there was the much bigger 2553cc six-pot engine, and yes, the car had more comfort to it, but its body was also substantially altered with more glass and slimmer roof pillars, a steeply inclined back window and an impressive chrome-laded front end characterised by four headlamps. Extra power over the Zephyr 6 meant 107bhp and a genuine 100mph. For 1965 to 1966, there was the Zodiac Executive which was pitched as a Jaguar rival.

SPECIFICATIONS

Years produced:	1962-1966 (79,285 in total)
Performance:	0-60mph: 13.4 secs (Top speed: 100mph)
Power & torque:	112bhp / 140lb/ft
Engine:	Normally aspirated, 2553cc in-line six, petrol, carburettor, 12 valves
Drivetrain:	Front-engine RWD
Suspension:	(F) Ind. coil spring, MacPherson strut. (R) Live axle, semi-elliptic lever spring
Bodyframe:	Monocoque
Transmission:	4-speed manual
Weight:	1283kgs

PRICE GUIDE

Launch price:	£813
Excellent:	£4500
Good:	£3500
Average:	£2000
Project:	£600

FORD
Lotus Cortina MkI

Dropping the 105bhp twin-cam into Ford's lightweight Cortina bodyshell created a saloon car legend. Almost all came in white with the green side flashes, and their minimalist quarter bumpers became de riguer for several generations of Ford tuners. The first year's production came with aluminium doors, bonnet and bootlid, along with an A-frame for the rear axle location. This is prone to cracking its mounts and was changed for leaf springs, but those earlier cars still command something like a 20% price premium.

SPECIFICATIONS

Years produced:	1963-1966 (3301 in total)
Performance:	0-60mph: 13.8 secs (Top speed: 108mph)
Power & torque:	115bhp / 108lb/ft
Engine:	Normally aspirated, 1558cc in-line four, petrol, carburettor, 8 valves
Drivetrain:	Front-engine RWD
Suspension:	(F) Ind. MacPherson strut. (R) Live rear axle with coil spring (later leaf spring)
Bodyframe:	Monocoque
Transmission:	4-speed manual
Weight:	842kgs
	PRICE GUIDE
Launch price:	£1100
Excellent:	£18,000
Good:	£15,000
Average:	£8750
Project:	£5000

FORD
Corsair

In the 1960s the Corsair was introduced to plug the void between Cortina and Zephyr. The handsome looks suggested Ford's Thunderbird reduced in size to British proportions. After two years the original 1498cc engine was replaced by a 1662cc V4 which, while it may have given more oomph, wasn't noted for its smoothness or sophistication. In 1967, capacity went up again, this time to 1996cc. This led to one of Ford's 'E' offshoots, the 2000E, which justified its Executive status with a different grille, wooden dash and a black vinyl roof.

SPECIFICATIONS

Years produced:	1963-1970 (294,591 in total)
Performance:	0-60mph: 13.5 secs (Top speed: 97mph)
Power & torque:	88bhp / 116lb/ft
Engine:	Normally aspirated, 1663cc V4, petrol, carburettor, 8 valves
Drivetrain:	Front-engine RWD
Suspension:	(F) Independent, MacPherson struts (R) Live axle, half-elliptic leaf springs
Bodyframe:	Monocoque
Transmission:	4-speed manual
Weight:	995kgs
	PRICE GUIDE
Launch price:	£650
Excellent:	£3300
Good:	£2500
Average:	£1250
Project:	£500

FORD
Mustang

The original Mustang was exactly the right car at the right time and thus this sports car for the masses sold a million in less than two years. Available as a notchback coupé, convertible or, from 1965, a fastback coupé, the array of trim and engine options meant that there was a 'Stang to satisfy anyone... although it was in powerful V8 form that this fast Ford was most fulfilling. While handling was to the usual American standards the other attractions of the Mustang meant other manufacturers were soon rushing to offer their own 'Pony Car' pretenders.

SPECIFICATIONS

Years produced:	1964-1966
Performance:	0-60mph: 7.6 secs (Top speed: 128mph)
Power & torque:	271bhp / 312lb/ft
Engine:	Normally aspirated 4728cc V8, petrol, carburettor, 16 valves
Drivetrain:	Front-engine RWD
Suspension:	(F) Independent, coil spring (R) Live axle, leaf springs
Bodyframe:	Monocoque
Transmission:	4-speed manual
Weight:	1182kgs
	PRICE GUIDE
Launch price:	£1925
Excellent:	£24,000
Good:	£18,000
Average:	£9000
Project:	£4000

FORD
GT40

It's the car built with the impudent idea of Ford giving Ferrari a slap in the face. And they did it at Le Mans. Four times. Obviously it was an out-and-out racer, so Ford then built seven MkIIIs purely as road cars, using 4.7-litre V8s. The racing versions used either 4.2, 4.7 or 5.0-litre Ford small block V8s or a 7.0-litre big block. Power outputs are recorded as high as 485 reliable bhp. Values are very hard to pin down as the cars differ so much and rarely come up for sale, but a racer with history might make more than our guide.

SPECIFICATIONS

Years produced:	1965-1969 (99 in total)
Performance:	0-60mph: 4.6 secs (Top speed: 187.5mph)
Power & torque:	350bhp / 275lb/ft
Engine:	4728cc V8, petrol, carburettor, 16 valves
Drivetrain:	Mid-engine RWD
Suspension:	(F) Ind. double wishbone, anti-roll bar, telescopic dampers. (R) Ind. double trailing arms, trans. top link
Bodyframe:	Monocoque
Transmission:	4-speed manual
Weight:	864kgs
	PRICE GUIDE
Launch price:	N/A
Excellent:	£1,250,000
Good:	£1000,000
Average:	£750,000
Project:	£600,000

FORD
Cortina MkII

While the MkII Cortina used much of the old MkI for its underpinnings, its well-proportioned and boxy body was all new, helping to spearhead the move in the UK towards less curvaceous looks for cars during the tail end of the 1960s. Appreciative customers were given a multitude of different trim and engine options from 1297cc to 1599cc and quite austere saloons and estates through to sporty and posh Executive versions. Like the first generation, this family of Cortinas was also made for just four years and clocked up a million sales.

SPECIFICATIONS

Years produced:	1966-1970 (963,750 in total)
Performance:	0-60mph: 15.1 secs (Top speed: 87mph)
Power & torque:	58bhp / 71lb/ft
Engine:	Normally aspirated 1298cc in-line four, petrol, carburettor, 8 valves
Drivetrain:	Front-engine RWD
Suspension:	(F) Independent, MacPherson strut, anti-roll bar. (R) Live rear axle, radius arms
Bodyframe:	Monocoque
Transmission:	4-speed manual
Weight:	875kgs
	PRICE GUIDE
Launch price:	£589
Excellent:	£4250
Good:	£3000
Average:	£1500
Project:	£500

FORD
Lotus Cortina MkII

Comes with slightly more power than the MkI, but to some extent the moment had passed and they were quickly overshadowed by the Escort Twin Cam that was launched the following year. They weren't as successful in competition as the MkI Lotus Cortinas and were built in higher numbers, so values fall well shy of their predecessors, and will remain that way. Still a handy tool, even if 109.5bhp doesn't feel as fast as it used to. Beware of fakes as rust and the unscrupulous means more than a few have been created from Cortina GT bodyshells over the years.

SPECIFICATIONS

Years produced: 1966-1970 (4032 in total)
Performance: 0-60mph: 9.9 secs (Top speed: 102mph)
Power & torque: 110bhp / 107lb/ft
Engine: Normally aspirated 1558cc in-line four, petrol, carburettor, 8 valves
Drivetrain: Front-engine RWD
Suspension: (F) Independent, coil spring, MacPherson strut. (R) Live axle
Bodyframe: Monocoque
Transmission: 4-speed manual
Weight: 905kgs

PRICE GUIDE

Launch price: £1068
Excellent: £10,000
Good: £8500
Average: £5000
Project: £2500

FORD
Zephyr/Zodiac MkIV

The Zephyr and Zodiac range had grown consistently with every new reincarnation but, for the MkIV, things just went over the top. With their enormously long bonnets and short, stubby ends, the 1966-72 range looked like aircraft carriers on wheels... and handled in a similar way. V-configuration engines were featured throughout; the Zephyr 4 had a 1996cc V4, the Zephyr 6 had a 2495cc V6 and the meaty Zodiac weighed in with a 2994cc V6. Top of the range was the Jaguar wannabe Executive model, loaded with occupant-pampering goodies and gadgets.

SPECIFICATIONS

Years produced: 1966-1972 (149,263 in total)
Performance: 0-60mph: 17.1 secs (Top speed: 95mph)
Power & torque: 88bhp / 123lb/ft
Engine: 1996cc V4, petrol, carburettor, 8 valves
Drivetrain: Front-engine RWD
Suspension: (F) Independent, MacPherson strut, co-axial coil spring, anti-roll bar. (R) Independent, semi-trailing arms
Bodyframe: Monocoque
Transmission: 4-speed manual
Weight: 1250kgs

PRICE GUIDE

Launch price: £933
Excellent: £4000
Good: £2750
Average: £1100
Project: £500

FORD
Cortina 1600E

There is one Cortina that is held in almost as much esteem as the Lotus versions, but, fortunately for those who love it, is rather more affordable to buy and less temperamental to look after. The 1600E was launched in late-1967, with its 'E for Executive' badging signifying that this Cortina was a big step upmarket. And it was a surprising effective package; an 88bhp 1599cc Kent engine, lowered Lotus suspension, Rostyle wheels, pinstriping, a black grille and a plush interior with a wooden dashboard. It proved a big hit.

SPECIFICATIONS

Years produced: 1967-1970 (57,524 in total)
Performance: 0-60mph: 11.8 secs (Top speed: 96mph)
Power & torque: 88bhp / 96lb/ft
Engine: 1599cc in-line four, petrol, carb. 8 valves
Drivetrain: Front-engine RWD
Suspension: (F) Independent, coil spring, MacPherson strut, anti-roll bar. (R) Live axle, half-elliptic leaf spring
Bodyframe: Monocoque
Transmission: 4-speed manual
Weight: 924kgs

PRICE GUIDE

Launch price: £799
Excellent: £5250
Good: £4250
Average: £2250
Project: £750

FORD
Escort MkI

Originally intended to be the new Anglia, the Escort name was adopted instead for the fresh small Ford after the formation of Ford of Europe in 1967. With less distinctive styling than the Anglia, it proved to be a huge hit, for its simplicity, neat appearance and good performance endeared it to millions. Even the basic 1098cc version proved surprisingly sporty, thanks to rack-and-pinion steering and effective MacPherson strut front suspension, while some of the higher-powered 'specialist' models were effectively rally machines for the road.

SPECIFICATIONS

Years produced: 1968-1975 (895,873 in total)
Performance: 0-60mph: 20.6 secs (Top speed: 83mph)
Power & torque: 58bhp / 72lb/ft
Engine: Normally aspirated 1098cc in-line four, petrol, carburettor, 8 valves
Drivetrain: Front-engine RWD
Suspension: (F) Independent, MacPherson strut, lower links. (R) Live axle
Bodyframe: Monocoque
Transmission: 4-speed manual
Weight: 745kgs

PRICE GUIDE

Launch price: £635
Excellent: £3250
Good: £2500
Average: £1250
Project: £650

FORD
Escort Twin Cam

The word 'Lotus' was silently attached to the Escort Twin Cam, for this model was basically the Lotus Cortina engine and running gear clothed in the lighter two-door Escort bodyshell; something which made it even more of a wolf in sheepish clothing. Available from the start of MkI production in 1968, this 1558cc-engined machine had a very usable 106bhp – more than double that of the standard Escort 1100 – and a top speed of around 113mph. Constructed in limited numbers for homologation purposes. Production ended in 1971.

SPECIFICATIONS

Years produced: 1968-1971
Performance: 0-60mph: 8.7 secs (Top speed: 113mph)
Power & torque: 109bhp / 106lb/ft
Engine: 1558cc in-line four, petrol, carb. 8 valves
Drivetrain: Front-engine RWD
Suspension: (F) Independent, MacPherson struts, lower links, anti-roll bar. (R) Live axle, half-elliptic leaf springs, radius arms
Bodyframe: Monocoque
Transmission: 4-speed manual
Weight: 785kgs

PRICE GUIDE

Launch price: £1263
Excellent: £22,500
Good: £19,000
Average: £13,500
Project: £9000

FORD
Capri MkI

According to Ford, this was 'The car you always promised yourself.' And, for 1.2-million customers, they were telling the truth, such was the sales success of this Mustang wannabe. The Capri was inspired by its American cousin and nobody cared that much that it was simply a Cortina in a party frock. The long bonnet swallowed up the four-cylinder 1300s and 1600s and even the V4 1996cc and V6 2994cc engines fitted with space to spare. GT badging was used to distinguish 1300, 1600 and 2000 models.

SPECIFICATIONS

Years produced: 1968-1973 (1,172,900 (all MkIs) in total)
Performance: 0-60mph: 13 secs (Top speed: 100mph)
Power & torque: 72bhp / 70lb/ft
Engine: Normally aspirated 1593cc in-line four, petrol, carburettor, 8 valves
Drivetrain: Front-engine RWD
Suspension: (F) Independent, MacPherson strut, coil spring. (R) Live axle, leaf spring
Bodyframe: Monocoque
Transmission: 4-speed manual
Weight: 920kgs

PRICE GUIDE

Launch price: £1041
Excellent: £3500
Good: £2500
Average: £1250
Project: £600

FORD
Capri MkI 3000

The big daddies of the mainstream MkI Capri range were the 3000 models, available as the performance-orientated 3000GT, the more luxury-focussed 3000E and (from 1972) the flagship 3000GXL. Trumpeted as Ford's fastest ever production line cars, with a maximum velocity around the 120mph mark, these big bruisers of the Capri world could be distinguished by their bonnet bulges... at least until the smaller-engined models also adopted these posing pouches in 1972 (even though they had nothing to fill them).

SPECIFICATIONS

Years produced: 1968-1973 (347,700 in total)
Performance: 0-60mph: 9.2 secs (Top speed: 114mph)
Power & torque: 128bhp / 173lb/ft
Engine: Normally aspirated 2994cc V6, petrol, carburettor, 12 valves
Drivetrain: Front-engine RWD
Suspension: (F) Independent, MacPherson strut, coil spring. (R) Live axle, leaf spring
Bodyframe: Monocoque
Transmission: 4-speed manual
Weight: 1057kgs

PRICE GUIDE

Launch price: £1087
Excellent: £5500
Good: £4000
Average: £2250
Project: £900

FORD
Escort RS1600 BDA

Ford set up their Advanced Vehicles Operation in Essex in 1970 and first-born was the RS1600. This was an extension of the Escort Twin Cam, fitted with the new 16-valve Cosworth BDA twin-cam. The engine was developed from a Formula 2 racing engine and even in detuned state it still made the Escort a furious machine, with the potential to hit almost 120mph. Most buyers ended up tuning them back up again and using them for competition. The Twin Cam demanded a lot of care and attention beyond the means of most 'ordinary' owners.

SPECIFICATIONS

Years produced: 1970-1973 (1200 in total)
Performance: 0-60mph: 8.3 secs (Top speed: 114mph)
Power & torque: 120bhp / 112lb/ft
Engine: Normally aspirated, 1599cc in-line four, petrol, carburettor, 8 valves
Drivetrain: Front-engine RWD
Suspension: (F) Ind. MacPherson strut, coil spring (R) Live axle, leaf spring
Bodyframe: Monocoque
Transmission: 4-speed manual
Weight: 785kgs

PRICE GUIDE

Launch price: £1447
Excellent: £25,000
Good: £21,000
Average: £15,000
Project: £9500

FORD
Escort Mexico/RS2000

Ford's victory in the tough and demanding 1970 World Cup Rally to Mexico gave them the perfect excuse to unleash another 'hotted up' Escort upon an unsuspecting public. Based on the RS1600, the Mexico forewent the specialist twin-cam engine of that car and opted for a simpler – and therefore more reliable – 1558cc Kent overhead valve engine instead. Although less powerful (at only 86bhp) than other fast Fords, it was still a sprightly machine and completely looked the part with lairy colour schemes featuring contrasting side stripes.

SPECIFICATIONS

Years produced: 1970-1975 (9382/4324 in total)
Performance: 0-60mph: 9.0 secs (Top speed: 108mph)
Power & torque: 100bhp / 108lb/ft
Engine: Normally aspirated, 1993cc in-line four, petrol, carburettor, 8 valves
Drivetrain: Front-engine RWD
Suspension: (F) Ind. coil spring, MacPherson strut. (R) Live axle, half elliptic leaf spring
Bodyframe: Monocoque
Transmission: 4-speed manual
Weight: 915kgs

PRICE GUIDE

Launch price: £1150/1586
Excellent: £14,500
Good: £10,000
Average: £5000
Project: £3000

FORD
Cortina MkIII

A new Cortina for a new decade... and the MkIII was ideal for the more flamboyant and funky era that was the Seventies. The 'Coke bottle' styling had overtones of American Fords and there was a mass of different options; X, XL, GT or GXL anyone? And would Sir like that with an 1100, 1300, 1600 or 2000 engine in his two-door or four-door saloon or estate? In all, there were 35 variants of Cortina at its launch. Whilst its predecessor had been a MkI makeover, the MkIII was completely fresh, with new coil and wishbone suspension .

SPECIFICATIONS

Years produced: 1970-1976 (1,126,559 in total)
Performance: 0-60mph: 12.9 secs (Top speed: 104mph)
Power & torque: 98bhp / 111lb/ft
Engine: Normally aspirated, 1298cc in-line four, petrol, carburettor, 8 valves
Drivetrain: Front-engine RWD
Suspension: (F) Ind., coil springs, wishbones. (R) Live axle, coil springs, radius arms
Bodyframe: Monocoque
Transmission: 4-speed manual
Weight: 965kgs

PRICE GUIDE

Launch price: £700
Excellent: £4000
Good: £3000
Average: £1500
Project: £600

FORD
Consul/Granada 3.0

Forever immortalised by *The Sweeney*, the 1972-77 Consul and Granada series was Ford's return to reality after the excesses of the previous Zephyr/Zodiac range. The Consuls served as the entry level models – with 1996cc V4 and 2495cc of 2994cc V6 engines – while the Granadas were the better-equipped and more expensive choice. Ford's recent purchase of Italian coachbuilder Ghia resulted in the luxurious Granada Ghia in 1974, soon joined by the Ghia Coupé. Consuls were discontinued in 1975 after which more basic Granadas filled the void.

SPECIFICATIONS

Years produced: 1972-1977 (50,747 in total)
Performance: 0-60mph: 10.4 secs (Top speed: 109mph)
Power & torque: 120bhp / 132lb/ft
Engine: Normally aspirated, 2495cc V6, petrol, carburettor, 12 valves
Drivetrain: Front-engine RWD
Suspension: (F) Ind. coil spring, double wishbone. (R) Ind. semi-trailing arms, coil springs
Bodyframe: Monocoque
Transmission: 4-speed manual
Weight: 1270kgs

PRICE GUIDE

Launch price: £1416
Excellent: £3750
Good: £2750
Average: £1500
Project: £500

FORD
Capri MkII/III

Falling sales caused Ford to have a rethink for the MkII Capri, launched in 1974. Some of the primitive raucousness of the original was taken away and replaced with more sophisticated practicality, with a hatchback rear instead of a boot. The body was also smoothed out, although not enough to make the car particularly aerodynamic. That had to wait until the MkIII model of 1978, which had a revamped front end with hooded quad-headlamps and a spoiler, plus other subtle touches to modernise it for the 1980s.

SPECIFICATIONS

Years produced: 1974-1977 (727,657 in total)
Performance: 0-60mph: 11.4 secs (Top speed: 104mph)
Power & torque: 57bhp / 87lb/ft
Engine: Normally aspirated 1297cc in-line four, petrol, carburettor, 8 valves
Drivetrain: Front-engine RWD
Suspension: (F) Independent, MacPherson strut, coil spring. (R) Live axle, leaf spring
Bodyframe: Monocoque
Transmission: 4-speed manual
Weight: 1010kgs

PRICE GUIDE

Launch price: £1336
Excellent: £3600
Good: £2250
Average: £1000
Project: £400

FORD
Escort MkII

In 1975, the MkII Escort came along and, like the Cortina before it, lost many of the curves of the original in favour of a square-cut look which many considered bland. However, bland often sells well if the rest of the package is good, and the MkII proved this, with around two-million sold during its five-year life. Underneath the boxy body, everything was much the same as on the MkI model, albeit with the addition of a 1599cc engine to complement the existing 1098cc and 1298cc ones. Trim levels were just as varied as before.

SPECIFICATIONS

Years produced: 1975-1980 (960,000 in total)
Performance: 0-60mph: 20.8 secs (Top speed: 79mph)
Power & torque: 41bhp / 52lb/ft
Engine: Normally aspirated 1097cc in-line four, petrol, carburettor, 8 valves
Drivetrain: Front-engine RWD
Suspension: (F) Independent, MacPherson strut, coil spring. (R) Live axle, leaf spring
Bodyframe: Monocoque
Transmission: 4-speed manual
Weight: 875kgs

PRICE GUIDE

Launch price: £1299
Excellent: £2750
Good: £2000
Average: £1000
Project: £450

FORD
Escort MkII Sport/RS Mexico

Ford continued to offer sporty Escorts for both the masses and more focussed drivers with the Mk2. Intended for more general consumption were the Sport and Mexico. The Sport used a 1599cc engine with 84bhp extracted from it, just enough to make it capable of the ton. However, to give the impression that it was capable of more, it had special wheels, spotlamps perched above its split front bumpers and pinstriping with '1600 Sport' branding. The Mexico, sold from 1976-78, did similar with its looks, but added touches from the RS2000.

SPECIFICATIONS

Years produced: 1975-1980
Performance: 0-60mph: 10.5 secs (Top speed: 107mph)
Power & torque: 95bhp / 92lb/ft
Engine: Normally aspirated, 1593cc in-line four, petrol, carburettor, 8 valves
Drivetrain: Front-engine RWD
Suspension: (F) Ind. MacPherson struts, coil spring. (R) Live axle, semi-elliptic leaf springs
Bodyframe: Monocoque
Transmission: 4-speed manual
Weight: 903kgs

PRICE GUIDE

Launch price: £2978
Excellent: £5500
Good: £4500
Average: £2500
Project: £1000

FORD
Escort MkII RS2000

When the MkII Escort was launched, the RS name continued with the Cosworth-engined RS1800, produced in tiny numbers. More widespread Rallye Sport production was initiated with the RS2000 of 1976 which substituted the diva-ish Cosworth unit for a sturdier two-litre Pinto powerhouse. However, the real talking point about the RS2000 was its polyurethane 'droop snoot' front end and air dam, a modification that clearly distinguished it from any other Escort. Poor sales led to the revamped version in 1978.

SPECIFICATIONS

Years produced: 1976-1980 (10,039 in total)
Performance: 0-60mph: 8.5 secs (Top speed: 108mph)
Power & torque: 110bhp / 119lb/ft
Engine: Normally aspirated, 1993cc in-line four, petrol, carburettor, 8 valves
Drivetrain: Front-engine RWD
Suspension: (F) Ind. MacPherson struts, coil struts (R) Live axle, semi-elliptic leaf springs
Bodyframe: Monocoque
Transmission: 4-speed manual
Weight: 925kgs

PRICE GUIDE

Launch price: £2857
Excellent: £10,500
Good: £9000
Average: £4750
Project: £2500

FORD
Granada MkII

MkII Granadas adopted Ford's new family appearance of squared-off lines. The angular appearance worked especially well with the larger proportions, cunningly disguising that what was underneath was mainly MkI. However, fresh V6 engines were added in 2293cc and 2792cc capacities plus, for those who prized economy over performance, a 2112cc diesel. Trim levels of L, GL, S and Ghia covered all bases and there were limited edition versions such as the Sapphire and leather-clad Chasseur.

SPECIFICATIONS

Years produced: 1977-1985 (918,969 in total)
Performance: 0-60mph: 8.9 secs (Top speed: 117mph)
Power & torque: 160bhp / 163lb/ft
Engine: Normally aspirated 2792cc V6, petrol, mechanical fuel injection, 12 valves
Drivetrain: Front-engine RWD
Suspension: (F) Ind. coil spring, double wishbones, anti-roll bar. (R) Ind. coil springs
Bodyframe: Monocoque
Transmission: 5-speed manual
Weight: 1455kgs

PRICE GUIDE

Launch price: £5913
Excellent: £3000
Good: £2250
Average: £950
Project: £300

FORD
Escort XR3/XR3i

With cars like the Volkswagen Golf stealing sales, the MkIII Escort of 1980 moved to a front-wheel-drive hatchback configuration to compete. The XR3 had the Golf GTI firmly as its target. A tuned 1597cc CVH engine produced 96bhp thanks to a twin-choke carburettor, while front and rear spoilers and blacked-out trim made it visually appealing to Eighties eyes. Better was to come though with the fuel injected XR3i of 1983. Boy racers soon fell in love with the XRs, in the same way their fathers had with the old rear-wheel-drive Escorts.

SPECIFICATIONS

Years produced: 1981-1986
Performance: 0-60mph: 9.7 secs (Top speed: 113mph)
Power & torque: 94bhp / 97lb/ft
Engine: 1598cc in-line four, petrol, carb. 8 valves
Drivetrain: Front-engine FWD
Suspension: (F) Independent, MacPherson struts, coil springs, anti-roll bar. (R) Independent, coil springs
Bodyframe: Monocoque
Transmission: 5-speed manual
Weight: 970kgs

PRICE GUIDE

Launch price: £5750
Excellent: £3250
Good: £2500
Average: £1000
Project: £300

FORD
Capri 2.8i/280

And so the end of a legend, with the final genuinely exciting Capris. With its market dominance threatened by the growth of the hot hatch and sales on the slide, Ford needed to do something to revitalise the Capri. The adoption of the 2792cc 'Cologne' V6 engine in 1981 for the 2.8i did just that, giving the breed back some of the vigour it had possessed in its earlier days, with 130mph possible from 160 horses. Best of all was the special edition 280, the last Capri of 'em all. Available only in Brooklands Green, a mere 1038 were made.

SPECIFICATIONS

Years produced: 1981-1987
Performance: 0-60mph: 8.2 secs (Top speed: 127mph)
Power & torque: 160bhp / 163lb/ft
Engine: Normally aspirated 2994cc V6, petrol, mechanical fuel injection, 12 valves
Drivetrain: Front-engine RWD
Suspension: (F) Independent, MacPherson strut, coil spring. (R) Live axle, leaf spring
Bodyframe: Monocoque
Transmission: 5-speed manual
Weight: 1230kgs

PRICE GUIDE

Launch price: £7995
Excellent: £4000
Good: £3000
Average: £1500
Project: £500

FORD
Fiesta XR2

Ford finally entered the mini car market in 1976 with the Fiesta; an unqualified success right from the word go. Surprisingly, it took nearly six years before a genuine performance version was added to the range, in the neat and tidy form of the XR2, with a larger, more powerful engine than any other Fiesta. Black plastic trim decorated the interior and exterior, there were alloy wheels and large circular headlamps were added. Ford's Cooper continued through the MkII and MkIII versions of the Fiesta, until dropped in 1994.

SPECIFICATIONS

Years produced: 1981-1989
Performance: 0-60mph: 9.4 secs (Top speed: 106mph)
Power & torque: 94bhp / 97lb/ft
Engine: Normally aspirated 1597cc in-line four, petrol, carburettor, 8 valves
Drivetrain: Front-engine FWD
Suspension: (F) Ind. MacPherson strut, coil spring (R) Dead axle, trailing links, coil spring
Bodyframe: Monocoque
Transmission: 5-speed manual
Weight: 840kgs

PRICE GUIDE

Launch price: £5713
Excellent: £3250
Good: £2500
Average: £1250
Project: £400

FORD
Escort RS1600i

In an even more serious vein than the XR3i was the RS1600i, built for homologation purposes to allow this fast Ford to go rallying in Group A competition. Although closely related to the XR3i – the fuel-injected engine was the same, for example – there were sufficient tweaks to raise power to 115bhp plus provide potential for future tuning. The 1980s was the era of flashy graphics, and the RS1600i was not one to disappoint, with extensive striping down its flanks and on its bonnet, plus prominent nose and boot spoilers and seven-spoke alloy wheels.

SPECIFICATIONS

Years produced: 1982-1983 (8659 in total)
Performance: 0-60mph: 8.7 secs (Top speed: 116mph)
Power & torque: 115bhp / 109lb/ft
Engine: Normally aspirated 1596cc in-line four, petrol, electronic fuel injection, 8 valves
Drivetrain: Front-engine FWD
Suspension: (F) Ind. MacPherson struts, coil springs, anti-roll bar. (R) Ind. anti-roll bar
Bodyframe: Monocoque
Transmission: 5-speed manual
Weight: 1105kgs

PRICE GUIDE

Launch price: £6834
Excellent: £4250
Good: £3250
Average: £1800
Project: £1000

FORD
Sierra XR4i

After the conservative Cortinas the radically-styled Sierra took some while to gain general acceptance. Eventually though they caught the public's imagination, helped in no small part by models like the XR4i, the first of the performance-orientated Sierras. It used a tuned version of Ford's fuel-injected 2994cc V6 engine along with a restyled version of the three-door bodyshell – with slightly bizarre multi-pillared rear windows – and made sure it caught any attention going with its prominent double rear spoiler.

SPECIFICATIONS

Years produced:	1983-1985 (27,400 in total)
Performance:	0-60mph: 7.7 secs (Top speed: 130mph)
Power & torque:	160bhp / 159lb/ft
Engine:	Normally aspirated 2792cc V6, petrol, electronic fuel injection, 12 valves
Drivetrain:	Front-engine RWD
Suspension:	(F) Ind. MacPherson strut, coil spring. (R) Ind. semi-trailing arms, coil spring
Bodyframe:	Monocoque
Transmission:	5-speed manual
Weight:	1175kgs
PRICE GUIDE	
Launch price:	£9946
Excellent:	£3000
Good:	£2250
Average:	£1000
Project:	£400

FORD
Escort RS Turbo

With the XR3i and RS1600i very close in both looks and performance, Ford decided to make the Escort RS line a little more enticing with 1985's RS Turbo. Mechanically, the car took the best features from the XR3i and RS1600i then bolted a Garrett T3 turbocharger onto the 1597cc CVH engine to up power to a very enjoyable 132bhp. This meant 125mph was attainable. Wide seven-spoke alloys, a body kit and the usual aerodynamic aids featured.

SPECIFICATIONS

Years produced:	1984-1990 (8604 in total)
Performance:	0-60mph: 8.2 secs (Top speed: 125mph)
Power & torque:	130bhp / 133lb/ft
Engine:	Turbocharged 1597cc in-line four, petrol, mechanical fuel injection, 8 valves
Drivetrain:	Front-engine FWD
Suspension:	(F) Ind. MacPherson struts, coil spring. (R) Ind. variable rate coil spring
Bodyframe:	Monocoque
Transmission:	5-speed manual
Weight:	940kgs
PRICE GUIDE	
Launch price:	£9951
Excellent:	£5500
Good:	£4500
Average:	£2850
Project:	£800

FORD
Sierra RS Cosworth

As if the grandiosity of the be-spoilered Sierra XR4i wasn't enough, Ford went even more extreme with the Sierra RS Cosworth. Launched in 1986, it used a 1993cc double-overhead camshaft engine, with the now requisite turbocharger attached, to give an output of 204bhp. Just 5545 were built, and insurance premiums were astronomical. It didn't help, of course, that a Cosworth Sierra was very obvious even from long distance, thanks to its massive whale-tail spoiler positioned halfway down the rear window.

SPECIFICATIONS

Years produced:	1985-1987 (6012 in total)
Performance:	0-60mph: 6.2 secs (Top speed: 142mph)
Power & torque:	204bhp / 203lb/ft
Engine:	Turbocharged 1993cc in-line four, petrol, electronic fuel injection, 16 valves
Drivetrain:	Front-engine RWD
Suspension:	(F) Ind. MacPherson strut, coil. (R) Ind. semi-trailing arms, coils,
Bodyframe:	Monocoque
Transmission:	5-speed manual
Weight:	1240kgs
PRICE GUIDE	
Launch price:	£15,950
Excellent:	£12,500
Good:	£10,000
Average:	£7000
Project:	£4250

FORD
Sierra Cosworth RS500

Why the RS500? Ford chose the name to indicate that only 500 of this 1987 successor to the original RS Cosworth would be built. This evolution of the Cosworth, constructed for motor sport homologation purposes, was put together by Aston Martin subsidiary Tickford. Mechanical modifications put power up to 224bhp. As well as uprated brakes and a modified front end, there was also the zenith of Ford's spoiler obsession with a second small one now hiding beneath the existing half-mast whale-tail contraption at the rear.

SPECIFICATIONS

Years produced:	1987-1987 (500 in total)
Performance:	0-60mph: 6.1 secs (Top speed: 154mph)
Power & torque:	224bhp / 204lb/ft
Engine:	Turbocharged 1993cc in-line four, petrol, electronic fuel injection, 16 valves
Drivetrain:	Front-engine RWD
Suspension:	(F) Ind. MacPherson strut, coil spring. (R) Ind. semi-trailing arms, coil spring
Bodyframe:	Monocoque
Transmission:	5-speed manual
Weight:	1240kgs
PRICE GUIDE	
Launch price:	£19,995
Excellent:	£22,000
Good:	£18,000
Average:	£11,000
Project:	£6500

FORD
Sierra Sapphire RS Cos.

Things calmed down with the launch of the Sapphire Cosworth in 1988, which was much more discreet and down-to-earth than previous Sierra Cosworths. As its name suggests, it was based on the Sapphire saloon version of the Sierra and used the existing 1993cc Cosworth twin-cam engine. Perhaps wisely, now missing were the flashy spoilers, replaced by just a small and subtle one on the bootlid. Even the two available colours were sensible too; White and Graphite Grey. 11,000 were made before the Sapphire RS Cosworth 4x4 replaced it in 1990.

SPECIFICATIONS

Years produced:	1987-1992 (20,250 in total)
Performance:	0-60mph: 6.5 secs (Top speed: 151mph)
Power & torque:	201bhp / 204lb/ft
Engine:	Turbocharged 1993cc in-line four, petrol, electronic fuel injection, 16 valves
Drivetrain:	Front-engine RWD
Suspension:	(F) Ind. MacPherson strut, anti-roll bar, (R) Ind. semi-trailing arms, coil spring
Bodyframe:	Monocoque
Transmission:	5-speed manual
Weight:	1250kgs
PRICE GUIDE	
Launch price:	£19,500
Excellent:	£8000
Good:	£6500
Average:	£4000
Project:	£2000

FORD
Escort RS Cosworth

Just like the pumped up Sierras that preceded it, the Escort RS Cosworth was a supercar for the people: brash, confident and up for anything. Backed up by a successful rallying career, over 7000 were sold, despite the crippling insurance premiums they attracted. The turbocharged two-litre twin-cam in original cars kicked out 227bhp. This dropped to 217bhp from 1994 when the turbo was changed to a smaller Garrett T25 unit. In compensation, this made the car much nicer to drive, with better throttle response.

SPECIFICATIONS

Years produced: 1992-1996 (7000 in total)
Performance: 0-60mph: 6.3 secs (Top speed: 138mph)
Power & torque: 224bhp / 220lb/ft
Engine: Turbocharged 1993cc in-line four, petrol, electronic fuel injection, 16 valves
Drivetrain: Front-engine AWD
Suspension: (F) Ind. MacPherson struts, anti-roll bar, (R) Torsion beam, trailing arm, coil spring
Bodyframe: Monocoque
Transmission: 5-speed manual
Weight: 1275kgs

PRICE GUIDE

Launch price: £25,825
Excellent: £17,000
Good: £14,500
Average: £11,500
Project: £8000

FRAZER NASH
Le Mans Replica

Following the privateer success for Frazer Nash in the 1949 Le Mans 24 Hour race, the company produced its own version following on from the tradition first started with the 1932 TT Replica. The Le Mans was powered by a 1971cc straight-six BMW engine delivering a healthy 120bhp, and in the lightweight 'High Speed' body proved prodigiously quick. Like all Nashes the Le Mans Replica was completely hand-built, with the customer getting the final say on engine configuration and suspension set-up.

SPECIFICATIONS

Years produced: 1948-1953 (34 in total)
Performance: 0-60mph: 8.8 secs (Top speed: 110mph)
Power & torque: 125bhp / N/A
Engine: Normally aspirated 1971cc in-line six, petrol, carburettor, 12 valves
Drivetrain: Front-engine RWD
Suspension: (F) Independent traverse leaf spring. (R) Beam axle, torsion bar
Bodyframe: Chassis and separate body
Transmission: 4-speed
Weight: 635kgs

PRICE GUIDE

Launch price: £3074
Excellent: £200,000
Good: £175,000
Average: £140,000
Project: £100,000

GILBERN
GT

Good looking little 2+2 from Wales, with a glassfibre body over a tube frame. To some degree or other the 277 built were sold as kit-cars to avoid purchase tax, so parts and spec can vary a little between cars. They were initially offered with A-series or MGA engines, but most survivors you'll find will have MGB power, along with front suspension from the same source. Thanks to an enthusiastic club parts sourcing is much better than you might expect, right down to repro bodies and chassis if necessary.

SPECIFICATIONS

Years produced: 1959-1967 (277 in total)
Performance: 0-60mph: 12.0 secs (Top speed: 111mph)
Power & torque: 95bhp / 110lb/ft
Engine: Normally aspirated 1798cc in-line four, petrol, carburettor, 8 valves
Drivetrain: Front-engine RWD
Suspension: (F) Independent, coil spring, (R) Live axle, coil spring
Bodyframe: Chassis and separate body
Transmission: 4-speed manual
Weight: 813kgs

PRICE GUIDE

Launch price: £748
Excellent: £6000
Good: £5000
Average: £2900
Project: £1000

GILBERN
Genie

Gilbern's move upmarket to full GT status. Larger, more angular body now contains a Ford Zephyr V6, mostly in 3.0 capacity, though some were sold with 2.5s. Another big change was that you could buy a Genie factory built as well as in component form. The first 30 or so came with MGB front suspension and rear axle, then these were upgraded to MGC spec. Somewhere close to 200 were built. Overdrive was an option worth finding now, and some even came with electric windows. Twin fuel tanks add to their kudos.

SPECIFICATIONS

Years produced: 1966-1970 (197 in total)
Performance: 0-60mph: 10.7 secs (Top speed: 115mph)
Power & torque: 141bhp / 181lb/ft
Engine: Normally aspirated 2994cc V6, petrol, carburettor, 12 valves
Drivetrain: Front-engine RWD
Suspension: (F) Independent, wishbone, coil spring, (R) Live axle, coil spring
Bodyframe: Spaceframe
Transmission: 4-speed manual
Weight: 965kgs

PRICE GUIDE

Launch price: £1752
Excellent: £6000
Good: £4750
Average: £2750
Project: £1000

GILBERN
Invader

The MkI and II Invaders differed visually only in detail from the Genie they replaced. Flush-fitting door handles and rear pillar vents are the biggest giveaways. Underneath, the front suspension is still MGC-based, but with double wishbones and coil-overs replacing the MG's lever-arm dampers. For 1971-72 there was also an estate version of which 105 were built. MkIII uses the same 3.0 engine, but a switch to Cortina MkIII axles and suspension brings the need for flared wheelarches. A full-width grille adds further distinction.

SPECIFICATIONS

Years produced: 1969-1974 (603 in total)
Performance: 0-60mph: 10.7 secs (Top speed: 115mph)
Power & torque: 141bhp / 181lb/ft
Engine: Normally aspirated 2994cc V6, petrol, carburettor, 12 valves
Drivetrain: Front-engine RWD
Suspension: (F) Independent, coil spring, wishbone, anti- roll bar. (R) Beam axle
Bodyframe: Spaceframe
Transmission: 4-speed manual
Weight: 903kgs

PRICE GUIDE

Launch price: N/A
Excellent: £6250
Good: £5000
Average: £2750
Project: £1000

GINETTA
G15

As a more obviously road-focused model it's clear why the G15 became Ginetta's best-selling model. Powered by the excellent Coventry Climax based Hillman Imp engine, mid-mounted in the lightweight glassfibre shell, weight distribution was near perfect and handling was predictably good as a result. The suspension set-up was a mixture of Triumph and Hillman and was used to great effect. A more powerful G15S was launched and pushed the top speed up to 115mph – but sadly the G15 was taken out of production in 1973.

SPECIFICATIONS

Years produced:	1968-1974 (800 in total)
Performance:	0-60mph: 12.9 secs (Top speed: 94mph)
Power & torque:	50bhp / 49lb/ft
Engine:	Normally aspirated 875cc in-line four, petrol, carburettor, 8 valves
Drivetrain:	Front-engine RWD
Suspension:	(F) Independent, coil spring. (R) Independent, coil spring
Bodyframe:	Spaceframe, glassfibre body
Transmission:	4-speed manual
Weight:	501kgs
	PRICE GUIDE
Launch price:	£1024
Excellent:	£8500
Good:	£6500
Average:	£3500
Project:	£1500

GINETTA
G21

The more upmarket G21 reflected Ginetta's ambitions in the wake of the collapse of the kit car market. The sleek glassfibre body was fitted over a new backbone tubular steel chassis and a choice of Sunbeam Rapier H120 or Ford V6 engines meant that there was real power on tap. The two-seat coupé wasn't offered with an opening rear door, and in the wake of the MGB and Ford Capri, this seemed like a oversight – but despite this, most of the 170 built were sold as complete cars, and not in kit form.

SPECIFICATIONS

Years produced:	1973-1978 (180 in total)
Performance:	0-60mph: 9.7 secs (Top speed: 112mph)
Power & torque:	85bhp / 91lb/ft
Engine:	Normally aspirated 1725cc in-line four, petrol, carburettor, 8 valves
Drivetrain:	Front-engine RWD
Suspension:	(F) Independent, coil spring. (R) Beam axle, coil spring
Bodyframe:	Spaceframe, glassfibre body
Transmission:	4-speed manual
Weight:	737kgs
	PRICE GUIDE
Launch price:	£1875
Excellent:	£8000
Good:	£6000
Average:	£3250
Project:	£1500

GINETTA
G32

A new look for the 1980s saw Ginetta going for the Toyota MR2 with its Ford-based mid-engined G32. Again, suspension was an off-the-shelf set-up taken from Ford, while the XR2 engine in the middle gave plenty of performance. After being in the business for so long, Ginetta had perfected getting a high quality finish from its glassfibre bodies, although the cunning use of the Fiesta's doors no doubt added to the feeling of solidity. Rare and unusual now, but satisfying if you can find the right one – and easy to keep on the road.

SPECIFICATIONS

Years produced:	1989-1992
Performance:	0-60mph: N/A (Top speed: N/A)
Power & torque:	90bhp / 98lb/ft
Engine:	Normally aspirated 1597cc in-line four, petrol, carburettor, 8 valves
Drivetrain:	Mid-engine RWD
Suspension:	(F) Independent, coil spring, double wishbone. (R) Independent, coil spring
Bodyframe:	Spaceframe, glassfibre body
Transmission:	5-speed manual
Weight:	753kg
	PRICE GUIDE
Launch price:	£10,490
Excellent:	£4750
Good:	£4000
Average:	£3000
Project:	£1750

GINETTA
G33 V8

The G33 saw the return of 'back to basics' at Ginetta. A development of the curvaceous G27 body (which harked back to the G4), with a Rover V8 engine shoehorned into the front provided TVR-rivalling thrills and soundtrack. But being a Ginetta it was more track focused than its Blackpool rival, making it a harder-edged alternative. The chassis was galvanised and hanging off it was a fully independent suspension set-up featuring double wishbones all-round and front and rear anti-roll bars.

SPECIFICATIONS

Years produced:	1990-1996
Performance:	0-60mph: 5.3 secs (Top speed: 137mph)
Power & torque:	198bhp / 220lb/ft
Engine:	Normally aspirated 3946cc V8, petrol, electronic fuel injection, 16 valves
Drivetrain:	Front-engine RWD
Suspension:	(F) Independent coil spring. (R) Independent coil spring
Bodyframe:	Spaceframe, glassfibre body
Transmission:	5-speed manual
Weight:	874kgs
	PRICE GUIDE
Launch price:	£18,187
Excellent:	£12,000
Good:	£10,000
Average:	£7500
Project:	£5000

GORDON-KEEBLE
GK1

With achingly pretty Giugiaro styling and the vocal accompaniment of a Corvette V8, you'd never know these were lovingly nailed together in a large shed near Southampton. Just 99 were built before the company folded for the second and last time, but enthusiastic support and a glassfibre body over a square tube chassis means that almost all of the cars survive. Commonly found (and much better to drive) with a power-assisted rack-and pinion steering conversion. Easy to drive fast and simple to look after.

SPECIFICATIONS

Years produced:	1964-1966 (99 in total)
Performance:	0-60mph: 7.5 secs (Top speed: 136mph)
Power & torque:	300bhp / 360lb/ft
Engine:	Normally aspirated 5354cc V8, petrol, carburettor, 16 valves
Drivetrain:	Front-engine RWD
Suspension:	(F) Independent, coil spring. (R) de Dion rear beam, coil spring
Bodyframe:	Chassis and separate body
Transmission:	4-speed manual
Weight:	1436kgs
	PRICE GUIDE
Launch price:	£2798
Excellent:	£36,500
Good:	£32,000
Average:	£24,000
Project:	£14,000

HEALEY Elliott

Former technical director at Triumph, Donald Healey, had been building his own cars since 1946, and the Elliott saloon was an important step in the development of his company. Considered to be the fastest closed four-seater available, these were thinly disguised racing cars, lightened with almost obsessive ruthlessness. At the Mille Miglia in 1948, Johnny Lurani and Giuglelmo Sandri won the production touring class in an Elliott, while Healey with his son, Geoffrey, finished ninth overall in a Westland Roadster.

SPECIFICATIONS

Years produced: 1948-1950 (64 in total)
Performance: 0-60mph: 12.3 secs (Top speed: 102mph)
Power & torque: 104bhp / 132lb/ft
Engine: Normally aspirated 2443cc in-line four, petrol, carburettor, 8 valves
Drivetrain: Front-engine RWD
Suspension: (F) Independent, coil springs. (R) Beam axle, coil springs
Bodyframe: Chassis and separate body
Transmission: 4-speed manual
Weight: 1143kgs

PRICE GUIDE

Launch price: £1566
Excellent: £15,000
Good: £12,000
Average: £9000
Project: £5000

HEALEY Silverstone

The Silverstone showed just how far Healey had come in such a short space of time – it was an excellent road- or competition-car, and proved itself more than capable of living with much more expensive machinery. The short-framed car had an anti-roll bar and tenacious handling on the circuit. The promising roadster was stylish, and Healey easily sold every car built. However, it was prematurely taken out of production when the deal between Nash and Healey to produce the Nash-Healey was concluded.

SPECIFICATIONS

Years produced: 1949-1950 (105 in total)
Performance: 0-60mph: 11.0 secs (Top speed: 105mph)
Power & torque: 104bhp / 132lb/ft
Engine: Normally aspirated 2443cc in-line four, petrol, carburettor, 8 valves
Drivetrain: Front-engine RWD
Suspension: (F) Independent, coil springs. (R) Beam axle, coil springs
Bodyframe: Chassis and separate body
Transmission: 4-speed manual
Weight: 940kgs

PRICE GUIDE

Launch price: £1246
Excellent: £32,500
Good: £27,500
Average: £20,000
Project: £12,500

HEALEY Abbott

The Westland Roadster was Healey's first production car, and although it was capable of great things in competition it wasn't ideal as a road car. It might have enjoyed the benefits of a stiff box section chassis, all-round coils and the Riley engine helped it to a 105mph top speed but it lacked creature comforts. The Abbott drophead coupé was introduced to put that right with sharper style, a more compliant ride and lower gearing to improve tractability. It might have been slower but it was a more accomplished all-rounder.

SPECIFICATIONS

Years produced: 1950-1954 (77 in total)
Performance: 0-60mph: 14.6 secs (Top speed: 104mph)
Power & torque: 106bhp / 136lb/ft
Engine: Normally aspirated 2443cc in-line four, petrol, carburettor, 8 valves
Drivetrain: Front-engine RWD
Suspension: (F) Independent, coil spring, trailing link. (R) Live axle, coil spring
Bodyframe: Body on steel ladder frame
Transmission: 4-speed manual
Weight: 1143kg

PRICE GUIDE

Launch price: £1854
Excellent: £20,000
Good: £16,000
Average: £10,500
Project: £6000

HEALEY Tickford

Based on the Elliott, but more stylishly executed, the Healey Tickford is far cleaner looking and more appealing than the original, perhaps taking the car away from its competition roots and into more exalted territory. Dynamically, it lost out to the Elliott, thanks to additional weight and a loss of agility, but instead, it received a proper boot and glass (instead of Perspex) side windows. In the end, it outsold the original by two-to-one proving that Healey's designs were good enough to warrant the premium.

SPECIFICATIONS

Years produced: 1950-1954 (224 in total)
Performance: 0-60mph: 14.6 secs (Top speed: 104mph)
Power & torque: 104bhp / 132lb/ft
Engine: Normally aspirated 2443cc in-line four, petrol, carburettor, 8 valves
Drivetrain: Front-engine RWD
Suspension: (F) Independent, coil springs. (R) Beam axle, coil springs
Bodyframe: Chassis and separate body
Transmission: 4-speed manual
Weight: 1546kgs

PRICE GUIDE

Launch price: £1854
Excellent: £15,000
Good: £12,500
Average: £9500
Project: £5000

HEINKEL/TROJAN Cabin Cruiser/200

The archetypal 'Bubble Car', the Heinkel was also produced in the UK by Trojan from 1961 as the Cabin Cruiser. Given its 197cc engine, cruiser was hardly an apt title for this economy special. As bubble cars go, the Heinkel was certainly an improvement over the original BMW – it had space (just) for four people, was lighter, and could cruise happily at up to 50mph. Survival rate of these cars is exceptionally high, and that is down simply to their great build quality – and there's excellent club and specialist support.

SPECIFICATIONS

Years produced: 1956-1965 (23,000 in total)
Performance: 0-60mph: N/A (Top speed: 53mph)
Power & torque: 9.2bhp / N/A
Engine: Normally aspirated cc, petrol, carburettor, 2 valves
Drivetrain: Rear-engine RWD
Suspension: (F) Independent, coil springs (R) Independent, coil springs
Bodyframe: Chassis and glassfibre body
Transmission: Single-speed
Weight: 279kg

PRICE GUIDE

Launch price: N/A
Excellent: £6000
Good: £5000
Average: £2500
Project: £1250

HILLMAN
Minx Phase I/II

While its upright looks were very traditional, the Hillman Minx Phase I was actually quite novel in some of its body design; not only was there half-unitary construction but also a rear-hinged bonnet rather than the then-usual cumbersome side-opening doors. Introduced in 1939, the car continued to be built for forces use during the war, returning to the civilian arena in 1945. The 1185cc 35bhp sidevalve engine and conventional suspension were little to get excited about, although at least the Phase II of 1947 added hydraulic brakes.

SPECIFICATIONS

Years produced: 1939-1948 (60,000 in total)
Performance: 0-60mph: N/A (Top speed: 59mph)
Power & torque: 35bhp / N/A
Engine: Normally aspirated 1185cc in-line four, petrol, carburettor, 8 valves
Drivetrain: Front-engine RWD
Suspension: (F) Beam axle, leaf springs. (R) Live axle, leaf springs
Bodyframe: Chassis and separate body
Transmission: 4-speed manual
Weight: 876kgs

PRICE GUIDE

Launch price: £397
Excellent: £3000
Good: £2250
Average: £900
Project: £400

HILLMAN
Minx Phase III-VIIIA

The pre-war looks of the Minx were revamped with the Phase III cars of 1948, which switched to 'full-width' styling, completely unitary construction and coil and wishbone independent front suspension. After that, Hillman continued with their process of annual Phase improvements, enlarging engines to give more power, upgrading the suspension and tweaking the bodywork to keep it fresh. The alterations were subtle, but ensured that the breed kept up with its rivals until it was replaced by the Series Minxes of 1956.

SPECIFICATIONS

Years produced: 1948-1957 (378,785 in total)
Performance: 0-60mph: 29.7 secs (Top speed: 73mph)
Power & torque: 35bhp / N/A
Engine: Normally aspirated 1185cc in-line four, petrol, carburettor, 8 valves
Drivetrain: Front-engine RWD
Suspension: (F) Independent, coil spring. (R) Live axle, semi-elliptic leaf spring
Bodyframe: Chassis and separate body
Transmission: 4-speed manual
Weight: 933kgs

PRICE GUIDE

Launch price: £505
Excellent: £2650
Good: £2000
Average: £900
Project: £400

HILLMAN
Minx Californian

The USA was always a big target for British car firms, and Hillman had a head start on their competitors thanks to Studebaker-inspired styling by American Raymond Loewy. As its name suggested the Californian coupé was blatantly aimed across the Atlantic, where style was often much more important than substance. In essence, it was a 1953 Minx drophead coupé with a permanent hardtop attached. And what a roof, for the split three-piece rear screen was very eye-catching and the roof's contrasting paint made the car stand out.

SPECIFICATIONS

Years produced: 1953-1956
Performance: 0-60mph: 34.7 secs (Top speed: 69mph)
Power & torque: 37bhp / 58lb/ft
Engine: Normally aspirated 875cc in-line four, petrol, carburettor, 8 valves
Drivetrain: Front-engine RWD
Suspension: (F) Independent, coil spring. (R) Live axle, semi-elliptic leaf spring
Bodyframe: Monocoque
Transmission: 4-speed manual
Weight: 990kgs

PRICE GUIDE

Launch price: £681
Excellent: £3250
Good: £2500
Average: £1300
Project: £500

HILLMAN
Minx Series I-IIIc

Hillman's new generation of family cars had smart and nicely-rounded styling, inspired by contemporary American trends. Sunbeam Rapiers and Singer Gazelles also used the same basic shell and body, but it was the Minx for the masses that was the big seller of course. With better performance and handling, plus more space inside, the Series cars were a significant step forward. Rootes fiddled with the formula almost every year; major changes included the 1390cc overhead valve engine rising to 1494cc with the Series III of 1958.

SPECIFICATIONS

Years produced: 1956-1963 (341,681 in total)
Performance: 0-60mph: 27.7 secs (Top speed: 77mph)
Power & torque: 48bhp / N/A
Engine: Normally aspirated 1390cc in-line four, petrol, carburettor, 8 valves
Drivetrain: Front-engine RWD
Suspension: (F) Independent, coil spring. (R) Live axle, semi-elliptic leaf spring
Bodyframe: Monocoque
Transmission: 4-speed manual
Weight: 965kgs

PRICE GUIDE

Launch price: £748
Excellent: £2500
Good: £1850
Average: £925
Project: £350

HILLMAN
Super Minx

What had been planned to be the new Minx eventually appeared in 1961 as the Hillman Super Minx. As it was bigger, heavier and (therefore) more expensive, Rootes had decided to release it as a separate model, with 'Super' added to highlight its improvements over the standard Minx. The bodyshell kept the family resemblance, underneath the mechanicals were mainly Minx. As well as the saloon and estate, there was a rather becoming four-seater convertible from 1962 (now worth double saloon prices).

SPECIFICATIONS

Years produced: 1961-1967
Performance: 0-60mph: 22.5 secs (Top speed: 83mph)
Power & torque: 58bhp / 86lb/ft
Engine: 1592cc in-line four, petrol, carb. 8 valves
Drivetrain: Front-engine RWD
Suspension: (F) Independent, coil spring. (R) Live axle, semi-elliptic leaf spring
Bodyframe: Monocoque
Transmission: 4-speed manual
Weight: 1069kgs

PRICE GUIDE

Launch price: £856
Excellent: £2000
Good: £1500
Average: £800
Project: £250

HILLMAN
Minx Series V/VI

In 1963, the Minx received a facelift to make it look less 1950s. Although the changes weren't that sweeping, they did succeed in making it look more like a car from the decade it lived in. The rear fins were greatly reduced, the roof was flattened, the rear wraparound window replaced and a new windscreen and grille were added. From today's viewpoint it was a less handsome vehicle but, back then, something needed to be done to boost the ageing Minx's appeal. The 1965 Series VI injected a bit more temptation with its 1725cc.

SPECIFICATIONS

Years produced: 1963-1967
Performance: 0-60mph: 18.6 secs (Top speed: 80mph)
Power & torque: 58bhp / 87lb/ft
Engine: Normally aspirated 1592cc in-line four, petrol, carburettor, 8 valves
Drivetrain: Front-engine RWD
Suspension: (F) Independent, coil spring. (R) Live axle, semi-elliptic leaf spring
Bodyframe: Monocoque
Transmission: 4-speed manual
Weight: 998kgs

PRICE GUIDE

Launch price: £635
Excellent: £2100
Good: £1600
Average: £800
Project: £250

HILLMAN
Imp

A heroic failure for Rootes, the 1963 Imp was the company's attempt to tackle the Mini. And it was a great little machine, with a 37bhp alloy 875cc Coventry Climax engine mounted in the back. The all-independent suspension made it nimble on bends and the opening rear screen added practicality. Had it come along before the Mini, it might have been the big little star rather than BMC's baby. However, reliability issues and suspicion about its unusual nature robbed it of sales and it never recovered, despite remaining on sale until 1976.

SPECIFICATIONS

Years produced: 1963-1976 (440,032 in total)
Performance: 0-60mph: 18.5 secs (Top speed: 81mph)
Power & torque: 39bhp / 52lb/ft
Engine: Normally aspirated 875cc in-line four, petrol, carburettor, 8 valves
Drivetrain: Rear-engine RWD
Suspension: (F) Independent, coil spring. (R) Independent, coil spring
Bodyframe: Monocoque
Transmission: 4-speed manual
Weight: 694kgs

PRICE GUIDE

Launch price: £508
Excellent: £2000
Good: £1500
Average: £850
Project: £275

HILLMAN
Minx/Hunter

Hillman turned its back on the past with the Hunter. The angular looks were penned with the help of noted stylist William Towns and were neat but hardly stirred the blood. The 1725cc engine was the only real link with Rootes history and, with MacPherson strut front suspension, front disc brakes and overdrive, the Hunter gave a good account of itself. The Minx variant was more downmarket, with a 1496cc engine, but the old name disappeared in 1970. The Hunter soldiered on, largely unloved, with the 88bhp GT and 93bhp GLSs its most exhilarating versions.

SPECIFICATIONS

Years produced: 1966-1977 (470,000 in total)
Performance: 0-60mph: 13.9 secs (Top speed: 83mph)
Power & torque: 79bhp / 91lb/ft
Engine: Normally aspirated 1725cc in-line four, petrol, carburettor, 8 valves
Drivetrain: Front-engine RWD
Suspension: (F) Independent, coil spring. (R) Live axle, leaf spring
Bodyframe: Monocoque
Transmission: 4-speed manual
Weight: 953kgs

PRICE GUIDE

Launch price: £838
Excellent: £1750
Good: £1350
Average: £650
Project: £250

HILLMAN
Avenger

This 1970 Hillman was a car Rootes/Chrysler intended to sell to the world... and did, to some extent, for it was also available in the USA as a Plymouth. However, although its styling was more appealing than the Hunter's and the fresh range of OHV engines – 1248cc and 1498cc from launch, 1295cc and 1598cc in 1973 – were lively enough, the Avenger never really captured the public's imagination. The one to have is the limited production competition-style Tiger of 1972-73, with lairy looks and 100mph potential.

SPECIFICATIONS

Years produced: 1970-1976 (638,631 in total)
Performance: 0-60mph: 19.8 secs (Top speed: 81mph)
Power & torque: 58bhp / 66lb/ft
Engine: Normally aspirated 1248cc in-line four, petrol, carburettor, 8 valves
Drivetrain: Front-engine RWD
Suspension: (F) Independent, coil spring. (R) Live axle, leaf spring
Bodyframe: Monocoque
Transmission: 4-speed manual
Weight: 830kgs

PRICE GUIDE

Launch price: £822
Excellent: £2250
Good: £1500
Average: £600
Project: £250

HONDA
S800

In true Honda tradition the S800's party piece was under the bonnet. Only Honda would create a 791cc engine capable of producing 70bhp at 8000rpm, giving the sports car an impressive top speed of over 100mph. This impressive performance was not at a cost of poor fuel economy, which came in at 35mpg. Available as a coupé or a roadster the car was loved by many, but with a shade over 10,000 sales worldwide it was not massively successful. The S800 was the last Honda to wear the S badge until the S2000 in 1999.

SPECIFICATIONS

Years produced: 1966-1971 (25,853 in total)
Performance: 0-60mph: 13.4 secs (Top speed: 94mph)
Power & torque: 70bhp / 49lb/ft
Engine: Normally aspirated 791cc in-line four, petrol, carburettor, 8 valves
Drivetrain: Front-engine RWD
Suspension: (F) Ind. double wishbone, torsion bar, anti-roll bar. (R) Live axle, trailing arms
Bodyframe: Monocoque
Transmission: 4-speed manual
Weight: 771kgs

PRICE GUIDE

Launch price: £779
Excellent: £6500
Good: £5000
Average: £3000
Project: £1500

HONDA
Z600 Coupé

In Japan, the most important sector of the market is the 'Kei Car' category. If your car falls into this class, below a certain size, engine capacity and weight you pay drastically reduced tax and insurance rates. Many Japanese car manufacturers embraced the Kei Car and Honda was one of them. The Z600 pushed the limits of the Kei Car regulations, but despite its limitations, the Z600 had no problem keeping up with traffic. All UK Z600s were painted Orange, with a 'Starsky and Hutch' style black stripe running along the flanks.

SPECIFICATIONS

Years produced: 1973-1974 (40,586 in total)
Performance: 0-60mph: 32.6 secs (Top speed: 78mph)
Power & torque: 32bhp / 32lb/ft
Engine: Normally aspirated 599cc, petrol, carburettor, 4 valves
Drivetrain: Front-engine FWD
Suspension: (F) Independent, coil spring. (R) Beam axle, semi-elliptic leaf spring
Bodyframe: Monocoque
Transmission: 5-speed manual
Weight: 580kgs

PRICE GUIDE

Launch price: £755
Excellent: £3500
Good: £2750
Average: £1650
Project: £350

HONDA
CR-X 1.6i/V-TEC

One of the important lessons learned from the early CR-X was that cars destined for Europe need a lot more rust protection than JDM equivalents. Barely any of these Series 1 CR-Xs survive today, as many of them lost their battle with rust many years ago. Honda took this on board with the second incarnation of the CR-X and with a line-up of more powerful engines, the CR-X was a big hit in Europe. The 1.6 VTEC engine was a real firecracker which like most Honda engines delivered all of its power near to its 7600RPM rev-limit.

SPECIFICATIONS

Years produced: 1984-1991
Performance: 0-60mph: 8.0 secs (Top speed: 132mph)
Power & torque: 158bhp / 111lb/ft
Engine: Normally aspirated 1595cc in-line four, petrol, electronic fuel injection, 16 valves
Drivetrain: Front-engine FWD
Suspension: (F) Independent, wishbone, coil spring. (R) Independent, wishbone, coil spring
Bodyframe: Monocoque
Transmission: 5-speed manual
Weight: 1105kgs

PRICE GUIDE

Launch price: £6950
Excellent: £3600
Good: £2850
Average: £1500
Project: £500

HONDA
NSX 3.0

Honda achieved what nobody before had, the supercar you could use every day. When the NSX was launched in 1990 it left the competition behind, in terms of reliability and practicality. The chassis was perfected at Suzuka, with input from F1 World Champion Ayrton Senna. Senna convinced Honda to stiffen the NSX even more and totally change the rear suspension geometry to give the NSX uncompromising traction. Honda wanted the NSX to be perfect and over its 15-year lifespan it was under constant development.

SPECIFICATIONS

Years produced: 1990-1997
Performance: 0-60mph: 5.8 secs (Top speed: 159mph)
Power & torque: 270bhp / 252lb/ft
Engine: Normally aspirated 2977cc V6, petrol, electronic fuel injection, 24 valves
Drivetrain: Mid-engine RWD
Suspension: (F) Ind. double wish. coils, tele.dampers, anti-roll bar. (R) Ind. double wish. coils
Bodyframe: Monocoque
Transmission: 5-speed manual
Weight: 1350kgs

PRICE GUIDE

Launch price: £52,000
Excellent: £24,000
Good: £20,000
Average: £16,000
Project: £12,000

HONDA
Integra Type-R

Honda went to extreme lengths to transform the Integra, previously a run of the mill coupé, into one of the most hardcore performance cars in the world. It went through a rigorous weight-loss programme which saw the standard windscreen thrown out in favour of a thinner sheet of glass. The Type-R was also stiffened, with front and rear strut-braces, along with highly tuned springs and dampers. A set of lightweight alloy wheels and a limited-slip differential finished the car off nicely, giving the front-wheel-drive car amazing levels of poise and grip.

SPECIFICATIONS

Years produced: 1996-2000
Performance: 0-60mph: 6.5 secs (Top speed: 145mph)
Power & torque: 187bhp / 178lb/ft
Engine: Normally aspirated 1797cc in-line four, petrol, electronic fuel injection, 16 valves
Drivetrain: Front-engine FWD
Suspension: (F) Ind. double wishbone, coil spring, anti-roll bar. (R) Ind. double wishbone
Bodyframe: Monocoque
Transmission: 5-Speed Manual
Weight: 1140kgs

PRICE GUIDE

Launch price: £19,500
Excellent: £8000
Good: £6750
Average: £4500
Project: £3000

HUMBER
Super Snipe/Pullman I

The Snipe of 1945 was the more upmarket version of the almost identical Hawk, fitted with a 2731cc six-cylinder engine. The further step up from this was the Super Snipe, which actually did have a few super things about it. For starters there was the huge and lazy 4086cc six-cylinder engine and some plusher touches to its make-up. The ultimate offshoot was the Pullman, intended to satisfy the wedding, funerals and mayoral market. Mechanically, it was the same as the Super Snipe but with a longer wheelbase.

SPECIFICATIONS

Years produced: 1945-1948
Performance: 0-60mph: 24.5 secs (Top speed: 80mph)
Power & torque: 100bhp / N/A
Engine: Normally aspirated 4086cc in-line six, petrol, carburettor, 12 valves
Drivetrain: Front-engine RWD
Suspension: (F) Independent, leaf spring. (R) Live axle, semi-elliptic leaf spring
Bodyframe: Chassis and separate body
Transmission: 4-speed manual
Weight: 1537kgs

PRICE GUIDE

Launch price: £889
Excellent: £8000
Good: £5500
Average: £2250
Project: £600

HUMBER Hawk MkI/II

Humber returned after World War 2 with the Hawk and the Snipe... both cars that owed an enormous debt of badge-engineering gratitude to the pre-war Hillman 14. While the Snipe had a six-cylinder engine, the Hawk also borrowed the four-cylinder 1944cc engine from its Hillman counterpart and slotted in below the Snipe as the Rootes Group's big luxury saloon for the more economy-minded. Advancements on what had gone before were hydraulic brakes, independent front suspension, larger boots and a sliding sunroof.

SPECIFICATIONS

Years produced: 1945-1949
Performance: 0-60mph: 42.1 secs (Top speed: 64mph)
Power & torque: 56bhp / N/A
Engine: Normally aspirated 1944cc in-line four, petrol, carburettor, 8 valves
Drivetrain: Front-engine RWD
Suspension: (F) Independent, transverse leaf spring. (R) Live axle, semi-elliptic leaf springs
Bodyframe: Chassis and separate body
Transmission: 4-speed manual
Weight: 1537kgs

PRICE GUIDE

Launch price: £684
Excellent: £6000
Good: £4500
Average: £2100
Project: £500

HUMBER Super Snipe/Pullman II-IV

A curious blend of the old style Super Snipes/ Pullmans and the freshly-redesigned Hawks. The cabin and rear end weren't touched, but the front was given a Raymond Loewy makeover, with headlamps now incorporated with the wings. And running boards, which had been dropped in 1940, enjoyed a surprise revival. Dropheads offered until 1950, and these can fetch up to double the quoted prices. Subtle improvements continued through until 1952 and the MkIV model, which finally adopted the complete Hawk body style.

SPECIFICATIONS

Years produced: 1948-1957 (56,935 in total)
Performance: 0-60mph: 20.6 secs (Top speed: 81mph)
Power & torque: 100bhp / N/A
Engine: Normally aspirated 4086cc in-line six, petrol, carburettor, 12 valves
Drivetrain: Front-engine RWD
Suspension: (F) Independent, coil spring. (R) Live axle, leaf spring
Bodyframe: Chassis and separate body
Transmission: 4-speed manual
Weight: 1247kgs

PRICE GUIDE

Launch price: £1144
Excellent: £7750
Good: £6000
Average: £2500
Project: £800

HUMBER Hawk MkIII-VIA

For the new Humber Hawk, the Rootes Group turned to legendary American stylist Raymond Loewy, who created an American-flavoured and modern design with a very imposing and elongated front end. The look endured to include the MkV1A version until this was dropped in 1957. Although the first MkIII cars used the same 1944cc four-cylinder sidevalve engine and gearbox as previous Hawks, independent front suspension was introduced. Further changes included a bigger engine for the 1950s MkIV.

SPECIFICATIONS

Years produced: 1949-1957 (59,282 in total)
Performance: 0-60mph: 30.7 secs (Top speed: 71mph)
Power & torque: 56bhp / N/A
Engine: Normally aspirated 1944cc in-line four, petrol, carburettor, 8 valves
Drivetrain: Front-engine RWD
Suspension: (F) Independent, coil spring. (R) Live axle, leaf springs
Bodyframe: Chassis and separate body
Transmission: 4-speed manual
Weight: 1247kgs

PRICE GUIDE

Launch price: £799
Excellent: £4500
Good: £3500
Average: £1750
Project: £500

HUMBER Hawk I-IV

Unitary construction reached Humber with the Hawk Series 1 of 1957. Trumpeted as the largest car bodyshell being built in the UK at the time, part of the size was due to the Transatlantic leanings, a big dollop of Detroit converted to Coventry dimensions. The 2267cc overhead valve engine from the previous generation of Hawk, giving 83mph from its 73bhp, was retained until the final MkIVA model. Series II cars had disc brakes, but the biggest change to the family came with the MkIV of 1964, when the cabin changed to a sleeker profile with more glass.

SPECIFICATIONS

Years produced: 1957-1967 (41,191 in total)
Performance: 0-60mph: 20.6 secs (Top speed: 83mph)
Power & torque: 73bhp / N/A
Engine: Normally aspirated 2267cc in-line four, petrol, carburettor, 8 valves
Drivetrain: Front-engine RWD
Suspension: (F) Independent, wishbone, coil spring. (R) Live axle, semi-elliptic leaf spring
Bodyframe: Monocoque
Transmission: 4-speed manual
Weight: 1433kgs

PRICE GUIDE

Launch price: £1261
Excellent: £4000
Good: £3000
Average: £1500
Project: £475

HUMBER Super Snipe I-VA

As was Rootes' way, the final generation of Humber Super Snipe continued with the practice of using the less powerful, less luxurious Hawk as its basis, but giving it more power (and two more cylinders) plus some extra class-conscious touches. The original 1958 Series Super Snipes had a 2651cc six-cylinder engine, this rose to 2965cc the following year. For 1960 the nose was smartly restyled with quad-headlamps, one of the first British cars to have this arrangement and something never bestowed upon the Hawk. The final Super Snipes were built in 1967.

SPECIFICATIONS

Years produced: 1958-1967 (30,031 in total)
Performance: 0-60mph: 19.0 secs (Top speed: 92mph)
Power & torque: 105bhp / N/A
Engine: Normally aspirated 2651cc in-line six, petrol, carburettor, 12 valves
Drivetrain: Front-engine RWD
Suspension: (F) Independent, coil spring. (R) Live axle, semi-elliptic leaf spring
Bodyframe: Monocoque
Transmission: 3-speed manual with overdrive
Weight: 1492kgs

PRICE GUIDE

Launch price: £1494
Excellent: £5000
Good: £4000
Average: £1800
Project: £500

HUMBER
Sceptre SI-II

Rootes introduced a new range of mid-sized cars in the early 1960s. At the top of this badge engineering tree, which also comprised the Hillman Super Minx and Singer Vogue, was the Humber Sceptre. More sporty than usual for a Humber – originally, the Sceptre was to be the new Sunbeam Rapier – the shell was considerably altered from the other offshoots with a wraparound screen, quad-headlamps and a lowered roofline. The Series II of 1965 saw Rootes' well-liked 1725cc engine adopted, albeit with a cheaper Hillman-influenced nose.

SPECIFICATIONS

Years produced:	1963-1967 (28,996 in total)
Performance:	0-60mph: 17.1 secs (Top speed: 90mph)
Power & torque:	80bhp / 91lb/ft
Engine:	Normally aspirated 1592cc in-line four, petrol, carburettor, 8 valves
Drivetrain:	Front-engine RWD
Suspension:	(F) Independent, coil spring. (R) Live axle, semi-elliptic leaf spring
Bodyframe:	Monocoque
Transmission:	4-speed manual
Weight:	1124kgs
PRICE GUIDE	
Launch price:	£977
Excellent:	£3250
Good:	£2500
Average:	£1200
Project:	£450

HUMBER
Sceptre SIII

Rootes, by now owned by the American Chrysler Corporation, swept away all their old models in 1966 and 1967 and replaced them with the Arrow range, personified by the Hillman Hunter and Avenger. The Series III Sceptre was an upmarket Hunter, with a quad-headlamp nose, vinyl roof, fancy wheeltrims and a side order of wood veneer inside. Coupled with this was an uprated 1725cc engine of 88bhp with overdrive as standard. It may have been badge engineering, but the additional touches did much to make the Humber desirable.

SPECIFICATIONS

Years produced:	1967-1976 (43,951 in total)
Performance:	0-60mph: 13.1 secs (Top speed: 98mph)
Power & torque:	79bhp / 91lb/ft
Engine:	Normally aspirated 1725cc in-line four, petrol, carburettor, 8 valves
Drivetrain:	Front-engine RWD
Suspension:	(F) Ind. coil spring, lower wishbone, anti-roll bar. (R) Live axle, leaf spring
Bodyframe:	Monocoque
Transmission:	4-speed manual with overdrive
Weight:	992kgs
PRICE GUIDE	
Launch price:	£1139
Excellent:	£2500
Good:	£1850
Average:	£1000
Project:	£300

ISO
Rivolta

The Rivolta was an example of the Italo-American breed that proved popular during the 1960s and '70s and which allowed drivers to sample Ferrari-style glamour and performance without the price. The Rivolta had all the credentials to deliver the goods: Giugiaro styling; Bizzarini chassis and a 140mph top speed from its General Motors-sourced V8. Under the skin its box-section frame with de Dion rear suspension was a recipe for success, and indeed, the Rivolta sold nearly 800 examples during its eight-year production run.

SPECIFICATIONS

Years produced:	1962-1970 (797 in total)
Performance:	0-60mph: 7.8 secs (Top speed: 135mph)
Power & torque:	300bhp / 360lb/ft
Engine:	Normally aspirated 5354cc V8, petrol, carburettor, 16 valves
Drivetrain:	Front-engine RWD
Suspension:	(F) Independent, wishbone, coil spring, anti-roll bar. (R) de Dion axle, coil spring
Bodyframe:	Chassis and separate body
Transmission:	4-speed manual
Weight:	1549kgs
PRICE GUIDE	
Launch price:	£3999
Excellent:	£25,000
Good:	£20,000
Average:	£14,000
Project:	£9000

ISO
Grifo

Continuing the Iso formula, the Grifo was another appealing 'bitza' that transcended the sum of its parts to become something of a supercar pacesetter. The Corvette power unit was good for 300bhp and gave the sleek Bertone bodied grand tourer a 150mph plus top speed with acceleration to match. Considered very much a rich playboy's supercar, the Grifo had the handling and poise to cut it against Ferrari, Maserati and Lamborghini's finest. Survival rate is reasonably good, although you'll struggle to find an unrestored car.

SPECIFICATIONS

Years produced:	1963-1974 (322 in total)
Performance:	0-60mph: 7.0 secs (Top speed: 143mph)
Power & torque:	300bhp / 360lb/ft
Engine:	Normally aspirated 5354cc V8, petrol, carburettor, 16 valves
Drivetrain:	Front-engine RWD
Suspension:	(F) Independent, wishbone, coil spring, anti-roll bar. (R) de Dion axle, coil spring
Bodyframe:	Chassis and separate body
Transmission:	4-speed manual
Weight:	1450kgs
PRICE GUIDE	
Launch price:	£5950
Excellent:	£75,000
Good:	£60,000
Average:	£45,000
Project:	£30,000

ISO
Grifo 7-Litre

Although it was no slouch Iso decided that the standard Grifo needed a shot of additional power to get on terms with the Ferrari Daytona and Maserati Ghibli. This was duly delivered thanks to a 7-litre (427ci) engine delivering no less than 390bhp. By 1968 supercar standards this was serious stuff and pushed Iso to the head of the pack. Top speed was a claimed 170mph and 0-60mph was around six seconds – quick even by today's standards. However, the Grifo disappeared off the new car price lists when Iso went out of business in 1974.

SPECIFICATIONS

Years produced:	1969-1974 (90 in total)
Performance:	0-60mph: 6.1 secs (Top speed: 171mph)
Power & torque:	390bhp / 460lb/ft
Engine:	Normally aspirated 6999cc V8, petrol, carburettor, 16 valves
Drivetrain:	Front-engine RWD
Suspension:	(F) Ind. coil spring, wishbone. (R) de Dion beam, coil spring, Watt linkage
Bodyframe:	Chassis and separate body
Transmission:	4-speed manual
Weight:	1410kgs
PRICE GUIDE	
Launch price:	£8700
Excellent:	£80,000
Good:	£65,000
Average:	£50,000
Project:	£35,000

ISO
Lele

Iso believed in platform sharing so it's understandable that the underpinnings used for the Grifo and Fidia were also put to good use when concocting a replacement for the Rivolta. Unlike the original car the Lele failed to impress buyers who were turned off by the clumsy Gandini styled coupé. Given that the 1973 oil crisis killed supercar sales stone dead, struggling Iso didn't have enough in the cupboard to ride the storm – disappearing from view in 1974. The last few Leles were powered by a Ford V8 and offered with automatic transmission.

SPECIFICATIONS

Years produced:	1969-1974 (317 in total)
Performance:	0-60mph: 7.3 secs (Top speed: 155mph)
Power & torque:	350bhp / 361lb/ft
Engine:	Normally aspirated 5358cc V8, petrol, carburettor, 16 valves
Drivetrain:	Front-engine RWD
Suspension:	(F) Independent, wishbone, coil spring, anti-roll bar. (R) de Dion axle, coil spring
Bodyframe:	Chassis and separate body
Transmission:	4-speed manual
Weight:	1640kg
	PRICE GUIDE
Launch price:	£7725
Excellent:	£20,000
Good:	£15,000
Average:	£10,000
Project:	£5000

JAGUAR
1.5 Litre Saloon

The entry level model in a threesome of elegant saloons that would go a very long way towards cementing Jaguar's position as the pre-eminent producer of sporting four-doors. Despite its modest engine capacity, the 1.5 Litre was quick enough to justify its styling. Introduced on the eve of world war two, and brought back shortly afterwards, its technical specification didn't look that advanced (a rigid axle was no great shakes by 1945), but the whole exceeded the sum of the parts. Values are modest considering their place in Jaguar's history.

SPECIFICATIONS

Years produced:	1938-1949 (13,046 in total)
Performance:	0-60mph: 25.1 secs (Top speed: 72mph)
Power & torque:	65bhp / 97lb/ft
Engine:	Normally aspirated 1776cc in-line four, petrol, carburettor, 8 valves
Drivetrain:	Front-engine RWD
Suspension:	(F) Feam axle, semi-elliptic leaf spring. (R) Beam axle, semi-elliptic leaf spring
Bodyframe:	Chassis and separate body
Transmission:	4-speed manual
Weight:	1346kgs
	PRICE GUIDE
Launch price:	£684
Excellent:	£15,000
Good:	£12,500
Average:	£7500
Project:	£3500

JAGUAR
3.5 Litre Saloon/DHC

Rather like the 1.5 Litre Jaguar, but with rather a lot more power on tap, the 3.5 really was the first of the new generation Jaguar saloons with the pace to back up its looks. The performance was impressive for a saloon car, especially for a pre-war car, thanks in no small part to the 125bhp it pushed out. Most of these cars ended up being exported, and as a result, these cars are scarce, but despite this, values lag behind the more illustrious sports cars – although the beautiful drophead version has been steadily rising in recent years.

SPECIFICATIONS

Years produced:	1938-1951 (14,215 in total)
Performance:	0-60mph: 14.7 secs (Top speed: 92mph)
Power & torque:	125bhp / 136lb/ft
Engine:	Normally aspirated 3485cc in-line six, petrol, carburettor, 12 valves
Drivetrain:	front-engine RWD
Suspension:	(F) Beam axle, semi-elliptic leaf spring. (R) Beam axle, semi-elliptic leaf spring
Bodyframe:	chassis and separate body
Transmission:	4-speed manual
Weight:	1626kgs
	PRICE GUIDE
Launch price:	£889
Excellent:	£22,000
Good:	£18,000
Average:	£11,500
Project:	£6000

JAGUAR
2.5-litre/Mark V Sal/DHC

The first genuinely new post-war Jaguar saloon, although it was actually a bit of a stop-gap between the pre-war cars and the all-new metal on the horizon. The sweeping bodywork was all-new, but quite similar to what came before, while the chassis would go on to be used to underpin all of Jaguar's '50s range of saloons. Independent front suspension finally made an appearance, bringing the Mark V in line with its rivals, and improving road manners. Limited production run – especially the drophead – means finding the right one takes time.

SPECIFICATIONS

Years produced:	1946-1951 (8905 in total)
Performance:	0-60mph: 17 secs (Top speed: 87mph)
Power & torque:	125bhp / N/A
Engine:	Normally aspirated 2663cc in-line six, petrol, carburettor, 12 valves
Drivetrain:	Front-engine RWD
Suspension:	(F) Independent torsion bar. (R) Beam axle, semi-elliptic leaf springs
Bodyframe:	Chassis and separate body
Transmission:	4-speed manual
Weight:	1676kgs
	PRICE GUIDE
Launch price:	£1189
Excellent:	£18,000
Good:	£15,000
Average:	£8500
Project:	£4250

JAGUAR
XK120

Quite simply, the XK120 was the sports car that elevated Jaguar into the big time. Introduced at the 1948 Earls Court Motor Show, featured an all-new straight-six twin-overhead camshaft engine that lived well into the '80s. Performance was excellent (the 120mph maximum speed was the reason for its name). However, the XK120's real forté was its sheer all-round driving pleasure for such a low price. The earliest aluminium roadsters are easily the most valuable, with SEs commanding a premium, and the later Drophead Coupés not far behind.

SPECIFICATIONS

Years produced:	1948-1954 (7612 in total)
Performance:	0-60mph: 10.1 secs (Top speed: 120mph)
Power & torque:	190bhp / 200lb/ft
Engine:	Normally aspirated 3442cc in-line six, petrol, carburettor, 12 valves
Drivetrain:	Front-engine RWD
Suspension:	(F) Independent, torsion bar, wishbone, anti-roll bar. (R) Beam axle
Bodyframe:	Chassis and separate body
Transmission:	4-speed manual
Weight:	1346kgs
	PRICE GUIDE
Launch price:	£1263
Excellent:	£47,500
Good:	£37,500
Average:	£22,500
Project:	£12,750

JAGUAR
XK120 FH Coupé

Once Jaguar had caught up with XK120 Roadster demand and production of steel-bodied examples was running smoothly, it developed the coupé to widen appeal. Aside from the obvious addition of a roof, the biggest difference between this and the Roadster is the use of a floorpan, mostly in steel, in place of plywood. As with all XK120s there was an SE option, which added 20bhp through the use of high-lift cams, plus uprated valve springs and a lightened flywheel. Wire wheels were fitted to SEs, and were a popular retro-fit on non-SE models.

SPECIFICATIONS

Years produced:	1951-1954 (2678 in total)
Performance:	0-60mph: 9.9 secs (Top speed: 120mph)
Power & torque:	160bhp / 195lb/ft
Engine:	Normally aspirated 3442cc in-line six, petrol, carburettor, 12 valves
Drivetrain:	Front-engine RWD
Suspension:	(F) Independent, torsion bar, wishbone, anti-roll bar. (R) Beam axle
Bodyframe:	Chassis and separate body
Transmission:	4-speed manual
Weight:	1143kgs
	PRICE GUIDE
Launch price:	£1389
Excellent:	£47,500
Good:	£37,500
Average:	£22,500
Project:	£12,750

JAGUAR
C-type

Based on the XK120, the C-type actually started out being referred to as the 120C, but the quickly applied nickname has stuck. The body, crafted by Malcolm Sayer, is completely different, considerably lighter thanks to its spaceframe chassis. Chassis featured torsion bars front and rear, the steering was by rack-and-pinion, and brakes were discs. The C-type's competition successes are legendary, with two victories at Le Mans (1951 and 1953) being the crowning glory. C-types rarely come up for sale, and attract considerable interest when they do.

SPECIFICATIONS

Years produced:	1951-1953 (54 in total)
Performance:	0-60mph: 8.1 secs (Top speed: 150mph)
Power & torque:	200bhp / 220lb/ft
Engine:	3442cc in-line six, petrol, carb. 12 valves
Drivetrain:	Front engine RWD
Suspension:	(F) Ind. via wishbone and torsion bar, tele.dampers, anti-roll bar. (R) Live axle suspended on trailing links
Bodyframe:	Spaceframe
Transmission:	4-speed manual
Weight:	939kgs
	PRICE GUIDE
Launch price:	£2327
Excellent:	£2,000,000
Good:	£1,500,000
Average:	£1,000,000
Project:	£750,000

JAGUAR
Mark VII-IX

Jaguar's post-war run of desirable and capable large saloons was truly kick-started with the arrival of the Mark VII in 1950. Although similar under the skin to the outgoing Mark V, the newer car's forward-looking styling and use of the XK engine, first seen in the XK120, meant the Mark VII was a genuine 100mph proposition. Subsequent revisions refined the big saloon and added even more power into the mix. Easy to find now, and not excessively expensive, the Mark VII-IX saloons lack the cult following of later cars but drive just as well.

SPECIFICATIONS

Years produced:	1951-1961 (47,190 in total)
Performance:	0-60mph: 13.6 secs (Top speed: 104mph)
Power & torque:	160bhp / 195lb/ft
Engine:	3442cc in-line six, petrol, carb. 12 valves
Drivetrain:	front-engine RWD
Suspension:	(F) Independent by wishbones, torsion bar, hydraulic dampers, anti-roll bar. (R) Beam axle, semi-elliptic leaf spring
Bodyframe:	Chassis and separate body
Transmission:	4-speed manual/3-speed automatic
Weight:	1753kgs
	PRICE GUIDE
Launch price:	£1276
Excellent:	£18,000
Good:	£15,000
Average:	£8000
Project:	£3500

JAGUAR
XK140 FHC

Introduced as a replacement to the XK120, the XK140 was a slightly bigger and heavier, but more powerful, car. These characteristics changed the whole driving experience, and rather than being an uncompromised sports car, it was a much more comfortable and relaxed long distance cruiser – unless you were in the coupé's tight rear seats. Upgrades included the standard fitment of rack and pinion steering (from the C-type) as well as optional power assisted steering. Coupés are worth less than roadsters, but are still very satisfying to drive.

SPECIFICATIONS

Years produced:	1954-57 (2808 in total)
Performance:	0-60mph: 8.4 secs (Top speed: 121mph)
Power & torque:	210bhp / 213lb/ft
Engine:	Normally aspirated 3442cc in-line six, petrol, carburettor, 12 valves
Drivetrain:	Front-engine RWD
Suspension:	(F) Independent torsion bar. (R) Beam axle, semi-elliptic leaf spring
Bodyframe:	Chassis and separate body
Transmission:	4-speed manual with overdrive
Weight:	1422kgs
	PRICE GUIDE
Launch price:	£1616
Excellent:	£37,500
Good:	£32,500
Average:	£19,000
Project:	£11,000

JAGUAR
XK140 Roadster

The additional weight of the XK140 over the XK120 was the most evident in the Roadster version. The older car was an unashamed sports car, while its replacement was softer and much more refined – no doubt a deliberate ploy to appeal to American customers. Some sold in Special Equipment form with C-type cylinder head and 210bhp, turning this car into a much more sporting prospect, and the perfect outside lane weapon for Britain's new motorway age. Worth rather less than the XK120, but the more intelligent choice for aficionados.

SPECIFICATIONS

Years produced:	1954-1957 (3354 in total)
Performance:	0-60mph: 8.4 secs (Top speed: 125mph)
Power & torque:	190bhp / 210lb/ft
Engine:	Normally aspirated 3442cc in-line six, petrol, carburettor, 12 valves
Drivetrain:	Front-engine RWD
Suspension:	(F) Independent torsion bar. (R) Beam axle, semi-elliptic leaf spring
Bodyframe:	Chassis and separate body
Transmission:	4-speed manual with overdrive
Weight:	1422kgs
	PRICE GUIDE
Launch price:	£1598
Excellent:	£50,000
Good:	£42,500
Average:	£25,000
Project:	£14,500

JAGUAR
XK140 DHC

Though similar in appearance to their predecessors, the XK140s came with a lot of small but significant differences. All are easily distinguished by their new seven-bar grilles and one-piece bumpers. The Drophead Coupé added a pair of rear seats, although they were of little use for anything other than small children. The Drophead Coupé was intelligently re-packaged – the battery was relocated behind the front wing, and the cockpit was shifted three inches forward. Well-priced compared with other XK Roadsters.

SPECIFICATIONS

Years produced:	1954-1957 (2889 in total)
Performance:	0-60mph: 11.0 secs (Top speed: 129mph)
Power & torque:	190bhp / 207lb/ft
Engine:	Normally aspirated 3442cc in-line six, petrol, carburettor, 12 valves
Drivetrain:	Front-engine RWD
Suspension:	(F) Independent, torsion bar, wishbone, anti-roll bar. (R) Beam axle
Bodyframe:	Chassis and separate body
Transmission:	4-speed manual
Weight:	1346kgs
	PRICE GUIDE
Launch price:	£1609
Excellent:	£45,000
Good:	£36,000
Average:	£21,000
Project:	£12,000

JAGUAR
MkI 2.4

The starting point in Jaguar's move into the compact sporting saloon market, even if from behind the wheel of an original 2.4 you'd be hard pushed to believe it, thanks to sluggish performance. Just like the D-type, the 2.4 featured unitary construction; the first roadgoing Jaguar to do so. The detuned, short-stroke 2.4-litre XK engine didn't tax the independent suspension set-up too much, but with overdrive, it was a restful cruiser. All-disc brakes and automatic transmission were offered in 1957, but today, the 2.4 is still seen as the runt of the litter.

SPECIFICATIONS

Years produced:	1955-1959 (19,992 in total)
Performance:	0-60mph: 14.4 secs (Top speed: 102mph)
Power & torque:	112bhp / 140lb/ft
Engine:	Normally aspirated 2483cc in-line six, petrol, carburettor, 12 valves
Drivetrain:	Front-engine RWD
Suspension:	(F) Independent coil spring. (R) Beam axle, half (semi)-elliptic leaf spring
Bodyframe:	Monocoque
Transmission:	4sp man, overdrive option. 3sp auto
Weight:	1372kgs
	PRICE GUIDE
Launch price:	£1344
Excellent:	£12,500
Good:	£9500
Average:	£5000
Project:	£2250

JAGUAR
MkI 3.4

Although the 2.4 was a significant car in Jaguar's evolution, the compact sporting saloon concept really came to life when the Coventry engineers crammed in the 3.4-litre engine from the XK140. Combined with the curvaceous styling and reasonably commodious interior, the potent 3.4-litre engine delivered performance previously reserved for the sports car sector. The 3.4 was launched as a sister car to the 2.4 and featured a wider grille, cutaway spats. Despite a higher price, the 3.4 sold nearly as many examples during its two-year run.

SPECIFICATIONS

Years produced:	1957-1959 (17,405 in total)
Performance:	0-60mph: 9.1 secs (Top speed: 120mph)
Power & torque:	210bhp / 216lb/ft
Engine:	Normally aspirated 3442cc in-line six, petrol, carburettor, 12 valves
Drivetrain:	Front-engine RWD
Suspension:	(F) Independent coil spring. (R) Beam axle, semi-elliptic leaf spring
Bodyframe:	Monocoque
Transmission:	4sp manual, overdrive option. 3sp auto
Weight:	1448kgs
	PRICE GUIDE
Launch price:	£1672
Excellent:	£16,000
Good:	£12,000
Average:	£7000
Project:	£2750

JAGUAR
XK150 3.4 FHC

At 1364kg, the XK150 was not the lightweight sports car the XK120 had once been. Certain aluminium panels were added to try and reduce the overall weight, but it still tipped the scales at 50kg more than the XK140. It was the first Jaguar available with all-round disc brakes. In 1958, the XK150S was launched. The uprated car came with an impressive 250bhp at first, then 265bhp a year later when the capacity increased to 3.8 litres. A limited-slip differential was needed to handle the extra power. A 3.4S is worth an extra 15%.

SPECIFICATIONS

Years produced:	1957-1961 (4450 in total)
Performance:	0-60mph: 8.5 secs (Top speed: 124mph)
Power & torque:	250bhp / 240lb/ft
Engine:	Normally aspirated 3442cc in-line six, petrol, carburettor, 12 valves
Drivetrain:	Front-engine RWD
Suspension:	(F) Independent, torsion bar. (R) Beam axle, semi-elliptic leaf spring
Bodyframe:	Monocoque
Transmission:	4-speed manual with overdrive
Weight:	1447kgs
	PRICE GUIDE
Launch price:	£1764
Excellent:	£36,500
Good:	£32,000
Average:	£18,500
Project:	£11,000

JAGUAR
XK150 Roadster

The Roadster differs from previous such XKs in having wind-up windows, though the hood is still quite rudimentary compared with the Drophead's. There's also a significant difference between these and other XK150s: the deletion of rear seats allowed the cockpit to be moved back four inches, so the Roadster has a correspondingly longer bonnet. Most came with 3.4-litre engines, but the 3.8 was added in 1959. Both had 'S' performance versions with an extra carburettor among other things. Add 12% for 3.4S prices and 30% for a 3.8S.

SPECIFICATIONS

Years produced:	1958-1960 (2263 in total)
Performance:	0-60mph: 7.9 secs (Top speed: 136mph)
Power & torque:	250bhp / 237lb/ft
Engine:	Normally aspirated 3442cc in-line six, petrol, carburettor, 12 valves
Drivetrain:	Front-engine RWD
Suspension:	(F) Independent, torsion bar. (R) Beam axle, semi-elliptic leaf spring
Bodyframe:	Chassis and separate body
Transmission:	4-speed manual
Weight:	1432kgs
	PRICE GUIDE
Launch price:	£1764
Excellent:	£50,000
Good:	£40,000
Average:	£26,000
Project:	£14,500

JAGUAR Mk2 2.4

Generally speaking, facelift cars don't look as good as the cars they are intended to replace. But Jaguar tore up the form book with the Mk2 saloons which, thanks to William Lyons, was transformed by the fitment of revised upper door pressings and a deeper windscreen as well as widening the rear track. The effect was to brighten the interior and update the overall style, and in doing so, create the most iconic '60s saloon of them all. The 2.4 was still a modest performer, despite an additional 8bhp over the (retrospectively named) Mk1.

SPECIFICATIONS

Years produced: 1959-1967 (83,976 of all Mk2s)
Performance: 0-60mph: 17.3 secs (Top speed: 96mph)
Power & torque: 120bhp / 144lb/ft
Engine: Normally aspirated 2483cc in-line six, petrol, carburettor, 12 valves
Drivetrain: Front-engine RWD
Suspension: (F) Independent, torsion bar. (R) Beam axle, leaf spring
Bodyframe: Monocoque
Transmission: 4-speed manual
Weight: 1448kgs

PRICE GUIDE

Launch price: £1534
Excellent: £15,000
Good: £11,000
Average: £6500
Project: £2500

JAGUAR Mk2 3.4

Previously, the 3.4-litre XK engine had been enough to top the compact saloon range, but all that changed with the arrival of the Mk2. But for 1959, the mid-range car had been significantly improved, thanks to a raft of small, but significant improvements. With more than enough power on board, the adoption of a wider front and rear track improved road manners, optimising a car that was hardly lacking in the first place. Heavier than before, the Mk2's performance was slightly blunted, but that was addressed by the arrival of the 3.8.

SPECIFICATIONS

Years produced: 1959-1967
Performance: 0-60mph: 11.9 secs (Top speed: 120mph)
Power & torque: 210bhp / 216lb/ft
Engine: Normally aspirated 3442cc in-line six, petrol, carburettor, 12 valves
Drivetrain: Front-engine RWD
Suspension: (F) Independent, torsion bar. (R) Beam axle, leaf spring
Bodyframe: Monocoque
Transmission: 4-speed manual
Weight: 1499kgs

PRICE GUIDE

Launch price: £1669
Excellent: £24,000
Good: £17,000
Average: £9000
Project: £4000

JAGUAR Mk2 3.8

The new flagship in the mid-sized saloon line-up certainly proved popular and profitable for Jaguar. But with a 125mph top speed and throttle-adjustable handling, the 3.8 became *the* car of choice for enthusiastic drivers. A limited-slip differential improved traction and controllability, while power assisted steering (a standard fitment from 1960) further improved the way the car drove. Considered the best of all Mk2s and market values reflect this, but some would argue that it's too high a premium for what is in effect a 10bhp upgrade.

SPECIFICATIONS

Years produced: 1959-1967
Performance: 0-60mph: 8.5 secs (Top speed: 125mph)
Power & torque: 220bhp / 240lb/ft
Engine: Normally aspirated 3781cc in-line six, petrol, carburettor, 12 valves
Drivetrain: Front-engine RWD
Suspension: (F) Independent, torsion bar. (R) Beam axle, leaf spring
Bodyframe: Monocoque
Transmission: 4-sp manual, overdrive option., 3-sp auto.
Weight: 1499kgs

PRICE GUIDE

Launch price: £1779
Excellent: £29,000
Good: £20,000
Average: £10,500
Project: £6000

JAGUAR E-type 3.8 FHC

When it exploded onto the automotive landscape in 1961, the E-type effectively redefined the way in which we all viewed sports cars, and how much you could expect for your money. Although the famous 150mph runs in pre-production models were never replicated by owners, the E-type was still fast enough to send supercar manufacturers back to their drawing boards. The recipe was simple enough – a 3.8-litre XK engine married to a beautiful and aerodynamic body designed by Malcolm Sayer, underpinned by all-independent suspension.

SPECIFICATIONS

Years produced: 1961-1964 (46,300 in total)
Performance: 0-60mph: 7.1 secs (Top speed: 149mph)
Power & torque: 265bhp / 260lb/ft
Engine: Normally aspirated 3781cc in-line six, petrol, carburettor, 12 valves
Drivetrain: Front-engine RWD
Suspension: (F) Independent torsion bar. (R) Independent coil spring
Bodyframe: Monocoque
Transmission: 4-speed manual
Weight: 1219kgs

PRICE GUIDE

Launch price: £2098
Excellent: £37,000
Good: £29,500
Average: £17,500
Project: £10,500

JAGUAR E-type 3.8 Roadster

Although the E-type coupé was the fastest and most useful of the breed, it's the Roadster that attracts by far the most attention these days. The underpinnings were well-considered and stiff enough to stave off the worst effects of scuttle shake, and that meant it was just as effective to drive as the Coupé. Hugely popular in the USA as well as Europe, and a high survival rate means that there are still plenty around, and that keeps values lower than they would be had the badge on the bonnet been Italian or German.

SPECIFICATIONS

Years produced: 1961-1974 (46,300 in total)
Performance: 0-60mph: 7.1 secs (Top speed: 149mph)
Power & torque: 265bhp / 260lb/ft
Engine: Normally aspirated 3781cc in-line six, petrol, carburettor, 12 valves
Drivetrain: front-engine RWD
Suspension: (F) Independent torsion bar. (R) Independent coil spring
Bodyframe: Monocoque
Transmission: 4-speed manual
Weight: 1206kgs

PRICE GUIDE

Launch price: £2098
Excellent: £52,000
Good: £44,000
Average: £24,000
Project: £14,000

JAGUAR
S-type

Because the XJ6 was still years away from making it into production, Jaguar decided that it needed an intermediate model to plug the gap between the Mk2 and the enormous MkX. Using the Mk2 as a starting point, the company created the S-type by adding the MkX's Independent rear suspension and extended rear end as well as improving its interior. The end result was a luxury sports saloon which actually drives better than the car it was based upon, extending the life of the Mk2 platform really quite usefully.

SPECIFICATIONS

Years produced:	1963-1968 (24,900 in total)
Performance:	0-60mph: 14.2 secs (Top speed: 114mph)
Power & torque:	210bhp / 216lb/ft
Engine:	Normally aspirated 3442cc in-line six, petrol, carburettor, 12 valves
Drivetrain:	Front-engine RWD
Suspension:	(F) Independent torsion bar (R) Independent coil springs
Bodyframe:	Monocoque
Transmission:	4-spd manual, o/d optional/3-spd auto
Weight:	1626kgs
	PRICE GUIDE
Launch price:	£1669
Excellent:	£17,000
Good:	£10,000
Average:	£4500
Project:	£1500

JAGUAR
E-type S1 4.2 Roadster

Never one to sit on its laurels, Jaguar continued to develop the E-type throughout its life. The first results of this programme of improvements came in 1964, when the newly-enlarged XK engine was installed under the E-type's bonnet. Although the maximum power output remained unchanged at 265bhp, torque was up usefully, improving driveability. Other improvements included the arrival of a fully-synchronised Moss gearbox. Worth slightly more than the 3.8-litre Roadsters because of the improvements.

SPECIFICATIONS

Years produced:	1964-1968 (46,300 in total)
Performance:	0-60mph: 7.4 secs (Top speed: 139mph)
Power & torque:	265bhp / 283lb/ft
Engine:	Normally aspirated 4235cc in-line six, petrol, carburettor, 12 valves
Drivetrain:	Front-engine RWD
Suspension:	(F) Independent torsion bar. (R) Independent coil spring
Bodyframe:	Monocoque
Transmission:	4-speed manual
Weight:	1295kgs
	PRICE GUIDE
Launch price:	£1896
Excellent:	£52,500
Good:	£45,000
Average:	£25,000
Project:	£14,000

JAGUAR
E-type S1 4.2 Coupé

Despite the additional torque from the 4.2-litre XK engine, 150mph remained an elusive target for those owners lucky enough to have access to de-restricted motorways. But despite being limited to a top speed of 'only' 149mph, the E-type in 4.2-litre form remained a long way ahead of the opposition – cars that could match its speed were far more expensive; while similarly priced sports cars wouldn't have seen which way it went. The 4.2 actually felt more grown up to drive, with its lower redline, prompting some to say the zest had gone.

SPECIFICATIONS

Years produced:	1964-1968 (10,930 in total)
Performance:	0-60mph: 7.4 secs (Top speed: 149mph)
Power & torque:	265bhp / 283lb/ft
Engine:	Normally aspirated 4235cc in-line six, petrol, carburettor, 12 valves
Drivetrain:	Front-engine RWD
Suspension:	(F) Independent torsion bar (R) Independent coil springs
Bodyframe:	Monocoque
Transmission:	4-speed manual
Weight:	1410kgs
	PRICE GUIDE
Launch price:	£2245
Excellent:	£37,500
Good:	£30,000
Average:	£17,500
Project:	£10,500

JAGUAR
E-type S1 2+2

Despite its global success and ringing accolades, Jaguar knew that E-type sales were being held back by the limitations of a two-seater. Enter the 2+2, created by extending the wheelbase and cabin by nine inches to make room for kids in the back. There's also a taller, more upright windscreen. And unlike some other two-plus-twos, you can actually get people with legs in there, as long as the driver isn't tall. The car was an instant sales success, outselling the fixed-head coupé from day one. An affordable way into E-type ownership.

SPECIFICATIONS

Years produced:	1966-1967 (5600 in total)
Performance:	0-60mph: 8.9 secs (Top speed: 136mph)
Power & torque:	256bhp / 280lb/ft
Engine:	Normally aspirated 4325cc in-line six, petrol, carburettor, 12 valves
Drivetrain:	Front-engine RWD
Suspension:	(F) Independent torsion bar (R) Independent coil springs
Bodyframe:	Metal monocoque
Transmission:	3-speed automatic
Weight:	1401kgs
	PRICE GUIDE
Launch price:	£2245
Excellent:	£23,500
Good:	£18,000
Average:	£13,000
Project:	£7500

JAGUAR
420

The Jaguar 420 was basically an S-type, with the 4.2-litre version of the XK engine fitted. The front end was completely restyled, previewing the upcoming XJ6 (as well as aping the 420G), and although it looked slightly unbalanced, there was no question over the way the 420 went. By the time of its launch in 1968, the Mk1/Mk2 platform had been stretched as far as possible in an attempt to maintain sales. The interior was further improved with the arrival of a padded fascia top, the first move towards the safety-led designs that followed.

SPECIFICATIONS

Years produced:	1966-1968 (9600 in total)
Performance:	0-60mph: 9.9 secs (Top speed: 123mph)
Power & torque:	245bhp / 283lb/ft
Engine:	Normally aspirated 4235cc in-line six, petrol, carburettor, 12 valves
Drivetrain:	Front-engine RWD
Suspension:	(F) Independent torsion bar (R) Independent coil springs
Bodyframe:	Metal monocoque
Transmission:	4-spd manual, o/d optional, 3-spd auto
Weight:	1676kgs
	PRICE GUIDE
Launch price:	£1930
Excellent:	£11,500
Good:	£8500
Average:	£4000
Project:	£1400

JAGUAR
240

After a good innings, the Mk2 was finally facelifted in 1967 to become the 240/340. These models were priced usefully below the outgoing cars, and evidence of cost-cutting was most notable inside, where leather gave way to lower-grade Ambla. Despite its popularity in the Mk2, power assisted steering wasn't even offered as an option in the 240, making the car feel a lot more ponderous than it needed to. The engine was upgraded with a 4.2-style cylinder head, and that finally gave it enough power to break the 100mph barrier.

SPECIFICATIONS

Years produced: 1967-1969 (6840 in total)
Performance: 0-60mph: 12.5 secs (Top speed: 106mph)
Power & torque: 133bhp / 146lb/ft
Engine: Normally aspirated 2483cc in-line six, petrol, carburettor, 12 valves
Drivetrain: Front-engine RWD
Suspension: (F) Independent coil spring. (R) Beam axle, leaf spring
Bodyframe: Metal monocoque
Transmission: 4-speed manual O/D/3-speed auto
Weight: 1448kgs

PRICE GUIDE

Launch price: £1365
Excellent: £12,500
Good: £9500
Average: £5000
Project: £2500

JAGUAR
340

With the XJ6 still a couple of years from production, the 240/340 ended up serving run-out duties for the Mk2 line for longer than anyone it Coventry would have hoped. But despite its advancing years, the 340 was still a car of great ability and proved a hit with buyers. With the same 210bhp engine as before, all of the performance that attracted buyers to the 3.4-litre Mk2 was there, but in a lower-priced package. Today, values lag behind the earlier cars because of their cost-constrained interiors, so for canny buyers, the 340 is a worthwhile purchase.

SPECIFICATIONS

Years produced: 1967-1969 (6840 in total)
Performance: 0-60mph: 8.8 secs (Top speed: 115mph)
Power & torque: 210bhp / 216lb/ft
Engine: Normally aspirated 3442cc in-line six, petrol, carburettor, 12 valves
Drivetrain: Front-engine RWD
Suspension: (F) Independent coil spring. (R) Beam axle, leaf spring
Bodyframe: Metal monocoque
Transmission: 4-speed manual O/D/3-speed auto
Weight: 1524kgs

PRICE GUIDE

Launch price: £1442
Excellent: £16,500
Good: £13,000
Average: £6500
Project: £3500

JAGUAR
E-type S1½/S2 Roadster

The Series 1.5 was, as the name suggests, a bridge between the SI and S2. Only current for a year, its main role seems to have been introducing the new style headlamps with no covers but more chrome trim. They may not have looked so good but they worked better. The S2 brought more significant changes, like the larger grille opening, heavier front bumpers and bigger light units. Mechanical changes were limited to an improved cooling system and (thank goodness!) better brakes, changed from Lockheed to Girling. Power steering was an option.

SPECIFICATIONS

Years produced: 1967-1970 (8630 in total)
Performance: 0-60mph: 7.4 secs (Top speed: 149mph)
Power & torque: 265bhp / 283lb/ft
Engine: Normally aspirated 4235cc in-line six, petrol, carburettor, 12 valves
Drivetrain: Front-engine RWD
Suspension: (F) Independent torsion bar. (R) Independent coil spring
Bodyframe: Metal monocoque
Transmission: 4-speed manual
Weight: 1295kgs

PRICE GUIDE

Launch price: £2117
Excellent: £42,000
Good: £35,000
Average: £20,000
Project: £11,000

JAGUAR
E-type S1½/2 2+2

With their uncovered headlamps and less desirable body shape, these 2+2s are now the entry level E-type – one you can buy for MGA money. And it has been pointed out that while it doesn't match up to Jaguar's coupé or roadster, it may still be the third best looking car in the world. One significant change over the previous 2+2 model was a new windscreen. The base of this was moved as far as the bulkhead and would allow more rake to the screen, improving aerodynamics. Because of the greater weight 2+2s were fitted with stiffer front torsion bars.

SPECIFICATIONS

Years produced: 1968-1970 (5330 in total)
Performance: 0-60mph: 8.9 secs (Top speed: 137mph)
Power & torque: 265bhp / 280lb/ft
Engine: Normally aspirated 4235cc in-line six, petrol, carburettor, 12 valves
Drivetrain: Front-engine RWD
Suspension: (F) Independent torsion bar. (R) Independent coil spring
Bodyframe: Metal monocoque
Transmission: 4-speed manual
Weight: 1401kgs

PRICE GUIDE

Launch price: £2284
Excellent: £21,500
Good: £17,500
Average: £12,000
Project: £7000

JAGUAR
E-type S1½/2 Coupé

Featuring all the changes made to the Roadsters, the main point of note about this series of coupés is that they are the rarest model of all the E-types. Not that that makes them any more valuable in this case. Having lost sales to the 2+2, fewer than 5000 were built, and the writing was on the wall for the shorter wheelbase coupé body style. The wire wheel locating nuts lost their 'ears' from March 1969 for safety legislation reasons, though as they are more aesthetically pleasing, you may find that eared spinners have been substituted at some point.

SPECIFICATIONS

Years produced: 1968-1970 (4860 in total)
Performance: 0-60mph: 7.1 secs (Top speed: 150mph)
Power & torque: 265bhp / 280lb/ft
Engine: Normally aspirated 4235cc in-line six, petrol, carburettor, 12 valves
Drivetrain: Front-engine RWD
Suspension: (F) Independent torsion bar. (R) Independent coil spring
Bodyframe: Metal monocoque
Transmission: 4-speed manual
Weight: 1407kgs

PRICE GUIDE

Launch price: £2117
Excellent: £31,000
Good: £25,000
Average: £15,000
Project: £9250

JAGUAR XJ6 SI 2.8

This was the first generation of the very successful XJ model range, and introduced a new platform strategy that saw a single range replace the mixed bag of previous models. The Series I XJ6 was not an entirely new car, but it was designed to reinvent the Jaguar brand, still echoing the important values of previous models, but moving it forwards. The XJ came with fully independent suspension all-round for a world-beating suspension set-up, as well as the well-travelled XK engine. In 2.8-litre form, it lacked urge, and wasn't free from reliability issues.

SPECIFICATIONS

Years produced: 1968-1973
Performance: 0-60mph: 11.3 secs (Top speed: 117mph)
Power & torque: 140bhp / 150lb/ft
Engine: Normally aspirated 2792cc in-line six, petrol, carburettor, 12 valves
Drivetrain: Front-engine RWD
Suspension: (F) Independent coil spring. (R) Independent, coil spring
Bodyframe: Metal monocoque
Transmission: 4-spd manual with overdrive/3-spd auto
Weight: 1537kgs

PRICE GUIDE

Launch price: £1797
Excellent: £5000
Good: £4000
Average: £1750
Project: £600

JAGUAR XJ6 SI 4.2

The optimum Jaguar XJ came with the XK engine in 4.2-litre form, and once again proved that Browns Lane was capable of producing the best affordable saloon in the world. Unlike the 2.8-litre version, of which few survive, the 4.2-litre XJ in Series I form was popular with buyers and has a good survival rate today. It's easy to see why, as the ride quality and interior comfort are astounding, and the roadholding is tenacious. Rust is a significant issue, though, and few unrestored cars remain. The best examples are now appreciating rapidly.

SPECIFICATIONS

Years produced: 1968-1973 (59,077 in total)
Performance: 0-60mph: 8.8 secs (Top speed: 124mph)
Power & torque: 245bhp / 280lb/ft
Engine: Normally aspirated 4235cc in-line six, petrol, carburettor, 12 valves
Drivetrain: Front-engine RWD
Suspension: (F) Independent coil spring. (R) Independent coil spring
Bodyframe: Metal monocoque
Transmission: 4-speed manual/3-speed automatic
Weight: 1537kgs

PRICE GUIDE

Launch price: £1797
Excellent: £6750
Good: £5500
Average: £2250
Project: £750

JAGUAR E-type S3 V12 2+2

Walter Hassan, one of Britain's pre-eminent post-war engineers, and mastermind behind the Coventry Climax Formula One engines worked with Harry Mundy to produce an all-new V12. As Jaguar's first production V12, the flat-head single overhead camshaft design was designed for maximum smoothness. When fitted in the E-type, the turbine-smooth V12 was hailed an immediate success, especially in the USA, where it was aimed at. Maxumum speed was still shy of 150mph, though, and fuel consumption was attrocious.

SPECIFICATIONS

Years produced: 1971-1975 (10,930 in total)
Performance: 0-60mph: 7.4 secs (Top speed: 139mph)
Power & torque: 265bhp / 283lb/ft
Engine: Normally aspirated 4235cc in-line six, petrol, carburettor, 12 valves
Drivetrain: Front-engine RWD
Suspension: (F) Independent torsion bar. (R) Independent coil spring
Bodyframe: Metal monocoque
Transmission: 4-speed manual/3-speed auto
Weight: 1410kgs

PRICE GUIDE

Launch price: £2245
Excellent: £26,000
Good: £21,000
Average: £11,500
Project: £7000

JAGUAR E-type S3 V12 Roadster

Although it's been criticised for being too much of a tourer, and not enough of a sports car, the E-type Series III still has massive appeal. The front-end styling with its prominent chrome grille lacks the grace of the earlier cars, and the suspension of these later cars was softer, but as Jaguar was looking towards the American market with, this was on message. The V12 was only 36kg heavier than the straight-six, and handling balance wasn't too drastically affected. In Europe, it became unsaleable overnight in the aftermath of the 1973 energy crisis.

SPECIFICATIONS

Years produced: 1971-1975 (15,290 in total)
Performance: 0-60mph: 6.4 secs (Top speed: 146mph)
Power & torque: 276bhp / 304lb/ft
Engine: Normally aspirated 5343cc V12, petrol, carburettor, 32 valves
Drivetrain: Front-engine RWD
Suspension: (F) Independent torsion bar. (R) Independent coil springs
Bodyframe: Metal monocoque
Transmission: 4-speed manual/3-speed auto
Weight: 1499kgs

PRICE GUIDE

Launch price: £3123
Excellent: £37,500
Good: £32,000
Average: £21,000
Project: £11,000

JAGUAR XJ12 SI-III

Although the Hassan-designed V12 impressed in the E-type Series III, it found its true home in the larger XJ bodyshell. With up to 300bhp in the later versions, it offered dominant performance and up to 150mph in the right circumstances. The XJ12's mechanical smoothness could be its undoing as age and unreliability took hold – engines could drop a cylinder or two without being too noticeable, while the complex suspension set-up could break the odd bush here or there without the driver feeling a thing. Engine and body restorations are expensive.

SPECIFICATIONS

Years produced: 1972-1993 (42,461 in total)
Performance: 0-60mph: 7.4 secs (Top speed: 146mph)
Power & torque: 265bhp / 304lb/ft
Engine: Normally aspirated 5343cc V12, petrol, carburettor, 24 valves
Drivetrain: Front-engine RWD
Suspension: (F) Independent coil spring. (R) Independent coil spring
Bodyframe: Metal monocoque
Transmission: Automatic
Weight: 1760kgs

PRICE GUIDE

Launch price: £3726
Excellent: £7500
Good: £5250
Average: £2200
Project: £750

JAGUAR
XJ 5.3C Coupé

Prematurely announced in the summer of 1973, it would be a further two years before the two-door XJ-C would finally go on sale. The timing wasn't exactly great, though, as at the point it went on sale, the world had been pushed into the midst of a fuel crsis, and then recession, that took the best part of a decade to recover from. A vinyl roof was fitted as standard to all models, and the frameless windows that caused so much trouble during development, were noisy at speed and often leaked. Fuel injection was added later, which caused further problems.

SPECIFICATIONS

Years produced:	1973-1977
Performance:	0-60mph: 7.6 secs (Top speed: 148mph)
Power & torque:	285bhp / 294lb/ft
Engine:	Normally aspirated 5343cc V12, petrol, carburettor, 24 valves
Drivetrain:	Front-engine RWD
Suspension:	(F) Independent coil spring. (R) Independent coil spring
Bodyframe:	Monocoque
Transmission:	3-speed automatic
Weight:	1762kgs
	PRICE GUIDE
Launch price:	£6850
Excellent:	£12,000
Good:	£9000
Average:	£5000
Project:	£1250

JAGUAR
XJ6 Coupé

The V12-powered XJ 5.3 Coupé might have stolen all of the glamour at the launch of the two-door XJ, but the 4.2-litre car was the one that comfortably sold the most. With a 20kg weight advantage over the four-door XJ, acceleration was slightly improved, but cruising really was this car's forté. Sales never met management's expectations, mainly because of the recession, but also because of a rapidly deteriorating reputation on the back of poor build quality during the 1970s. Never made it into Series III form, which hints at unfulfilled potential.

SPECIFICATIONS

Years produced:	1973-1977 (8378 in total)
Performance:	0-60mph: 8.8 secs (Top speed: 124mph)
Power & torque:	173bhp / 227lb/ft
Engine:	Normally aspirated 4235cc in-line six, petrol, carburettor, 12 valves
Drivetrain:	Front-engine RWD
Suspension:	(F) Independent coil spring. (R) Independent coil spring
Bodyframe:	Monocoque
Transmission:	4-spd manual overdrive/3-spd automatic
Weight:	1689kgs
	PRICE GUIDE
Launch price:	£5480
Excellent:	£10,000
Good:	£8000
Average:	£4000
Project:	£1000

JAGUAR
XJ6 S2/S3

Jaguar made many detail improvements to the Jaguar XJ to create the Series II. The new heating and ventilation system was welcome, as was the improved fuel economy thanks to an updated engine. The interior received a substantial update, but the only visual differences externally were the smaller grille and raised bumpers, to help the XJ meet US safety regulations. Unfortunately, the Series II was plagued with poor build quality and reliability issues, and that hit Jaguar's hard-earned reputation for quality.

SPECIFICATIONS

Years produced:	1973-1986
Performance:	0-60mph: 8.8 secs (Top speed: 124mph)
Power & torque:	167bhp / 230lb/ft
Engine:	Normally aspirated 4235cc in-line six, petrol, carburettor, 12 valves
Drivetrain:	Front-engine RWD
Suspension:	(F) Independent coil spring. (R) Independent coil spring
Bodyframe:	Metal monocoque
Transmission:	4-spd manual with overdrive/3-spd auto
Weight:	1680kgs
	PRICE GUIDE
Launch price:	£2253
Excellent:	£5750
Good:	£4000
Average:	£1900
Project:	£650

JAGUAR
XJ-S

Based on a shortened XJ6 chassis, the XJ-S was the long awaited E-type replacement, that ended up missing the mark by several miles, even if it successfully continued in the spirit of the Series III. The new car was not a sporting drive in the way the earlier E-types were, but a more sedate Grand Tourer, with over-light power assisted steering. The XJ-S remained in production for over 20 years – the longest run of any Jaguar – and went on to become a financial success for the company, with the last car coming off the line in 1996.

SPECIFICATIONS

Years produced:	1975-1981
Performance:	0-60mph: 6.9 secs (Top speed: 153mph)
Power & torque:	285bhp / 294lb/ft
Engine:	Normally aspirated 5343cc V12, petrol, electronic fuel injection, 12 valves
Drivetrain:	Front-engine RWD
Suspension:	(F) Independent coil spring. (R) Independent coil spring
Transmission:	5-speed manual/3-speed automatic
Weight:	1770kgs
	PRICE GUIDE
Launch price:	£8900
Excellent:	£5000
Good:	£4000
Average:	£2000
Project:	£500

JAGUAR
XJ-S 5.3 HE

After a lean period in the late-1970s, where at one point, Jaguar actually stopped building XJ-Ss, 1981 saw the beginning of an unprecedented rennaissance for the XJ-S. Swiss engineer, Michael May designed a new high compression cylinder head that not only freed more power from the V12, but significantly improved economy – in real world, an XJ-S would now return 16mpg, rather than 12mpg. Its arrival coincided with an upturn in Jaguar build quality, and dealer service – and vastly improved sales were the result.

SPECIFICATIONS

Years produced: 1981-1985
Performance: 0-60mph: 6.6 secs (Top speed: 151mph)
Power & torque: 295bhp / 318lb/ft
Engine: Normally aspirated 5343cc V12, petrol, electronic fuel injection, 24 valves
Drivetrain: Front-engine RWD
Suspension: (F) Independent coil spring. (R) Independent coil spring
Bodyframe: Monocoque
Transmission: 3-speed automatic
Weight: 1774kgs

PRICE GUIDE

Launch price: £19,187
Excellent: £6000
Good: £4500
Average: £2250
Project: £700

JAGUAR
XJ-SC 3.6 Cabriolet

The launch of a new Jaguar engine isn't exactly a common event, and is usually executed in stages. As is the case when the first V12s were fitted to the E-type sports car, when Jaguar finished its slant-six engine known as the AJ6, it installed it in the XJ-S in 1983 before making it available to saloon car buyers, three years later. The Cabriolet version of the XJ-S was a half-way house to full open-topped motoring, as it retained a heavy (and ugly) roll-over structure, and the coupé's passenger doors. Paved the way for a full convertible in later years.

SPECIFICATIONS

Years produced: 1983-1987
Performance: 0-60mph: 8.7 secs (Top speed: 136mph)
Power & torque: 223bhp / 277lb/ft
Engine: Normally aspirated 3980cc in-line six, petrol, electronic fuel injection, 24 valves
Drivetrain: Front-engine RWD
Suspension: (F) Independent coil spring. (R) Independent coil spring
Bodyframe: Monocoque
Transmission: 5-speed manual/3-speed automatic
Weight: 1611kgs

PRICE GUIDE

Launch price: £33,400
Excellent: £7500
Good: £6000
Average: £3500
Project: £1200

JAGUAR
XJ-S 3.6

As well as ushering in the Cabriolet bodyshell, the arrival of the AJ6 engine gave Jaguar the chance to refocus the car's marketing. Although it lacked the ultimate grunt of the V12, the new engine and manual transmission package added spporting appeal into the mix, and although it shouldn't have worked, the six-cylinder XJ-S actually went on to sell rather well. Sport versions were introduced later on to reflect the tastes of the '80s; as well as a range of questionable body kits and trim options, diluting the original car's appeal.

SPECIFICATIONS

Years produced: 1983-1991 (92,750 in total)
Performance: 0-60mph: 7.4 secs (Top speed: 142mph)
Power & torque: 225bhp / 240lb/ft
Engine: Normally aspirated 3690cc in-line six, petrol, electronic fuel injection, 24 valves
Drivetrain: Front-engine RWD
Suspension: (F) Independent coil spring. (R) Independent coil spring
Bodyframe: Monocoque
Transmission: 5-speed manual/Automatic
Weight: 1660kgs

PRICE GUIDE

Launch price: £19,249
Excellent: £6000
Good: £4250
Average: £2400
Project: £700

JAGUAR
XJ-S 5.3 Cabriolet

Like the six-cylinder XJ-SC, the V12 Cabriolet wasn't open-topped Jaguar motoring at its best. The roll-over structure engineered by Tickford cluttered the styling, even if it helped retain the structural integrity of such a large car. As with the coupé version, V12 power resulted in effortless performance and magnificent long distance touring ability, hampered only by the car's great thirst. Despite retaining the closed coupé's interior, the rear seats were dropped, and turned into a neat little storage area with lidded bins.

SPECIFICATIONS

Years produced: 1985-1988 (16.790 in total)
Performance: 0-60mph: 7.6 secs (Top speed: 161mph)
Power & torque: 308bhp / 355lb/ft
Engine: Normally aspirated 5994cc V12, petrol, electronic fuel injection, 24 valves
Drivetrain: Front-engine RWD
Suspension: (F) Independent coil spring. (R) Independent coil spring
Bodyframe: Monocoque
Transmission: 3-speed automatic
Weight: 1985kgs

PRICE GUIDE

Launch price: £45,100
Excellent: £7500
Good: £6000
Average: £3500
Project: £1500

JAGUAR
XJ6 2.9/3.2 (XJ40)

Development work on the XJ40 started back in 1973, and led to a protracted gestation period of more than 15 years. The long wait was down to the 1973 fuel crisis, then a lack of funding and management direction from BL. The project was continually delayed until it finally made its debut in 1986, by which time, its styling had become all retro. Despite its elderly looks the XJ40 was great to drive, although the single cam straight six was breathless and lacked power. Later 3.2-litre versions were vastly improved and have genuine classic appeal.

SPECIFICATIONS

Years produced: 1986-1994 (204,474 in total)
Performance: 0-60mph: 9.8 secs (Top speed: 117mph)
Power & torque: 165bhp / 176lb/ft
Engine: Normally aspirated 2919cc in-line six, petrol, electronic fuel injection, 12 valves
Drivetrain: Front-engine RWD
Suspension: (F) Independent coil spring. (R) Independent coil spring
Bodyframe: metal monocoque
Transmission: 5-speed manual/automatic
Weight: 1720kgs

PRICE GUIDE

Launch price: £16,495
Excellent: £3000
Good: £2200
Average: £1100
Project: £250

JAGUAR
XJ6 3.6/4.0 (XJ40)

The larger six-cylinder engined XJ40s were an entertaining mixture of old-school styling and cutting edge dynamics. The earliest 3.6-litre cars with their 'Tokyo-by-night' dashboards were riddled with electrical niggles that ended up frustrating their hapless owners. But following Ford's takeover and a significant injection of cash, the much-improved revised 4-litre cars appeared in 1990. The larger engined cars featured conventional instrumentation, uprated electrics and a much torquier engine, making them easier to drive.

SPECIFICATIONS

Years produced: 1986-1994
Performance: 0-60mph: 8.2 secs (Top speed: 141mph)
Power & torque: 223bhp / 278lb/ft
Engine: Normally aspirated 3980cc in-line six, petrol, electronic fuel injection, 24 valves
Drivetrain: Front-engine RWD
Suspension: (F) Independent coil spring. (R) Independent coil spring
Bodyframe: Metal monocoque
Transmission: 5-speed manual/4-speed automatic
Weight: 1810kgs

PRICE GUIDE

Launch price: £25,200
Excellent: £3350
Good: £2500
Average: £1200
Project: £300

JAGUAR
XJ-S V12 Convertible

This is the best of the XJ-S range, a full convertible this time, with an electrically operated hood that incorporates a heated glass rear window. And as if to confirm its status, the XJ-S Convertible was only available with the V12 engine and an automatic gearbox. To make up for the loss of the Cabriolet's strengthening roof supports, there's a new subframe at the front to brace the body, though they are still not completely free of scuttle shake. The V12 Convertible made a comeback from 1993-95 with a 6-litre engine and 2+2 seating.

SPECIFICATIONS

Years produced: 1988-1991 (7420 in total)
Performance: 0-60mph: 8.0 secs (Top speed: 150mph)
Power & torque: 285bhp / 309lb/ft
Engine: Normally aspirated 5343cc V12, petrol, electronic fuel injection, 24 valves
Drivetrain: Front-engine RWD
Suspension: (F) Independent coil spring. (R) Independent coil spring
Bodyframe: Metal monocoque
Transmission: 3-speed automatic
Weight: 1900kgs

PRICE GUIDE

Launch price: £36,000
Excellent: £9500
Good: £8000
Average: £6000
Project: £3750

JAGUAR
XJS 4.0

1991's restyle of the XJS (note the lack of hyphen now) brought longer rear side windows and a much smoother tail, along with a redesigned interior that features even more wood trim. There are many changes under the skin too, including the increase in engine capacity for the six-cylinder to create this 4.0 version. Further changes were made in 1993, the most obvious being the body-coloured bumpers. There's also a Convertible model now, with extra bracing to improve the body's rigidity. Add another 50% to the prices for these cars.

SPECIFICATIONS

Years produced: 1991-1996
Performance: 0-60mph: 7.5 secs (Top speed: 141mph)
Power & torque: 223bhp / 278lb/ft
Engine: Normally aspirated 3980cc in-line six, petrol, carburettor, 24 valves
Drivetrain: Front-engine RWD
Suspension: (F) Independent coil spring. (R) Independent coil spring
Bodyframe: Metal monocoque
Transmission: 5-speed manual
Weight: 1830kgs

PRICE GUIDE

Launch price: £33,400
Excellent: £7500
Good: £6000
Average: £4500
Project: £1400

JAGUAR
XJ220

When the XJ220 was unveiled at the 1988 British Motor Show, the crowds were awe-struck. The V12 powered 200mph supercar had been developed by engineers in their own time and promised to beat the Italians at their own game. Deposits were taken, and production was promised for 1990. Two years later, and the V6 powered twin-turbo XJ220 was a very different beast – still capable of over 200mph, its MG Metro 6R4-derived engine didn't have quite the same appeal. Buyers demanded their deposits back and sales were rather slower than anticipated.

SPECIFICATIONS

Years produced: 1992-1994 (271 in total)
Performance: 0-60mph: 3.6 secs (Top speed: 213mph)
Power & torque: 542bhp / 475lb/ft
Engine: Normally aspirated 3498cc V6, petrol, electronic fuel injection, 24 valves
Drivetrain: Mid-engine RWD
Suspension: (F&R) Independent, double wishbone, spring/damper unit, anti-roll bar
Bodyframe: Monocoque
Transmission: 5-speed manual
Weight: 1996kgs

PRICE GUIDE

Launch price: £403,000
Excellent: £130,000
Good: £115,000
Average: £90,000
Project: N/A

JAGUAR
XJR 4.0 Supercharged

Mechanically similar to the XJ40, the styling of Jaguar's next generation reverted to something similar to the earlier XJ models, with the trademark curvaceous bonnet and quad round headlamps making a return. The X300 also made huge steps forward in terms of build quality and reliability, and buyers lapped it up. The pride of the fleet was the XJR, which thanks to the addition of a supercharger to Jaguar's straight-six developed BMW M5 rivalling power. Manual versions are rare and desirable and well worth seeking out.

SPECIFICATIONS

Years produced: 1994-1997
Performance: 0-60mph: 5.7 secs (Top speed: 153mph)
Power & torque: 321bhp / 378lb/ft
Engine: Normally aspirated 3980cc in-line six, petrol, electronic fuel injection, 24 valves
Drivetrain: Front-engine RWD
Suspension: (F) Independent coil spring. (R) Independent coil spring
Bodyframe: Metal monocoque
Transmission: 5-speed manual/4-speed automatic
Weight: 1875kgs

PRICE GUIDE

Launch price: £45,450
Excellent: £6750
Good: £4500
Average: £2250
Project: £1000

JENSEN 541

Although launched in 1953, specialist manufacturer Jensen didn't manage to get their aerodynamically-styled 541 into production until 1955, by which time the decision had been taken to use glassfibre for its body. Most of the running gear came courtesy of Austin, with the hefty 3993cc six-cylinder engine borrowed from the Princess. In a lighter Grand Tourer like the 541 it gave a much better account of itself than in BMC's big limos. 1957's 541R had more power, while 1960's 541S was longer and wider for greater space inside.

SPECIFICATIONS

Years produced: 1954-1962 (549 in total)
Performance: 0-60mph: 9.2 secs (Top speed: 116mph)
Power & torque: 130bhp
Engine: Normally aspirated 3990cc in-line six, petrol, carburettor, 12 valves
Drivetrain: Front-engine RWD
Suspension: (F) Independent, coil springs. (R) Beam axle, semi-elliptic leaf spring
Bodyframe: Chassis and glassfibre body
Transmission: 4-speed manual
Weight: 1422kgs

PRICE GUIDE

Launch price: £2147
Excellent: £21,000
Good: £16,500
Average: £9000
Project: £3750

JENSEN C-V8

Jensen furthered its knowledge of glassfibre construction with 1962's CV-8, a striking-looking machine characterised by slanting quad headlamps. This time round an enormous 5916cc Chrysler V8 replaced the Austin engine. Mated to an automatic transmission it was capable of pushing the C-V8 to 130mph, but this wasn't enough for Jensen so in 1964 in went a 335bhp 6276cc. This raised the potential velocity to 140mph but also meant horrendous fuel consumption. 1965's MkIII saw further tweaks to those front lights.

SPECIFICATIONS

Years produced: 1962-1965 (499 in total)
Performance: 0-60mph: 8.4 secs (Top speed: 129mph)
Power & torque: 305bhp / N/A
Engine: Normally aspirated 5916cc V8, petrol, carburettor, 16 valves
Drivetrain: Front-engine RWD
Suspension: (F) Independent, wishbone, coil spring. (R) Live axle, semi-elliptic leaf spring
Bodyframe: Chassis and glassfibre body
Transmission: 3-speed manual
Weight: 1517kgs

PRICE GUIDE

Launch price: £3861
Excellent: £18,500
Good: £15,000
Average: £8000
Project: £4250

JENSEN Interceptor

One of the biggest and best British bruisers of the luxury Grand Tourer world 1966's Interceptor propelled Jensen into the limelight. The handsome lines were styled by Touring of Milan and initially, the bodies (steel now instead of glassfibre) were built by Vignale in Italy before Jensen switched production to the UK. The standard car's most distinctive feature was a curved glass hatchback but even without this it was still a very eye-catching and imposing creation, as the accompanying convertibles and notchback coupé proved.

SPECIFICATIONS

Years produced: 1966-1974 (6175 in total)
Performance: 0-60mph: 7.3 secs (Top speed: 133mph)
Power & torque: 325bhp / 425lb/ft
Engine: Normally aspirated 6286cc V8, petrol, carburettor, 16 valves
Drivetrain: Front-engine RWD
Suspension: (F) Independent, coil springs. (R) Beam axle, semi-elliptic leaf spring
Bodyframe: Chassis and separate body
Transmission: 3-speed automatic
Weight: 1768kgs

PRICE GUIDE

Launch price: £8334
Excellent: £15,000
Good: £12,000
Average: £6250
Project: £3250

JENSEN Interceptor Convertible

Cutting the roof off the Interceptor resulted in a surprisingly stylish machine, despite the loss of the car's trademark curved glass hatchback. Conceived as a flagship to boost Jensen sales in the USA the mechanical side of the convertible was the same as the tin-top cars – thus the 7212cc Chrysler V8 with TorqueFlite automatic transmission – but changes to the body (aside from the obvious missing roof) included strengthening around the sills and the windscreen pillars, plus a spacious boot. Production ended in mid-1976 after 508 cars.

SPECIFICATIONS

Years produced: 1966-1976 (508 in total)
Performance: 0-60mph: 7.3 secs (Top speed: 135mph)
Power & torque: 300bhp / 410lb/ft
Engine: Normally aspirated 6286cc V8, petrol, carburettor, 16 valves
Drivetrain: Front-engine RWD
Suspension: (F) Independent, coil springs. (R) Live axle, semi-elliptic leaf spring
Bodyframe: Chassis and separate body
Transmission: 3-speed automatic
Weight: 1588kgs

PRICE GUIDE

Launch price: £6744
Excellent: £30,000
Good: £24,000
Average: £12,500
Project: £7500

JENSEN FF

The advanced and forward-thinking Jensen FF was the world's first road-only car with permanent four-wheel-drive and anti-lock brakes. Introduced in 1966, alongside the Interceptor, it was closely related to that car but had a longer wheelbase, twin vents in the front wings and a bonnet scoop. Mechanically it was very different of course, although the same Chrysler 6276cc V8 did business under the bonnet. FF stood for Ferguson Formula, the tractor company behind the all-wheel-drive, while the ABS was by Dunlop.

SPECIFICATIONS

Years produced: 1968-1971 (320 in total)
Performance: 0-60mph: 8.4 secs (Top speed: 130mph)
Power & torque: 325bhp / 425lb/ft
Engine: Normally aspirated 6276cc V8, petrol, carburettor, 16 valves
Drivetrain: Front-engine AWD
Suspension: (F) Independent, coil springs. (R) Beam axle, semi-elliptic leaf spring
Bodyframe: Chassis and separate body
Transmission: 3-speed automatic
Weight: 1828kgs

PRICE GUIDE

Launch price: £5340
Excellent: £19,500
Good: £16,500
Average: £11,000
Project: £5000

JENSEN
Interceptor SP

The 'SP' stood for 'Six-Pack' and denoted that these 1971-1973 Jensen Interceptors were rather special, with their Chrysler V8 engines sporting three twin-barrel Holley carburettors in a 'six-pack' configuration. The designation also hinted at their macho and hairy-chested nature, for the SPs were the most powerful Jensens ever built. Their 7212cc powerhouses peaked at 385bhp, which meant a speed of 150mph was attainable. However, the SP didn't shout about its capabilities in the same way many other 1970s high performance cars did.

SPECIFICATIONS

Years produced: 1971-1973 (232 in total)
Performance: 0-60mph: 6.4 secs (Top speed: 137mph)
Power & torque: 330bhp / 425lb/ft
Engine: Normally aspirated 7212cc V8, petrol, carburettor, 16 valves
Drivetrain: Front-engine RWD
Suspension: (F) Independent, coil springs. (B) Beam axle, semi-elliptic leaf spring
Bodyframe: Chassis and separate body
Transmission: 3-speed automatic
Weight: 1649kgs

PRICE GUIDE

Launch price: £6744
Excellent: £16,000
Good: £13,000
Average: £7500
Project: £3750

JENSEN
GT Estate

With Healey's connection with Jensen now ended, the 1975 sporting estate that grew out of the Jensen-Healey convertible in 1975 was simply known as the Jensen GT. It used the same mechanicals – a 1973cc Lotus twin-cam engine mated to a Getrag five-speed gearbox – which by now was reliable. However, grafting a fixed roof onto what was basically the convertible body still failed to produce a great car, despite the extra practicality and luxurious touches such as a walnut dashboard and electric windows.

SPECIFICATIONS

Years produced: 1975-1976 (473 in total)
Performance: 0-60mph: 8.7 secs (Top speed: 119mph)
Power & torque: 144bhp / 134lb/ft
Engine: Normally aspirated 1973cc in-line four, petrol, carburettor, 8 valves
Drivetrain: Front-engine RWD
Suspension: (F) Independent, coil springs. (R) Beam axle, coil springs
Bodyframe: Chassis and separate body
Transmission: 5-speed manual
Weight: 1096kgs

PRICE GUIDE

Launch price: £4178
Excellent: £6000
Good: £4750
Average: £3000
Project: £1000

JENSEN-HEALEY
Jensen-Healey

After British Leyland dropped its range of Austin-Healey sports cars, Donald and Geoffrey Healey joined Jensen to develop a successor. They came up with the body design for the 1972 convertible sportscar simply known as the Jensen-Healey, using a mix of different parts from other manufacturers. The 1973cc twin-cam 16-valve engine was from Lotus, the suspension and steering from Vauxhall's Viva and the gearbox was a Sunbeam item. Unfortunately, nothing gelled together that well.

SPECIFICATIONS

Years produced: 1972-1976 (10,504 in total)
Performance: 0-60mph: 7.8 secs (Top speed: 119mph)
Power & torque: 144bhp / 134lb/ft
Engine: Normally aspirated 1973cc in-line four, petrol, carburettor, 8 valves
Drivetrain: Front-engine RWD
Suspension: (F) Independent, coil springs. (R) Beam axle, coil springs
Bodyframe: Chassis and glassfibre body
Transmission: 4-speed manual
Weight: 1061kgs

PRICE GUIDE

Launch price: £1810
Excellent: £6250
Good: £5000
Average: £3250
Project: £1000

JOWETT
Javelin

A brave attempt by this small British manufacturer, and technologically advanced for the immediate post-war period. The Javelin was designed by Gerald Palmer to give sporting performance and handling, good aerodynamics and comfortable seating for five. It succeeded on all fronts and they were snapped up by professionals. Innovative and well-built, with torsion bar suspension and lightweight flat-four engine, they still feel surprisingly good to drive today and cruise happily at 65-70mph .

SPECIFICATIONS

Years produced: 1947-1953 (23,307 in total)
Performance: 0-60mph: 22.2 secs (Top speed: 78mph)
Power & torque: 50bhp / N/A
Engine: Normally aspirated 1486cc flat 4, petrol, carburettor, 8 valves
Drivetrain: Front-engine RWD
Suspension: (F) Independent, torsion bar. (R) Live axle, torsion bar
Bodyframe: Separate body and chassis
Transmission: 4-speed manual
Weight: 1003kgs

PRICE GUIDE

Launch price: £819
Excellent: £7250
Good: £6000
Average: £3250
Project: £1600

JOWETT
Jupiter

This was Jowett's only sports car and was created by using Javelin mechanical bits in a tubular spaceframe. Though no beauty in the conventional sense, with its high nose and low tail, the body is at least distinctive and was created from a mixture of steel and aluminium panels. The whole front hinges upwards to give superb engine access. The MkIA from 1952 has a larger boot, with a bootlid this time. Three class wins at Le Mans and one in the Monte Carlo rally proved the Jupiter's worth and attracted enthusiast buyers.

SPECIFICATIONS

Years produced: 1950-1953 (825 in total)
Performance: 0-60mph: 16.8 secs (Top speed: 84mph)
Power & torque: 60bhp / N/A
Engine: Normally aspirated 1486cc flat 4, petrol, carburettor, 8 valves
Drivetrain: Front-engine RWD
Suspension: (F) Independent, torsion bar. (R) Live axle, torsion bar
Bodyframe: Separate body and chassis
Transmission: 4-speed manual
Weight: 1003kgs

PRICE GUIDE

Launch price: £1017
Excellent: £16,500
Good: £13,000
Average: £9500
Project: £5500

LAGONDA
2.6/2.9

Lagonda's 2.6 was introduced in 1946, just before David Brown took the company over to combine it with Aston Martin. A smaller car than pre-war Lagondas, WO Bentley designed its engine and chassis. The latter was advanced for the time, with all-independent suspension. Bodies were saloon and drophead coupé, the latter now worth more than twice the quoted saloon prices. Metamorphosed into a 2.9-litre in 1953, with the same chassis, a larger bore engine well-proven in competition, and a body penned by Tickford.

SPECIFICATIONS

Years produced: 1948-1957 (780 in total)
Performance: 0-60mph: 18.8 secs (Top speed: 100mph)
Power & torque: 105bhp / 133lb/ft
Engine: Normally aspirated 2580cc in-line six, petrol, carburettor, 12 valves
Drivetrain: Front-engine RWD
Suspension: (F) Independent, coil spring. (R) de Dion axle, torsion bar
Bodyframe: Chassis and separate body
Transmission: 4-speed manual
Weight: 1471kgs

PRICE GUIDE

Launch price: £3110
Excellent: £25,000
Good: £20,000
Average: £10,000
Project: £5000

LAGONDA
Rapide

From the front wheels back, Lagonda's 1961 to 1964 Rapide was a handsome and dignified machine. Unfortunately, ahead of that, it was also visually shocking thanks to a sloped quad-headlamp nose and outlandish grilles. Given that it was designed by Touring this look was a big disappointment and no doubt contributed to only 54 of these machines being built. The car used an elongated DB4 chassis, with suspension tweaks, and a 236bhp 4-litre six-cylinder engine that wouldn't graduate to the Aston Martin until the DB5 three years later.

SPECIFICATIONS

Years produced: 1961-1964 (55 in total)
Performance: 0-60mph: N/A (Top speed: 130mph)
Power & torque: 236bhp / 265lb/ft
Engine: Normally aspirated 3995cc in-line six, petrol, carburettor, 12 valves
Drivetrain: Front-engine RWD
Suspension: (F) Independent, coil spring, wishbone. (R) de Dion axle, torsion bar
Bodyframe: Chassis and superleggera
Transmission: 3-speed automatic or 4-speed manual
Weight: 1715kgs

PRICE GUIDE

Launch price: £4950
Excellent: £32,000
Good: £25,000
Average: £16,000
Project: £10,000

LAMBORGHINI
350 GT

Here's where it all began, allegedly because Ferruccio Lamborghini was unhappy with the level of service he received Enzo Ferrari when a car he bought from the Scuderia went wrong. When Lamborghini started his sports car company, he poached a number of Ferrari engineers to help create his first car – most notably Giotto Bizzarini, who created the V12 engine, and Giampaolo Dallara, who sorted out the chassis. When the Touring bodied 350GT arrived on the scene, it made a huge impact that resonated across Italy – and from that moment on, Enzo took Ferruccio seriously.

SPECIFICATIONS

Years produced: 1964-1966 (120 in total)
Performance: 0-60mph: 6.8 secs (Top speed: 155mph)
Power & torque: 320bhp / 241lb/ft
Engine: Normally aspirated 3464cc V12, petrol, carburettor, 24 valves
Drivetrain: Front-engine RWD
Suspension: (F&R) All-independent, coil spring, tubular wishbone, anti-roll bar
Bodyframe: Spaceframe
Transmission: 5-speed manual
Weight: 1200kgs

PRICE GUIDE

Launch price: £6950
Excellent: £185,000
Good: £160,000
Average: £120,000
Project: £80,000

LAMBORGHINI
400 GT 2+2

Extending the Lamborghini range, Ferruccio took the step of commissioning Touring to extend the 350GT. The coachbuilder came up with an all-new body based on a lengthened wheelbase that managed to incorporate a pair of occasional rear seats – it may have looked almost identical to the smaller car, but every panel was changed. To keep keen drivers happy, the newly developed 4-litre version of Bizzarni's V12 was installed, maintaining supercar-style performance. Although the more accomplished cars, values favour the 350GT.

SPECIFICATIONS

Years produced: 1966-1968 (242 in total)
Performance: 0-60mph: 7.5 secs (Top speed: 155mph)
Power & torque: 320bhp / 276lb/ft
Engine: Normally aspirated 3929cc V12, petrol, carburettor, 24 valves
Drivetrain: Front-engine RWD
Suspension: (F&R) All-independent, coil spring, tubular wishbone, anti-roll bar
Bodyframe: Spaceframe
Transmission: 5-speed manual
Weight: 1380kgs

PRICE GUIDE

Launch price: £7995
Excellent: £130,000
Good: £105,000
Average: £80,000
Project: £55,000

LAMBORGHINI
Miura P400

The Miura made its first appearance in chassis form at the 1965 Turin show, attracting much interest with orders and deposits coming in before the body itself was even designed. Its box steel chassis full of holes for lightness housed an engine and transmission placed transversely just ahead of the rear wheels. The V12 engine sat on top of the gearbox with the two sharing the same oil. Nothing like it had been seen before and it captured the imaginations of many. Every coachbuilder in Italy clamored for the opportunity to clothe the spectacular chassis. Bertone was chosen.

SPECIFICATIONS

Years produced: 1966-1968 (475 in total)
Performance: 0-60mph: 6.2 secs (Top speed: 172mph)
Power & torque: 350bhp / 272lb/ft
Engine: Normally aspirated 3929cc V12, petrol, carburettor, 24 valves
Drivetrain: Mid-engine RWD
Suspension: (F&R) Independent, double wishbone, coil spring, anti roll bar
Bodyframe: Spaceframe
Transmission: 5-speed manual
Weight: 1292kgs

PRICE GUIDE

Launch price: £6425
Excellent: £200,000
Good: £175,000
Average: £140,000
Project: £100,000

LAMBORGHINI
Islero

The Islero was introduced to the public at the 1968 Geneva Motor Show. It was not as aggressive as the Espada or Miura, catering more for the grand touring crowd. However, it did offer luxurious benefits such as air conditioning and larger interior, and was designed with one eye on the American market. An S version followed in 1969 which was shortlived, with only 100 being produced. The Islero is named after a fighting bull that killed the famous matador Manuel Rodriquez in August of 1947.

SPECIFICATIONS

Years produced: 1968-1970 (125 in total)
Performance: 0-60mph: 6.2 secs (Top speed: 165mph)
Power & torque: 350bhp / 290lb/ft
Engine: Normally aspirated 3929cc V12, petrol, carburettor, 24 valves
Drivetrain: Front-engine RWD
Suspension: (F&R) Independent, coil spring, tubular wishbone, anti-roll bar
Bodyframe: Spaceframe
Transmission: 5-speed manual
Weight: 1460kgs

PRICE GUIDE

Launch price: £7950
Excellent: £75,000
Good: £60,000
Average: £40,000
Project: £22,500

LAMBORGHINI
Miura P400 S

If the 350/400GTs paved the way for Lamborghini to become a major player in the supercar scene, the trendsetting Miura left Ferrari floundering in its wake. At a time when mid-engined cars were very much for competition and niche cars, Lamborghini embraced the layout for its range-topping sports car. For many, the Miura was the first supercar. It wasn't without faults – if you were tall, forget driving it, and if you wanted to go fast, you had to compensate for its flexing chassis and iffy aerodynamics. But despite that, it's an all-time great, and one that remains undervalued.

SPECIFICATIONS

Years produced: 1968-1971 (140 in total)
Performance: 0-60mph: 5.5 secs (Top speed: 177mph)
Power & torque: 370bhp / 286lb/ft
Engine: Normally aspirated 3939cc V12, petrol, carburettor, 24 valves
Drivetrain: Mid-engine RWD
Suspension: (F&R) Independent, coil spring, tubular wishbone, anti-roll bar
Bodyframe: Spaceframe
Transmission: 5-speed manual
Weight: 1040kgs

PRICE GUIDE

Launch price: £10,860
Excellent: £240,000
Good: £200,000
Average: £160,000
Project: £110,000

LAMBORGHINI
Espada

In 1968, Ferruccio decided to built a full four-seater Gran Turismo, and it was presented as the Espada 400 GT. Its styling was inspired by the memorable Marzal concept car of 1966, and maintained that car's expansive proportions, despite now being front-engined. The first Espada prototype retained the Marzal's gullwing door-design, but this was abandoned for the production model. The styling of the Espada was sensational, a real head-turner. Despite its four-seater layout, the Espada handled its two-seater sisters.

SPECIFICATIONS

Years produced: 1968-1978 (186 in total)
Performance: 0-60mph: 6.5 secs (Top speed: 155mph)
Power & torque: 325bhp / 276lb/ft
Engine: Normally aspirated 3939cc V12, petrol, carburettor, 24 valves
Drivetrain: Front-engine RWD
Suspension: (F&R) Independent, coil spring, tubular wishbone, anti-roll bar
Bodyframe: Spaceframe
Transmission: 5-speed manual/3-speed automatic
Weight: 1480kgs

PRICE GUIDE

Launch price: £10,295
Excellent: £30,000
Good: £25,000
Average: £16,000
Project: £9000

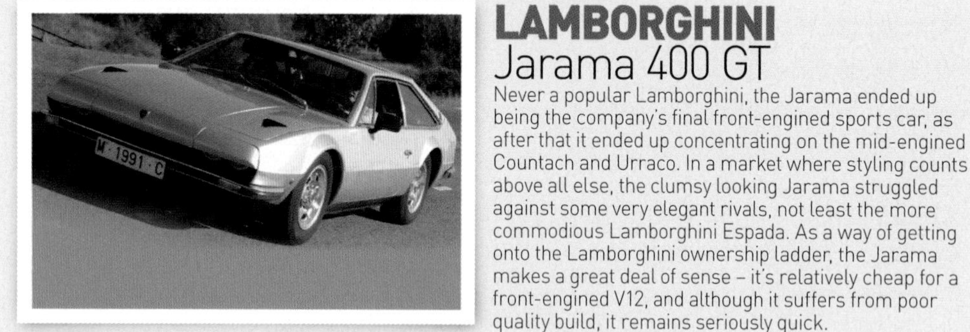

LAMBORGHINI
Jarama 400 GT

Never a popular Lamborghini, the Jarama ended up being the company's final front-engined sports car, as after that it ended up concentrating on the mid-engined Countach and Urraco. In a market where styling counts above all else, the clumsy looking Jarama struggled against some very elegant rivals, not least the more commodious Lamborghini Espada. As a way of getting onto the Lamborghini ownership ladder, the Jarama makes a great deal of sense – it's relatively cheap for a front-engined V12, and although it suffers from poor quality build, it remains seriously quick.

SPECIFICATIONS

Years produced: 1970-1973 (177 in total)
Performance: 0-60mph: 7.2 secs (Top speed: 162mph)
Power & torque: 350bhp / 290lb/ft
Engine: Normally aspirated 3939cc V12, petrol, carburettor, 24 valves
Drivetrain: Front-engine RWD
Suspension: (F&R) Independent, coil spring, tubular wishbone, anti-roll bar
Bodyframe: Chassis and separate body
Transmission: 5-speed manual
Weight: 1540kgs

PRICE GUIDE

Launch price: £9800
Excellent: £25,000
Good: £21,000
Average: £14,000
Project: £8000

LAMBORGHINI
Urraco P250

In 1970, Ferruccio Lamborghini sought to introduce a low-cost Lamborghini to compete with the Porsche 911 and the Dino 246 by Ferrari. Ferruccio insisted that his new junior supercar have a 2+2 layout and a V8 engine to get one over on the two-seat V6 Dino. Bertone designed and built two prototypes, but Lamborghini decided to use an original and elegant design by Marcello Gandini, who was also responsible for the Miura and Espada. The car was shown to the public on the 1970 Turin Auto Show in November and aroused considerable interest, if not sales.

SPECIFICATIONS

Years produced: 1972-1976 (520 in total)
Performance: 0-60mph: 8.5 secs (Top speed: 149mph)
Power & torque: 220bhp / 166lb/ft
Engine: Normally aspirated 2463cc V8, petrol, carburettor, 16 valves
Drivetrain: Mid-engine RWD
Suspension: (F&R) Independent, coil spring, tubular wishbone, anti-roll bar
Bodyframe: Spaceframe
Transmission: 5-speed manual
Weight: 1100kgs

PRICE GUIDE

Launch price: £5950
Excellent: £19,000
Good: £15,000
Average: £10,000
Project: £5000

LAMBORGHINI Urraco P300

The P300 was a direct answer to Ferrari's new 308 GT4, the successor to the famous Dino. The original P250 needed changing; the price was too high and the workmanship wasn't up to the desired level. The Urraco should have been a big success, but with poor build quality and limp-wristed performance in P250 form it failed to take off. The 265bhp P300 put right the latter problem, pushing the Urraco to over 160mph, but the former was a more deep-seated issue that failed to get resolved. A 2-litre tax break P200 model was sold in Italy, and it's not uncommon to find one for sale now.

SPECIFICATIONS

Years produced: 1974-1979 (190 in total)
Performance: 0-60mph: 7.4 secs (Top speed: 161mph)
Power & torque: 265bhp / 195lb/ft
Engine: Normally aspirated 2996cc V8, petrol, carburettor, 16 valves
Drivetrain: Mid-engine RWD
Suspension: (F&R) Independent, coil spring, tubular wishbone, anti-roll bar
Bodyframe: Spaceframe
Transmission: 5-speed manual
Weight: 1300kgs

PRICE GUIDE

Launch price: £9975
Excellent: £23,000
Good: £19,000
Average: £14,000
Project: £7000

LAMBORGHINI Countach LP400

Although the Miura was a tough act to follow, Lamborghini did it in style with the Countach, perhaps the most iconic bedroom poster car of all. With a dramatic wedge style, scissor doors and a claimed maximum speed approaching 200mph from its 375bhp V12, the Countach was a concept car for the road. It also put right many of the Miura's most serious problems, most notably its shocking aerodynamics. Cramped, noisy and impossible to see out of, the Countach is a true great – and currently undervalued compared with its forebear. For how much longer though?

SPECIFICATIONS

Years produced: 1974-1978 (150 in total)
Performance: 0-60mph: 6.8 secs (Top speed: 196mph)
Power & torque: 375bhp / 268lb/ft
Engine: Normally aspirated 3929cc V12, petrol, carburettor, 24 valves
Drivetrain: Mid-engine RWD
Suspension: (F&R) Independent, coil spring, tubular wishbone, anti-roll bar
Bodyframe: Spaceframe
Transmission: 5-speed manual
Weight: 1065kgs

PRICE GUIDE

Launch price: £17,285
Excellent: £100,000
Good: £90,000
Average: £50,000
Project: £30,000

LAMBORGHINI Countach LP500 QV

Later Countaches might have lost the design purity of the original, but the addition of fat low-profile P7 rubber and engine and aero upgrades kept it on the pace into the '80s. The Quattrovalvole engine saw power leap to over 400bhp but, in truth, road testers never got anywhere close to matching the fanciful claimed top speed of over 190mph. That didn't really matter too much – it was still faster than a Ferrari Boxer, and could stop traffic with those looks. The cars that followed it continued the formula most successfully.

SPECIFICATIONS

Years produced: 1985-1988 (610 in total)
Performance: 0-60mph: 4.8 secs (Top speed: 182mph)
Power & torque: 455bhp / 369lb/ft
Engine: Normally aspirated 4754cc V12, petrol, carburettor, 24 valves
Drivetrain: Mid-engine RWD
Suspension: (F&R) Independent, coil spring, tubular wishbone, anti-roll bar
Bodyframe: Spaceframe
Transmission: 5-speed manual
Weight: 1490kgs

PRICE GUIDE

Launch price: £49,500
Excellent: £62,500
Good: £55,000
Average: £35,000
Project: £25,000

LAMBORGHINI Silhouette P300

Based on the Urraco P300, the Silhouette was an ultimately unsuccessful attempt to take on the Ferrari 308 GTS. An appealing looking car with tele-dial alloys and ultra-low profile tyres – just like a Countach – it wasn't strong enough to make the grade. It fell by the wayside when Lamborghini went through horrendous financial problems during the late 1970s, a time when Sant Agata's model range was reduced to the Countach only. With 54 built, the Silhouette is rare and rapidly gaining desirability – but not as nice to drive as a 308.

SPECIFICATIONS

Years produced: 1976-1979 (52 in total)
Performance: 0-60mph:6.8 secs (Top speed: 160mph)
Power & torque: 260bhp / 210lb/ft
Engine: Normally aspirated 2996cc V8, petrol, carburettor, 16 valves
Drivetrain: Mid-engine RWD
Suspension: (F&R) Independent, coil spring, tubular wishbone, anti-roll bar
Bodyframe: Spaceframe
Transmission: 5-speed manual
Weight: 1240kgs

PRICE GUIDE

Launch price: £13,684
Excellent: £25,000
Good: £22,000
Average: £15,000
Project: £8000

LAMBORGHINI Jalpa

The Jalpa was Lamborghini's last throw of the Urraco dice. Given that the Silhouette had been out of production for two years, it was an odd decision to revamp it for another attack on the 308, but that's what Lamborghini did. The Jalpa was usefully quicker thanks to its enlarged (by Alfieri) 3.5-litre V8 engine, but the '70s throwback styling and Airfix interior should have been a barrier to sales. However, during its decade-long production run, the Jalpa bucked the trend and sold up to 200 per year, becoming Lamborghini's most successful V8 yet.

SPECIFICATIONS

Years produced: 1981-1988 (410 in total)
Performance: 0-60mph: 7.3 secs (Top speed: 146mph)
Power & torque: 255bhp / 231lb/ft
Engine: Normally aspirated 3485cc V8, petrol, carburettor, 16 valves
Drivetrain: Mid-engine RWD
Suspension: (F&R) Independent, coil spring, tubular wishbone, anti-roll bar
Bodyframe: Metal monocoque
Transmission: 5-speed manual
Weight: 1510kgs

PRICE GUIDE

Launch price: £26,001
Excellent: £27,500
Good: £25,000
Average: £16,000
Project: £9000

LAMBORGHINI Diablo

A straightforward replacement for the Countach, brought up to date, and suitably scaled up. The original design had been penned by Marcello Gandini (who was responsible for the Miura and Countach), but following Chrysler's takeover in 1987 the design was softened, causing problems between the stylist and Lamborghini. Most significantly, though, after its launch in 1990, the Countach officially became the company's first 200mph road car. The original Diablo pushed out 492bhp, but this was subsequently increased, culminating with 540bhp from the 1996 SV-R model.

SPECIFICATIONS

Years produced: 1990-1998 (900 in total)
Performance: 0-60mph: 3.9 secs (Top speed: 203mph)
Power & torque: 492bhp / 428lb/ft
Engine: Normally aspirated 5709cc V12, petrol, electronic fuel injection, 48 valves
Drivetrain: Mid-engine RWD
Suspension: (F&R) Independent, coil spring, tubular wishbone, anti-roll bar
Bodyframe: Spaceframe
Transmission: 5-speed manual
Weight: 1576kgs

PRICE GUIDE

Launch price: £152,614
Excellent: £70,000
Good: £65,000
Average: £54,000
Project: £39,000

LANCHESTER LD10

Had World War 2 not intervened, Lanchester would have launched the LD10 in 1940. In the event, it was postponed until 1946. Vaguely American from the front thanks to its prominent cascading front grille, the 10 was quite clever underneath where coil-sprung independent front suspension meant a compliant ride and well-behaved handling. The overhead valve 1287cc engine was lively and the pre-selector gearbox meant extra versatility. A special version was the Barker saloon of 1949 with an aluminium body.

SPECIFICATIONS

Years produced: 1946-1951 (3050 in total)
Performance: 0-60mph: 36.8 secs (Top speed: 68mph)
Power & torque: 40bhp / N/A
Engine: Normally aspirated 1287cc in-line four, petrol, carburettor, 8 valves
Drivetrain: Front-engine RWD
Suspension: (F) Independent, coil spring. (R) Live axle, semi-elliptic leaf spring
Bodyframe: Chassis and separate body
Transmission: 4-speed pre-select manual
Weight: 1118kgs

PRICE GUIDE

Launch price: £672
Excellent: £4750
Good: £3500
Average: £1750
Project: £900

LANCHESTER Fourteen/Leda

Both Lanchester and Daimler were owned by BSA, giving the parent company a great excuse to experiment with badge engineering in the 1950s. Lanchester's 14 was the first version of what would become better known as the Daimler Conquest. With a four-cylinder engine of 2-litres and 60bhp, it was pedestrian in both performance and looks, although the drophead coupé cut a dash. The Leda name was used abroad, to denote cars that had a steel frame instead of the wooden one of the UK cars. The last car to wear the Lanchester name.

SPECIFICATIONS

Years produced: 1951-1954 (2100 in total)
Performance: 0-60mph: N/A (Top speed: 75mph)
Power & torque: 60bhp / N/A
Engine: Normally aspirated 1968cc in-line four, petrol, carburettor, 8 valves
Drivetrain: Front-engine RWD
Suspension: (F) Independent, torsion bar. (R) Live axle, semi-elliptic leaf springs
Bodyframe: Chassis and separate body
Transmission: 4-speed pre-select manual
Weight: 1410kgs

PRICE GUIDE

Launch price: £1144
Excellent: £6000
Good: £4750
Average: £3250
Project: £1600

LANCIA Aprilia

Looking at the Aprilia's specification sheet, it's easy to see that it was light years ahead of its time. The features list included monocoque construction, independent suspension all-round, pillarless styling honed in the wind tunnel, and a jewel-like 1354cc V4-engine that produced enough power to allow the car to run round much more glamorous rivals. Three wheelbases were offered, and you could also buy coachbuilt versions. Post-war examples were upgraded with 1.5-litre engines, and remained in production until 1949.

SPECIFICATIONS

Years produced: 1937-1949 (27,635 in total)
Performance: 0-60mph: N/A (Top speed: 80mph)
Power & torque: 46bhp / N/A
Engine: Normally aspirated 1352cc V4, petrol, carburettor, 8 valves
Drivetrain: Front-engine RWD
Suspension: (F) Independent, transverse leaf spring. (R) Independent, torsion bar
Bodyframe: Monocoque
Transmission: 4-speed manual
Weight: 850kgs

PRICE GUIDE

Launch price: N/A
Excellent: £16,500
Good: £13,000
Average: £8000
Project: £3500

LANCIA Aurelia Saloon

Considering the Aprilia blazed such a trail, it's scarcely believable that Lancia went and did the same with the Aurelia. The main advance was the engine – the world's first production V6; a 60-degree design developed during World War Two. It was smooth and lusty, and proved the perfect power unit for long distance touring – and in the B10 saloon version was initially available in 1754 and 1991cc forms. The wind-cheating styling was developed with assistance from Pininfarina and, looking at it today, it seems amazing that it first hit the streets in 1951.

SPECIFICATIONS

Years produced: 1950-1958 (12,705 in total)
Performance: 0-60mph: 17.9 secs (Top speed: 91mph)
Power & torque: 87bhp / 118lb/ft
Engine: Normally aspirated 226cc V6, petrol, carburettor, 12 valves
Drivetrain: Front-engine RWD
Suspension: (F) Independent coils spring. (R) de Dion, semi-elliptic leaf spring
Bodyframe: Monocoque
Transmission: 4-speed manual
Weight: 1232kgs

PRICE GUIDE

Launch price: £2863
Excellent: £17,500
Good: £14,000
Average: £8500
Project: £4500

LANCIA
Aurelia B20 Gran Turismo

Pininfarina was also responsible for the B20 GT coupé (it built the Ghia styled bodies), and it shows in the elegant proportions and exquisite detailing. Now considered to be the first Gran Turismo, the 2- and 2.5-litre versions were quick, smooth and effortless. Fewer than 4000 B20 GTs were built, and those that remain have risen steeply in value in recent years as demand continues to outstrip supply for these thoroughbreds. In all, six series of Aurelias were built, with trim and performance upgrades being drafted in on an almost annual basis.

SPECIFICATIONS

Years produced: 1953-1958 (3424 in total)
Performance: 0-60mph: 12.3 secs (Top speed: 103mph)
Power & torque: 75bhp / 89lb/ft
Engine: Normally aspirated 1991cc V6, petrol, carburettor, 12 valves
Drivetrain: Front-engine RWD
Suspension: (F) Independent, coil spring, (R) de Dion, semi-elliptic leaf spring
Bodyframe: Monocoque
Transmission: 4-speed manual
Weight: 1194kgs

PRICE GUIDE

Launch price: £3472
Excellent: £65,000
Good: £50,000
Average: £30,000
Project: £16,000

LANCIA
Appia Saloon

Designed as an entry-level model, the Appia was unashamedly stylish and advanced. Not only was it aerodynamic but it was light, too, featuring aluminium body panels – and that made the 43bhp 1.1-litre car move along at a fair old pace. The Appia was developed constantly throughout its life, mutating into the Series 2. The styling may have been rejigged to provide a bigger boot, but it still looked good, and was light years ahead of the opposition. These cars are almost impossible to find in the UK, especially the coachbuilt models from Vignale, Farina and Zagato.

SPECIFICATIONS

Years produced: 1953-1959 (98,006 in total)
Performance: 0-60mph: 32.5 secs (Top speed: 76mph)
Power & torque: 38bhp / 52lb/ft
Engine: Normally aspirated 1090cc V4, petrol, carburettor, 8 valves
Drivetrain: Front-engine RWD
Suspension: (F) Independent, coil spring. (R) Beam axle, semi-elliptic leaf spring
Bodyframe: Monocoque
Transmission: 4-speed manual
Weight: 813kgs

PRICE GUIDE

Launch price: £1772
Excellent: £8000
Good: £6500
Average: £4000
Project: £1500

LANCIA
Aurelia B24 Spider

In 1954, to coincide with the arrival of the fourth series cars, the most desirable of all the Aurelias (unless you carry passengers), the B24 Spider, was unveiled. Although its front end styling was similar to the B10 and B20 GT from front wheels back, it was radically different. The wheelbase was shortened by 203mm and Pininfarina produced the sensational coachwork. Production was limited, although many cars have survived – but with higher market values to match their elevated styling and engineering. In the end, the Spider name was rather short-lived.

SPECIFICATIONS

Years produced: 1955-1956 (240 in total)
Performance: 0-60mph: N/A (Top speed: 115mph)
Power & torque: 118bhp / 127lb/ft
Engine: Normally aspirated 2451cc V6, petrol, carburettor, 12 valves
Drivetrain: Front-engine RWD
Suspension: (F) Independent, coil spring. (R) de Dion, semi-elliptic leaf spring
Bodyframe: Monocoque
Transmission: 4-speed manual
Weight: 1070kgs

PRICE GUIDE

Launch price: £N/A
Excellent: £250,000
Good: £200,000
Average: £150,000
Project: £120,000

LANCIA
Aurelia B24 Convertible

For the penultimate round of changes to the Aurelia, and just over a year after it first appeared, the B24 was revised. In the process it lost the Spider name, becoming the B24 Convertible. Alongside the fifth series B20 GTs, which received a sturdier transaxle, the B24 gained wind-up windows, improved seating, and a new windscreen that lost its wraparound. However, the conventional screen with opening quarter lights would prove more useful when motoring with the hood up. Because there were more Convertibles than Spiders, values are correspondingly lower.

SPECIFICATIONS

Years produced: 1957-1958 (510 in total)
Performance: 0-60mph: 12.7 secs (Top speed: 107mph)
Power & torque: 110bhp / 125lb/ft
Engine: Normally aspirated 2451cc V6, petrol, carburettor, 12 valves
Drivetrain: Front-engine RWD
Suspension: (F) Independent, coil spring. (R) de Dion, semi-elliptic leaf spring
Bodyframe: Monocoque
Transmission: 4-speed manual
Weight: 1215kgs

PRICE GUIDE

Launch price: £N/A
Excellent: £140,000
Good: £120,000
Average: £90,000
Project: £60,000

LANCIA
Flaminia 2.8

Replacing the Aurelia was never going to be easy but with the Flaminia, Lancia managed the task with considerable style, although the two cars' production runs overlapped by a couple of years just to confuse matters. The new car heralded a new design direction, with Pininfarina going for a more angular (if conventionally beautiful) style. A new 2458cc V6 was developed for the Flaminia, and wishbone and coil sprung front suspension replaced the old car's more conventional set-up. Fewer than 4000 Berlinas were produced in total and few remain.

SPECIFICATIONS

Years produced: 1957-1970 (3424 in total)
Performance: 0-60mph: N/A (Top speed: 121mph)
Power & torque: 148bhp / 165lb/ft
Engine: Normally aspirated 2775cc V6, petrol, carburettor, 12 valves
Drivetrain: Front-engine RWD
Suspension: (F) Independent, coil spring. (R) de Dion, semi-elliptic leaf spring
Bodyframe: Monocoque
Transmission: 4-speed manual
Weight: 1247kgs

PRICE GUIDE

Launch price: £2847
Excellent: £7250
Good: £6000
Average: £3500
Project: £1500

LANCIA
Flaminia Coupé/GT

Like the Berlina, the Flaminia Coupé was penned by Pininfarina, displaying a strong family resemblance to the four-door car. Built on a shortened wheelbase that was shared with all other two-door versions, the Coupé were handsome and desirable. Again, this was not a mass-produced car – 5282 Coupés were built, excluding the Carrozzeria Touring designed GT, which featured different styling and a two-seat cabin. The Flaminia was the last Lancia to be offered in so many coachbuilt variations. Values are high as a consequence, although not in the Aurelia league. Yet.

SPECIFICATIONS

Years produced: 1959-1967 (5282/1718 in total)
Performance: 0-60mph: 13.6 secs (Top speed: 106mph)
Power & torque: 119bhp / 137lb/ft
Engine: Normally aspirated 2458cc V6, petrol, carburettor, 12 valves
Drivetrain: Front-engine RWD
Suspension: (F) Independent, coil spring. (R) de Dion, semi-elliptic leaf spring
Bodyframe: Monocoque
Transmission: 4-speed manual
Weight: 1481kgs

PRICE GUIDE

Launch price: £3869
Excellent: £18,500
Good: £14,000
Average: £7000
Project: £3250

LANCIA
Flaminia Convertible

The Convertible was perhaps the best looking of all the Flaminias thanks to a carefully considered roof chop of the Touring-styled GT. Offered with the optional hardtop, and uprated 2775cc V6 engine, it remained in production until 1964 with a production total of a mere 847. The one to have is most definitely the 2.8-litre version, of which just 180 were built. However, finding one is always tough, and when you do, be prepared to pay top money for the best examples, as demand for this particularly striking car remains as strong as ever.

SPECIFICATIONS

Years produced: 1959-1967 (847 in total)
Performance: 0-60mph: N/A (Top speed: 110mph)
Power & torque: 148bhp / 164lb/ft
Engine: Normally aspirated 2775cc V6, petrol, carburettor, 12 valves
Drivetrain: Front-engine RWD
Suspension: (F) Independent, coil spring. (R) de Dion, semi-elliptic leaf spring
Bodyframe: Monocoque
Transmission: 4-speed manual
Weight: 1360kgs

PRICE GUIDE

Launch price: N/A
Excellent: £32,500
Good: £25,000
Average: £15,000
Project: £8000

LANCIA
Flaminia Sport Zagato

The Flaminia Sport was coachbuilt by Zagato, and was almost incomparably handsome as a result. The Sport sat on the same wheelbase chassis as the GT, and unlike the Pininfarina and Touring cars, which were angular, the aluminium bodied Sport was more rounded, harking back to the more timeless style of the B20 GT. It became the Super Sport in 1964, the new name reflecting the additional performance from its 2.8-litre V6. Zagato styling signatures, such as the pop-out doorhandles, were retained, although the Sport and Super Sport's styling differed significantly.

SPECIFICATIONS

Years produced: 1960-1967 (593 in total)
Performance: 0-60mph: 12.7 secs (Top speed: 112mph)
Power & torque: 119bhp / 127lb/ft
Engine: Normally aspirated 2458cc V6, petrol, carburettor, 12 valves
Drivetrain: Front-engine RWD
Suspension: (F) Independent, coil spring. (R) de Dion, semi-elliptic leaf spring
Bodyframe: Monocoque
Transmission: 4-speed manual
Weight: 1520kgs

PRICE GUIDE

Launch price: £3888
Excellent: £75,000
Good: £60,000
Average: £40,000
Project: £20,000

LANCIA
Flavia Saloon

Like every other post-war Lancia, the Flavia was innovative compared with the class of 1960. It was the first front-wheel-drive Lancia, making the Italian company one of the earliest adopters of this transmission layout, beating BMC into the 1500cc sector by eight years. But it didn't stop there – the V4 engine was new for Lancia, as was the all-disc brake set-up. The Berlina was styled in-house, and it showed – its boxy styling doing a great job of hiding the groundbreaking technical specification under a cloud of mediocrity.

SPECIFICATIONS

Years produced: 1961-1974 (79,764 in total)
Performance: 0-60mph: 14.3 secs (Top speed: 103mph)
Power & torque: 102bhp / 113lb/ft
Engine: Normally aspirated 1800cc V4, petrol, carburettor, 8 valves
Drivetrain: Front-engine RWD
Suspension: (F) Independent, transverse leaf spring. (R) Beam axle, semi-elliptic leaf spring
Bodyframe: Monocoque
Transmission: 4-speed manual
Weight: 1199kgs

PRICE GUIDE

Launch price: £2075
Excellent: £4000
Good: £3000
Average: £1500
Project: £400

LANCIA
Flavia Sport Zagato

Once again, Zagato was drafted in to create an individual looking Sport, although for the Flavia it was more outlandish than usual. The curvaceous bodywork was a long way away from the square-rigged conventionality of the Berlina, and even the Coupé looked restrained in comparison. However in lightweight form and with twin carburettors, the Sport lived up to its name, proving quick and agile on the road. However, sales weren't good, and in the wake of the Fiat takeover of Lancia in 1969, bespoke models such as this were very much off the menu.

SPECIFICATIONS

Years produced: 1962-1969
Performance: 0-60mph: 11.9 secs (Top speed: 117mph)
Power & torque: 101bhp / 103lb/ft
Engine: Normally aspirated 1800cc V4, petrol, carburettor, 8 valves
Drivetrain: Front-engine RWD
Suspension: (F) Independent, transverse leaf spring. (R) Beam axle, semi-elliptic leaf spring
Bodyframe: Chassis and superleggera
Transmission: 4-speed manual
Weight: 1800kgs

PRICE GUIDE

Launch price: £2736
Excellent: £17,500
Good: £15,000
Average: £9500
Project: £3000

LANCIA
Flavia Coupé

A year after the arrival of the Flavia saloon, the eye-catching Coupé model arrived. Continuing a long tradition of co-operation with Pininfarina, its pretty two-door body style moved Lancia styling away from the classicism of the earlier models. The Coupé initially came with a 90bhp twin carburettor version of the 1.5-litre V4, but this was uprated to 100bhp and 1.8-litres in 1963, before going to the full 126bhp and 2-litres in 1971. Rust has been the main enemy of these cars, although many have now been restored – and values are sure to continue rising.

SPECIFICATIONS

Years produced: 1962-1973 (26,084 in total)
Performance: 0-60mph: 13.2 secs (Top speed: 103mph)
Power & torque: 91bhp / 108lb/ft
Engine: Normally aspirated 1800cc V4, petrol, carburettor, 8 valves
Drivetrain: Front-engine RWD
Suspension: (F) Independent, transverse leaf spring. (R) Beam axle, semi-elliptic leaf spring
Bodyframe: Monocoque
Transmission: 4-speed manual
Weight: 1160kgs

PRICE GUIDE

Launch price: £2275
Excellent: £12,500
Good: £9000
Average: £4000
Project: £1500

LANCIA
Fulvia Berlina

Following on from the Appia in 1963, it seemed that Lancia had skipped a generation when going to the Fulvia, as in many ways it appeared to be a miniature version of the recently launched Flavia. Although the all-new V4 engine shared the same layout as its predecessor, the boxy styling, front wheel drive transmission, suspension set-up and all-disc brake set-up were almost pure Flavia. The Fulvia proved to be the perfect entry level model for Lancia, and although it initially was powered by a 58bhp 1098cc engine, it had the same brio as its larger cousins.

SPECIFICATIONS

Years produced: 1963-1972 (192,097 in total)
Performance: 0-60mph: 23.5 secs (Top speed: 85mph)
Power & torque: 58bhp / 62lb/ft
Engine: Normally aspirated 1091cc V4, petrol, carburettor, Overhead valves
Drivetrain: Front-engine RWD
Suspension: (F) Independent, transverse leaf spring. (R) Beam axle, semi-elliptic leaf spring
Bodyframe: Metal monocoque
Transmission: 4-speed manual
Weight: 984kgs

PRICE GUIDE

Launch price: £1389
Excellent: £4500
Good: £3500
Average: £1600
Project: £500

LANCIA
Fulvia Coupé

After a couple of years in production, the special variations of the Fulvia started to get released. The major news was the two-door Coupé, which like the Flavia was distinguished by its handsome bodywork mounted on a shortened floorpan. It also shared no exterior panels with the saloon. Performance was improved with a 1.2-litre 80bhp version of the engine being installed at launch, but upgraded to a 90bhp 1290cc power unit later in its life. Handling was known for its precision and neutrality, a point devastatingly proved in motor sport with the more potent HF.

SPECIFICATIONS

Years produced: 1965-1976 (139,817 in total)
Performance: 0-60mph: 15.8 secs (Top speed: 100mph)
Power & torque: 80bhp / 77lb/ft
Engine: Normally aspirated 1216cc V4, petrol, carburettor, 8 valves
Drivetrain: front-engine RWD
Suspension: Independent, transverse leaf springs Beam axle, semi-elliptic leaf springs
Bodyframe: metal monocoque
Transmission: 4-speed manual
Weight: 940kgs

PRICE GUIDE

Launch price: £1490
Excellent: £6500
Good: £5000
Average: £2500
Project: £800

LANCIA
Fulvia Coupé HF

The Fulvia's crowning achievement was to win the 1972 International Rally Championship with the HF Rallye, the competition version of a model had been around since 1965. Powered by a tuned version of the 1216cc engine producing 88bhp, the HF was lighter than the standard Coupé, thanks to the aluminium bonnet, doors and bootlid along with with plexiglass windows. Considered too raw for the road, the HF was further developed into the Rallye 1.6 HF; a fire breathing 1584cc version developing 115bhp. Today HFs are the most soughtafter versions, with values to match.

SPECIFICATIONS

Years produced: 1965-1976 (139,817 in total)
Performance: 0-60mph: 11.9 secs (Top speed: 103mph)
Power & torque: 87bhp / 83lb/ft
Engine: Normally aspirated 1298cc V4, petrol, carburettor, 8 valves
Drivetrain: Front-engine RWD
Suspension: (F) Independent, transverse leaf spring. (R) Beam axle, semi-elliptic leaf spring
Bodyframe: Monocoque
Transmission: 4-speed Manual
Weight: 894kgs

PRICE GUIDE

Launch price: £1548
Excellent: £12,000
Good: £9500
Average: £4750
Project: £2500

LANCIA
Fulvia Sport Zagato

Slightly more palatable looking than the Zagato-bodied Sport Flavia, the aluminium Fulvia was still a challenging looking thing. But those concept car looks promised a great driving experience and, thankfully, the Sport Zagato lived up to the off-the-wall styling. Like the HF, the Zagato was lighter than the standard Coupé, and the power-to-weight ratio delivered by the lively V4 power units was enhanced usefully. Upgraded during its life, the Sport Zagato even picked up luxury fitments such as electric windows later in life, a sure sign that drivers were demanding more into the 1970s.

SPECIFICATIONS

Years produced: 1968-1972
Performance: 0-60mph: 13.0 secs (Top speed: 109mph)
Power & torque: 87bhp / 84lb/ft
Engine: Normally aspirated 1298cc V4, petrol, carburettor, 8 valves
Drivetrain: Front-engine FWD
Suspension: (F) Independent, transverse leaf spring. (R) Beam axle, semi-elliptic leaf spring
Bodyframe: Monocoque
Transmission: 5-speed manual
Weight: 960kgs

PRICE GUIDE

Launch price: N/A
Excellent: £11,000
Good: £9000
Average: £4500
Project: £2250

LANCIA
Beta Berlina

A gem of a saloon that was streets ahead of other family offerings when it appeared in 1972 with four-wheel disc brakes, twin-cam engine, independent suspension and a five-speed gearbox. Rust in front subframes and wings, with ferocious media hype around it, saw to the car's UK demise, despite the '76 S2 being vastly better and Lancia's introduction of a six-year anti-corrosion warranty before the troubles came to light. Most of the afflicted S1 Betas have gone to the crusher, but there are still cared-for S2s to be found.

SPECIFICATIONS

Years produced: 1972-1981 (194,914 in total)
Performance: 0-60mph: 10.5 secs (Top speed: 109mph)
Power & torque: 110bhp / 106lb/ft
Engine: Normally aspirated 1756cc in-line four, petrol, carburettor, 8 valves
Drivetrain: Front-engine FWD
Suspension: [F] Independent, wishbone, coil spring. [R] Independent, wishbone, coil spring
Bodyframe: Monocoque
Transmission: 5-speed manual
Weight: 1095kgs

PRICE GUIDE

Launch price: £1594
Excellent: £2200
Good: £1650
Average: £700
Project: £125

LANCIA
Stratos

It started life as a Bertone concept car in 1970, but the Lancia competition director, Cesare Fiorio saw something in the squat little wedge that no one else did: a potential rally car. Fiorio knew that the Dino V6 engine from Ferrari was now within his grasp. A plan was hatched, and within three years, a production version was released (and 500 built), while the rally car was developed from it. From this inspired idea, Lancia's domination of world rallying ensued. Road versions were hard to sell, and some languished in showrooms, unsold, for up to five years.

SPECIFICATIONS

Years produced: 1973-1975 (492 in total)
Performance: 0-60mph: 6.0 secs (Top speed: 4.3mph)
Power & torque: 187bhp / 166lb/ft
Engine: Normally aspirated 2419cc V6, petrol, carburettor, 12 valves
Drivetrain: Mid-engine RWD
Suspension: [F] Independent, wishbone, coil spring. [R] Independent, wishbone, coil spring
Bodyframe: chassis and glassfibre body
Transmission: 5-speed manual
Weight: 980kgs

PRICE GUIDE

Launch price: £7000
Excellent: £50,000
Good: £42,500
Average: £30,000
Project: £20,000

LANCIA
Beta Coupé

Launched a year after the saloon it was based on, the Coupé used a 19cm shortened floorpan but still found room for full-sized adults in the rear seats. That shorter wheelbase combines well with a reduction of 90kg from the saloon's weight, creating a car that is even sharper to drive and suffers less from the lack of power steering. Engine options are the same rev-happy 1300-2000 twin-cams as the saloon, with Bosch injection from 1981 and the addition of a supercharged version, badged Volumex, for 1983-84.

SPECIFICATIONS

Years produced: 1973-1984 (111,801 in total)
Performance: 0-60mph: 9.8 secs (Top speed: 114mph)
Power & torque: 108bhp / 114lb/ft
Engine: Normally aspirated 1585cc in-line four, petrol, carburettor, 8 valves
Drivetrain: Front-engine FWD
Suspension: [F] Independent, wishbone, coil spring. [R] Independent, wishbone, coil spring
Bodyframe: Monocoque
Transmission: 5-speed manual
Weight: 1000kgs

PRICE GUIDE

Launch price: £2153
Excellent: £3000
Good: £2400
Average: £1000
Project: £500

LANCIA
Beta Spider

In theory this is just a Beta Coupé with a clever roof, but this is Lancia so it's more complicated than that. The Targa top with folding rear window section and different door window frames was designed by Pininfarina and built by Zagato, which was enough for the car to be badged Lancia Zagato in America. They also changed the tail-lights for units shared with the Bristol Beaufighter. Unusually it's a four-seater convertible. Only sold with 1600 or 2000 engines, though there's not that much difference in performance between them.

SPECIFICATIONS

Years produced: 1975-1982 (9390 in total)
Performance: 0-60mph: 9.5 secs (Top speed: 115mph)
Power & torque: 119bhp / 129lb/ft
Engine: Normally aspirated 1995cc in-line four, petrol, carburettor, 8 valves
Drivetrain: Front-engine FWD
Suspension: [F] Independent, wishbone, coil spring. [R] Independent, wishbone, coil spring
Bodyframe: Monocoque
Transmission: 5-speed manual
Weight: 1048kgs

PRICE GUIDE

Launch price: £3128
Excellent: £3750
Good: £3200
Average: £1600
Project: £700

LANCIA
Beta Montecarlo

This is only actually a Beta in name, with the only parts shared with the rest of the range being the engine block and internal door lock buttons. It's a mid-engined two-seater, originally envisaged as the Fiat X1/20. Then someone realised it could be priced higher with a Lancia badge. Only sold with a two-litre engine in Europe, S1 versions had problems with locking front brakes, cured simply by removing the servo. 1980-on S2s were better in other ways too. With fine handling balance and expressive steering, these are under-rated driver's cars.

SPECIFICATIONS

Years produced: 1975-1984 (7595 in total)
Performance: 0-60mph: 8.6 secs (Top speed: 120mph)
Power & torque: 118bhp / 122lb/ft
Engine: Normally aspirated 1995cc in-line four, petrol, carburettor, 8 valves
Drivetrain: Mid-engine RWD
Suspension: [F] Independent, wishbone, coil spring. [R] Independent, wishbone, coil spring
Bodyframe: Monocoque
Transmission: 5-speed manual
Weight: 970kgs

PRICE GUIDE

Launch price: £5927
Excellent: £7200
Good: £6000
Average: £3000
Project: £1500

LANCIA
Gamma Berlina

If one car summed up the bitter-sweet nature of large Italian cars of the 1970s, it had to be the Gamma. Originally conceived as part of a joint venture with Citroën that never bore fruit, the Gamma ended up being developed by Lancia alone. The Gamma drove well, but its undoing was its new flat-four – it leaked oil, overheated and snapped its cambelt for good measure. And then, it rusted away. If you can see past the faults, there's a great car trying to escape, but there are so few survivors now that few people will ever find out.

SPECIFICATIONS

Years produced: 1975-1984 (15,296 in total)
Performance: 0-60mph: N/A (Top speed: 115mph)
Power & torque: 115bhp / 127lb/ft
Engine: Normally aspirated 1999cc Flat 4, petrol, carburettor, 8 valves
Drivetrain: Front-engine FWD
Suspension: [F] Independent, wishbone, coil spring. [R] Independent, wishbone, coil spring
Bodyframe: Monocoque
Transmission: 5-speed manual
Weight: 1320kgs

PRICE GUIDE

Launch price: £7136
Excellent: £2500
Good: £1750
Average: £900
Project: £200

LANCIA
Beta HPE

The initials stand for High Performance Estate, created by fitting a Coupé front end and doors (with different window frames) to a saloon floorpan and finishing off with a hatchback rear section that pays homage to the Reliant Scimitar GTE. The result is a lot more stylish than that sounds, and you get the softer ride of the saloon with the lower seating position of the Coupé. In keeping with its superior intentions, only 1600 and 2000 engines were offered, with an optional 135bhp supercharged version of the two-litre for the last year of production.

SPECIFICATIONS

Years produced: 1975-1985 (71,258 in total)
Performance: 0-60mph: 10.6 secs (Top speed: 116mph)
Power & torque: 115bhp / 130lb/ft
Engine: Normally aspirated 1995cc in-line four, petrol, carburettor, 8 valves
Drivetrain: Front-engine FWD
Suspension: [F] Independent, wishbone, coil spring. [R] Independent, wishbone, coil spring
Bodyframe: Monocoque
Transmission: 5-speed manual
Weight: 1060kgs

PRICE GUIDE

Launch price: £3688
Excellent: £3200
Good: £2500
Average: £1250
Project: £250

LANCIA
Gamma Coupé

The Gamma Berlina was perhaps the ultimate evolution of Pininfarina's BMC 1800 Aerodynamica concept car, first shown in 1966. The fastback saloon echoed the times perfectly, but somehow failed to capture buyers' imaginations. However, the Coupé – also styled by Pininfarina – emerged as one of the finest-looking cars of the 1970s. It might have been saddled with the same problems as the Berlina, but owners have been more prepared to restore and repair than to throw away, and that's down purely to the way the Coupé looks. Buy by all means, but treat like a China doll.

SPECIFICATIONS

Years produced: 1976-1984 (6789 in total)
Performance: 0-60mph: 9.4 secs (Top speed: 120mph)
Power & torque: 140bhp / 154lb/ft
Engine: Normally aspirated 2484cc Flat 4, petrol, electronic fuel injection, 8 valves
Drivetrain: Front-engine FWD
Suspension: [F] Ind. wishbone, coil spring, anti-roll bar. [R] Ind. wishbone, coil spring, anti-roll bar
Bodyframe: Monocoque
Transmission: 5-speed manual
Weight: 1290kgs

PRICE GUIDE

Launch price: £9186
Excellent: £3750
Good: £2750
Average: £1250
Project: £300

LANCIA
Delta HF Turbo

In an attempt to join the 1980s hot hatch club, Lancia uprated its stylish Delta with a turbocharged version of the classic Fiat twin-cam under the bonnet. Performance was predictably rapid, and thanks to Martini stripes on all-white paintwork (for the early cars), it stood out from the crowd, too. Sales in the UK were never that rapid, thanks to the Escort XR3i and Golf GTI's dominance of the sector, but despite its obscurity the Delta HF Turbo earned itself a reputation for being fast and fun. Not the last word in finesse or refinement, but a hoot to drive.

SPECIFICATIONS

Years produced: 1984-1990
Performance: 0-60mph: 8.5 secs (Top speed: 126mph)
Power & torque: 140bhp / 141lb/ft
Engine: Turbocharged 1585cc in-line four, petrol, electronic fuel injection, 8 valves
Drivetrain: Front-engine FWD
Suspension: (F&R) Ind. strut, coil spring, wishbone, telescopic damper, anti-roll bar
Bodyframe: Monocoque
Transmission: 5-speed manual
Weight: 1000kgs

PRICE GUIDE

Launch price: £8790
Excellent: £3500
Good: £2500
Average: £1000
Project: £350

LANCIA
Delta HF Integrale 8v

The first Integrale an for many enthusiasts, the best. For this rally homologation special, a 2-litre version of the venerable Fiat twin-cam had a full-pressure turbo to deliver 165bhp. Combine this with permanent four-wheel-drive and wide tyres and the ensuing super-hot hatch was fast-agile and grippy, with none of the torque steer than afflicted lesser rivals. Although part of the UK Lancia range, the Integrale was never converted to right hand drive, so if you come across a right-hooker check to see which company carried out the conversion.

SPECIFICATIONS

Years produced: 1987-1989
Performance: 0-60mph: 6.2 secs (Top speed: 128mph)
Power & torque: 185bhp / 224lb/ft
Engine: Turbocharged 1995cc in-line four, petrol, electronic fuel injection, 8 valves
Drivetrain: Front-engine AWD
Suspension: (F&R) Ind. strut, coil spring, wishbone, telescopic damper, anti-roll bar
Bodyframe: Monocoque
Transmission: 5-speed manual
Weight: 1267kgs

PRICE GUIDE

Launch price: £13,980
Excellent: £8000
Good: £5750
Average: £3000
Project: £1250

LANCIA
Thema 8.32

The Ferrari V8 that was shoehorned into Lancia's Type Four chassis was not actually assembled by Ferrari. The job of screwing it together was outsourced to Ducati engineers. Although similar to that found in the 308 qv, it was tuned differently to suit the Lancia's more relaxed driving style. The epic soundtrack and moderate performance were not enough to sell it, and UK sales were dire, with just nine 8.32s officially sold. It did slightly better in Europe, but the killer for this car was the Thema Turbo i.e which was actually quicker in a straight line.

SPECIFICATIONS

Years produced:	1988-1990 (3971 in total)
Performance:	0-60mph: 6.8 secs (Top speed: 149mph)
Power & torque:	215bhp / 210lb/ft
Engine:	Normally aspirated 2927cc V8, petrol, electronic fuel injection, 32 valves
Drivetrain:	Front-engine FWD
Suspension:	(F) Ind. struts, coil spring, anti-roll bar. (R) Ind. struts, coil spring, anti-roll bar
Bodyframe:	Metal monocoque
Transmission:	5-speed manual
Weight:	1400kgs
	PRICE GUIDE
Launch price:	£40,095
Excellent:	£9000
Good:	£7250
Average:	£3750
Project:	£1500

LAND ROVER
Series I

In the aftermath of World War Two, Rover's chief engineer, Maurice Wilks, owned a 'demobbed' Jeep and was impressed with its abilities. However, it was worn out and as there was no British replacement on the market he decided to build his own. In 1948, that vehicle appeared as the Land Rover and proved so popular that demand massively outstripped supply – and went on to become an enduring success that helped keep the rest of Rover afloat during the lean years of the 1950s. Now known as the S1, these early cars are enduring classics.

SPECIFICATIONS

Years produced:	1948-1957
Performance:	0-60mph: N/A (Top speed: 55mph)
Power & torque:	50bhp / N/A
Engine:	Normally aspirated 1595cc in-line four, petrol, carburettor, 8 valves
Drivetrain:	front-engine AWD
Suspension:	(F&R) Beam axle, semi-elliptic leaf spring
Bodyframe:	Chassis and separate body
Transmission:	4-speed manual with selectable high and low ratios
Weight:	1177kgs
	PRICE GUIDE
Launch price:	£450
Excellent:	£6750
Good:	£5500
Average:	£2850
Project:	£1850

LAND ROVER
SII/SIIA

A decade after its launch and still hugely popular, the Series II Land Rover appeared. Easily identifiable by its revised styling and powered by a new 2.25-litre petrol engine, this design stayed in production – basically unchanged – until 1990. The Series IIA that followed 18 months later was further improved to include a 2.6-litre petrol engine in the LWB version, and a new 2.25-litre diesel, significantly expanding the car's appeal in export markets. Considered the ultimate DIY car, Land Rovers are revered for the ease with which you can work on them.

SPECIFICATIONS

Years produced:	1958-1971
Performance:	0-60mph: 36.1 secs (Top speed: 65mph)
Power & torque:	77bhp / N/A
Engine:	Normally aspirated 2286cc in-line four, petrol, carburettor, 8 valves
Drivetrain:	Front-engine AWD
Suspension:	(F) Beam axle, leaf springs. (R) Beam axle, leaf springs
Bodyframe:	Chassis and separate body
Transmission:	4-speed manual
Weight:	1092kgs
	PRICE GUIDE
Launch price:	£640
Excellent:	£4250
Good:	£3000
Average:	£1400
Project:	£500

LAND ROVER
S III

Series III improvements are easy to spot thanks to the repositioned headlights (late SIIAs had them, too) and updated plastic radiator grille. The updated – more safety conscious – interior and all synchromesh gearbox acknowledged the opposition was catching up, and the option of overdrive catered for those who needed their Land Rovers for serious on-road work. It was during the Series III production that the Rover V8 engine was added to the range, initially in low compression form to allow it to run on whatever grade fuel its owner threw at it.

SPECIFICATIONS

Years produced:	1971-1985
Performance:	0-60mph: 29.1 secs (Top speed: 68mph)
Power & torque:	70bhp / 119lb/ft
Engine:	Normally aspirated 2286cc in-line four, petrol, carburettor, 8 valves
Drivetrain:	Front-engine AWD
Suspension:	(F) Live axle, semi-elliptic leaf springs. (R) Live axle, semi-elliptic leaf springs
Bodyframe:	chassis and separate body
Transmission:	4-speed manual
Weight:	1380kgs
	PRICE GUIDE
Launch price:	£1002
Excellent:	£4000
Good:	£3000
Average:	£1300
Project:	£400

LEA FRANCIS
14 Saloon

One of the original British motor industry players, the pre-war years had been good for Lea Francis. Its competition cars had proved themselves and had earned an enviable reputation with enthusiasts. After the war, the firm concentrated on saloon car production, initially with its 14hp saloon. The 14 sat very much at the upper end of the market, and found fewer buyers than anticipated, but the addition of a 2.5-litre engine in 1949 widened appeal. Lea Francis continued with this line until 1953, then abandoned car production to concentrate on other activities.

SPECIFICATIONS

Years produced:	1946-1954 (3137 in total)
Performance:	0-60mph: N/A (Top speed: 70mph)
Power & torque:	55bhp / N/A
Engine:	Normally aspirated 1469cc in-line four, petrol, carburettor, 8 valves
Drivetrain:	Front-engine RWD
Suspension:	(F) Beam axle, semi-elliptic leaf springs. (R) Beam axle, semi-elliptic leaf springs
Bodyframe:	Chassis and separate body
Transmission:	4-speed manual
Weight:	1270kgs
	PRICE GUIDE
Launch price:	£951
Excellent:	£8750
Good:	£7250
Average:	£3750
Project:	£1650

LEA FRANCIS
14hp/2.5-litre Sports

The Sports was a classic English sports car powered by the saloon's 1.8-litre engine, and closely following the established template that proved so popular in export markets. The engine itself was intriguing because it aped Riley's pre-war design, and delivered enough power for a top speed of 85mph. Later models gained independent front suspension, and proved to be excellent handling cars, while the 2.5-litre Sports that followed in 1950 added extra power into the mix, becoming a genuine 100mph four-seater sports car in the process.

SPECIFICATIONS

Years produced: 1947-1953 (186 in total)
Performance: 0-60mph: 19.2 secs (Top speed: 87mph)
Power & torque: 87bhp / N/A
Engine: Normally aspirated 1767cc in-line four, petrol, carburettor, 8 valves
Drivetrain: front-engine RWD
Suspension: (F) Beam axle, leaf spring. (R) Beam axle, leaf spring
Bodyframe: Chassis and separate body
Transmission: 4-speed manual
Weight: 1016kgs

PRICE GUIDE

Launch price: £1266
Excellent: £18,250
Good: £15,000
Average: £11,000
Project: £6000

LOTUS
Six

Intended as a street-legal weekend racer, the predecessor to the legendary Seven uses a lightweight spaceframe clothed in alloy panels (often left bare) and fitted with Ford brakes and rear axle. All were sold in kit form, so specification can vary widely from car to car. Most commonly used engines were Ford, either in sidevalve 1172cc or OHV 1500 form, though some are known to have been fitted with 1250cc MG units. In all cases the lack of weight means they provide a lot more fun and performance than you might expect.

SPECIFICATIONS

Years produced: 1953-1956 (100 in total)
Performance: 0-60mph: N/A (Top speed: 93mph)
Power & torque: 36bhp / N/A
Engine: Normally aspirated 1172cc in-line four, petrol, carburettor, 8 valves
Drivetrain: Front-engine RWD
Suspension: (F) Independent, coil spring. (R) Beam axle, coil spring
Bodyframe: Spaceframe with alloy panels
Transmission: 3-speed manual
Weight: N/A

PRICE GUIDE

Launch price: £185
Excellent: £20,000
Good: £16,500
Average: £12,500
Project: £9000

LOTUS
Seven S1/S2

A legend is born that lives on today. Refinements over the VI it is based on include wishbone front suspension and hydraulic brakes, and that's just for starters. S1s initially sold with Ford's sidevalve engine, with later S1s and S2s offered with the 948cc BMC A-series and its four-speed 'box; from 1961 there was also the option of the 997cc Anglia engines. Don't be surprised by later upgrades though. S2s are distinguished by their glassfibre nosecones, but they also have a less complex spaceframe and revised rear axle location. Short of space for those of large frame or large feet.

SPECIFICATIONS

Years produced: 1957-1968 (242/1350 in total)
Performance: 0-60mph: 17.8 secs (Top speed: 76mph)
Power & torque: 40bhp / 58lb/ft
Engine: Normally aspirated 1172cc in-line four, petrol, carburettor, 8 valves
Drivetrain: Front-engine RWD
Suspension: (F) Independent, coil springs. (R) Beam axle, coil springs
Bodyframe: Spaceframe with alloy/glassfibre pabels
Transmission: 3-speed manual
Weight: 457kgs

PRICE GUIDE

Launch price: £1036
Excellent: £17,500
Good: £15,000
Average: £10,000
Project: £6500

LOTUS
Super Seven

Really pushing the racecar for the road theme, the Super Sevens came with longer glassfibre front wings and Cosworth-tuned Ford engines of 1340, 1500 or 1600cc capacity and phenomenal performance. To reign this back, those with the larger engines came with the welcome addition of disc brakes. Many were still sold as kits, and they've always appealed to those of a tinkering nature, so expect the unexpected as far as specification goes. A dozen or so 'Super Sevens' were fitted with Lotus twin-cam engines, but only genuine ones are worth the extra these command.

SPECIFICATIONS

Years produced: 1957-1968 (500+ in total)
Performance: 0-60mph: 9.0 secs (Top speed: 102mph)
Power & torque: 95bhp / 103lb/ft
Engine: Normally aspirated 1498cc in-line four, petrol, carburettor, 8 valves
Drivetrain: Front-engine RWD
Suspension: (F) Independent, coil springs. (R) Beam axle, coil springs
Bodyframe: Spaceframe with glassfibre panels
Transmission: 4-speed manual
Weight: 435kgs

PRICE GUIDE

Launch price: £1250
Excellent: £18,500
Good: £16,000
Average: £11,000
Project: £7500

LOTUS
Elite

The undoubted star of the 1957 Earl's Court Motor Show, but Lotus kept buyers waiting until the summer of 1959 to enjoy this technical marvel of great beauty. Use of a chassis-less glassfibre monocoque and aluminium Coventry-Climax 1200cc 75bhp engine resulted in the incredibly light weight that made this car perform and handle so well; 1960 brought a Series II model with improved rear suspension and trim, plus the SE with its close-ratio ZF gearbox and optional breathing package for an extra 10bhp. Be aware, they are noisy inside, and quite a squeeze for six-footers.

SPECIFICATIONS

Years produced: 1958-1963 (988 in total)
Performance: 0-60mph: 11.4 secs (Top speed: 112mph)
Power & torque: 71bhp / 77lb/ft
Engine: Normally aspirated 1216cc in-line four, petrol, carburettor, 8 valves
Drivetrain: Front-engine RWD
Suspension: (F) Independent, coil springs, wishbone. (R) Ind. coil springs, Chapman strut
Bodyframe: Glassfibre monocoque
Transmission: 4-speed manual
Weight: 660kgs

PRICE GUIDE

Launch price: £1951
Excellent: £35,000
Good: £30,000
Average: £18,500
Project: £10,000

LOTUS
Elan DHC

The lightweight sports car against whose handling all other would be measured for decades. All-independent suspension on a backbone chassis was the stuff of genius, and makes the indifferent fit and finish of the glassfibre bodies almost irrelevant. Gradually improved through four series, each of which outsold the last: S2 gained larger front brake calipers; S3 (from 1966) has frames for the windows, centre lock alloy wheels and a higher final drive ratio; S4 got a bonnet bulge to cover its twin Stromberg carbs, but reverted to Webers in late 1969. SE means 115bhp and close-ratio 'box.

SPECIFICATIONS

Years produced:	1962-1971 (12,200 (all Elans) in total)
Performance:	0-60mph: 8.0 secs (Top speed: 110mph)
Power & torque:	100bhp / 102lb/ft
Engine:	Normally aspirated 1499cc in-line four, petrol, carburettor, 8 valves
Drivetrain:	Front-engine RWD
Suspension:	(F) Independent, coil springs. (R) Independent, coil springs
Bodyframe:	Chassis and separate body
Transmission:	4-speed manual
Weight:	585kgs

PRICE GUIDE

Launch price:	£1499
Excellent:	£17,000
Good:	£14,000
Average:	£8500
Project:	£4250

LOTUS
Elan S3/S4 Coupé

Hardtop version of the Elan was used to introduce the S3, and arrived the year before its soft-top brother. In line with Lotus's intention to move upmarket and justify their 'quality' prices, fit and finish was improved over the earlier Elans, and the Coupé came with a smarter dashboard and frames for the door windows to greatly reduce wind noise. The windows themselves were now electrically operated. SE model was offered from July 1966 with 115bhp engine, standard servo brakes, a close ratio gearbox, plus a slightly taller rear axle ratio to make things a little quieter at high speeds.

SPECIFICATIONS

Years produced:	1965-1971 (5650 (all Elans) in total)
Performance:	0-60mph: 8.7 secs (Top speed: 114mph)
Power & torque:	105bhp / 108lb/ft
Engine:	Normally aspirated 1558cc in-line four, petrol, carburettor, 8 valves
Drivetrain:	Front-engine RWD
Suspension:	(F) Ind. wishbone, coil springs. (R) Ind. lower wishbone, coil springs
Bodyframe:	Chassis and separate body
Transmission:	4-speed manual
Weight:	688kgs

PRICE GUIDE

Launch price:	£1312
Excellent:	£13,000
Good:	£11,000
Average:	£6250
Project:	£3500

LOTUS
Europa S1/S2

Colin Chapman's first mid-engined road car was aimed squarely at the glamorous European market, where Italians were making inroads with the layout. Based around Renault 16 running gear, all S1s went for export. They also had their glassfibre body bonded to the steel chassis, making repairs a nightmare. Europa S2s were sold in the UK, from 1969, and only differed from the S1 in being bolted to the chassis and having elecric windows. All but US exports came with 1470cc engines, though many larger 1565cc units have since been transplanted in from dead Renaults.

SPECIFICATIONS

Years produced:	1967-1971
Performance:	0-60mph: 9.3 secs (Top speed: 117mph)
Power & torque:	78bhp / 76lb/ft
Engine:	Normally aspirated 1470cc in-line four, petrol, carburettor, 8 valves
Drivetrain:	Mid-engine RWD
Suspension:	(F) Independent, coil spring. (R) Independent, coil spring
Bodyframe:	Chassis and separate body
Transmission:	4-speed manual
Weight:	706kgs

PRICE GUIDE

Launch price:	£1996
Excellent:	£9000
Good:	£7500
Average:	£4000
Project:	£2000

LOTUS
Seven S3

Sold alongside the Super Seven, the S3s came with their Ford engines in a saner state of tune, though all sizes from 1300-1600 were available. Tuning options came from Holbay, not Cosworth for these. This is the car that was revived officially by Caterham and unofficially by everyone else, but the 350 or so originals command a decent premium for all that heritage. Still largely sold as kits originally, which means fit and finish has always been variable, and is likely to have been redone several times over a car's life. Hard to value, but the fun factor is always the same.

SPECIFICATIONS

Years produced:	1968-1970 (1413 in total)
Performance:	0-60mph: 7.7 secs (Top speed: 99mph)
Power & torque:	84bhp / 96lb/ft
Engine:	Normally aspirated 1598cc in-line four, petrol, carburettor, 8 valves
Drivetrain:	Front-engine RWD
Suspension:	(F) Independent, coil springs. (R) Beam axle, coil springs
Bodyframe:	Spaceframe with alloy/glassfibre panels
Transmission:	4-speed manual
Weight:	549kgs

PRICE GUIDE

Launch price:	£775
Excellent:	£16,000
Good:	£14,000
Average:	£9000
Project:	£5500

LOTUS
Elan Plus 2

Taking one step further away from the racetrack, Lotus widened its range to include something for buyers with young families. By stretching the Elan's chassis by a foot and widening the track, child-sized rear seats could be accommodated. This was also the first Lotus not to be sold in kit form, which at least evens out build quality; the 118bhp engine tune helps with the extra weight, and this was raised to 126bhp from 1970 for the Plus 2S/130 is identifiable by its silver metalflake roof. Better quality trim is a feature, and from 1972 the 130-5 comes with a five-speed gearbox.

SPECIFICATIONS

Years produced:	1969-1974 (3300 in total)
Performance:	0-60mph: 8.2 secs (Top speed: 123mph)
Power & torque:	118bhp / 112lb/ft
Engine:	Normally aspirated 1558cc in-line four, petrol, carburettor, 8 valves
Drivetrain:	Front-engine RWD
Suspension:	(F) Independent, coil springs. (R) Independent, coil springs
Bodyframe:	Chassis and separate body
Transmission:	4-speed manual
Weight:	854kgs

PRICE GUIDE

Launch price:	£1923
Excellent:	£10,250
Good:	£8750
Average:	£5000
Project:	£2000

LOTUS
Seven S4

The lower prices today tell you Lotus lost the plot a bit with the S4. In some ways it's a better car, with decent legroom at last, improved front and rear suspension and all-glassfibre bodywork over a new steel chassis. Unfortunately that all added an extra couple of hundred pounds to the weight, slightly blunting the scorching performance and handling that Sevens are all about. Plus that new bodywork falls somewhere between archaic special and racing beach buggy. It offers a way in to Seven ownership, but you can see why Caterham went back to the S3 when they took over manufacture.

SPECIFICATIONS

Years produced: 1970-1973 (887 in total)
Performance: 0-60mph: 8.7 secs (Top speed: 116mph)
Power & torque: 115bhp / 108lb/ft
Engine: Normally aspirated 1598cc in-line four, petrol, carburettor, 8 valves
Drivetrain: Front-engine RWD
Suspension: (F) Independent, coil springs. (R) Beam axle, coil springs
Bodyframe: Spaceframe with glassfibre body
Transmission: 4-speed manual
Weight: 579kgs

PRICE GUIDE

Launch price: £1245
Excellent: £8500
Good: £7000
Average: £4500
Project: £2000

LOTUS
Elan Sprint

Introduced to boost flagging sales, the Sprint justified its name thanks to a substantial boost in the engine department. A big-valve head with high-lift cams and a raised compression ratio raised output to 126bhp and the drivetrain was suitably toughened and braced to cope. Both coupé and roadster versions were built, with gold-painted bumpers and two-tone paint to set them apart from other Elans. Single colour paint was also available, but as an extra cost option. With prices approaching those of E-type Jags, only around 1000 were sold, some of the last with five-speed gearboxes.

SPECIFICATIONS

Years produced: 1971-1973
Performance: 0-60mph: 6.7 secs (Top speed: 121mph)
Power & torque: 126bhp / 113lb/ft
Engine: Normally aspirated 1558cc in-line four, petrol, carburettor, 8 valves
Drivetrain: Front-engine RWD
Suspension: (F) Ind. wishbone, coil spring, anti-roll bar. (R) Ind. coil spring, lower wishbone
Bodyframe: Chassis and separate body
Transmission: 4-speed manual
Weight: 721kgs

PRICE GUIDE

Launch price: £1706
Excellent: £18,000
Good: £14,500
Average: £8500
Project: £4500

LOTUS
Europa Twin Cam/Special

Accusations that the Europa was underpowered were dealt with by the simple expedient of fitting the Lotus twin-cam unit, initially in 105bhp form, but with 126bhp in the Special a year later in 1972. Most of these celebrated Lotus' Grand Prix success by being painted John Player Special colours. Both of these Europas still used the Renault 16 gearbox (with an improved gear linkage), though the Specials could also be had with a five-speed version from the 17TS. Visually, these twin-cam models differed from the S1/S2 by having cut-down rear 'buttresses' to improve visibility.

SPECIFICATIONS

Years produced: 1971-1975 (1580 in total)
Performance: 0-60mph: 7.7 secs (Top speed: 109mph)
Power & torque: 105bhp / 108lb/ft
Engine: Normally aspirated 1558cc in-line four, petrol, carburettor, 8 valves
Drivetrain: Front-engine RWD
Suspension: (F) Independent, coil springs. (R) Independent, coil springs
Bodyframe: Chassis and separate body
Transmission: 4-speed manual
Weight: 737kgs

PRICE GUIDE

Launch price: £1996
Excellent: £15,000
Good: £11,000
Average: £5500
Project: £2500

LOTUS
Elite/Eclat

In an effort to shed its kit car image, Lotus took a giant leap upmarket in 1974 with the Elite – a four-seater coupe with a kind of hatchback. As the American market didn't take to the styling, it was joined the next year by the Eclat, pretty much the same car but with the rear panels reshaped into a more familiar fastback form, also losing about 45kg in weight in the process. The all-new two-litre Lotus twin-cam engine was increased to 2.2 litres from 1980, with the same peak power output but substantially more torque. A Getrag five-speed gearbox was also used from this point.

SPECIFICATIONS

Years produced: 1974-1983 (2398/1299 in total)
Performance: 0-60mph: 7.8 secs (Top speed: 124mph)
Power & torque: 160bhp / 140lb/ft
Engine: Normally aspirated 1973cc in-line four, petrol, carburettor, 8 valves
Drivetrain: Front-engine RWD
Suspension: (F) Independent, wishbone, coil springs. (R) Independent, wishbone, coil springs
Bodyframe: Chassis and glassfibre body
Transmission: 5-speed manual
Weight: 1107kgs

PRICE GUIDE

Launch price: £5445
Excellent: £5000
Good: £4000
Average: XXXXX
Project: £900

LOTUS
Esprit S1

Lotus turned to Giugiaro to design them a flagship that gained instant pin-up status, and an appearance as a Bond car/submarine in *The Spy Who Loved Me*. Still using the established Elan system of a glassfibre body over a backbone chassis, the Esprit had its two-litre twin-cam engine mid-mounted. The S2's minor mods included 'ears' behind the rear side windows to improve engine airflow, Speedline alloys and upturned Rover SD1 taillights. For the last year of production it was fitted with the 2.2-litre engine, these models being commonly referred to as the S2.2.

SPECIFICATIONS

Years produced: 1976-1977 (718/1060 in total)
Performance: 0-60mph: 8.4 secs (Top speed: 135mph)
Power & torque: 160bhp / 140lb/ft
Engine: Normally aspirated 1973cc in-line four, petrol, carburettor, 16 valves
Drivetrain: Mid-engine RWD
Suspension: (F) Independent, wishbone, coil springs. (R) Independent, wishbone, coil springs
Bodyframe: Chassis and separate body
Transmission: 5-speed manual
Weight: 1006kgs

PRICE GUIDE

Launch price: £7883
Excellent: £11,000
Good: £9000
Average: £5000
Project: £3000

LOTUS
Esprit Turbo

Lotus was now touching supercar territory, with a car that beat the psychological milestones of 150mph and 0-60mph in under six seconds. With almost peerless handling they could now be compared with Porsches and Ferraris. The extra 50bhp over the normal 2.2-litre Esprit comes from a Garrett T3 turbocharger, though the whole of the engine was re-engineered to cope. The first 104 were in Essex Petroleum livery. In 1985 the suspension was revised to use more Toyota and less Triumph parts. Short-lived HC version for 1987 only gets extra 5bhp and 20lb/ft of torque.

SPECIFICATIONS

Years produced:	1980-1987 (1658 in total)
Performance:	0-60mph: 5.6 secs (Top speed: 141mph)
Power & torque:	215bhp / 220lb/ft
Engine:	Turbocharged 2174cc in-line four, petrol, carburettor, 16 valves
Drivetrain:	Mid-engine RWD
Suspension:	(F) Independent, coil springs. (R) Independent, coil springs
Bodyframe:	Chassis and separate body
Transmission:	5-speed manual
Weight:	1148kgs

PRICE GUIDE

Launch price:	£25,980
Excellent:	£12,500
Good:	£10,000
Average:	£7000
Project:	£3500

LOTUS
Esprit S3

Wearing most of the body, chassis and interior revisions introduced for the Turbo model the year before, the Esprit S3 also signalled a major leap forward in quality and reliability. There's a lot more sound insulation too, allegedly reducing noise levels inside by 50%. Despite the larger bumpers and sided air scoops, the design stays true to Giugiaro's concept. The rear wheels and tyres are larger, and lower profile rubber is used to further sharpen the Esprit's superb handling and grip. Despite now being cheaper, experts say these are a much better bet than the S1 and S2.

SPECIFICATIONS

Years produced:	1981-1987 (767 in total)
Performance:	0-60mph: 6.5 secs (Top speed: 135mph)
Power & torque:	160bhp / 160lb/ft
Engine:	Normally aspirated 2174cc in-line four, petrol, carburettor, 16 valves
Drivetrain:	Mid-engine RWD
Suspension:	(F) Independent, wishbone, coil springs. (R) Independent, wishbone, coil springs
Bodyframe:	Chassis and separate body
Transmission:	5-speed manual
Weight:	1020kgs

PRICE GUIDE

Launch price:	£13,461
Excellent:	£9500
Good:	£8000
Average:	£4500
Project:	£2750

LOTUS
Excel

Thoroughly revised version of the Eclat, sold at first as the Eclat Excel to avoid the expense of putting the new car through Type Approval. Most body changes are on the back half of the car, but the big stuff is underneath the skin with a five-speed Toyota Supra transmission and brakes, plus broader, lower rear wishbones. The chassis was galvanised, too. The body was revised again in 1984 with quattro-style blister flares, and from 1986 the SE version offers 180bhp, up 20bhp from the standard car. The same year the SA was launched with a ZF four-speed automatic gearbox.

SPECIFICATIONS

Years produced:	1982-1992 (2074 in total)
Performance:	0-60mph: 7.4 secs (Top speed: 128mph)
Power & torque:	160bhp / 160lb/ft
Engine:	Normally aspirated 2174cc in-line four, petrol, carburettor, 16 valves
Drivetrain:	Front-engine RWD
Suspension:	(F) Independent, coil springs. (R) Independent, coil springs
Bodyframe:	Chassis and separate body
Transmission:	5-speed manual
Weight:	1135kgs

PRICE GUIDE

Launch price:	£13,787
Excellent:	£6000
Good:	£4750
Average:	£2750
Project:	£1250

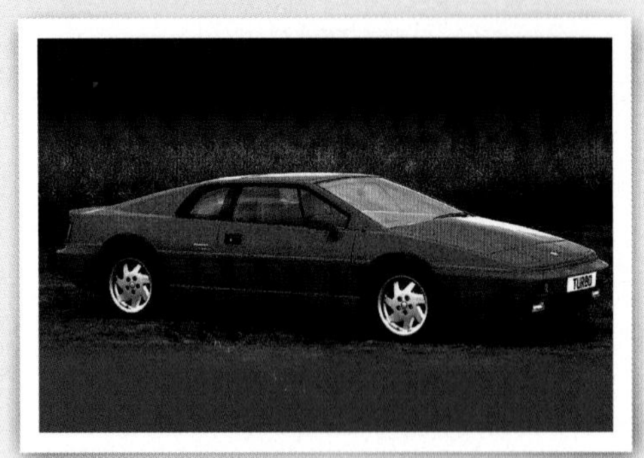

LOTUS
Esprit Turbo/SE (X180)

A subtle redesign by Peter Stevens knocks some of the sharp edges off Giugiaro's original styling, and the opportunity is also used to create more interior space. Mechanically, both normally aspirated and Turbo versions carry on as before, with the exception of a little extra power in the lesser car to pull more weight. Also the Citroën SM transmissions have become obsolete, so Renault GTA units are used instead, along with outboard rear brakes. For spotters, the Turbo has flush glass covering the space between the rear buttresses, while there's none on the standard car.

SPECIFICATIONS

Years produced:	1987-1992 (3120 in total)
Performance:	0-60mph: 5.4 secs (Top speed: 150mph)
Power & torque:	215bhp / 220lb/ft
Engine:	Turbocharged 2174cc in-line four, petrol, electronic fuel injection, 16 valves
Drivetrain:	Mid-engine RWD
Suspension:	(F&R) Independent, wishbone, coil springs, anti-roll bar
Bodyframe:	Chassis and separate body
Transmission:	5-speed manual
Weight:	1270kgs

PRICE GUIDE

Launch price:	£28,900
Excellent:	£13,250
Good:	£11,000
Average:	£8500
Project:	£5000

LOTUS
Elan M100

Conclusive proof that sports cars can be front-wheel-drive as Lotus once again leads the pack in handling technology. Almost all the first batch were turbocharged SE versions, though some 130bhp non-turbo models were sold; all use a long-lived Isuzu 1600 engine that Lotus had helped to design. Sadly, Lotus were losing money on every one of the 3855 Elans sold, so the plug was pulled after two years. When Bugatti bought Lotus in 1994 another run of 800 was made, using up spare engine stock and subtly improved. These were badged S2 and are more sought after today.

SPECIFICATIONS

Years produced:	1989-1994 (4655 in total)
Performance:	0-60mph: 6.5 secs (Top speed: 136mph)
Power & torque:	165bhp / 148lb/ft
Engine:	Turbocharged 1588cc in-line four, petrol, electronic fuel injection, 16 valves
Drivetrain:	Front-engine FWD
Suspension:	(F) Independent, coil springs. (R) Independent, coil springs
Bodyframe:	Metal monocoque
Transmission:	5-speed manual
Weight:	1085kgs

PRICE GUIDE

Launch price:	£19,850
Excellent:	£10,500
Good:	£8500
Average:	£6000
Project:	£3000

LOTUS Carlton

Ford had dominated the performance saloon market in the UK for too long with its Cosworth Sierras. Vauxhall hit back in grand style with the Lotus Carlton in 1989. Back then Lotus was part of the General Motors empire, so it reworked the suspension, steering and brakes of the Carlton saloon while, from elsewhere in GM, a twin-turbocharged Chevrolet Corvette ZR-1 V8 engine with six-speed transmission was adopted. This transformed a fairly ordinary Vauxhall into a blistering five-person express, with supercar levels of speed (177mph) and handling. But it did cost £48,000...

SPECIFICATIONS

Years produced: 1990-1992 (440 in total)
Performance: 0-60mph: 5.4 secs (Top speed: 177mph)
Power & torque: 377bhp / 419lb/ft
Engine: Twin-turbocharged 3615cc in-line six, petrol, electronic fuel injection, 24 valves
Drivetrain: Front-engine RWD
Suspension: (F&R) Ind. tele dampers, coil springs and anti-roll bars. (R) Semi-trailing arms
Bodyframe: Metal monocoque
Transmission: 6-speed manual
Weight: 1663kgs

PRICE GUIDE

Launch price: £48,000
Excellent: £22,000
Good: £16,500
Average: £12,000
Project: £7500

LOTUS Esprit 300 Sport

Developed from the race car, the Esprit 300 Sport is distinct due to its new front airdam and rear spoiler, plus flared arches. A lighter weight composite body helps to shave 91kg off the weight compared to a standard Esprit and it's stiffer too, as is the backbone chassis. Brakes and suspension are uprated and thanks to a hybrid T3/T4 turbo and more efficient chargecooler, power from the 2.2-litre engine goes up to 300bhp – hence the name. Fittings are in place for a rollcage and race seats. Just 50 examples were built.

SPECIFICATIONS

Years produced: 1993 (50 in total)
Performance: 0-60mph: 4.5 secs (Top speed: 165mph)
Power & torque: 300bhp / 300lb/ft
Engine: Turbocharged 2174cc in-line four, petrol, electronic fuel injection, 16 valves
Drivetrain: Mid-engine RWD
Suspension: (F&R) Independent, double wishbone, coil springs, anti-roll bar
Bodyframe: Chassis and separate composite body
Transmission: 5-speed manual
Weight: 1338kgs

PRICE GUIDE

Launch price: £64,995
Excellent: £20,000
Good: £17,500
Average: £15,000
Project: £12,000

LOTUS Esprit S4 Turbo

With a thorough makeover that adorns the car with all manner of scoops, ducts, spoilers and bulges, the Esprit takes on an even more stunningly dramatic persona; one that works a lot better than the description might sound. It came with the muscle to back all that up too, with a water-cooled turbocharger boosting power all the way to 264bhp. To cope with this there's a new high-torque five-speed transmission, plus further major advances in suspension dynamics to keep Lotus ahead in the game it plays best. Power steering is fitted as standard to an Esprit for the first time.

SPECIFICATIONS

Years produced: 1993-1996
Performance: 0-60mph: 4.7 secs (Top speed: 165mph)
Power & torque: 264bhp / 261lb/ft
Engine: Normally aspirated 2174cc in-line four, petrol, electronic fuel injection, 16 valves
Drivetrain: Mid-engine RWD
Suspension: (F& R) Independent, double wishbone, coil springs, anti-roll bars
Bodyframe: Chassis and separate body
Transmission: 5-speed manual
Weight: 1175kgs

PRICE GUIDE

Launch price: £XXXX
Excellent: £16,000
Good: £14,000
Average: £12,000
Project: £10,000

LOTUS Elise S1

A technological marvel that not only took Lotus back to its stripped down lightweight roots, but also created the fastest and best-selling Lotus of all time. Nearly 9000 S1s were shifted in five years. It's built by attaching composite panels to a very light but strong chassis tub made from extruded aluminium and literally glued together. It does without (and doesn't need) such things as a brake servo and power steering, but combines electrifying performance with the feeling that it sucks the road like a vacuum cleaner. Now at affordable levels, but don't expect that to last forever.

SPECIFICATIONS

Years produced: 1995-2001 (12,200 in total)
Performance: 0-60mph: 5.5 secs (Top speed: 124mph)
Power & torque: 118bhp / 122lb/ft
Engine: Normally aspirated 1796cc in-line four, petrol, electronic fuel injection, 16 valves
Drivetrain: Mid-engine RWD
Suspension: (F&R) Independent coil springs
Bodyframe: Chassis with composite panels
Transmission: 5-speed manual
Weight: 674kgs

PRICE GUIDE

Launch price: £18,950
Excellent: £12,000
Good: £9750
Average: £7250
Project: £5500

LOTUS 340R

Originally a concept car created in conjunction with *Autocar* magazine, the 340R simply proved too good – and created too much interest – for it not to be built. Using the Elise's aluminium chassis and all the best bits from sporty Elise variants, everything else – including much of the bodywork – was stripped away to create the purest driving experience possible. In combination with a 177bhp version of Rover's K-Series engine, this added up to a power-to-weight ratio of 272bhp per tonne that many supercars fail to match. Fittingly, production was limited to 340 examples.

SPECIFICATIONS

Years produced: 2000 (340 in total)
Performance: 0-60mph: 4.5 secs (Top speed: 132mph)
Power & torque: 177bhp / 176lb/ft
Engine: Normally aspirated 1796cc in-line four, petrol, electronic fuel injection, 16 valves
Drivetrain: Mid-engine RWD
Suspension: (F&R) Independent, coil springs
Bodyframe: Chassis with composite panels
Transmission: 5-speed manual
Weight: 675kgs

PRICE GUIDE

Launch price: £35,000
Excellent: £18,000
Good: £16,500
Average: £15,000
Project: £13,500

LOTUS
Exige S1

This racecar-based coupé version of the Elise was built with trackday action in mind and styled by someone who appears to have watched far too many avantgarde sci-fi movies. It lacks creature comforts, borders on the impractical and offers appalling rearward visibility. But would you change anything about it? An instant classic, obviously. The engine is the full-on VHPD version of the K-Series, as used in the 340R, and good for 177bhp. Always priced well above the Elise it's based on, and a lot less were sold, so don't expect Exige values to drop to the same levels.

SPECIFICATIONS

Years produced:	2000-2004
Performance:	0-60mph: 4.7 secs (Top speed: 136mph)
Power & torque:	177bhp / 127lb/ft
Engine:	Normally aspirated 1796cc in-line four, petrol, electronic fuel injection, 16 valves
Drivetrain:	Mid-engine RWD
Suspension:	(F&R) Independent, double wishbones, coil springs, anti-roll bar
Bodyframe:	Chassis with composite panels
Transmission:	5-speed manual
Weight:	785kgs
	PRICE GUIDE
Launch price:	£32,995
Excellent:	£20,000
Good:	£18,000
Average:	£16,000
Project:	£14,000

MARCOS
1800 GT

Founded by Jem Marsh and Frank Costin, Marcos' core values revolved around sports cars designed for maximum efficiency and lightness – unusually for cars of their era, extensive use of wood was used in their construction. The 1800 GT was introduced to move Marcos into the MGB market, despite being available in kit form. Powered by a Volvo engine (an unusual step for a British specialist at the time), and featuring an advanced suspension layout, it was a quick and fine-handling alternative. However, the price was on the high side, and sales remained disappointing.

SPECIFICATIONS

Years produced:	1964-1968 (99 in total)
Performance:	0-60mph: 9.1 secs (Top speed: 115mph)
Power & torque:	114bhp / 110lb/ft
Engine:	Normally aspirated 1778cc in-line four, petrol, carburettor, 8 valves
Drivetrain:	Front-engine RWD
Suspension:	(F) Independent, coil spring. (R) Independent, coil spring
Bodyframe:	Wooden/metal chassis, glassfibre body
Transmission:	4-speed manual with overdrive
Weight:	767kgs
	PRICE GUIDE
Launch price:	£1645
Excellent:	£13,000
Good:	£10,000
Average:	£4000
Project:	£2000

MARCOS
Mini-Marcos

An cottage industry of specialists had emerged making the humble BMC Mini do things that its creator, Alec Issignonis, had never imagined for it. The Mini-Marcos was one such car, combining a lightweight low-drag fibreglass monocoque with the front-wheel-drive car's drivetrain and suspension. It proved a successful combination, not only dynamically, but commercially, too – and when Marcos folded in 1971, the Mini-Marcos continued in various guises, and arguably inspired the Midas of the 1980s. The original has plenty of appeal, though – and good examples fetch strong money.

SPECIFICATIONS

Years produced:	1965-1974 (700 in total)
Performance:	0-60mph: N/A (Top speed: 75mph)
Power & torque:	34bhp / 44lb/ft
Engine:	Normally aspirated 848cc in-line four, petrol, carburettor, 8 valves
Drivetrain:	Front-engine FWD
Suspension:	(F&R) Independent, rubber spring and damper units
Bodyframe:	Glassfibre monocoque
Transmission:	4-speed manual
Weight:	483kgs
	PRICE GUIDE
Launch price:	£199
Excellent:	£3600
Good:	£3000
Average:	£1500
Project:	£800

MARCOS
1500/1600

In an attempt to widen the appeal of the GT, Ford engines replaced the expensive Volvo, while the sophisticated semi-trailing arm/de Dion rear suspension layout of the 1800 was thrown out in favour of a simpler live axle. Price was usefully lower and in kit form the 1500 proved a more popular choice than its more exotic predecessor – although only 290 were made in total. Performance predictably suffered, and the roadholding wasn't as good, but widely available parts and specialist back-up today make them a sensible and charismatic DIY sports car.

SPECIFICATIONS

Years produced:	1966-1965 (82/192 in total)
Performance:	0-60mph: 8.7 secs (Top speed: 120mph)
Power & torque:	120bhp / 126lb/ft
Engine:	Normally aspirated 1652cc in-line four, petrol, carburettor, 8 valves
Drivetrain:	Front-engine RWD
Suspension:	(F) Ind. coil spring. (R) de Dion axle, coil spring
Bodyframe:	Wooden/metal chassis, glassfibre body
Transmission:	4-speed manual
Weight:	750kgs
	PRICE GUIDE
Launch price:	£1606
Excellent:	£8000
Good:	£6750
Average:	£3500
Project:	£2000

MARCOS
3-litre

Marcos finally abandoned its plywood underpinnings for the 3-litre and went for a square tube chassis that cost less to build, was easier to maintain, and ultimately made it easier to sell. The 3-litre was a clear indicator that Marcos was moving upmarket, and although the Ford V6-powered car looked near identical to its four-cylinder cousins, it offered much more performance – and therefore, sales appeal. However it wasn't cheap, and in moving away from its competition roots, Marcos struggled to find new buyers – especially in the wake of the launch of the cheap and plentiful Ford Capri 3000.

SPECIFICATIONS

Years produced:	1968-1972 (561 in total)
Performance:	0-60mph: 7.8 secs (Top speed: 125mph)
Power & torque:	136bhp / 193lb/ft
Engine:	Normally aspirated 2994cc V6, petrol, carburettor, 12 valves
Drivetrain:	front-engine RWD
Suspension:	(F) Independent, coil spring. (R) Beam axle, coil spring
Bodyframe:	Chassis, glassfibre body
Transmission:	4-speed manual with overdrive
Weight:	884kgs
	PRICE GUIDE
Launch price:	£2350
Excellent:	£9250
Good:	£7500
Average:	£4750
Project:	£2500

MARCOS
Mantula

The Mantula was a welcome return to basics for the reborn Marcos company of the 1980s. Powered by the venerable Rover V8 engine, and featuring a body that was a subtle development of the Dennis Adams-styled body, but with more effective aerodynamics, the Mantula continued offered big-engined thrills for a modest outlay. In 1986, a Spyder version was introduced for the first time, and an updated independent suspension set-up helped keep all of that power on the road. More modest Cortina-powered versions were also available.

SPECIFICATIONS

Years produced:	1984-1989
Performance:	0-60mph: 5.7 secs (Top speed: 155mph)
Power & torque:	190bhp / 220lb/ft
Engine:	Normally aspirated 3532cc V8, petrol, electronic fuel injection, 16 valves
Drivetrain:	Front-engine RWD
Suspension:	(F) Independent, wishbone, coil spring. (R) Live axle, Panhard rod, coil spring
Bodyframe:	Spaceframe
Transmission:	5-speed manual
Weight:	900kgs

PRICE GUIDE

Launch price:	£16,694
Excellent:	£10,000
Good:	£8250
Average:	£6500
Project:	£3500

MARCOS
Mantara

Once again, Marcos attempted to go upmarket, but this time, with a little more success. In 1992, it left the kit car business, and introduced the Marcos Mantara – a further extension of the original GT styling, which by this time appeared as if it had been on a course of steroids. Once again, the Rover V8 (now in 3.9- and 4.6-litre form) provided the power, and once again Marcos found itself going head to head with TVR. The Mantara ended up campaigning in GT racing, with the ultimate version – the LM600 – powered by a 6-litre Chevrolet V8.

SPECIFICATIONS

Years produced:	1993-1997
Performance:	0-60mph: 6.0 secs (Top speed: 131mph)
Power & torque:	190bhp / 235lb/ft
Engine:	Normally aspirated 3946cc V8, petrol, mechanical fuel injection, 16 valves
Drivetrain:	Front-engine RWD
Suspension:	(F) Coil spring, MacPherson strut. (R) Upper/lower wishbones, coil springs
Bodyframe:	Spaceframe
Transmission:	5-speed manual
Weight:	1020kgs

PRICE GUIDE

Launch price:	£
Excellent:	£16,000
Good:	£14,000
Average:	£12,000
Project:	£9500

MASERATI
3500GT

Maserati made its name in motor racing, having produced the legendary 250F, which took Juan Manuel to World Championship glory in 1957. However, in 1957, the company turned its full attention to the business of building road cars, unveiling the 3500GT. With this car, Maserati evolved into a serious producer of road cars (the A6 models were always low volume semi-racers), competing strongly with Ferrari. The Touring bodied coupé certainly looked the part, and with an Alfieri designed engine and racer-derived chassis, the 3500GT was as good to drive as it was to look at.

SPECIFICATIONS

Years produced:	1957-1964 (2000 in total)
Performance:	0-60mph: 7.6 secs (Top speed: 145mph)
Power & torque:	220bhp/ 253lb/ft
Engine:	Normally aspirated 3485cc in-line six, petrol, carburettor, 12 valves
Drivetrain:	Front-engine RWD
Suspension:	(F) Independent, coil spring. (R) Beam axle, semi-elliptic leaf spring
Bodyframe:	Metal monocoque
Transmission:	4-speed manual
Weight:	1270kgs

PRICE GUIDE

Launch price:	£5800
Excellent:	£75,000
Good:	£60,000
Average:	£40,000
Project:	£25,000

MASERATI
3500GT Spyder

During its seven year production run, the 3500GT became an established member of the sporting elite, with the coupé taking the lion's share of sales. But the lighter Vignale-bodied Spider was every bit as capable as its hard-top sister car, sitting on a shortened wheelbase. During its production run, it was regularly upgraded, gaining front disc brakes and Borani wire wheels in 1959 and a five-speed gearbox the following year. In 1961 the 3500GT also gained Lucas fuel injection. A handful of one-offs were also produced, and are now fabulously valuable.

SPECIFICATIONS

Years produced:	1959-1964 (227 in total)
Performance:	0-60mph: 7.6 secs (Top speed: 136mph)
Power & torque:	235bhp/ 232lb/ft
Engine:	Normally aspirated 3485cc in-line six, petrol, carburettor, 12 valves
Drivetrain:	Front-engine RWD
Suspension:	(F) Independent, coil spring. (R) Beam axle, semi-elliptic leaf spring
Bodyframe:	Chassis and separate body
Transmission:	4-speed manual
Weight:	1406kgs

PRICE GUIDE

Launch price:	£4450
Excellent:	£125,000
Good:	£100,000
Average:	£75,000
Project:	£40,000

MASERATI
Sebring

In essence, the Sebring was a shortened 3500GT that wore a beautiful Vignale body, styled by Giovanni Michelotti. In terms of looks, the Sebring was a perfect car for its time, although the straight-six engine was beginning to look a little outclassed compared with the latest opposition from Ferrari. But this car was designed for America, and it was style and equipment that were the prime motivators in the creation of the car – so air conditioning and an automatic gearbox were on the options list. For the Sebring II, a 4-litre version of the straight-six was fitted.

SPECIFICATIONS

Years produced:	1963-1969 (438 in total)
Performance:	0-60mph: 8.4 secs (Top speed: 137mph)
Power & torque:	235bhp/ 232lb/ft
Engine:	Normally aspirated 3485cc in-line six, petrol, carburettor, 12 valves
Drivetrain:	Front-engine RWD
Suspension:	(F) Independent, coils spring. (R) Beam axle, semi-elliptic leaf spring
Bodyframe:	Chassis and separate body
Transmission:	5-speed manual
Weight:	1510kgs

PRICE GUIDE

Launch price:	£4801
Excellent:	£60,000
Good:	£50,000
Average:	£32,500
Project:	£15,000

MASERATI
Mistral Coupé

The Frua-bodied Mistral was the last of the six-cylinder line of Maseratis that started with the 3500GT. Its name comes from the wind that blows across the south of France every year, and was the first Maserati to be named that way. The power unit was a direct descendent of the 350S engine, and proved lusty and long-lasting. The engine line-up was identical to the Sebring's, but few 3.5-litre versions found their way under the bonnet of the newer car. Performance was usefully improved, because the short wheelbase Mistral weighed 200kg less than the Sebring.

SPECIFICATIONS

Years produced: 1963-1970 (948 in total)
Performance: 0-60mph: 6.9 secs (Top speed: 152mph)
Power & torque: 265bhp / 261lb/ft
Engine: Normally aspirated 3485cc in-line six, petrol, carburettor, 12 valves
Drivetrain: Front-engine RWD
Suspension: (F) Independent, coil spring. (R) Beam axle, semi-elliptic leaf spring
Bodyframe: Metal monocoque
Transmission: 5-speed manual
Weight: 1270kgs

PRICE GUIDE

Launch price: £5980
Excellent: £37,500
Good: £30,000
Average: £17,500
Project: £8500

MASERATI
Mistral Spider

Slightly happier looking than the coupe, the Mistral Spyder bears an uncanny resemblance to the later AC 428 – both styled by Pietro Frua. It was so close that there's some parts interchangeability between the two, a side benefit of being built in the same factory. Unusually, the Mistral was offered with either aluminium or steel body, with no discernible difference in weight. However, the survival of the former is much higher than for the latter. The final 4-litre Mistral was a genuinely quick car, though, and had a top speed of over 140mph.

SPECIFICATIONS

Years produced: 1963-1970 (120 in total)
Performance: 0-60mph: 6.8 secs (Top speed: 147mph)
Power & torque: 255bhp / 267lb/ft
Engine: Normally aspirated 4012cc in-line six, petrol, carburettor, 12 valves
Drivetrain: Front-engine RWD
Suspension: (F) Independent, coil spring. (R) Beam axle, semi-elliptic leaf spring
Bodyframe: Metal monocoque
Transmission: 5-speed manual
Weight: 1300kgs

PRICE GUIDE

Launch price: £5980
Excellent: £100,000
Good: £80,000
Average: £60,000
Project: £35,000

MASERATI
Quattroporte I/II

One name, two very different cars – the Quattroporte I was significant for Maserati because it was the first of its cars to be powered by the new V8 engine, initially in 4.1-litre form (later 4.7). The family resemblance with the Mistral was strong, as it was also a Frua design; while underneath it was built on a sports car like tubular frame. The second generation Quattroporte was far less successful, with a production run of five. Powered by the 3-litre SM engine and automatic gearbox, it simply wasn't fast or appealing enough to survive the recession of the mid-1970s.

SPECIFICATIONS

Years produced: 1963-1971 (760 in total)
Performance: 0-60mph: 8.3 secs (Top speed: 130mph)
Power & torque: 260bhp / 267lb/ft
Engine: Normally aspirated 4136cc V8, petrol, carburettor, 16 valves
Drivetrain: Front-engine RWD
Suspension: (F) Ind. coil springs. (R) de Dion, coil spring (later beam axle, leaf spring)
Bodyframe: Metal monocoque
Transmission: 5-speed manual
Weight: 1728kgs

PRICE GUIDE

Launch price: £5986
Excellent: £10,000
Good: £8500
Average: £6500
Project: £2500

MASERATI
Mexico

Following on from the Quattroporte I in 1965, the Mexico was the next Maserati to be fitted with the new V8 engine. The four-seater coupé was styled by Vignale, and after the exuberance of the previous Frua bodied cars, it lacked the visual drama to go with its high price. However, with the later 4.7-litre V8 fitted, it was seriously quick, with more than enough muscle to replace the Sebring. Sadly the new car failed to emulate its predecessor's sales success in the USA – a situation that hurt Maserati's finances significantly.

SPECIFICATIONS

Years produced: 1966-1972 (250 in total)
Performance: 0-60mph: N/A (Top speed: 143mph)
Power & torque: 260bhp / 268lb/ft
Engine: Normally aspirated 4136cc V8, petrol, carburettor, 16 valves
Drivetrain: Front-engine RWD
Suspension: (F) Independent, coil spring. (R) Beam axle, semi-elliptic leaf spring
Bodyframe: Metal monocoque
Transmission: 5-speed manual
Weight: 1651kgs

PRICE GUIDE

Launch price: £7216
Excellent: £25,000
Good: £20,000
Average: £12,500
Project: £7000

MASERATI
Ghibli

Sitting at the top of the Maserati range, and vying with the very best from Ferrari for the title 'fastest car in the world', the Ghibli is one of the finest GT cars to emerge from the 1960s. Subsequently overshadowed by the Daytona and Miura, the Ghibli combined Giorgetto Giugiaro's styling (while he was still at Ghia) with Maserati's muscle to create a genuine 170mph road burner. The chassis engineering was beginning to look a little old hat, as it was a further variation of the Quattroporte's tubular frame – but it was effective nevertheless.

SPECIFICATIONS

Years produced: 1969-1974 (1274 in total)
Performance: 0-60mph: 7.5 secs (Top speed: 154mph)
Power & torque: 330bhp / 290lb/ft
Engine: Normally aspirated 4719cc V8, petrol, carburettor, 16 valves
Drivetrain: Front-engine RWD
Suspension: (F) Independent, coil springs; (R) Beam axle, semi-elliptic leaf spring
Bodyframe: Metal monocoque
Transmission: 5-speed manual
Weight: 1352kgs

PRICE GUIDE

Launch price: £10,180
Excellent: £50,000
Good: £42,500
Average: £25,000
Project: £14,000

MASERATI
Indy

This was more like it – based on a shortened version of the Quattroporte's chassis, but with a wider track, the Vignale-styled Indy looked every inch the supercar it was supposed to. Compared with the Mexico it replaced, the Indy was a huge success. The 2+2 coupé also saw a change in Maserati construction technique, as the chassis and body were now welded (instead of bolted) together, described as a unitary body. None of that mattered on the road where, in 4.7-litre form, the Indy could exceed 160mph in the right conditions, making it one of the world's fastest four-seater cars.

SPECIFICATIONS

Years produced: 1969-1974 (1136 in total)
Performance: 0-60mph: 7.2 secs (Top speed: 140mph)
Power & torque: 260bhp / 268lb/ft
Engine: Normally aspirated 4136cc V8, petrol, carburettor, 16 valves
Drivetrain: Front-engine RWD
Suspension: (F) Independent, coil springs. (R) Beam axle, semi-elliptic leaf spring
Bodyframe: Metal monocoque
Transmission: 5-speed manual
Weight: 1651kgs

PRICE GUIDE

Launch price: £8320
Excellent: £22,000
Good: £17,500
Average: £11,000
Project: £6000

MASERATI
Bora

Considering it was a relative latecomer to the mid-engined supercar club (although it beat the Ferrari BB to the market by two years), the Maserati Bora established itself as a front-runner in the fast club. Like the Ghibli, the Bora was styled by Giugiaro, who had by now gone it alone to form Ital Design, but the design studio had also devised the all-new steel unitary construction underneath it. The Bora was fitted with the Indy V8 in 4.7- and 4.9-litre form. As part of its association with Citroën, high pressure hydraulics powered the brakes and steering.

SPECIFICATIONS

Years produced: 1971-1978 (524 in total)
Performance: 0-60mph: 6.5 secs (Top speed: 165mph)
Power & torque: 310bhp / 339lb/ft
Engine: Normally aspirated 4719cc V8, petrol, carburettor, 16 valves
Drivetrain: Mid-engine RWD
Suspension: (F) Ind. coil springs, wishbones. (R) Ind. coil springs, wishbones
Bodyframe: Metal monocoque
Transmission: 5-speed manual
Weight: 1550kgs

PRICE GUIDE

Launch price: £22,911
Excellent: £45,000
Good: £37,500
Average: £22,500
Project: £12,500

MASERATI
Khamsin

To show its commitment to the front-engined cause, Maserati introduced the Khamsin to sell alongside the Bora/Merak twins. Styling and body engineering was by Marcello Gandini at Bertone, and it was a most arresting design. The suspension and steering were closely related to the mid-engined cars but the high geared power assisted steering was lifted from the Citroën SM, and proved remarkably successful once owners had acclimatised to it. Poor interior layout and visibility were negated by the 320bhp from its 4.9-litre Indy engine – over 150mph was possible.

SPECIFICATIONS

Years produced: 1973-1982 (421 in total)
Performance: 0-60mph: 8.1 secs (Top speed: 171mph)
Power & torque: 320bhp / 354lb/ft
Engine: Normally aspirated 4930cc V8, petrol, carburettor, 16 valves
Drivetrain: Front-engine RWD
Suspension: (F) Independent, coil spring. (R) Independent, coil spring
Bodyframe: Metal monocoque
Transmission: 5-speed manual
Weight: 1530kgs

PRICE GUIDE

Launch price: £13,999
Excellent: £45,000
Good: £37,500
Average: £20,000
Project: £10,000

MASERATI
Merak

Created to fight the Ferrari 308 and Lamborghini Urraco, the Maserati Merak was a super-stylish parts-bin special that proved rather effective. The body was a lightly revised version of the Bora's (losing its flush rear window in the process), and the engine was a lightly tuned version of the Maserati-designed Citroën SM 3-litre, now boasting 190bhp. Never a light car, the Merak struggled to keep up with its rivals, but the 220bhp SS version did much to make amends. Like the Bora, its values lag behind those of its Lamborghini and Ferrari rivals, making a Merak a wise investment.

SPECIFICATIONS

Years produced: 1974-1982 (1699 in total)
Performance: 0-60mph: 8.2 secs (Top speed: 135mph)
Power & torque: 190bhp / 188lb/ft
Engine: Normally aspirated 2965cc V8, petrol, carburettor, 16 valves
Drivetrain: Mid-engine RWD
Suspension: (F) Independent, coil spring. (R) Independent, coil spring
Bodyframe: metal monocoque
Transmission: 5-speed manual
Weight: 1339kgs

PRICE GUIDE

Launch price: £7996
Excellent: £23,000
Good: £18,500
Average: £11,000
Project: £4500

MASERATI
Kyalami

After De Tomaso's takeover of Maserati, badge engineering was introduced. The De Tomaso Longchamp was slightly facelifted, fitted with the Indy V8 (initially in 4.1-litre form), and re-marketed as the Maserati Kyalami. Although this version of the Ghia-styled car looked better than the original, it was not appealing enough to bring in a significant number of new buyers. Perhaps it was the price – which had taken a significant hike over the Ford engined car it was based upon – but more likely, there was simply no market for it in the late 1970s.

SPECIFICATIONS

Years produced: 1976-1983 (187 in total)
Performance: 0-60mph: 7.6 secs (Top speed: 147mph)
Power & torque: 270bhp / 289lb/ft
Engine: Normally aspirated 4136cc V8, petrol, carburettor, 16 valves
Drivetrain: Front-engine RWD
Suspension: (F) Independent, coil spring. (R) Independent, coil spring
Bodyframe: Metal monocoque
Transmission: 5-speed manual
Weight: 1740kgs

PRICE GUIDE

Launch price: £21,996
Excellent: £16,000
Good: £12,500
Average: £7000
Project: £4000

MASERATI Quattroporte III

Another back to basics offering, and none the worse for it. Where the Quattroporte II had flopped on its unconventional engineering and anodyne styling, its replacement returned to the formula that made the original car so successful – a big V8, discrete styling, and a supercar driving experience combined with additional accommodation. Sales were not as strong as they could have been, although in 4.9-litre form the Quatroporte III remained in production throughout the 1980s to be sold alongside the new Biturbo – perhaps as a reminder of greater times?

SPECIFICATIONS

Years produced: 1979-1990 (1876 in total)
Performance: 0-60mph: N/A (Top speed: 143mph)
Power & torque: 280bhp / 289lb/ft
Engine: Normally aspirated 4930cc V8, petrol, carburettor, 16 valves
Drivetrain: Front-engine RWD
Suspension: (F&R) Independent, wishbones, coil spring, anti-roll bar
Bodyframe: Metal monocoque
Transmission: 3-speed automatic
Weight: 1900kgs

PRICE GUIDE

Launch price: £56,912
Excellent: £9500
Good: £8000
Average: £4500
Project: £1750

MASERATI Biturbo 220-425

In 1981, Maserati model development took a new direction. The supercar market was surrendered to Ferrari and Lamborghini as the company chased volume with its new BMW 3-Series rivalling Biturbo. At the heart of the new car was an elegant new three valves per cylinder quad-cam 2-litre V6, which pushed out 180bhp thanks to its brace of turbos. The interior was plush – and its centrepiece clock was a real novelty. It was an interesting new direction, although big sales were never forthcoming. The four-door 425, introduced in 1983, added appeal.

SPECIFICATIONS

Years produced: 1981-1994
Performance: 0-60mph: 7.2 secs (Top speed: 126mph)
Power & torque: 192bhp / 220lb/ft
Engine: turbocharged 2491cc V6, petrol, carburettor, 18 valves
Drivetrain: Front-engine RWD
Suspension: (F) Independent, coil spring. (R) Independent, coil spring
Bodyframe: metal monocoque
Transmission: 5-speed manual
Weight: 1242kgs

PRICE GUIDE

Launch price: £28,795
Excellent: £6000
Good: £4600
Average: £2250
Project: £1000

MASERATI Biturbo Spyder

In 1984, Maserati chopped off the roof of the Biturbo to create this stylish four-seater convertible. Like the tin-topped versions, it wasn't without issues, and as well as suffering from niggling build and quality issues, premature corrosion was a very real problem. Image and prices dropped massively in a short amount of time, from which the Biturbo is only now beginning to emerge. Despite low classic values, there's a real sense of the exotic when it comes to keeping a Biturbo on the road, while restoration costs can be horrifying – especially when it comes to the engine.

SPECIFICATIONS

Years produced: 1984-1991
Performance: 0-60mph: 6.1 secs (Top speed: 140mph)
Power & torque: 241bhp / 246lb/ft
Engine: Turbocharged 1996cc V6, petrol, electronic fuel injection, 24 valves
Drivetrain: Front-engine RWD
Suspension: (F) Independent, coil spring. (R) Independent, coil spring
Bodyframe: Metal monocoque
Transmission: 5-speed manual
Weight: 1251kgs

PRICE GUIDE

Launch price: N/A
Excellent: £8000
Good: £6750
Average: £4000
Project: £2000

MASERATI Shamal

The Biturbo platform was certainly adaptable – in 1989 the exterior was heavily revised (by Marcello Gandini), and a quad-cam 32-valve 3.2-litre V8 was shoehorned under the bonnet. Inside, it was just as luxurious as the Biturbo, and made extensive use of wood and leather – while retaining that clock. It certainly looked different, but the main draw for the Shamal was its performance – with 325bhp on tap, it topped out at nearly 170mph, making it one of the fastest Maseratis ever produced. Handling was excellent, helped by the electronic active control suspension – when it was working...

SPECIFICATIONS

Years produced: 1989-1995
Performance: 0-60mph: 5.1 secs (Top speed: 169mph)
Power & torque: 326bhp / 321lb/ft
Engine: Normally aspirated 3217cc V6, petrol, electronic fuel injection, 24 valves
Drivetrain: Front-engine RWD
Suspension: (F) Independent, coil spring. (R) Independent, coil spring
Bodyframe: Metal monocoque
Transmission: 6-speed manual
Weight: 1415kgs

PRICE GUIDE

Launch price: £63,450
Excellent: £20,000
Good: £16,000
Average: £12,000
Project: £9000

MASERATI Ghibli II

A great name returned in 1992 with the arrival of the Ghibli II. Clearly based upon the Shamal, it was actually a lower powered variation of the theme, retaining the Biturbo's V6 power units. In top-of-the-range form, the 2.8-litre V6 was available with a six-speed manual or four-speed auto. However, the 2-litre V6 was the real headline grabber, pushing out a remarkable 306bhp – giving the two-door a real turn of speed. It formed the basis of a GT racer, and special editions based on this specification (such as the Ghibli Open Cup) are highly soughtafter today.

SPECIFICATIONS

Years produced: 1992-1997
Performance: 0-60mph: 5.6 secs (Top speed: 153mph)
Power & torque: 302bhp / 275lb/ft
Engine: Normally aspirated 2790cc V6, petrol, electronic fuel injection, 24 valves
Drivetrain: Front-engine RWD
Suspension: (F) Independent, coil spring. (R) Independent, coil spring
Bodyframe: metal monocoque
Transmission: 5-speed manual
Weight: 1365kgs

PRICE GUIDE

Launch price: £42,813
Excellent: £12,500
Good: £11,000
Average: £8500
Project: £5000

MASERATI
3200 GT

In 1998, Maserati was reinvented. After becoming part of the Fiat Group, finances were finally poured into the once-great marque's development, as it sought a new identity within the group alongside Ferrari. With the 3200GT, Maserati was repositioned below the Scuderia, to take on cars such as the Jaguar XK and BMW 6-Series. The V8 engine was a development of that found in the Ferrari 355. Despite being slightly rough around the edges, the 3200GT was a great success, and has sired a generation of successors that have turned around the marque's fortunes completely.

SPECIFICATIONS

Years produced:	1998-2001
Performance:	0-60mph: 5.1 secs (Top speed: 174mph)
Power & torque:	370bhp / 362lb/ft
Engine:	Turbocharged 3217cc V8, petrol, electronic fuel injection, 32 valves
Drivetrain:	Front-engine RWD
Suspension:	(F&R) Independent, coil spring, double wishbones, electronic dampers
Bodyframe:	Metal monocoque
Transmission:	6-speed manual
Weight:	1587kgs
	PRICE GUIDE
Launch price:	£53,000
Excellent:	£18,500
Good:	£16,000
Average:	£13,500
Project:	£11,500

MATRA
Bagheera

The Matra-Simca Bagheera was one of the most innovative sports cars produced in over a decade. Featuring three-abreast seating, composite panels draped over steel spaceframe, and mid-engined power pack, the Bagheera was cheap, stylish and interesting. Performance never matched its looks, but the Simca-derived power units were willing enough, if unrefined. On the road, the Bagheera could run rings around far more expensive cars. Structural corrosion has been the Bagheera's enemy, but plenty survive, and backup from the enthusiast clubs is excellent.

SPECIFICATIONS

Years produced:	1973-1980
Performance:	0-60mph: 12.3 secs (Top speed: 101mph)
Power & torque:	82bhp / 78lb/ft
Engine:	Normally aspirated 1294cc in-line four, petrol, carburettor, 8 valves
Drivetrain:	Mid-engine RWD
Suspension:	(F&R) Torsion bars, wishbones
Bodyframe:	Chassis and composite body
Transmission:	4-speed manual
Weight:	885kgs
	PRICE GUIDE
Launch price:	£5370 (UK launch, 1977)
Excellent:	£4000
Good:	£3250
Average:	£2000
Project:	£600

MATRA
Murena

The Murena was a logical development of the Bagheera. It was clothed in a new aerodynamic body and, importantly, underpinned by a galvanised steel spaceframe which would prove resistant to rust. The top engine option was a 2.2-litre Talbot Tagora engine, which provided the go to match its excellent handling – something that the Bagheera had lacked. Sadly, politics between Peugeot-Talbot and Matra saw the Murena prematurely halted in 1985, by which time the innovative French company was gearing up to produce the Espace.

SPECIFICATIONS

Years produced:	1980-1983
Performance:	0-60mph: 9.2 secs (Top speed: 124mph)
Power & torque:	118bhp / 139lb/ft
Engine:	Normally aspirated 2155cc in-line four, petrol, carburettor, 8 valves
Drivetrain:	Mid-engine RWD
Suspension:	(F) Ind. wishbones, torsion bar. (R) Ind. wishbones, coil spring
Bodyframe:	Composite body, steel chassis
Transmission:	5-speed manual
Weight:	1050kgs
	PRICE GUIDE
Launch price:	£
Excellent:	£5000
Good:	£4000
Average:	£2500
Project:	£1000

MAZDA
RX-7 Series 1

This was Mazda's attempt to make the world take the rotary engine seriously. In terms of over half-a-million sales of this first series RX-7, it worked. However, the seemingly unassailable problem of these engines' poor economy means they'll never go mainstream. The RX-7 makes the most of the engine's light weight, with perfect 50/50 weight distribution. The early version is best left to enthusiasts; from 1981 it was a better car, with an extra 10bhp, rear disc brakes, a spoiler on the back and more comprehensive equipment.

SPECIFICATIONS

Years produced:	1979-1985 (471,018 in total)
Performance:	0-60mph: 9.5 secs (Top speed: 115mph)
Power & torque:	105bhp / 106lb/ft
Engine:	Normally aspirated 2292cc twin-rotor, petrol, carburettor
Drivetrain:	Front-engine RWD
Suspension:	(F) Independent, coil spring, MacPherson strut; (R) Rigid axle, coil spring
Bodyframe:	Metal monocoque
Transmission:	5-speed manual
Weight:	980kgs
	PRICE GUIDE
Launch price:	£8549
Excellent:	£3750
Good:	£3000
Average:	£1600
Project:	£750

MAZDA
RX-7 Series 2

The second generation RX-7's all-new styling stole a lot of cues from the Porsche 928 and managed to look more substantial without growing in size, and only adding an extra 80lb in weight. It gave safer handling thanks to new rear suspension, and sharper steering from rack-and-pinion instead of recirculating ball. The revised '13A' engine kicks out more power – especially in the Turbo version that became available in the UK from 1988 with up to 200bhp. The following year a convertible was added to the range, though these are harder to find.

SPECIFICATIONS

Years produced:	1986-1992 (272,027 in total)
Performance:	0-60mph: 8.5 secs (Top speed: 134mph)
Power & torque:	149bhp / 135lb/ft
Engine:	Turbocharged 2254cc twin-rotor, petrol, electronic fuel injection
Drivetrain:	Front-engine RWD
Suspension:	(F) Independent, MacPherson strut; (R) Independent, multi-link, coil springs
Bodyframe:	Metal monocoque
Transmission:	5-speed manual
Weight:	1221kgs
	PRICE GUIDE
Launch price:	£13,995
Excellent:	£4250
Good:	£3500
Average:	£1900
Project:	£600

MAZDA
MX-5 MkI

The perfect roadster for those who want the traditional British sports car experience without the associated worries of rust and unreliability. With a twin-cam engine that's more powerful than the Elan it apes, the MX-5 offers sufficient performance, though not enough to trouble the fine handling and grip. The MX-5 has proved totally dependable over high mileages and the only rust you are likely to find is where the sills join the rear wings. The lighter early 1.6s are favoured, but avoid the budget-spec post-1994 1.6 engines as they are down on power.

SPECIFICATIONS

Years produced: 1990-1997 (421,107 in total)
Performance: 0-60mph: 8.6 secs (Top speed: 116mph)
Power & torque: 114bhp / 100lb/ft
Engine: Normally aspirated 1597cc in-line four, petrol, electronic fuel injection, 16 valves
Drivetrain: Front-engine RWD
Suspension: (F) Ind. transverse arms, coil spring. (R) Ind. transverse arms, coil spring
Bodyframe: metal monocoque
Transmission: 5-speed manual
Weight: 970kgs

PRICE GUIDE

Launch price: £14,249
Excellent: £5000
Good: £4000
Average: £2000
Project: £850

MAZDA
MX-3 V6

Just establishing itself as a classic, and worth both saving and savouring. Often misunderstood, the MX-3 may be a small coupé, but despite looks it still manages to offer generous rear seating area. For your delectation there is also crisp steering, a fine handling balance, precision gearbox and strong brakes. However, the real accolades are saved for what's under the bonnet: a turbine-like four-cam engine of just 1850cc that laid claim to being the world's smallest production V6. On that score alone it deserves proper recognition.

SPECIFICATIONS

Years produced: 1991-1998
Performance: 0-60mph: 8.9 secs (Top speed: 124mph)
Power & torque: 133bhp / 116lb/ft
Engine: Normally aspirated 1845cc V6, petrol, mechanical fuel injection, 12 valves
Drivetrain: Front-engine FWD
Suspension: (F) Independent, coil, strut. (R) Independent, coil, strut
Bodyframe: Metal monocoque
Transmission: 5-speed manual
Weight: 1133kgs

PRICE GUIDE

Launch price: £15,445
Excellent: £2950
Good: £2250
Average: £1000
Project: £300

MAZDA
RX-7 Series 3

For the third generation, Mazda got serious. This can now be considered an uncompromising, hardcore sport car, with heaps more power from a twin-turbo '13B' rotary engine – 252bhp going up to 280bhp in late examples. With a low centre of gravity and perfect weight distribution, it's no surprise that their handling has been highly praised. Not that many were sold in the UK by Mazda, but their numbers have been more than doubled by 'grey' imports, so take care that you actually know which of the many specs of car you are looking at.

SPECIFICATIONS

Years produced: 1992-2002 (68,589 in total)
Performance: 0-60mph: 5.9 secs (Top speed: 156mph)
Power & torque: 236bhp / 217lb/ft
Engine: Turbocharged 2616cc twin-rotor, petrol, electronic fuel injection, valves
Drivetrain: Front-engine RWD
Suspension: (F) Independent, coils, struts; (R) Independent, coil springs, wishbones.
Bodyframe: Metal monocoque
Transmission: 5-speed manual
Weight: 1310kgs

PRICE GUIDE

Launch price: £34,000
Excellent: £8500
Good: £7000
Average: £4500
Project: £2400

McLAREN
F1

After a decade of Formula One success, McLaren turned to the task of producing a roadgoing supercar. Given that Gordon Murray was the project's co-ordinator, and he had an obsession for lightness and detail, it was clear that the new car would be far from ordinary. When it emerged, the 627bhp BMW-powered, Peter Stevens-styled three-seater was a masterpiece. 0-150mph in 12.8 seconds and a top speed of 231mph might seem like an irrelevance, but it's a glorious one – and one that its £1m-plus market value clearly reflects.

SPECIFICATIONS

Years produced: 1993-1998
Performance: 0-60mph: 3.2 secs (Top speed: 240mph)
Power & torque: 627bhp / 455lb/ft
Engine: Normally aspirated 6064cc V12, petrol, electronic fuel injection, 48 valves
Drivetrain: Mid-engine RWD
Suspension: (F) Independent, double wishbones, coil. (R) Independent, double wishbones, coil
Bodyframe: Carbon fibre monocoque
Transmission: 6-speed manual
Weight: 1138kgs

PRICE GUIDE

Launch price: £540,000
Excellent: £1,500,000
Good: £1,000,000
Average: £650,000
Project: £n/a

MERCEDES-BENZ
300 Cabriolet D

This convertible version of the 300 saloon was built in limited numbers and was most commonly seem with the leaders of any number of nations waving from the rear seats. Side windows and frames lower fully to make it a full convertible. A car with enormous presence, it also requires an enormous wallet should you need to undertake restoration work, though the value of a good one does go some way towards reflecting this. As with the saloons, the later the version you buy, the better equipment it will have, and the better you'll enjoy the driving experience.

SPECIFICATIONS

Years produced:	1951-1956 (707 in total)
Performance:	0-60mph: 17.0 secs (Top speed: 99mph)
Power & torque:	123bhp / 163lb/ft
Engine:	Normally aspirated 2996cc in-line six, petrol, carburettor, 12 valves
Drivetrain:	Front-engine RWD
Suspension:	(F) Independent, coil spring, wishbone. (R) Swing axle, coil spring
Bodyframe:	Separate chassis, steel body
Transmission:	4-speed manual
Weight:	1940kgs
PRICE GUIDE	
Launch price:	N?A
Excellent:	£85,000
Good:	£65,000
Average:	£40,000
Project:	£20,000

MERCEDES-BENZ
300A/B/C/D

Mercedes' return to the production of prestige automobiles six years after the end of WW2 resulted in this 4000lb giant. The range has since been dubbed 'Adenauer' as the car became closely associated with the German chancellor of the time, Dr Konrad Adenauer. Built on the X-frame chassis of its pre-war counterparts, the engine is an alloy-headed straight-six. Sold in the UK from 1953, and better from 1954 when a servo was fitted to the braking system. 1957's 300D was restyled above the waist with thinner pillars and a greater glass area.

SPECIFICATIONS

Years produced:	1951-1962 (11,430 in total)
Performance:	0-60mph: 15.0 secs (Top speed: 109mph)
Power & torque:	148bhp / 178lb/ft
Engine:	Normally aspirated 2996cc in-line four, petrol, carburettor, 12 valves
Drivetrain:	Front-engine RWD
Suspension:	(F) Independent, coil spring, double wishbone. (R) Swing axle, coil spring
Bodyframe:	Separate chassis, steel body
Transmission:	4-speed manual/3-speed auto
Weight:	1740kgs
PRICE GUIDE	
Launch price:	£3500
Excellent:	£15,000
Good:	£12,000
Average:	£7000
Project:	£3500

MERCEDES-BENZ
300S/Sc Cabriolet/Roadster

Built on a six inch shortened 300 saloon chassis, this still-giant two-seater harked back to the 540K of Mercedes' pre-war glory days. Using a predecessor of its engine, the S was actually more expensive than the 300SL Gullwing in 1954. The quick way to tell the Cabriolet and Roadster apart is that the former has 'pram irons' on the side of the folding top. The Sc was introduced in 1955, the small 'c' denoting that the engine has Bosch fuel injection.

SPECIFICATIONS

Years produced:	1952-1958 (760 in total)
Performance:	0-60mph: 15.0 secs (Top speed: 109mph)
Power & torque:	148bhp / 178lb/ft
Engine:	Normally aspirated 2996cc in-line six, petrol, carburettor, 12 valves
Drivetrain:	Front-engine RWD
Suspension:	(F) Independent, double wishbone, coil spring. (R) Swing axle, coil spring
Bodyframe:	Separate chassis, steel body
Transmission:	4-speed manual
Weight:	N/A
PRICE GUIDE	
Launch price:	£5529
Excellent:	£150,000
Good:	£125,000
Average:	£90,000
Project:	£65,000

MERCEDES-BENZ
180-220S Ponton

These are generally referred to by their 'Ponton' nickname, which is German for pontoon and refers to the slab-sided appearance. The 180 and 190 have four-cylinder engines and were much better from 1957-on when they received an overhead-cam engine in place of the old sidevalve unit. There was also a popular though underpowered 180D diesel option. 220s sit on a longer wheelbase and have six-cylinder engines, so they are of course worth more. These were the cars that started Mercedes' reputation for build quality and dependability.

SPECIFICATIONS

Years produced:	1953-1962 (280,807 in total)
Performance:	0-60mph: 15.2 secs (Top speed: N/A)
Power & torque:	58bhp / 82lb/ft
Engine:	Normally aspirated 1767cc in-line four, petrol, carburettor, 8 valves
Drivetrain:	Front-engine RWD
Suspension:	(F) Independent, coil spring. (R) Independent, coil spring
Bodyframe:	Metal monocoque
Transmission:	4-speed manual
Weight:	1070kgs
PRICE GUIDE	
Launch price:	£1694
Excellent:	£8500
Good:	£6000
Average:	£2750
Project:	£1500

MERCEDES-BENZ
300SL Gullwing

Rarely seen but instantly recognised, this is not just a car but a true icon, generally known simply by the name Gullwing. Behind the legend is a high quality sports coupé with a racing heritage, built over a spaceframe chassis, and with the world's first production fuel-injected engine. The rest of the spec seems a little less impressive today: drum brakes, a four-speed gearbox, and swing-axle rear suspension. Most had steel bodies, but 29 were built in aluminium, for which you will have to double the prices given.

SPECIFICATIONS

Years produced:	1954-1957 (1400 in total)
Performance:	0-60mph: 8.8 secs (Top speed: 135mph)
Power & torque:	215bhp / 203lb/ft
Engine:	Normally aspirated 2996cc in-line six, petrol, mechanical injection, 12 valves
Drivetrain:	Front-engine RWD
Suspension:	(F) Independent, coil spring. (R) Independent, coil spring, swing axle
Bodyframe:	Separate chassis, steel (or alloy) body
Transmission:	4-speed manual
Weight:	1293kgs
PRICE GUIDE	
Launch price:	£4393
Excellent:	£375,000
Good:	£325,000
Average:	£250,000
Project:	£190,000

MERCEDES-BENZ
190SL Roadster

The 'SL' tag is supposed to translate as super-light, but despite aluminium doors, bonnet and bootlid, the 190SL is still too heavy to do anything properly sporting with its 1.9-litre four-cylinder engine. Settle for the fact that it is a good, if not exhilarating to drive, with bags of style. In fact it's just the thing for those who can't afford ten times the price for the larger 300SL. Build quality is superb, and they've survived in good enough numbers to make finding one simple enough. You may have to pay a bit more if it comes with both soft and hard tops.

SPECIFICATIONS

Years produced: 1955-1963 (25,881 in total)
Performance: 0-60mph: 13.3 secs (Top speed: 109mph)
Power & torque: 104bhp / 114lb/ft
Engine: Normally aspirated 1897cc in-line four, petrol, carburettor, 8 valves
Drivetrain: Front-engine RWD
Suspension: (F) Independent, coil spring. (R) Independent, coil spring, swing axle
Bodyframe: Steel monocoque
Transmission: 4-speed manual
Weight: 1140kgs

PRICE GUIDE

Launch price: £2693
Excellent: £40,000
Good: £32,000
Average: £17,500
Project: £9000

MERCEDES-BENZ
220S/SE Cabriolet

Based on the 220 Ponton saloon but on a five-inch shorter floorpan, with much prettier bodywork distinguished by really long doors. Priced roughly 75% higher than a saloon when new, they sold in small numbers. The 220S had a 100bhp six-cylinder engine with twin Solex carburettors, and this was joined in 1958 by the 220SE, with the 'E' standing for fuel injection, a Bosch unit that added 15bhp – and even more to the car's already high price. They remained in production a year longer than their saloon counterparts.

SPECIFICATIONS

Years produced: 1956-1960
Performance: 0-60mph: 15.2 secs (Top speed: 101mph)
Power & torque: 98bhp / 119lb/ft
Engine: Normally aspirated 2195cc in-line six, petrol, carburettor, 12 valves
Drivetrain: Front-engine RWD
Suspension: (F) Ind. double wishbone, coil spring. (R) Independent, coil spring, swing axle
Bodyframe: Metal moncoque
Transmission: 4-speed manual
Weight: N?A

PRICE GUIDE

Launch price: £3715
Excellent: £60,000
Good: £50,000
Average: £27,500
Project: £15,000

MERCEDES-BENZ
220S/SE Coupé

Launched a year later than the Cabriolet, the Coupé version is identical apart from the fixed roof and upright rather than slanted frames for the rear of the side window. Being based on a saloon floorpan means it's a full four-seater, and that US-influenced hardtop styling ensures plenty of headroom, even for those in the back. Built from the best materials, but before the era of rust protection so many will have suffered. Fuel-injected SE is preferred, so you may find the carburettor S version for less than the prices listed here. Both are rare in right-hand-drive.

SPECIFICATIONS

Years produced: 1957-1960
Performance: 0-60mph: 17.1 secs (Top speed: 100mph)
Power & torque: 98bhp / 119lb/ft
Engine: Normally aspirated 2195cc in-line six, petrol, carburettor, 12 valves
Drivetrain: Front-engine RWD
Suspension: (F) Ind. double wishbones, coil spring. (R) Swing axle, coil spring, torsion bar
Bodyframe: Metal monocoque
Transmission: 4-speed manual
Weight: 1350kgs

PRICE GUIDE

Launch price: N/A
Excellent: £30,000
Good: £22,000
Average: £14,000
Project: £8000

MERCEDES-BENZ
300SL Roadster

The replacement for the Gullwing, the Roadster has a revised spaceframe chassis to make room for normal doors, which added 200lb to the weight. It's a softer and more relaxing car to drive and is actually better all round. The more extensive use of chrome, inside and out, isn't to all tastes, but the Roadster did enjoy disc brakes from 1961, then got a much lighter aluminium engine block the following year. Expect to pay a premium for cars so equipped. Expensive to buy, but then they cost more than a detached house in a London suburb when new.

SPECIFICATIONS

Years produced: 1957-1963 (1856 in total)
Performance: 0-60mph: 8.1 secs (Top speed: 130mph)
Power & torque: 215bhp / 228lb/ft
Engine: Normally aspirated 2996cc in-line six, petrol, mechanical injection, 12 valves
Drivetrain: Front-engine RWD
Suspension: (F) Ind. coil spring, double wishbone; (R) Independent, coil spring
Bodyframe: Separate chassis, steel body
Transmission: 4-speed manual
Weight: 1383kgs

PRICE GUIDE

Launch price: £4393
Excellent: £325,000
Good: £275,000
Average: £200,000
Project: £150,000

MERCEDES-BENZ
190-230 Fintail Saloon

Those tail fins that gave these cars their nickname were shamelessly tacked on to attract American buyers, and it worked: the Fintail Mercs sold extremely well, but without looking like some Pontiac pastiche. They proved handy for rallying too, with a 220SE winning the Monte Carlo rally. Low rent models have single round headlights, with the more desirable versions treated to stacked headlamps and double-decked bumpers. Four and six-cylinder versions are available, with diesel options for the former that sold well to taxi drivers.

SPECIFICATIONS

Years produced: 1959-1968 (966,085 in total)
Performance: 0-60mph: 12.8 secs (Top speed: 90mph)
Power & torque: 90bhp / 113lb/ft
Engine: Normally aspirated 1897cc in-line four, petrol, carburettor, 8 valves
Drivetrain: Front-engine RWD
Suspension: (F) Independent, wishbone, coil spring, anti-roll bar. (R) Live axle, coil spring
Bodyframe: Steel monocoque
Transmission: 4-speed manual
Weight: 1224kgs

PRICE GUIDE

Launch price: £1987
Excellent: £7500
Good: £5500
Average: £2750
Project: £1000

MERCEDES-BENZ
220SEb Coupé/Cabriolet

First incarnations of Paul Bracq's elegant coupé and convertible body designs which lasted over a decade and are regarded by some as the best looking Mercedes of the classic era. Interior trimmings are also of the highest quality, beautifully detailed. It may not had had anything like the same performance, but you can see why these cost similar money to an Aston Martin DB4 back in 1962. Four-speed automatics were standard fitment, and you won't find many with the optional four-speed manual gearbox. Add 50% for Cabrio prices.

SPECIFICATIONS

Years produced: 1961-1965 (16,902 in total)
Performance: 0-60mph: 12.8 secs (Top speed: 106mph)
Power & torque: 120bhp / 139lb/ft
Engine: Normally aspirated, 2195cc in-line six, petrol, 12 valves
Drivetrain: Front-engine RWD
Suspension: (F) Independent, double wishbone, coil spring. (R) Swing axle, coil spring
Bodyframe: Metal monocoque
Transmission: 4-speed automatic
Weight: 1410kgs

PRICE GUIDE

Launch price: £4288
Excellent: £20,000
Good: £15,000
Average: £8000
Project: £4500

MERCEDES-BENZ
300SE Fintail Saloon

The range-topping 300SE gets a mention of its own as there's so much more to it. Extra chrome helps it stand out, but underneath there are real changes. Riding on self-levelling air suspension, the car also benefits from all-wheel disc brakes and has power steering as standard. That three-litre straight-six is a detuned version of the engine used in the 300SL, and there was a choice of four-speed manual or automatic transmission. From 1963 there is also a 300SEL, providing more room thanks to a four inch longer wheelbase.

SPECIFICATIONS

Years produced: 1961-1965 (6748 in total)
Performance: 0-60mph: 10.9 secs (Top speed: 115mph)
Power & torque: 157bhp / 185lb/ft
Engine: Normally aspirated 2996cc in-line six, petrol, mechanical injection, 12 valves
Drivetrain: Front-engine RWD
Suspension: (F) Ind. double wishbone, air suspension. (R) Swing axle, air suspension
Bodyframe: Metal monocoque
Transmission: 4-speed manual
Weight: N/A

PRICE GUIDE

Launch price: £3814
Excellent: £9000
Good: £7000
Average: £3500
Project: £1500

MERCEDES-BENZ
300SE Coupé/Cabriolet

Delivered some of the performance lacking in the 220SEb models thanks to 160bhp and then 170bhp versions of the big fuel-injected six-cylinder engine. The 300SEs also employed the self-levelling air suspension of the 300 saloons, giving them the sort of ride you would comment favourably on in a modern luxury car. With prices approaching those of Bentleys in the UK, along with a propensity for rust, there aren't a lot about. Good ones are sought after. That air suspension can also be troublesome if neglected. Again add 50% for Cabrios.

SPECIFICATIONS

Years produced: 1962-1967 (3127 in total)
Performance: 0-60mph: 10.7 secs (Top speed: 115mph)
Power & torque: 167bhp / 184lb/ft
Engine: Normally aspirated 2996cc in-line six, petrol, mechanical injection, 12 valves
Drivetrain: Front-engine RWD
Suspension: (F) Independent, double wishbone, air spring. (R) Swing axle, air spring
Bodyframe: Metal monocoque
Transmission: 4-speed automatic
Weight: 1600kgs

PRICE GUIDE

Launch price: £4931
Excellent: £24,000
Good: £18,000
Average: £12,000
Project: £6000

MERCEDES-BENZ
230/250SL

In keeping with the fashion to apply generic names to Mercedes ranges to help cut through the maze of numbers, you'll find 'Pagoda' commonly attached to these sports cars, thanks to the kicked up edges to the roofline of the optional hardtop. Offering more power and performance than the 190SL it replaced, the 230SL. Proving its worth, one won the Spa-Sofia-Liège rally. The 250SL superseded it, but was only around for 1967. Other than the larger engine, which offered no more bhp but extra torque, there were only small detail differences.

SPECIFICATIONS

Years produced: 1963-1968 (19,831/5196 in total)
Performance: 0-60mph: 10.5 secs (Top speed: 124mph)
Power & torque: 148bhp / 145lb/ft
Engine: Normally aspirated 2308cc in-line six, petrol, mechanical injection, 12 valves
Drivetrain: Front-engine RWD
Suspension: (F) Independent, coil spring, double wishbone. (R) Swing axle, coil spring
Bodyframe: Metal monocoque
Transmission: 4-speed manual/4-speed automatic
Weight: 1295kgs

PRICE GUIDE

Launch price: £3595
Excellent: £29,500
Good: £22,500
Average: £15,000
Project: £8000

MERCEDES-BENZ
600

Mercedes threw everything but the kitchen sink at this technical tour de force, designed to be bought by governments rather than mere business magnates. They weighed in at 2.5 tonnes (or more for the long wheelbase seven-seater Pullman), and that was before the bullet-proof glass was added. There's air suspension, vacuum central locking, two heating and ventilation systems, and to haul it around, a new 6.3-litre V8 engine with Bosch fuel injection. The limo stayed in production for 18 years and notched up a remarkable number of sales.

SPECIFICATIONS

Years produced: 1964-1981 (2677 in total)
Performance: 0-60mph: 9.7 secs (Top speed: 127mph)
Power & torque: 247bhp / 369lb/ft
Engine: Normally aspirated 6332cc V8, petrol, mechanical fuel injection, 16 valves
Drivetrain: Front-engine RWD
Suspension: (F) Independent, wishbone, radius arm. (R) Independent, semi-swing axle
Bodyframe: Metal monocoque
Transmission: 4-speed automatic
Weight: 2475kgs

PRICE GUIDE

Launch price: £8752
Excellent: £45,000
Good: £35,000
Average: £22,500
Project: £12,500

MERCEDES-BENZ 300SE/SEL (W108/W109)

Packed with luxuries and safety items, the 300s sat comfortably at the top of the new S-class range, with the SEL – four inches longer than the standard cars – roughly twice the price of the entry level 250S. The 300s came as standard with a four-speed automatic gearbox, later supplemented by an optional five-speed manual. All used the older all-alloy three-litre straight-six, up until late 1968 when the SE was dropped and the 300SEL, rather confusingly for those starting to understand Mercedes models, got the 280SE's 2.8-litre engine.

SPECIFICATIONS

Years produced: 1965-1969 (7625 in total)
Performance: 0-60mph: 11.2 secs (Top speed: 115mph)
Power & torque: 168bhp / 184lb/ft
Engine: Normally aspirated 2996cc in-line six, petrol, mechanical injection, 12 valves
Drivetrain: Front-engine RWD
Suspension: (F) Independent, double wishbone, air spring. (R) Ind. swing axle, air spring
Bodyframe: Metal monocoque
Transmission: 4-speed automatic
Weight: 1575kgs

PRICE GUIDE

Launch price: £5669
Excellent: £6500
Good: £5000
Average: £3000
Project: £1250

MERCEDES-BENZ 250/280/SE Saloon (W108)

This was the dawn of the S-class, styled in a timeless, if less than exciting manner, by Paul Bracq. Entry level was provided by the 250S with twin Solex carbs and 130bhp, with the Bosch fuel-injected 250SE offering another 20bhp and shaving two seconds off the car's 0-60mph time. In 1968 the engines were increased to 2.8 litres, still with a carburetted S and fuel injected SE option, and the long wheelbase bodyshell previously only offered on the top-of-the-range 300SEL now comes with the smaller engine as well, badged 280SEL.

SPECIFICATIONS

Years produced: 1965-1972 (325,562 in total)
Performance: 0-60mph: 11.8 secs (Top speed: 118mph)
Power & torque: 148bhp / 159lb/ft
Engine: Normally aspirated 2497cc in-line six, petrol, mechanical injection, 12 valves
Drivetrain: Front-engine RWD
Suspension: (F) Independent, double wishbone, air spring; (R) Ind. swing axle, air spring
Bodyframe: Metal monocoque
Transmission: 4-speed manual/4-speed automatic
Weight: 1480kgs

PRICE GUIDE

Launch price: £2575
Excellent: £5750
Good: £4500
Average: £2400
Project: £800

MERCEDES-BENZ 250/280SE Coupé/Cabrio

With the 1965 launch of the S-class saloon, the smaller engined versions of the Coupé and Cabriolet were both improved and rationalised by being given the 2.5-litre engine from the new cars. That added 30bhp, and rear disc brakes were added at the same time. Two years later, when the 300SE was dropped, the 280SE replaced both that and the 250SE with its 2.8-litre 160bhp straight-six with revised fuel injection for better economy. From 1969 a five-speed manual gearbox became an option. Cabriolets are worth around 70% more than Coupés.

SPECIFICATIONS

Years produced: 1965-1972 (6213 in total)
Performance: 0-60mph: 11.8 secs (Top speed: 118mph)
Power & torque: 148bhp / 159lb/ft
Engine: Normally aspirated 2497cc in-line six, petrol, mechanical injection, 12 valves
Drivetrain: Front-engine RWD
Suspension: (F) Independent, double wishbone, air spring. (R) Ind. swing axle, air spring
Bodyframe: Metal monocoque
Transmission: 4-speed manual
Weight: 1480kgs

PRICE GUIDE

Launch price: £4275
Excellent: £20,000
Good: £15,000
Average: £9000
Project: £5000

MERCEDES-BENZ 280SL

The final version of the Pagoda roadsters also turned out to be the best selling. With the engine bored out to 2.8 litres, even with the restrictions caused by new emission controls it offered more power and torque this time. Some of the benefits of this were lost due to the weight the car had gained. The suspension was also retuned a little in favour of ride comfort, which means the 280SL doesn't have quite the same handling prowess as previous SLs. None of that has stopped it from becoming the favoured version of the range with buyers.

SPECIFICATIONS

Years produced: 1967-1971 (23,885 in total)
Performance: 0-60mph: 9.0 secs (Top speed: 124mph)
Power & torque: 168bhp / 177lb/ft
Engine: Normally aspirated 2778cc in-line six, petrol, mechanical injection, 12 valves
Drivetrain: Front-engine RWD
Suspension: (F) Independent, double wishbone, coil spring. (R) Swing axle, coil spring
Bodyframe: Metal monocoque
Transmission: 4-speed manual/4-speed automatic
Weight: 1360kgs

PRICE GUIDE

Launch price: £3850
Excellent: £31,000
Good: £25,000
Average: £16,000
Project: £8500

MERCEDES-BENZ 300SEL 6.3 (W109)

In 1968, Mercedes engineers went slightly bonkers and dropped the 6.3-litre V8 from the 600 into the longer wheelbase 300's bodyshell, but keeping all the luxuries like air suspension. With the engine's massive torque, the result was a muscle car in disguise, and unlike most American muscle cars it came with dual-circuit four-wheel disc brakes. This was a luxury saloon that could outpace most of the sports cars on sale at the time, though you did have to cough up more than the price of a Ferrari Daytona for the pleasure.

SPECIFICATIONS

Years produced: 1967-1972 (6526 in total)
Performance: 0-60mph: 5.7 secs (Top speed: 141mph)
Power & torque: 247bhp / 369lb/ft
Engine: Normally aspirated 6332cc V8, petrol, carburettor, 16 valves
Drivetrain: Front-engine RWD
Suspension: (F) Independent, air suspension. (R) Independent, air suspension
Bodyframe: Metal monocoque
Transmission: 4-speed automatic
Weight: 1780kgs

PRICE GUIDE

Launch price: £7743
Excellent: £13,500
Good: £10,000
Average: £6500
Project: £3500

MERCEDES-BENZ
200/220/230.4 Saloon (W115)

These were the lesser of the New Generation cars, built to replace the four-cylinder Fintails. In Mercedes-speak they are known as the W115 range. There was a strong family resemblance to the S-class, but these were shorter and lighter cars, though being on the same wheelbase as the S-class means they have excellent interior space. Engines range from a 95bhp two-litre to 110bhp 2.3, with a 105bhp 2.2 in the middle. At least the model names follow the engine capacities, with the 230.4 denoting the four-cylinder – see also the 230.6 (below).

SPECIFICATIONS

Years produced: 1967-1976 (1,450,298 in total)
Performance: 0-60mph: 15.2 secs (Top speed: 99mph)
Power & torque: 93bhp / 115lb/ft
Engine: Normally aspirated 1988cc in-line four, petrol, carburettor, 8 valves
Drivetrain: Front-engine RWD
Suspension: (F) Ind. coil spring, double wishbone. (R) Ind. coil spring, semi-trailing arms
Bodyframe: Metal monocoque
Transmission: 4-speed manual
Weight: 1330kgs

PRICE GUIDE

Launch price: £2388
Excellent: £4500
Good: £3500
Average: £2000
Project: £400

MERCEDES-BENZ
230.6/250/280E Saloon

These saloons use the same bodyshell as the W115 cars but have six-cylinder engines, giving them the Mercedes range designation W114. Entry level is the 230.6 with 120bhp, joined at first by the 130bhp 250. The confusion starts in 1970 when the 250 is given a single-overhead-cam 2.8-litre engine, though the regular 250 continued for two years. Then in 1971 a 280 joined the range, using a different version of the 2.8-litre engine, this time with twin camshafts. This came in carburettor form, or as the 280E, with fuel injection, and only the latter came to the UK.

SPECIFICATIONS

Years produced: 1967-1976 ((W114) in total)
Performance: 0-60mph: 12.8 secs (Top speed: 112mph)
Power & torque: 128bhp / 147lb/ft
Engine: Normally aspirated 2496cc in-line six, petrol, carburettor, 12 valves
Drivetrain: front-engine RWD
Suspension: (F) Ind. coil spring, double wishbone. (R) Ind. coil spring, semi-trailing arm
Bodyframe: Metal monocoque
Transmission: 4-speed manual
Weight: 1375kgs

PRICE GUIDE

Launch price: £4753
Excellent: £5500
Good: £4000
Average: £2250
Project: £600

MERCEDES-BENZ
250/280CE Coupé (W114)

Only the fuel-injected versions of these pillarless coupés came to the UK market, though carburettor versions were sold elsewhere, without the 'E' on the end of their name. They were based on the W114 saloons, retaining their length and wheelbase but with a shortened passenger compartment and a roof that was two inches lower. The 150bhp 250CE gave way to the 280CE in 1972. This latter car came with the 185bhp twin-cam 2.8-litre engine. In some markets, like the US, there was also a version of the 250 with a single-cam 2.8 engine on carbs.

SPECIFICATIONS

Years produced: 1968-1976 (21,787/11,518 in total)
Performance: 0-60mph: 8.9 secs (Top speed: 118mph)
Power & torque: 150bhp / 174lb/ft
Engine: Normally aspirated 2497cc in-line six, petrol, mechanical injection, 12 valves
Drivetrain: Front-engine RWD
Suspension: (F) Independent, coil spring. (R) Independent, coil spring
Bodyframe: Metal monocoque
Transmission: 3-speed automatic
Weight: 1360kgs

PRICE GUIDE

Launch price: £3475
Excellent: £7000
Good: £5500
Average: £3250
Project: £1250

MERCEDES-BENZ
280SE 3.5 Coupé/ Cabriolet (W111)

These are the ones that everyone wants but few can afford. From late 1969 Mercedes dropped their 3.5-litre V8s into the Coupés and Cabrios to create a reassuringly expensive range-topper with 25% more power than the six-cylinder cars. Today, the SE 3.5s have become cooler than a penguin's fridge. It is of course the much rarer Cabriolets that take top honours, with prices more than double those given for Coupés.

SPECIFICATIONS

Years produced: 1969-1971 (4502 in total)
Performance: 0-60mph: 9.0 secs (Top speed: 130mph)
Power & torque: 197bhp / 211lb/ft
Engine: Normally aspirated 3499cc V8, petrol, mechanical fuel injection, 16 valves
Drivetrain: Front-engine RWD
Suspension: (F) Independent, double wishbone, coil spring. (R) Swing axle, coil spring
Bodyframe: Metal monocoque
Transmission: 4-speed automatic
Weight: 1570kgs

PRICE GUIDE

Launch price: £5158
Excellent: £35,000
Good: £28,000
Average: £20,000
Project: £12,000

MERCEDES-BENZ
280SE 3.5/300SEL 3.5 (W108/W109)

For anyone enjoying the puzzle of the 2.8-litre 300SEL, here we have the same S-class bodies fitted with 3.5-litre V8s to bridge the gap between the six-cylinder cars and the crazy 300SEL 6.3. So the best versions of the W108/109 S-class saloons remain something of an enigma. The 300 still has air suspension, so mechanically shy buyers might prefer a 280. There was also a 280SEL 3.5, but that seemed one choice too many and only 951 were built.

SPECIFICATIONS

Years produced: 1969-1972 (11,309/9483 in total)
Performance: 0-60mph: 8.4 secs (Top speed: 115mph)
Power & torque: 157bhp / 185lb/ft
Engine: Normally aspirated 2996cc in-line six, petrol, mechanical injection, 12 valves
Drivetrain: Front-engine RWD
Suspension: (F) Ind. double wishbone, air spring (R) Swing axle, air spring
Bodyframe: Metal monocoque
Transmission: 4-speed automatic
Weight: 1673kgs

PRICE GUIDE

Launch price: £5158
Excellent: £8250
Good: £6500
Average: £3400
Project: £1500

MERCEDES-BENZ
350/450SLC (C107)

Mercedes took a bit of a shortcut to creating these 2+2 coupés. In effect, what you have is an R107 roadster with 14 inches added to the wheelbase, a fixed roof and some rear seats. Of course there's a bit more to it that that, as the job was achieved whilst only adding 110lb to the car's weight. Launched with a 3.5-litre V8, this was joined the following year by a 4.5-litre version that outsold the smaller engine by more than two to one. Elegant and well detailed, they are also considerably cheaper than the soft-tops.

SPECIFICATIONS

Years produced: 1971-1980 (13,925/31,739 in total)
Performance: 0-60mph: 9.3 secs (Top speed: 130mph)
Power & torque: 217bhp / 265lb/ft
Engine: Normally aspirated 4520cc V8, petrol, mechanical fuel injection, 16 valves
Drivetrain: Front-engine RWD
Suspension: (F) Independent, wishbone, coil spring. (R) Ind. semi-trailing arms, coil springs
Bodyframe: Metal monocoque
Transmission: 3-speed automatic
Weight: 1630kgs

PRICE GUIDE

Launch price: £7875
Excellent: £8000
Good: £6500
Average: £3250
Project: £1000

MERCEDES-BENZ
350SL (R107)

The 350SL was introduced as a replacement for the Pagoda 280SL, and once again both soft and hard tops were offered. There's more than a passing resemblance between the two cars, but the 350SL's body is three inches longer and 300lb heavier. That means much of the benefit of fitting a 3.5-litre V8 has been lost. Both cars share 0-60mph times, but the new car's taller rear axle ratio, allowed by the V8's extra torque, means it can pull a higher top speed. Not that they were supposed to be sporting cars, being aimed more at the luxury market.

SPECIFICATIONS

Years produced: 1971-1980 (15,304 in total)
Performance: 0-60mph: 9.3 secs (Top speed: 126mph)
Power & torque: 200bhp / 211lb/ft
Engine: Normally aspirated 3499cc V8, petrol, electronic fuel injection, 16 valves
Drivetrain: Front-engine RWD
Suspension: (F) Independent, coil springs (R) Independent, coil springs
Bodyframe: Metal monocoque
Transmission: 4-speed manual/3-speed auto
Weight: 1545kgs

PRICE GUIDE

Launch price: £7395
Excellent: £12,500
Good: £10,000
Average: £5250
Project: £2500

MERCEDES-BENZ
450SL

Though the 4.5-litre V8 had been available as an option for American market 350SLs since 1971 (largely to compensate for Federal emissions controls), Europe had to wait until 1973 for the official 450SL model. The extra litre didn't add much in the way of bhp, but the torque figure took a big leap and allowed the larger-engined car to be fitted with a much taller rear axle ratio. That makes it even more of a lazy cruiser than the 350SL, but does help out on the economy front. You'll find a fair proportion fitted with automatic gearboxes.

SPECIFICATIONS

Years produced: 1971-1981 (66,298 in total)
Performance: 0-60mph: 9.2 secs (Top speed: 133mph)
Power & torque: 217bhp / 265lb/ft
Engine: Normally aspirated 4520cc V8, petrol, electronic fuel injection, 16 valves
Drivetrain: Front-engine RWD
Suspension: (F) Independent, wishbone, coil spring. (R) Ind. semi-trailing arm, coil spring
Bodyframe: Metal monocoque
Transmission: 3-speed automatic
Weight: 1580kgs

PRICE GUIDE

Launch price: £8598
Excellent: £13,500
Good: £10,000
Average: £6000
Project: £3000

MERCEDES-BENZ
280S/SE (W116)

This is the second generation of S-class cars, and the one that cemented Mercedes' reputation at the top of the saloon car pecking order. The 280s were the basic models, though not that basic, and came with a twin-cam straight-six that produced either 160bhp with carbs (S) or 185bhp using fuel injection (SE). To say they led the market in safety features might sound boring, but they also had a fair turn of speed and excellent roadholding thanks to their new semi-trailing arm rear suspension. Now much cheaper than they deserve to be.

SPECIFICATIONS

Years produced: 1972-1980 (273,623 in total)
Performance: 0-60mph: 10.5 secs (Top speed: 124mph)
Power & torque: 182bhp / 176lb/ft
Engine: Normally aspirated 2746cc in-line six, petrol, mechanical fuel injection, 12 valves
Drivetrain: Front-engine RWD
Suspension: (F) Independent, wishbone, coil spring. (R) Ind. semi-trailing arm, coil spring
Bodyframe: Metal monocoque
Transmission: 4-speed manual
Weight: 1610kgs

PRICE GUIDE

Launch price: £5597
Excellent: £4750
Good: £3750
Average: £2000
Project: £750

MERCEDES-BENZ
350/450SE/SEL (W116)

Provocatively dubbed 'the best cars in the world' when new, the V8-engined versions of the S-class also become one of the few truly deserving winners of the Car of the Year award. Their build quality and equipment levels set new standards and you can still be impressed by driving one that's over 30 years old. Model numbers represent the 3.5 and 4.5-litre V8s, and there's also a 450 SEL with an extra six inches in the wheelbase, mostly for the benefit of rear legroom. Good ones are still not that expensive to buy, but a poor one could quickly become so.

SPECIFICATIONS

Years produced: 1972-1980 (156,585 in total)
Performance: 0-60mph: 9.3 secs (Top speed: 130mph)
Power & torque: 221bhp / 279lb/ft
Engine: Normally aspirated 4520cc V8, petrol, mechanical fuel injection, 16 valves
Drivetrain: Front-engine RWD
Suspension: (F) Ind. double wishbone, coil spring. (R) Ind. semi-trailing arm, coil spring
Bodyframe: Metal monocoque
Transmission: 3-speed automatic
Weight: 1765kgs

PRICE GUIDE

Launch price: £6995
Excellent: £6000
Good: £4750
Average: £2000
Project: £800

MERCEDES-BENZ 450SEL 6.9 Saloon (W116)

With its all-dominating S-class cars selling so well the range was losing the cache of exclusivity, and Mercedes-Benz needed something extra for the image conscious plutocrat. A 6.9-litre V8 engine did the trick, along with self-levelling Hydropneumatic suspension. Reassuringly expensive, the same money would buy you two XJ-S V12s and a Lancia Beta HPE, but the 450SEL 6.9 still sold in surprising numbers. Now prices are a little closer to earth, but you still need a comfortable income to meet the running costs.

SPECIFICATIONS

Years produced: 1975-1980 (7380 in total)
Performance: 0-60mph: 7.5 secs (Top speed: 140mph)
Power & torque: 286bhp / 405lb/ft
Engine: Normally aspirated 6834cc V8, petrol, mechanical fuel injection, 16 valves
Drivetrain: Front-engine RWD
Suspension: (F&R) Self-levelling hydro-pneumatic
Bodyframe: Metal monocoque
Transmission: 3-speed automatic
Weight: 1935kgs

PRICE GUIDE

Launch price: £21,995
Excellent: £9750
Good: £7500
Average: £3500
Project: £1500

MERCEDES-BENZ 230/280CE (C123)

Based on the W123 saloons, but with 10cm nipped out of the wheelbase, these pillarless coupés shared the same sumptuous interior. Top of the range was the fuel-injected 177bhp 280CE, while entry level was covered by the 230C, which put out 109bhp on carbs. Some markets got the in-between 280C with 156bhp, again on carbs. Both of those were dropped in 1980 to make way for the 230CE, which not only got fuel injection, but an new 2.3-litre engine to go with it. Output was now 136bhp, while the 280CE crept up to 185bhp.

SPECIFICATIONS

Years produced: 1977-1985 (79,147 in total)
Performance: 0-60mph: 11.5 secs (Top speed: 112mph)
Power & torque: 134bhp / 151lb/ft
Engine: Normally aspirated 2299cc in-line four, petrol, mechanical injection, 8 valves
Drivetrain: Front-engine RWD
Suspension: (F) Ind. double wishbone, coil spring. (R) Ind. semi-trailing arm, coil spring
Bodyframe: Metal monocoque
Transmission: 4-speed manual
Weight: 1380kgs

PRICE GUIDE

Launch price: £8951
Excellent: £4750
Good: £3500
Average: £1900
Project: £600

MERCEDES-BENZ 280/300SL (R107)

The strong-selling R107 roadsters were given a makeover in 1980. Nothing you'd really notice in the body, as this was still considered too good to mess with, but there were plenty of improvements under the skin. Main change was upgrading the standard gearbox from a four- to a five-speed manual. In September 1985 the six-cylinder twin-cam engine's capacity was increased to three litres. That only added an extra 5bhp, but the torque figure was up by 21lb/ft, produced at lower revs. Both versions were good sellers that now hold their values well.

SPECIFICATIONS

Years produced: 1980-1986
Performance: 0-60mph: 11.0 secs (Top speed: 124mph)
Power & torque: 185bhp / 177lb/ft
Engine: Normally aspirated 2746cc in-line six, petrol, mechanical injection, 12 valves
Drivetrain: Front-engine RWD
Suspension: (F) Independent, wishbone, coil spring. (R) Ind. semi-trailing arms, coil springs
Bodyframe: Metal monocoque
Transmission: 4-speed automatic
Weight: 1500kgs

PRICE GUIDE

Launch price: £16,599
Excellent: £10,000
Good: £8000
Average: £5500
Project: £2500

MERCEDES-BENZ 380/420SL (R107)

These 'junior' versions of Mercedes' V8 roadster started with the 380SL. In September 1981, after just a year in production, the engine was changed for a small-bore/long stroke V8 of the same capacity but with a slight drop in power and something like a 10% improvement in fuel economy. From 1985 the capacity was upped to 4.2 litres, which at least restored power figures to their original level of 218bhp. All have automatic gearboxes, but it's the highly-regarded four-speed unit and not the three-speed used in pre-1980 SLs.

SPECIFICATIONS

Years produced: 1980-1989
Performance: 0-60mph: 7.7 secs (Top speed: 134mph)
Power & torque: 245bhp / 294lb/ft
Engine: Normally aspirated 4973cc V8, petrol, mechanical fuel injection, 16 valves
Drivetrain: Front-engine RWD
Suspension: (F) Ind. double wishbones, coil springs. (R) Ind. semi-trailing arms, coil springs
Bodyframe: Monocoque
Transmission: 4-speed automatic
Weight: 1605kgs

PRICE GUIDE

Launch price: £18,300
Excellent: £11,000
Good: £9000
Average: £6000
Project: £3000

MERCEDES-BENZ 380/420/500 SEC (C126)

If the S-class saloon was the best car in the world during the '80s then this – built on a four-inch shortened S-class floorpan – must have been the best coupé. The 380 came with 204bhp and steel wheels, with ABS only an optional extra until 1985. The 420 replaced it at the 1986 facelift, when the SE grew fatter bumpers and side skirts, and was good for 218bhp. The range-topper for five years until the 560 arrived, the 500SEC came with 240bhp, electric seats, ABS and a walnut-veneered dash. Fast and comfortable, they offer a lot for your money.

SPECIFICATIONS

Years produced: 1981-1991
Performance: 0-60mph: 7.9 secs (Top speed: 140mph)
Power & torque: 228bhp / 299lb/ft
Engine: Normally aspirated 4973cc V8, petrol, mechanical fuel injection, 16 valves
Drivetrain: Front-engine RWD
Suspension: (F) Ind. coil spring, anti-roll bar. (R) Ind. semi-trailing arms, coil spring
Bodyframe: Monocoque
Transmission: 4-speed automatic
Weight: 1610kgs

PRICE GUIDE

Launch price: £25,700
Excellent: £9750
Good: £7500
Average: £3250
Project: £1000

MERCEDES-BENZ 500/560SL (R107)

Expensive flagships of the SL range, though they turned out to be the best-selling models. 500SL was there from the start, standing out from lesser SLs by the addition of a fairly subtle bootlid lip spoiler. They lost a little power when re-tuned for economy in September 1981, gaining a taller diff ratio at the same time, so those early cars are more sought after. The 560SL joined the 500 in 1985 but didn't displace it, merely adding power, badge one-upmanship, and a thirst for fuel. All SLs should be considered as tourers rather than sports cars.

SPECIFICATIONS

Years produced: 1982-1989
Performance: 0-60mph: 7.7 secs (Top speed: 134mph)
Power & torque: 245bhp / 294lb/ft
Engine: Normally aspirated 4973cc V8, petrol, mechanical fuel injection, 16 valves
Drivetrain: Front-engine RWD
Suspension: (F) Ind, double wishbones, coil springs. (R) Ind. semi-trailing arms, coil springs
Bodyframe: Monocoque
Transmission: 4-speed automatic
Weight: 1605kgs

PRICE GUIDE

Launch price: £20,300
Excellent: £12,000
Good: £9750
Average: £6500
Project: £3500

MERCEDES-BENZ 190 Saloon (W201)

Darlings of the '80s upwardly mobile, almost two million 190s rolled out of the factory. Mercedes-Benz did an excellent job of scaling its big car looks down into a BMW 3-series-sized package, and barely lost any interior space. Largely ignored by the classic car market until recently, good examples are starting to be snapped up for what look like bargain prices. Only the Cosworth-tweaked and spoiler-clad 16V models, in 2.3 and 2.5-litre form, have attracted much enthusiast attention, and prices for those can be double those quoted for everyday 190s.

SPECIFICATIONS

Years produced: 1982-1993 (1,874,668 in total)
Performance: 0-60mph: 13.4 secs (Top speed: 109mph)
Power & torque: 88bhp / 122lb/ft
Engine: Normally aspirated 1997cc in-line four, petrol, carburettor, 8 valves
Drivetrain: Front-engine RWD
Suspension: (F) Independent, MacPherson strut. (R) Independent, multi-link, coil spring
Bodyframe: Monocoque
Transmission: 5-speed manual
Weight: 1080kgs

PRICE GUIDE

Launch price: £9685
Excellent: £3250
Good: £2500
Average: £1200
Project: £400

MERCEDES-BENZ 560SEC (C126)

Quite simply the best four-seater coupé you could buy in the '80s, and there still can't be a lot to compare them to today. Mercedes-Benz created something special by taking the best of the other SECs and adding fatter tyres, flared arches and a limited-slip diff. Climate control came as standard, as from 1988 did heated seats. With the aid of a mechanical/electronic fuel injection system, the 560's engine put out 20% more power than even the 500SEC. There was a price to match - by the end of the '80s these cars cost a massive £63,000.

SPECIFICATIONS

Years produced: 1985-1991
Performance: 0-60mph: 6.8 secs (Top speed: 156mph)
Power & torque: 295bhp / 335lb/ft
Engine: Normally aspirated 5547cc V8, petrol, mechanical fuel injection, 16 valves
Drivetrain: Front-engine RWD
Suspension: (F) Independent, coil spring, anti-roll bar. (R) Ind. semi-trailing arms, coil spring
Bodyframe: Monocoque
Transmission: 4-speed automatic
Weight: 1748kgs

PRICE GUIDE

Launch price: £52,185
Excellent: £11,000
Good: £8500
Average: £4000
Project: £1750

MERCEDES-BENZ 300 CE Coupé (W124)

This sleek coupé was based on a shortened saloon floorpan, in this case that of the surprisingly entertaining and almost indestructible E-class. The 300CE drives even better than it looks, and started out with a 188bhp 12-valve engine. This was joined for the 1990 model year by a 24-valve version with 231bhp. You may have to pay a little more than suggested for one of those, especially if it comes with manual transmission. Most of both versions were sold with Mercedes' tough four-speed auto, but the manual cars are the more coveted now.

SPECIFICATIONS

Years produced: 1987-1993 (19,320 in total)
Performance: 0-60mph: 8.1 secs (Top speed: 140mph)
Power & torque: 177bhp / 188lb/ft
Engine: Normally aspirated 2962cc in-line six, petrol, mechanical injection, 12 valves
Drivetrain: Front-engine RWD
Suspension: (F) Independent, a-arm, coil spring. (R) Independent, coil spring, multi-link
Bodyframe: Metal monocoque
Transmission: 5-speed manual
Weight: 1390kgs

PRICE GUIDE

Launch price: £30,100
Excellent: £4250
Good: £3250
Average: £1750
Project: £1000

MERCEDES-BENZ SL300/500 (R129)

Finally ditching the classic looks of the SL roadsters, Mercedes-Benz came up with this more aggressive and almost chrome-free offering. Filled with toys like a power-operated roof, pop-up roll-over bar and dual-range four-speed automatic gearbox, some even came with suspension that lowers itself at speed. Six-cylinder 300 has either 190bhp or 231bhp in 24-valve twin-cam form; the 500 packs a 326bhp V8 and later ones could be had with a five-speed auto. Unlike earlier SLs, these have the performance to be considered proper sports cars.

SPECIFICATIONS

Years produced: 1989-1993
Performance: 0-60mph: 6.3 secs (Top speed: 155mph)
Power & torque: 322bhp / 332lb/ft
Engine: Normally aspirated 4973cc V8, petrol, mechanical fuel injection, 32 valves
Drivetrain: Front-engine RWD
Suspension: (F) Independent, MacPherson strut. (R) Independent, 5-link, coil spring
Bodyframe: Metal monocoque
Transmission: 4-speed automatic
Weight: 1889kgs

PRICE GUIDE

Launch price: £42,130
Excellent: £10,000
Good: £8000
Average: £6000
Project: £3500

MERCEDES-BENZ
500E (W124)

This is perhaps the ultimate undercover performance car. Only the slightly flared arches tell you that it might be more than E-class fodder for a Latvian taxi rank. But lift the bonnet and you find a mighty five-litre V8. Not that it's a mere shoehorn job, in fact the car was completely re-engineered and even assembled by Porsche. Excited now? Sadly the 500E was only ever sold in left-hand-drive, which combined with a juicy £57,000 price tag means only seven of these M5-baiters were sold in the UK, though others have joined them since.

SPECIFICATIONS

Years produced:	1992-1994 (10,479 in total)
Performance:	0-60mph: 5.9 secs (Top speed: 155mph)
Power & torque:	320bhp / 346lb/ft
Engine:	Normally aspirated 4973cc V8, petrol, mechanical fuel injection, 32 valves
Drivetrain:	Front-engine RWD
Suspension:	(F) Ind. MacPherson strut, wishbone, coil spring. (R) Ind. multi-link, coil spring
Bodyframe:	Metal monocoque
Transmission:	4-speed automatic
Weight:	1730kgs
	PRICE GUIDE
Launch price:	£57,220
Excellent:	£12,500
Good:	£11,000
Average:	£8500
Project:	£6000

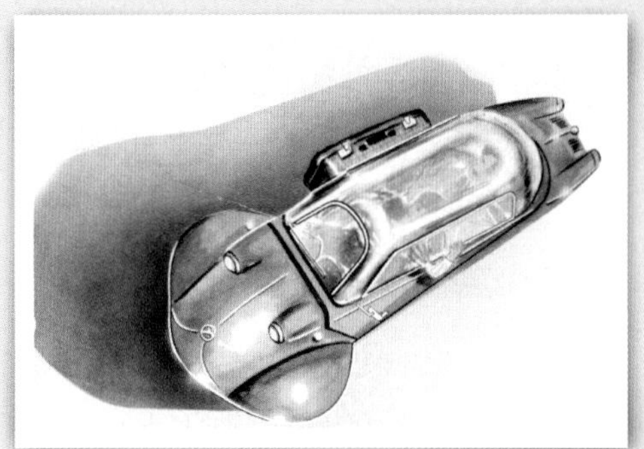

MESSERSCHMITT
KR175

The Messerschmitt KR175 (for Kabinroller) was introduced for up-and-coming German families who needed inexpensive transport during tough times. Aircraft engineer Fritz Fend was behind the bubble car and based it on the cockpit of a Messerschmitt 'plane. Initially powered by a single-cylinder engine, the lightweight machine was capable of 60mph – quite a feat considering the top speeds of standard family cars of the time. High levels of build quality and simple construction means that the survival rate is high, reflecting the cult status these cars now enjoy.

SPECIFICATIONS

Years produced:	1953-1964 (19,668 in total)
Performance:	0-60mph: (Top speed: 50 mph)
Power & torque:	9bhp / N/A
Engine:	Normally aspirated 123cc single-cylinder, petrol, carburettor, 2-stroke
Drivetrain:	rear-engine RWD
Suspension:	(F&R) Independent, rubber springing medium
Bodyframe:	Tubular chassis, steel body
Transmission:	4 speed and chain to single rear wheel
Weight:	220kgs
	PRICE GUIDE
Launch price:	DM 2100
Excellent:	£13,500
Good:	£10,000
Average:	£6250
Project:	£3250

MESSERSCHMITT
Tg500 Tiger

The main difference between the Tg500 and its lower powered predecessors was the extra wheel. Now with the full complement of four, the uprated 500cc 20bhp Sachs twin-cylinder was housed in a more suitable chassis. Performance of the ultimate go-faster bubble car was verging on the silly, with a top speed of over 75mph and a 0-60mph time of 18.7 seconds – enough to see off full-sized cars such as the Austin A30 and Morris Minor with ease. Sales were slow, though, with fewer than 500 built, and that makes the Tiger highly collectable today.

SPECIFICATIONS

Years produced:	1958-1961 (320 in total)
Performance:	0-60mph: 28.1 secs (Top speed: 78 mph)
Power & torque:	19.5bhp / 24lb/ft
Engine:	Normally aspirated 460cc twin-cylinder, petrol, carburettor, 2-stroke
Drivetrain:	Rear-engine RWD
Suspension:	(F) Independent, rubber springing medium. (R) Ind. spring, wishbone
Bodyframe:	Tubular chassis, steel body
Transmission:	4 speed and chain to single rear wheel
Weight:	370kgs
	PRICE GUIDE
Launch price:	DM 3650
Excellent:	£60,000
Good:	£50,000
Average:	£40,000
Project:	£30,000

MG
TA/TB

The original MG Midget: a development of PB-type, but featuring a larger body and powered by a 1292cc pushrod ohv four-cylinder engine (50bhp at 4000rpm). Twin SU carburettors and four-speed gearbox were typically sporting fitments, while the hydraulic brakings and half-elliptic springs added driver confidence. The TB, introduced in May 1939, had more of the same: larger carburettors, 54bhp at 5200rpm, and synchromesh on the top three gears. Two-seater sports, Tickford DHC and fixed-head Airline Coupé bodies were poular alternatives.

SPECIFICATIONS

Years produced:	1936-1939 (3003/379 in total)
Performance:	0-60mph: 17.6 secs (Top speed: 78mph)
Power & torque:	50bhp / N/A
Engine:	Normally aspirated 1292cc in-line four, petrol, carburettor, 8 valves
Drivetrain:	Front-engine RWD
Suspension:	(F) Beam axle, semi-elliptic leaf spring. (R) Beam axle, semi-elliptic leaf spring
Bodyframe:	Chassis and separate body
Transmission:	4-speed manual crash box
Weight:	801kgs
	PRICE GUIDE
Launch price:	£222
Excellent:	£20,000
Good:	£17,000
Average:	£12,000
Project:	£7000

MG
WA

This was MG's worthy attempt to move in on the luxury sports saloon market exploited by SS Jaguar. The war intervened before that many had been built. Available in saloon or Tickford-bodied drophead coupé, there are still roughly 25 survivors of each model worldwide. They turned out to be better appointed than the equivalent SS-Jaguars with lots of wood, leather and MG logos, and have better steering and road manners. Usually snapped up quickly when they come up for sale, add 20% to the prices given for one of those Tickford dropheads.

SPECIFICATIONS

Years produced:	1938-1939 (370 in total)
Performance:	0-60mph: N/A (Top speed: 91mph)
Power & torque:	96bhp / N/A
Engine:	Normally aspirated 2561cc in-line six, petrol, carburettor, 12 valves
Drivetrain:	Front-engine RWD
Suspension:	(F) Ind. semi-elliptic leaf spring. (R) Beam axle, semi-elliptic leaf spring.
Bodyframe:	chassis and separate body
Transmission:	4-speed manual
Weight:	1232kgs
	PRICE GUIDE
Launch price:	£442
Excellent:	£50,000
Good:	£40,000
Average:	£30,000
Project:	£10,000

MG
TC

First post-war MG, almost identical to TB, but with a body four inches wider, and additional (much-needed) interior space. Easily identifiable from the earlier car by its alternative instrumentation. Underneath, it featured shackles instead of sliding trunnions for the front and rear springs, and that had a positive effect on ride quality. Powered by the 1250cc, four-cylinder, overhead valve engine (54.4bhp at 5200rpm) a top speed of nearly 80mph was on the cards, and twin SU carburettors improve breathing. Two-seater sports body only.

SPECIFICATIONS

Years produced: 1945-1949 (10,001 in total)
Performance: 0-60mph: 27.25 secs (Top speed: 78mph)
Power & torque: 54.4bhp / 64lb/ft
Engine: Normally aspirated 1250cc in-line four, petrol, carburettor, 8 valves
Drivetrain: Front-engine RWD
Suspension: [F] Beam axle, semi-elliptic leaf spring. [R] Live axle, semi-elliptic leaf spring
Bodyframe: Chassis and separate body
Transmission: 4-speed manual
Weight: 838kgs

PRICE GUIDE

Launch price: £526
Excellent: £20,000
Good: £16,500
Average: £12,000
Project: £7000

MG
Y-type 1.25-litre

MG's first post-war saloon car had plenty of pre-war style and panache, although it lacked genuine performance. But the good value four-seater saloon proved a mainstay in the range while the T-types continued to evolve. The Y-type's engine was shared with its open-toppped cousins – the single-carburettor version of XPAG TC engine (46bhp at 4800rpm). New to the saloons was independent front suspension, rack-and-pinion steering and bolt-on disc wheels. Various open and closed model variations were introduced, although few remain.

SPECIFICATIONS

Years produced: 1947-1953 (8336 in total)
Performance: 0-60mph: 27.3 secs (Top speed: 71mph)
Power & torque: 46bhp / 58lb/ft
Engine: Normally aspirated 1250cc in-line four, petrol, carburettor, 8 valves
Drivetrain: Front-engine RWD
Suspension: [F] Independent, coil spring. [R] Live axle, semi elliptic leaf spring
Bodyframe: Chassis and separate body
Transmission: 4-speed manual
Weight: 1060kgs

PRICE GUIDE

Launch price: £565
Excellent: £7250
Good: £6000
Average: £3500
Project: £1500

MG
TD

Follow up to the much-loved TC, with most finding their way overseas during the austere years of the post-war era. The new rack-and-pinion steering and Y-Type's chassis sharpened up the Midget's game considerably, and the more rigid chassis improved durability. These cars were offered with left-hand drive, which obviously helped with the export drive. Engine-wise, it was the same story as before, with the 1250cc XPAG engine in 54bhp form putting in a fine performance, although an upgrade in 1950 to 57bhp for the MkII livened things up.

SPECIFICATIONS

Years produced: 1949-1953 (29,664 in total)
Performance: 0-60mph: 18.2 secs (Top speed: 78mph)
Power & torque: 54bhp / 64lb/ft
Engine: Normally aspirated 1250cc in-line four, petrol, carburettor, 8 valves
Drivetrain: Front-engine RWD
Suspension: [F] Independent, coil spring, wishbone. [R] Live axle, semi-elliptic leaf spring
Bodyframe: Chassis and separate body
Transmission: 4-speed manual
Weight: 876kgs

PRICE GUIDE

Launch price: £751
Excellent: £17,500
Good: £14,000
Average: £10,000
Project: £5000

MG
TF

The final flowering of the pre-war Midget concept was the TF which, like its predecessors, proved massively popular in the USA. It was a straightforward development of TD MkII, and the TF's most obvious changes from the older car are its raked radiator grille, lowered bonnet line and faired-in headlamps. Despite this, it was looking rather old by 1953, and sales in the UK were consequently slowing. Originally powered by the TD's engine, but later 1500 (July 1954 on) had XPEG engine of 1466cc and a top speed of nearly 90mph.

SPECIFICATIONS

Years produced: 1953-1955 (9600 in total)
Performance: 0-60mph: 18.9 secs (Top speed: 81mph)
Power & torque: 57bhp / 65lb/ft
Engine: Normally aspirated 1250cc in-line four, petrol, carburettor, 8 valves
Drivetrain: Front-engine RWD
Suspension: (F) Independent, wishbone, coil spring (R) Live axle, semi-elliptic leaf spring
Bodyframe: Chassis and separate body
Transmission: 4-speed manual
Weight: 916kgs

PRICE GUIDE

Launch price: £780
Excellent: £21,000
Good: £18,000
Average: £13,000
Project: £7500

MG
Magnette ZA/ZB

Nothing less than a quantum leap into the mainstream, this post-BMC MG, designed by Gerald Palmer, was elegant and affordable. Chassis-less saloon design, based on Wolseley 4/44, with indpendent front suspension, rack-and-pinion steering and BMC B-series power sold well, and established MG as part of BMC's badge-engineering portfolio. The 60bhp B-Series engine lacked sparkle, even with twin SU carburettors, but was helped in ZB form when power was uprated to 68bhp. Varitone version had larger rear window.

SPECIFICATIONS

Years produced: 1953-1958 (36,650 in total)
Performance: 0-60mph: 22.6 secs (Top speed: 82mph)
Power & torque: 60bhp / 71lb/ft
Engine: Normally aspirated 1489cc in-line four, petrol, carburettor, 8 valves
Drivetrain: Front-engine RWD
Suspension: (F) Independent, coil spring, wishbone. (R) Live axle, semi-elliptic leaf spring
Bodyframe: Monocoque
Transmission: 4-speed manual
Weight: 1118kgs

PRICE GUIDE

Launch price: £713
Excellent: £6500
Good: £5250
Average: £2750
Project: £1250

MG
MGA Roadster

This aerodynamic and beautiful two-seater roadster was a huge leap forward from the T-type Midgets. With twin-carburettor B-series engine, independent front suspension and rack-and-pinion steering, the differences were night and day. Initially offered with the 1489cc, four cylinder, B-Series ohv engine with 68bhp, but uprated to MGA 1600 specification in May 1959. Lockheed front discs made their first appearance with the larger 80bhp engine, significantly improving braking. Revered today and valued significantly ahead of the MGB.

SPECIFICATIONS

Years produced: 1955-1962 (101,000 in total)
Performance: 0-60mph: 15.6 secs (Top speed: 98mph)
Power & torque: 68bhp / 77lb/ft
Engine: Normally aspirated 1489cc in-line four, petrol, carburettor, 8 valves
Drivetrain: Front-engine RWD
Suspension: (F) Independent, coil spring, wishbone. (R) Live axle, semi-elliptic leaf spring
Bodyframe: Chassis and separate body
Transmission: 4-speed manual
Weight: 890kgs

PRICE GUIDE

Launch price: £894
Excellent: £17,000
Good: £14,000
Average: £9000
Project: £5500

MG
MGA Coupé

When it was launched in 1955, the beautiful MGA ushered in a new era of modernity at Abingdon – out went the pre-war cycle wings of the T-series car, and in came a slippery new body with Le Mans inspired styling. The MGA made liberal use of the BMC parts bin, with its B-series power unit coming straight from the Morris Oxford. Performance was hardly sparkling, but quick enough to impress the Americans, who bought the MGA in their container loads. For those who wanted more performance, the Twin Cam that followed was just the ticket.

SPECIFICATIONS

Years produced: 1956-1962
Performance: 0-60mph: 15.0 secs (Top speed: 100mph)
Power & torque: 72bhp / N/A
Engine: Normally aspirated 1489cc in-line four, petrol, carburettor, 8 valves
Drivetrain: Front-engine RWD
Suspension: (F) Independent, coil spring. (F) Beam axle, semi-elliptic leaf spring
Bodyframe: Chassis and separate body
Transmission: 4-speed manual
Weight: 927kgs

PRICE GUIDE

Launch price: £894
Excellent: £13,500
Good: £11,000
Average: £7000
Project: £3500

MG
MGA Twin Cam Roadster

The trouble with the MGA was always its lack of power. Although most owners were happy with the standard 1500 and 1600cc cars, there was demand from a certain hard core of buyers who wanted more. MG was happy to oblige when it came up with the Twin Cam. Racing car builder, Harry Weslake came up with a new twin-cam head for the B-Series, which improved breathing and top end power. Only ever offered as an option, the 108bhp upgrade was enough to satisfy MGA owners with a need for speed to match the beautiful styling.

SPECIFICATIONS

Years produced: 1958-1960 (2111 inc. Coupé in total)
Performance: 0-60mph: 9.1 secs (Top speed: 113mph)
Power & torque: 108bhp / N/A
Engine: Normally aspirated 1588cc in-line four, petrol, carburettor, 8 valves
Drivetrain: front-engine RWD
Suspension: (F) Independent, coil spring. (R) Live axle, semi-elliptic leaf spring.
Bodyframe: Chassis and separate body
Transmission: 4-speed manual
Weight: 952kgs

PRICE GUIDE

Launch price: £1266
Excellent: £24,000
Good: £20,000
Average: £12,500
Project: £7500

MG
MGA Twin Cam Coupé

Although it's an all-time classic, the MGA Twin Cam was far from trouble-free. For a start, it was an expensive engine to build, and that extra cost was passed on to the customer – a mere 2111 were sold during the late 1950s, and for those that did unreliability reared its ugly head. The engine gained a reputation for piston damage, and because of this few original cars survive. With a 110mph top speed, they were fun while they lasted. Visual differences between the Twin Cam and other MGAs were kept to a minimum, making these excellent Q-cars.

SPECIFICATIONS

Years produced: 1958-1960 (see Roadster in total)
Performance: 0-60mph: 9.1 secs (Top speed: 113mph)
Power & torque: 108bhp / 105lb/ft
Engine: Normally aspirated 1588cc in-line four, petrol, carburettor, 8 valves
Drivetrain: Front-engine RWD
Suspension: (F) Independent, coil spring. (R) Live axle, semi-elliptic leaf spring
Bodyframe: Chassis and separate body
Transmission: 4-speed manual
Weight: 952kgs

PRICE GUIDE

Launch price: £1266
Excellent: £19,000
Good: £15,000
Average: £9250
Project: £6000

MG
Magnette MkIII/IV

With a stable full of marques, BMC used its quota to the maximum with the Farina saloons. Few would have thought the staid and podgy B-Series powered car was a suitable basis for a new-age MG Magnette, but with a twin carburettor set-up and a wood and leather lined interior, they just about managed to pass it off. Later MkIVs are the ones to have with their 1622cc 68bhp engines providing just enough performance to keep up with the flow. Today, these cars are still readily available for relatively little money, and provide plenty of enjoyment.

SPECIFICATIONS

Years produced: 1959-1968 (31,104 in total)
Performance: 0-60mph: 20.6 secs (Top speed: 84mph)
Power & torque: 64bhp / N/A
Engine: Normally aspirated 1489cc in-line four, petrol, carburettor, 8 valves
Drivetrain: Front-engine RWD
Suspension: (F) Independent, coil spring. (R) Live axle, semi-elliptic leaf spring
Bodyframe: Metal monocoque
Transmission: 4-speed manual
Weight: 1118kgs

PRICE GUIDE

Launch price: £1013
Excellent: £3750
Good: £3000
Average: £1500
Project: £500

MG
Midget MkI-III

This unit-construction sports two-seater, developed from the Austin-Healey Sprite, was MG's most successful badge engineered model. It was initially powered by the BMC A-series 948cc, twin-carburettor, four-cylinder, ohv engine, and featured a four-speed gearbox, rack-and-pinion steering and independent front suspension. A hoot to drive despite the low power output, although the arrival of the 1098cc version helped. Disc brakes were added in 1962, before becoming the MkII in 1964 – with wind-up windows. MkIII upgunned to 1275cc.

SPECIFICATIONS

Years produced: 1961-1974 (152,158 in total)
Performance: 0-60mph: 10.8 secs (Top speed: 95mph)
Power & torque: 65bhp / 72lb/ft
Engine: Normally aspirated 1275cc in-line four, petrol, carburettor, 8 valves
Drivetrain: Front-engine RWD
Suspension: [F] Independent, wishbones and coil. [R] Rigid axle, semi-elliptic leaf spring
Bodyframe: Monocoque
Transmission: 4-speed manual
Weight: 685kgs

PRICE GUIDE

Launch price: £670
Excellent: £5000
Good: £4000
Average: £2500
Project: £900

MG
MGB Roadster MkI

Although MG found sucess with its T-type Midgets and MGA, the 'B took sales to a new level, eventually becoming the world's best-selling car until the arrival of the Datsun 240Z. A contemporary specification meant the 'B was a delight to drive compared with its rivals, and there was plenty of power on tap, thanks to its recently upgraded 1.8-litre B-series engine. Four-speed gearbox (overdrive available), rack-and-pinion steering, independent front suspension, and disc brakes were standard fitments right from the start.

SPECIFICATIONS

Years produced: 1962-1967 (513,276 in total)
Performance: 0-60mph: 12.2 secs (Top speed: 103mph)
Power & torque: 95bhp / 110lb/ft
Engine: Normally aspirated 1798cc in-line four, petrol, carburettor, 8 valves
Drivetrain: front-engine RWD
Suspension: [F] Independent, wishbones and coil. [R] Rigid axle, semi-elliptic leaf spring
Bodyframe: Monocoque
Transmission: 4-speed manual
Weight: 920kgs

PRICE GUIDE

Launch price: £690
Excellent: £11,250
Good: £9000
Average: £4500
Project: £2000

MG
1100/1300

The humble Austin 1100 initially seemed like an unsuitable starting point for an MG version, but as it happens, the small saloon acquitted itself very well indeed. Tenacious front-wheel-drive handling and a well-appointed interior made the MG 1100 a genuinely sporting saloon. It wasn't perfect, though – it proved difficult for mechanics to work on, and had a terrible reputation for rust, which was rightly deserved. Survival rate is low considering the huge number produced, but those that are left are not expensive to buy, and cost peanuts to run.

SPECIFICATIONS

Years produced: 1962-1971 (124,860/32,549 in total)
Performance: 0-60mph: 15.6 secs (Top speed: 78mph)
Power & torque: 48bhp / 60lb/ft
Engine: Normally aspirated 1098cc in-line four, petrol, carburettor, 8 valves
Drivetrain: Front-engine FWD
Suspension: I(F&R) Independent wishbone with Hydrolastic displacers
Bodyframe: Monocoque
Transmission: 4-speed manual
Weight: 832kgs

PRICE GUIDE

Launch price: £949
Excellent: £3250
Good: £2500
Average: £1200
Project: £500

MG
MGB GT

It's sometimes easy to forget just how much of an impact the MGB GT made on the marketplace. That fastback style roof, designed by Pininfarina, followed conventional GT styling cues, but for a fraction of the price. The raised windscreen height and side windows meant that there was a realistic amount of headroom for those in the front, although rear seat passengers didn't get such an easy ride. Underneath the glamorous new skin, the GT was pure Roadster, and that meant tidy handling and excellent performance.

SPECIFICATIONS

Years produced: 1965-1967 (21,835 in total)
Performance: 0-60mph: 13.0 secs (Top speed: 104mph)
Power & torque: 97bhp / 105lb/ft
Engine: Normally aspirated 1798cc in-line four, petrol, carburettor, 8 valves
Drivetrain: front-engine RWD
Suspension: [F] Independent, wishbones and coil. [R] Rigid axle, semi-elliptic leaf spring
Bodyframe: Monocoque
Transmission: 4-speed manual
Weight: 1108kgs

PRICE GUIDE

Launch price: £834
Excellent: £7000
Good: £5000
Average: £2500
Project: £1200

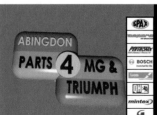

MG
MGC

In an attempt to extend the appeal of the MGB and also plug the gap in BMC's range with the demise of the big Healeys, the Abingdon engineers came up with the bright idea of fitting a C-series engine. The power and torque figures were adequate for this potential upmarket GT's ambitions, but those looking for sporting handling would end up being disapppointed with the understeery handling balance. Later development has tamed much of these handling indelicacies and, with proper tuning, the lumbering C-series can also deliver.

SPECIFICATIONS

Years produced: 1967-1969 (9002 in total)
Performance: 0-60mph: 10.2 secs (Top speed: 120mph)
Power & torque: 145bhp / 170lb/ft
Engine: Normally aspirated 2912cc in-line six, petrol, carburettor, 12 valves
Drivetrain: front-engine RWD
Suspension: [F] Independent, wishbones and coil. [R] Rigid axle, semi-elliptic leaf spring
Bodyframe: Monocoque
Transmission: 4-speed manual with overdrive
Weight: 1116kgs

PRICE GUIDE

Launch price: £1102
Excellent: £11,750
Good: £9250
Average: £6000
Project: £2750

MG
MGB Mk II/III

Upgrading the evergreen MGB to MkII specification was enough to keep Abingdon busy and sales on a high. The four-speed gearbox finally received synchromesh on all forward ratios, and an optional Borg-Warner automatic gearbox became available. In 1970 the MkII was treated to a BL style front end, which did away with the chrome grille surround and slats. MG fans hated the cost-constrained new style, and it was soon canned. The return to chrome ushered in the MkIII, which received a number of improvements to keep the MGB looking fresh.

SPECIFICATIONS

Years produced: 1967-1971 (310,077 in total)
Performance: 0-60mph: 13 secs (Top speed: 104mph)
Power & torque: 84bhp / 105lb/ft
Engine: Normally aspirated 1798cc in-line four, petrol, carburettor, 8 valves
Drivetrain: Front-engine RWD
Suspension: [F] Independent, wishbones and coil. [R] Rigid axle, semi-elliptic leaf spring
Bodyframe: Monocoque
Transmission: 4-speed manual
Weight: 1158kgs

PRICE GUIDE

Launch price: Not known
Excellent: £10,000
Good: £8000
Average: £4250
Project: £1750

MG
MGB GT V8

The concept of a V8 engined MGB was hardly new; Ken Costello had been making a good living converting MGBs to Rover engines for some time, and even MG had a go with the Edward Turner V8 before building the MGC instead. When production of the C-series was cut, MG finally introduced its own Rover V8-engined version, just as the effects of the 1973 energy crisis were hitting hard. Although a great car, the MGB GT V8 sold poorly, a victim of circumstance and poor marketing. Today it offers great value, but watch out for home conversions.

SPECIFICATIONS

Years produced: 1973-1976 (2591 in total)
Performance: 0-60mph: 9 secs (Top speed: 125mph)
Power & torque: 137bhp / 192lb/ft
Engine: Normally aspirated 3528cc V8, petrol, carburettor, 16 valves
Drivetrain: Front-engine RWD
Suspension: [F] Independent, wishbones and coil. [R] Rigid axle, semi-elliptic leaf spring
Bodyframe: Monocoque
Transmission: 4-speed manual
Weight: 1158kgs

PRICE GUIDE

Launch price: Not known
Excellent: £9750
Good: £7750
Average: £4500
Project: £2000

MG
MGB (Rubber Bumper)

North American regulations requested a raised ride height and polyurethane-covered bumpers required to withstand 5mph impacts without sustaining damage. Although condemned at the time by fans, the federalised MGB was actually a successful styling job compared with its Italian rivals. Later B-series engines in North America were reduced to a single Zenith Stromberg carb, emission equipment and a catalyst. Now these black bumper cars offer the best regular use practicality and value of all the MGBs.

SPECIFICATIONS

Years produced: 1974-1980 (128,653 in total)
Performance: 0-60mph: 13.0 secs (Top speed: 104mph)
Power & torque: 60bhp / 104lb/ft
Engine: Normally aspirated 1798cc in-line four, petrol, carburettor, 8 valves
Drivetrain: Front-engine RWD
Suspension: [F] Independent, wishbones and coil. [R] Rigid axle, semi-elliptic leaf spring
Bodyframe: Monocoque
Transmission: 4-speed manual
Weight: 971kgs

PRICE GUIDE

Launch price: Not known
Excellent: £8000
Good: £5750
Average: £2850
Project: £1100

MG
Metro/Metro Turbo

The first MG to appear after the closure of Abingdon in 1980 was a return to the badge-engineering ways of old. In becoming an MG in 1981, the Austin Metro received a trim upgrade package, and an uprated A-series engine delivering an additional 12bhp. Just over a year later, the Metro Turbo was added to the MG line-up and became a big seller in the GTi market. Featuring a Garrett T3 turbo, the engine was worked on by Lotus to develop 93bhp. It could have been more, but power was capped to prolong gearbox life. Most have now succumbed to rust.

SPECIFICATIONS

Years produced: 1982-1990 (37,500/21,968 in total)
Performance: 0-60mph: 9.9 secs (Top speed: 112mph)
Power & torque: 93bhp / 87lb/ft
Engine: Turbocharged 1275cc in-line four, petrol, carburettor, 8 valves
Drivetrain: front-engine FWD
Suspension: [F] Independent wishbones, Hydragas. [R] Independent trailing arms, Hydragas
Bodyframe: Metal monocoque
Transmission: 4-speed manual
Weight: 840kgs

PRICE GUIDE

Launch price: £4799
Excellent: £1750
Good: £1100
Average: £575
Project: £250

MG
Maestro 2.0EFi/Turbo

The early MG Maestro was fitted with a 1600cc engine derived from the Austin Maxi, and proved troublesome in use thanks to a hastily conceived twin-Weber carburettor set-up. The 2-litre O-series injection engine that was fitted to the 2.0 EFi model at the end of 1984 was much more like it, delivering ample performance and economy. After five years in production, the Montego Turbo's engine finally found its way into the Maestro, and with the help of Tickford a run of 505 was produced. Genuinely fast when new, but rare now thanks to extensive rust.

SPECIFICATIONS

Years produced: 1983-1991 (5740/3500 in total)
Performance: 0-60mph: 8.5 secs (Top speed: 115mph)
Power & torque: 115bhp / 134lb/ft
Engine: Normally aspirated 1994cc in-line four, petrol, electronic fuel injection, 8 valves
Drivetrain: Front-engine FWD
Suspension: [F] Independent, coil spring. [R] Dead beam, coil spring
Bodyframe: Monocoque
Transmission: 5-speed manual
Weight: 984kgs

PRICE GUIDE

Launch price: £7279
Excellent: £3000
Good: £2300
Average: £1400
Project: £400

MG
Montego EFi/Turbo

Sharing an engine with the Maestro, the 2.0 EFi Montego was MG's flagship model. It was quick, but when the turbocharged O-series made its debut, the EFi was left standing. The Montego Turbo was the fastest production MG, boasting a 0-60mph time of 7.2 seconds and a top speed of 128mph. It had its fair share of problems in the beginning, most notably the torque-steer, but over the next three years constant development transformed the Montego into an unfussed executive express. Now on the critical list with the Maestro and Metro.

SPECIFICATIONS

Years produced: 1985-1991 (57,900/23,000 in total)
Performance: 0-60mph: 7.5 secs (Top speed: 129mph)
Power & torque: 150bhp / 169lb/ft
Engine: Turbocharged 1994cc in-line four, petrol, carburettor, 8 valves
Drivetrain: Front-engine FWD
Suspension: [F] Independent, coil spring. [R] Dead beam, coil spring
Bodyframe: Monocoque
Transmission: 5-speed manual
Weight: 1098kgs

PRICE GUIDE

Launch price: £10,301
Excellent: £2000
Good: £1500
Average: £900
Project: £250

MG
RV8

In this incarnation of the MGB, the rubber bumper spec body was taken and modified to accept a new set of outer panels. The engine was a 3.9-litre Range Rover EFi V8 with 185bhp. A five-speed gearbox, derived from the Rover SD1, was used along with a new Salisbury axle. Very significant modifications were made to the suspension and brakes to bring the car up to date. The interior featured magnolia leather and burr elm. Most RV8s made were sold in Japan, but many of them have made their way back to the UK.

SPECIFICATIONS

Years produced: 1993-1995 (1983 in total)
Performance: 0-60mph: 6.0 secs (Top speed: 135mph)
Power & torque: 185bhp / 235lb/ft
Engine: Normally aspirated 3947cc V8, petrol, electronic fuel injection, 16 valves
Drivetrain: Front-engine RWD
Suspension: [F] Independent, wishbones and coil. [R] Rigid axle, semi-elliptic leaf spring
Bodyframe: Monocoque
Transmission: 5-speed manual
Weight: 1280kgs

PRICE GUIDE

Launch price: £26,500
Excellent: £14,000
Good: £12,000
Average: £9500
Project: £6000

MG
MGF

The MGF was the first production MG to feature a mid-mounted transverse engine. This has many advantages over the more conventional front mounted engine, the main being the superb weight distribution. This layout, coupled with the clever Hydragas suspension system, makes the MGF a unique driving experience. There are two engines available, the 1.8i K-series 1796cc 16v and the 1.8i VVC (Variable Valve Control). The power figures are 120PS and 145PS respectively which give a 0-60 time of 8.5 (1.8i) and 7.0 (VVC) seconds.

SPECIFICATIONS

Years produced: 1995-2002 (77,269 in total)
Performance: 0-60mph: 7.0 secs (Top speed: 126mph)
Power & torque: 143bhp / 128lb/ft
Engine: Normally aspirated 1796cc in-line four, petrol, electronic fuel injection, 16 valves
Drivetrain: Mid-engine RWD
Suspension: [F] Independent wishbones, Hydragas. [R] Independent trailing arms, Hydragas
Bodyframe: Metal monocoque
Transmission: 5-speed manual
Weight: 1070kgs

PRICE GUIDE

Launch price: £17,540
Excellent: £5500
Good: £4000
Average: £2000
Project: £900

MG
TF

Successor to the MGF saw replacement of Hydragas suspension with coil springs and multi-link rear axle. Steering was sharpened, the body gained 20% increase in torsional stiffness. The revised frontal elevation and aerodynamic package included an integrated lip spoiler on the bootlid. TF 115 1.6 litre entry-level model, mainstream TF 135 1.8 litre, the TF 120 Stepspeed 1.8 litre and the range-topping TF 160 VVC. Production stopped in 2005 but was re-launched under the ownership of Nanjing's MG UK as the MG TF LE500.

SPECIFICATIONS

Years produced: 2002-2005 (39,249 in total)
Performance: 0-60mph: 7.4 secs (Top speed: 137mph)
Power & torque: 157bhp / 128lb/ft
Engine: Normally aspirated 1795cc in-line four, petrol, electronic fuel injection, 16 valves
Drivetrain: Mid-engine RWD
Suspension: [F] Independent, double wishbones. [R] Independent, multi-link, coil springs
Bodyframe: Metal monocoque
Transmission: 5-speed manual
Weight: 1115kgs

PRICE GUIDE

Launch price: £15,200
Excellent: £7250
Good: £5500
Average: £4000
Project: £2750

MINI
MkI

Alec Issigonis' cheap small car for BMC was innovative with its front-wheel-drive and space-saving transverse engine layout but, more than that, it was incredibly entertaining to drive. The Mini had a personality that few small cars had displayed before, and it soon became a best-seller. The Austin version was initially called the Seven, but became the Mini in 1961. The 848cc A-series engine was used throughout the life of the MkI; one significant change was the adoption of Hydrolastic suspension in place of the original rubber cone type in 1964.

SPECIFICATIONS

Years produced:	1959-1967 (1,572,756 in total)
Performance:	0-60mph: 27.1 secs (Top speed: 72mph)
Power & torque:	34bhp / 33lb/ft
Engine:	Normally aspirated 848cc in-line four, petrol, carburettor, 8 valves
Drivetrain:	Front-engine RWD
Suspension:	(F&R) Independent, rubber springing medium (later Hydrolastic)
Bodyframe:	Metal monocoque
Transmission:	4-speed manual
Weight:	626kgs
PRICE GUIDE	
Launch price:	£537
Excellent:	£4250
Good:	£3250
Average:	£1750
Project:	£850

MINI
Cooper 997/998

Mini creator Alec Issigonis was against the idea of a performance Mini. Fortunately, his wishes didn't prevail, and a legend was born in the form of the 1961 Mini-Cooper, as tweaked by F1 guru John Cooper. The first cars used a 997cc twin-carb A-series; this was changed for a 998cc unit from 1964. Front disc brakes were standard and Coopers stood out by their two-tone paint schemes and special grilles. Speeds of around 90mph may not have been all-out fast, but it was the Cooper's handling brilliance that turned it into such a potent rally tool.

SPECIFICATIONS

Years produced:	1961-1969 (64,224 in total)
Performance:	0-60mph: 17.2 secs (Top speed: 85mph)
Power & torque:	55bhp / 54lb/ft
Engine:	Normally aspirated 997cc in-line four, petrol, carburettor, 8 valves
Drivetrain:	Front-engine FWD
Suspension:	(F&R) Independent, rubber springing medium (later Hydrolastic)
Bodyframe:	Metal monocoque
Transmission:	4-speed manual
Weight:	584kgs
PRICE GUIDE	
Launch price:	£679
Excellent:	£7500
Good:	£6000
Average:	£3000
Project:	£1250

MINI
Cooper 1071S

Cooper had more experience with A-series engines in the 1100cc racing class and put that knowledge to good use with the first Mini-Cooper S. Its enlarged 1071cc engine managed 70bhp and there were larger disc brakes to cope with its extra performance. Nothing much changed on the outside; the S looked the same as the Cooper save for 'S' badges on the bonnet and boot, and ventilated steel wheels. Inside, the upholstery was finished to more luxurious Mini Super De Luxe specification. A petite but potent rocket but even better was soon to follow...

SPECIFICATIONS

Years produced:	1963-1964 (4031 in total)
Performance:	0-60mph: 13.5 secs (Top speed: 90mph)
Power & torque:	70bhp / 62lb/ft
Engine:	Normally aspirated 1071cc in-line four, petrol, carburettor, 8 valves
Drivetrain:	Front-engine FWD
Suspension:	(F&R) Independent, rubber springing medium (later Hydrolastic)
Bodyframe:	Metal monocoque
Transmission:	4-speed manual
Weight:	686kgs
PRICE GUIDE	
Launch price:	£695
Excellent:	£10,250
Good:	£8250
Average:	£5000
Project:	£2600

MINI
Cooper 970S

The reduction in engine size and power for 1964's 970S Cooper might have seemed a strange move but it was built simply as a homologation special with a short-stroke 970cc engine developing 65bhp. The specialist engine was pricy to manufacture and so BMC made it a special order model; thus very few were sold. Aside from the engine, the mechanical specification was the same as the 1071S. Hydrolastic suspension made an appearance three months after launch but the car itself only lasted a further seven months after this change.

SPECIFICATIONS

Years produced:	1964-1965 (963 in total)
Performance:	0-60mph: N/A (Top speed: 92mph)
Power & torque:	65bhp / N/A
Engine:	Normally aspirated 970cc in-line four, petrol, carburettor, 8 valves
Drivetrain:	Front-engine FWD
Suspension:	(F&R) Independent, rubber springing medium (later Hydrolastic)
Bodyframe:	Metal monocoque
Transmission:	4-speed manual
Weight:	650kgs
PRICE GUIDE	
Launch price:	£671
Excellent:	£11,000
Good:	£9000
Average:	£5500
Project:	£2750

MINI
Cooper 1275S Mk I

Cooper's crowning glory was the 1275S, the MkI version of which lasted from 1964 to 1967. It was these Coopers that ruled the Monte Carlo rallies of the 1960s. The long-stroke 1275cc A-series gave 76bhp, enough to launch the car to nigh on 100mph. Single colour paint schemes were available alongside the usual two-tone ones meaning that these Coopers were great little Q-cars, as there wasn't too much else to distinguish them from a standard Mini. Hydrolastic suspension came along in 1964, with an oil cooler and twin fuel tanks from 1966.

SPECIFICATIONS

Years produced:	1964-1967 (21,141 in total)
Performance:	0-60mph: 11.2 secs (Top speed: 96mph)
Power & torque:	76bhp / 79lb/ft
Engine:	Normally aspirated 1275cc in-line four, petrol, carburettor, 8 valves
Drivetrain:	Front-engine FWD
Suspension:	(F&R) Independent, rubber springing medium (later Hydrolastic)
Bodyframe:	Metal monocoque
Transmission:	4-speed manual
Weight:	650kgs
PRICE GUIDE	
Launch price:	£756
Excellent:	£12,000
Good:	£9500
Average:	£6000
Project:	£3000

MINI
Moke

The Moke was developed as a military vehicle... but the forces failed to appreciate it. So, instead, BMC sold it as a fun fashion accessory. You weren't one of the in-crowd unless you'd driven down Carnaby Street in one. Unless, of course, you were Patrick McGoohan in *The Prisoner* instead. Production switched to Australia in 1968, with a rise in engine size from 848cc to 998cc, and then 1098cc with the MkII of 1969. The Moke Californian of 1971 had a 1275cc unit. Portuguese manufacture began in 1980 and ended in 1993.

SPECIFICATIONS

Years produced:	1964-1968 (14,518 in total)
Performance:	0-60mph: 21.8 secs (Top speed: 65mph)
Power & torque:	34bhp / N/A
Engine:	Normally aspirated 848cc in-line four, petrol, carburettor, 8 valves
Drivetrain:	Front-engine FWD
Suspension:	(F&R) Independent, rubber spring and damper units
Bodyframe:	Metal monocoque
Transmission:	4-speed manual
Weight:	406kgs
	PRICE GUIDE
Launch price:	£405
Excellent:	£7250
Good:	£6000
Average:	£3500
Project:	£2000

MINI
Cooper S MkII/III

The 1275cc Cooper S continued into MkII guise, with the same changes as the humbler Minis such as a reshaped grille, bigger rear window and enlarged back lights. Other Minis had dispensed with their marque names but the S continued to be available in Austin and Morris forms. The 998cc variant was dropped in 1969 but the 1275 Cooper S made it through to MkIII form with concealed door hinges and wind-up windows. It kept Hydrolastic suspension until British Leyland's agreement with Cooper was cancelled in 1971 and the type disappeared.

SPECIFICATIONS

Years produced:	1967-1971 (16,396 in total)
Performance:	0-60mph: 10.9 secs (Top speed: 96mph)
Power & torque:	76bhp / 79lb/ft
Engine:	Normally aspirated 1275cc in-line four, petrol, carburettor, 8 valves
Drivetrain:	Front-engine FWD
Suspension:	(F&R) Independent, Hydrolastic
Bodyframe:	Metal monocoque
Transmission:	4-speed manual
Weight:	640kgs
	PRICE GUIDE
Launch price:	£631
Excellent:	£9000
Good:	£7000
Average:	£4250
Project:	£1850

MINI
MkII-V

The short-lived MkII (1967-69) had a new grille and the option of a 998cc engine while the MkIII (1969-76) hid the door hinges and replaced the sliding windows with wind-up ones. The old Austin and Morris badges were dropped, with the Mini now a marque in its own right. Hydrolastic suspension – which had proved more expensive to fit – was dropped in favour of the original rubber cone type. Changes for the MkIV (1976-84) were more subtle, with alterations to the interior and subframe. The MkV took over from 1985-92, with 12in wheels and front disc brakes.

SPECIFICATIONS

Years produced:	1967-1992
Performance:	0-60mph: 27.1 secs (Top speed: 72mph)
Power & torque:	39bhp / 51lb/ft
Engine:	Normally aspirated 998cc in-line four, petrol, carburettor, 8 valves
Drivetrain:	front-engine RWD
Suspension:	(F&R) Independent, Hydrolastic (later rubber spring and damper units)
Bodyframe:	Metal monocoque
Transmission:	4-speed manual
Weight:	616kgs
	PRICE GUIDE
Launch price:	£509
Excellent:	£3250
Good:	£2500
Average:	£950
Project:	£300

MINI
1275GT

Seeking to save money, British Leyland replaced the Mini-Cooper with an uprated version of the Mini Clubman. However, just as the blunt-fronted Clubman lacked the character of the original Mini, so the 1275GT was a disappointment compared to the Cooper with only a single-carburettor 1275cc engine of 59bhp. In essence, it wasn't that bad a car, with front disc brakes and more sophisticated equipment inside, and at least it stood out more than other Minis with its Rostyle wheels and side decals. But it tried to supersede a legend. And that's tough to do...

SPECIFICATIONS

Years produced:	1969-1980 (110,673 in total)
Performance:	0-60mph: 13.3 secs (Top speed: 90mph)
Power & torque:	55bhp / 67lb/ft
Engine:	Normally aspirated 1275cc in-line four, petrol, carburettor, 8 valves
Drivetrain:	Front-engine FWD
Suspension:	Independent, wishbone, rubber spring and damper units
Bodyframe:	Metal monocoque
Transmission:	4-speed manual
Weight:	675kgs
	PRICE GUIDE
Launch price:	£834
Excellent:	£3500
Good:	£2500
Average:	£1275
Project:	£500

MINI
Clubman

Despite its sales success, the original Mini had never made any money for BMC. So, successor British Leyland launched what they regarded as an enhanced version in 1969, which was accordingly more expensive. The Clubman had a longer, squared-off nose. The interior was enhanced with instruments now in front of the driver instead of in the centre and Hydrolastic suspension was retained until 1971. An estate was available from launch, complete with fake plastic wood trim down the sides. A cheap way into Mini ownership these days.

SPECIFICATIONS

Years produced:	1969-1982 (473,189 in total)
Performance:	0-60mph: 21.0 secs (Top speed: 75mph)
Power & torque:	38bhp / N/A
Engine:	Normally aspirated 998cc in-line four, petrol, carburettor, 8 valves
Drivetrain:	Front-engine FWD
Suspension:	(F&R) Independent, wishbone, rubber spring and damper units
Bodyframe:	Metal monocoque
Transmission:	4-speed manual
Weight:	675kgs
	PRICE GUIDE
Launch price:	£720
Excellent:	£2500
Good:	£1650
Average:	£750
Project:	£250

MINI
RSP Cooper 1.3

Rover brought back the Cooper in 1990 as a limited edition of just 1000. Such was the interest in it that the decision was taken to reintroduce it as a mainstream model, with a 1275cc engine plus alloy wheels, white roof and more sporting interior. An 'S' package from John Cooper boosted power to 78bhp. Fuel injection from 1991 increased the power of both types even more, but from 1996, this changed from single- to multi-point with electronic ignition as well. The 40th birthday celebration Cooper S Works of 1999 was the most powerful of them all, with 90bhp.

SPECIFICATIONS

Years produced:	1991-2000
Performance:	0-60mph: 13.2 secs (Top speed: 94mph)
Power & torque:	63bhp / 70lb/ft
Engine:	Normally aspirated 1275cc in-line four, petrol, electronic fuel injection, 8 valves
Drivetrain:	Front-engine FWD
Suspension:	(F&R) Independent, wishbone, rubber spring and damper units
Bodyframe:	Metal monocoque
Transmission:	4-speed manual
Weight:	690kgs
	PRICE GUIDE
Launch price:	£6995
Excellent:	£6500
Good:	£5250
Average:	£2750
Project:	£1000

MORGAN
4/4 S1

The first post-war Morgan was similar to its pre-war cousin in styling, and almost identical underneath. The chassis was tubular, featuring Z-section side members, while the Morgan sliding pillar suspension and coil springs were just as before. For the first 4/4, a special overhead cam Standard engine was used, mated to a Moss gearbox. It was a recipe that worked, and would continue to do so for a very long time indeed. Some of the features, such as cable brakes, remained in place, but over time, these would be replaced by contemporary set-ups.

SPECIFICATIONS

Years produced:	1945-1950 (249 in total)
Performance:	0-60mph: N/A (Top speed: 77mph)
Power & torque:	40bhp / N/A
Engine:	Normally aspirated 1267cc in-line four, petrol, carburettor, 8 valves
Drivetrain:	Front-engine RWD
Suspension:	(F) Independent, torsion bar. (R) Beam axle, semi-elliptic leaf spring
Bodyframe:	Chassis and separate body
Transmission:	4-speed manual
Weight:	721kgs
	PRICE GUIDE
Launch price:	£455
Excellent:	£20,000
Good:	£17,000
Average:	£12,000
Project:	£7000

MORGAN
Plus 4

Adding four inches to the wheelbase of the 4/4 to make room for a second row of seats was a wise move, as it opened up the appeal of these vintage sports cars to those with small families. A move to hydraulically assisted brakes was a welcome move, as was the lightly restyled front end. During its 19-year run, it went through a 2.1-litre Standard Vanguard engine before moving to a Triumph TR2 engine. Front disc brakes were finally fitted as standard in 1961, which was a good thing, as the final TR4 engined models were genuine 100mph cars.

SPECIFICATIONS

Years produced:	1950-1969 (3737 in total)
Performance:	0-60mph: 14.1 secs (Top speed: 85mph)
Power & torque:	68bhp / 113lb/ft
Engine:	Normally aspirated 1993cc in-line four, petrol, carburettor, 8 valves
Drivetrain:	Front-engine RWD
Suspension:	(F) Independent, coil spring. (R) Live axle, coil spring
Bodyframe:	Chassis and separate body
Transmission:	4-speed manual
Weight:	838kgs
	PRICE GUIDE
Launch price:	£652
Excellent:	£18,500
Good:	£15,000
Average:	£11,000
Project:	£5000

MORGAN
4/4 SII-V

After a hiatus of four years, the 4/4 was put back into production. The number of TR2 engines used in the Plus 4 models was being restricted by Triumph so Morgan turned to Ford to use the cheap and readily available 1172cc sidevalve engine to create a new entry-level model. The wheelbase of the 4/4 was standardised with the Plus 4, thus streamlining production. The Series IV received a widened, better looking body, disc brakes and a larger Ford 1340cc engine. Despite not changing its style, the 4/4 remained consistently popular though the years.

SPECIFICATIONS

Years produced:	1955-1968 (1197 in total)
Performance:	0-60mph: 29.4 secs (Top speed: 71mph)
Power & torque:	36bhp / N/A
Engine:	Normally aspirated 1172cc in-line four, petrol, carburettor, 8 valves
Drivetrain:	Front-engine RWD
Suspension:	(F) Independent, coil spring. (R) Beam axle, leaf springs
Bodyframe:	Chassis and separate body
Transmission:	4-speed manual
Weight:	660kgs
	PRICE GUIDE
Launch price:	£639
Excellent:	£14,000
Good:	£11,000
Average:	£8000
Project:	£5000

MORGAN
Plus 8

The Rover V8 engine found its way under the bonnet of a bewildering array of cars. However, Morgan's decision to buy up a stockpile of the ex-GM engines was the most surprising but satisfying once it became clear just how much fun the Plus 8 actually was. It was a pragmatic move by Morgan, though, as supplies of suitable four-cylinder engines were beginning to dry up. The earliest examples made 143bhp – identical to the Rover P6 V8 – and endowed the lightweight 4/4 derived sports car with explosive acceleration and exciting handling.

SPECIFICATIONS

Years produced: 1968-1972 (482 in total)
Performance: 0-60mph: 6.7 secs (Top speed: 124mph)
Power & torque: 161bhp / N/A
Engine: Normally aspirated 3528cc V8, petrol, carburettor, 16 valves
Drivetrain: Front-engine RWD
Suspension: (F) Independent, coil spring. (R) Beam axle, leaf spring
Bodyframe: Chassis and separate body
Transmission: 4-speed manual
Weight: 839kgs

PRICE GUIDE

Launch price: £1478
Excellent: £30,000
Good: £25,000
Average: £17,500
Project: £11,000

MORGAN
4/4 1600

For increasingly affluent car buyers, the rather austere and underpowered 4/4 was looking a little bit out of its depth. There was nothing wrong with the way it looked, but rather the way it went. Morgan rectified this in 1968 by fitting the Ford Kent engine, boosting power to a more palatable 74bhp. The Plus 4 model was dropped, with the option of 2+2 seating being passed on to the 4/4 line. It remained available in this form until 1982, when the Ford CVH used in the front-wheel-drive Escort was dropped in, improving power and economy, if not refinement.

SPECIFICATIONS

Years produced: 1968-1981 (3708 in total)
Performance: 0-60mph: 9.8 secs (Top speed: 100mph)
Power & torque: 95bhp / 98lb/ft
Engine: Normally aspirated 1599cc in-line four, petrol, carburettor, 8 valves
Drivetrain: Front-engine RWD
Suspension: (F) Independent, coil springs. (R) Beam axle, semi-elliptic leaf spring
Bodyframe: Chassis and separate body
Transmission: 4-speed manual
Weight: 688kgs

PRICE GUIDE

Launch price: £858
Excellent: £14,500
Good: £12,000
Average: £8750
Project: £5000

MORGAN
Plus 8 (1973-86)

Morgan continued to develop the Plus 8, and by 1973, the aluminium-engined vintage-style hot-rod had the worst of its handling foibles sorted out. A all-synchromesh Rover 2000 gearbox was also installed to replace the old Moss unit. A higher output SD1-tune V8 was installed later, and in 1977, along with the much needed five-speed gearbox, the option of aluminium body panels was introduced. Sales continued steadily throughout the worst of the 1970s recession, and supply was carefully managed by keeping the waiting list long, at around eight years.

SPECIFICATIONS

Years produced: 1973-1986
Performance: 0-60mph: 6.7 secs (Top speed: 124mph)
Power & torque: 161bhp / 210lb/ft
Engine: Normally aspirated 3528cc V8, petrol, carburettor, 16 valves
Drivetrain: Front-engine RWD
Suspension: (F) Independent, coil springs. (R) Beam axle, semi-elliptic leaf spring
Bodyframe: Chassis and separate body
Transmission: 5-speed manual
Weight: 898kgs

PRICE GUIDE

Launch price: £1478
Excellent: £25,000
Good: £21,000
Average: £15,000
Project: £9000

MORGAN
Plus 8 Injection

Following the arrival of the Rover SD1 Vitesse in 1982, Morgan kept pace with developments by introducing its Lucas injected 190bhp power unit into the Plus 8. Given the Morgan's interesting handling, it seemed that the last thing it needed was additional grunt. However the power hikes continued long into the 21st century, first with the 3.9-litre Range Rover V8 (again with 190bhp, but more torque), and then with a 4.6-litre pushing out 240bhp. It was a recipe that worked though, and sales remained strong right through to the launch of the current Aero models.

SPECIFICATIONS

Years produced: 1984-1990
Performance: 0-60mph: 5.6 secs (Top speed: 120mph)
Power & torque: 190bhp / 220lb/ft
Engine: Normally aspirated 3528cc V8, petrol, electronic fuel injection, 16 valves
Drivetrain: Front-engine RWD
Suspension: (F) Independent, coil springs. (R) Beam axle, semi-elliptic leaf spring
Bodyframe: Chassis and separate body
Transmission: 5-speed manual
Weight: 839kgs

PRICE GUIDE

Launch price: £12,999
Excellent: £22,500
Good: £19,000
Average: £15,000
Project: £9000

MORGAN
Plus 4

For 1987, the Plus Four made a return, initially powered by the 1600cc Ford CVH, and then by an optional 1585cc Fiat Twin Cam. Typically, these Fiat-engined cars proved lively to drive and much faster than their Ford-engined counterparts. The 'Plus Four' name continued after the end of these 1600cc cars, thanks to the arrival of the 2-litre twin cam Rover M16 engine, which offered 138bhp and a top speed of over 110mph. However, these four-seat Morgans never achieved the popularity of their two-seat counterparts.

SPECIFICATIONS

Years produced: 1985-2000
Performance: 0-60mph: 9.0 secs (Top speed: 112mph)
Power & torque: 122bhp / 127lb/ft
Engine: Normally aspirated 1995cc in-line four, petrol, electronic fuel injection, 8 valves
Drivetrain: Front-engine RWD
Suspension: (F) Independent, coil springs. (R) Beam axle, semi-elliptic leaf spring
Bodyframe: Chassis and separate body
Transmission: 5-speed manual
Weight: 848kgs

PRICE GUIDE

Launch price: £10,901
Excellent: £17,500
Good: £13,500
Average: £10,000
Project: £8000

MORRIS
Minor Series MM

The original Minor, complete with sidevalve engine, is a sedate performer, but delightful handling aids its progress. At first, only sold as a two-door saloon or Tourer, with grille-mounted headlamps, until the four-door saloon was introduced in September 1950. These had their headlamps mounted in restyled front wings, and this change was adopted by two-doors and Tourers from January 1951. It's the early 'lowlamp' Minors that attract collectors. Prices are for lowlamp saloons. Add 40% for Tourers, deduct 20% for high-headlamp MMs.

SPECIFICATIONS

Years produced: 1948-1953 (176,002 in total)
Performance: 0-60mph: 36.5 secs (Top speed: 62mph)
Power & torque: 27bhp / N/A
Engine: Normally aspirated 918cc in-line four, petrol, carburettor, 8 valves
Drivetrain: Front-engine RWD
Suspension: (F) Independent, torsion beam. (R) Beam axle, leaf springs
Bodyframe: Metal monocoque
Transmission: 4-speed manual
Weight: 787kgs

PRICE GUIDE

Launch price: £359
Excellent: £4750
Good: £3500
Average: £2000
Project: £600

MORRIS
Six

Morris's top-of-the-range early post-war offering combines the rounded main body styling of the Minor/Oxford MO with the long bonnet and upright grille of pre-war offerings. It's not the most comfortable mix, but salvation lies in the straight-six engine that gives the car a decent turn of speed. The Six actually uses the MO's body from the screen back, but with different front door pressings and a 13in longer wheelbase. It uses cam steering, which isn't as good as the Oxford's rack-and-pinion. Not made in great numbers and survivors are rare.

SPECIFICATIONS

Years produced: 1948-1953 (12,400 in total)
Performance: 0-60mph: 22.4 secs (Top speed: 83mph)
Power & torque: 70bhp / 100lb/ft
Engine: Normally aspirated 2215cc in-line six, petrol, carburettor, 12 valves
Drivetrain: Front-engine RWD
Suspension: (F) Independent, torsion bar (R) Beam axle, leaf spring
Bodyframe: Metal monocoque
Transmission: 4-speed manual
Weight: 1276kgs

PRICE GUIDE

Launch price: £608
Excellent: £4750
Good: £3500
Average: £1650
Project: £650

MORRIS
Oxford MO

In effect a big brother to the Minor, the Oxford promises more of everything but the extra bulk it carries means that none of its works quite as well. The 1500cc sidevalve engine, though ploddingly reliable, is rather gutless with just 41bhp. The column-change for the four-speed gearbox borders on bearable. A wood-framed Traveller estate version was introduced in 1952, pre-dating the similar Minor by a year. These do have collector appeal, are now very rare and should be worth significantly more than the saloon values quoted.

SPECIFICATIONS

Years produced: 1948-1954 (159,960 in total)
Performance: 0-60mph: 31.1 secs (Top speed: 71mph)
Power & torque: 41bhp / 67lb/ft
Engine: Normally aspirated 1476cc in-line four, petrol, carburettor, 8 valves
Drivetrain: Front-engine RWD
Suspension: (F) Independent, torsion bar. (R) Beam axle, leaf spring
Bodyframe: Metal monocoque
Transmission: 4-speed manual
Weight: 1092kgs

PRICE GUIDE

Launch price: £505
Excellent: £3650
Good: £2500
Average: £1000
Project: £450

MORRIS
Minor Series II

Still with the charm of a split windscreen, but now powered by the A-series engine from Austin's A30. This engine only appeared in four-door models during 1952, but all models received it from February '53. Later that year the wood-framed Traveller is added to the range. From late '54 there's a new face with five horizontal grille slats, plus a new dashboard. Many of these cars have been fitted with the stronger 948cc engine from a later Minor. This has no detrimental affect on their value. Add 75% for Convertible and Traveller prices.

SPECIFICATIONS

Years produced: 1952-1956 (269,838 in total)
Performance: 0-60mph: N/A (Top speed: 62mph)
Power & torque: 30bhp / 40lb/ft
Engine: Normally aspirated 803cc in-line four, petrol, carburettor, 8 valves
Drivetrain: Front-engine RWD
Suspension: (F) Independent, torsion bar. (R) Live axle, semi-elliptic leaf spring
Bodyframe: Metal monocoque
Transmission: 4-speed manual
Weight: 787kgs

PRICE GUIDE

Launch price: £582
Excellent: £4000
Good: £2750
Average: £1300
Project: £400

MORRIS
Cowley

A poverty-spec version of the Series II/III Oxford, the first series of Cowleys were sold with a 1200cc B-series engine, from the Austin Somerset. They also used smaller front brakes and came with PVC upholstery instead of leather. Chrome side trim and over-riders were also missing. Series II versions, known as the Cowley 1500, did get the Oxford's 1489cc engine, but otherwise retained their austerity. Over six times as many Oxfords were built, but the Cowley's rarity counts for nothing and the few survivors can be picked up very cheaply.

SPECIFICATIONS
Years produced: 1954-1959 (22,036 in total)
Performance: 0-60mph: 37.5 secs (Top speed: 65mph)
Power & torque: 42bhp / 58lb/ft
Engine: Normally aspirated 1200cc in-line four, petrol, carburettor, 8 valves
Drivetrain: Front-engine RWD
Suspension: (F) Independent, torsion bar (R) Live axle, leaf springs
Bodyframe: Metal monocoque
Transmission: 4-speed manual
Weight: 1030kgs

PRICE GUIDE
Launch price: £702
Excellent: £2000
Good: £1500
Average: £900
Project: £200

MORRIS
Oxford II/III/IV

A big step forward from the Oxford MO, with an all-new body and 1500cc B-series engine. Becomes the Series III in October 1956 thanks to a facelift that includes a more stylish fluted bonnet and finned rear wings. Drives better than it looks thanks to torsion bar front suspension and rack-and-pinion steering. Wood-framed two-door Traveller estate version of the SII/III is worth double the price of a saloon. It was replaced in 1957 by the estate-only Series IV Oxford, with an all-steel four-door body. These command about 25% more than saloons.

SPECIFICATIONS
Years produced: 1954-1960 (145,458 in total)
Performance: 0-60mph: 29.0 secs (Top speed: 73mph)
Power & torque: 52bhp / 78lb/ft
Engine: Normally aspirated 1489cc in-line four, petrol, carburettor, 8 valves
Drivetrain: Front-engine RWD
Suspension: (F) Independent, torsion bar. (R) Beam axle, leaf spring
Bodyframe: Metal monocoque
Transmission: 4-speed manual
Weight: 1067kgs

PRICE GUIDE
Launch price: £745
Excellent: £3000
Good: £2200
Average: £1100
Project: £350

MORRIS
Isis

Much like the Six it replaced, the Isis is based closely on the Oxford, but this time the front end is stretched by eight inches to make room for a single-carb version of the six-cylinder C-series engine. On later cars mesh rather than painted slats in the grille sets it apart from the lesser car, though occupants will notice the right-hand floor-change for the gearbox, to allow three-abreast seating. Updates for rarer Series II in 1956 include fluted bonnet, rear fins, and an extra 4bhp. Highly prized and hard-to-find estates worth about a third more than saloons.

SPECIFICATIONS
Years produced: 1955-1958 (12,155 in total)
Performance: 0-60mph: 17.8 secs (Top speed: 86mph)
Power & torque: 86bhp / N/A
Engine: Normally aspirated 2639cc in-line six, petrol, carburettor, 12 valves
Drivetrain: Front-engine RWD
Suspension: (F) Independent, torsion bar. (R) Beam axle, leaf spring
Bodyframe: Metal monocoque
Transmission: 4-speed manual
Weight: 1397kgs

PRICE GUIDE
Launch price: £802
Excellent: £3750
Good: £3000
Average: £1600
Project: £650

MORRIS
Minor 1000

These are the best Minors for those who want one to drive as well as show. The larger A-series engines finally provided power to match the cars' handling, more so after September 1962 when a 1098cc engine replaced the 948. Larger front brakes were added at the same time. The 1000s are easily distinguished by their curved one-piece windscreen and larger rear window. Convertibles were dropped in June 1969, saloon production ended in November 1970, but Travellers soldiered on until April 1971. Add 50% for Convertible/Traveller prices.

SPECIFICATIONS
Years produced: 1956-1971 (847,491 in total)
Performance: 0-60mph: 22.2 secs (Top speed: 77mph)
Power & torque: 48bhp / 60lb/ft
Engine: Normally aspirated 1098cc in-line four, petrol, carburettor, 8 valves
Drivetrain: Front-engine RWD
Suspension: (F) Independent, torsion bar. (R) Beam axle, semi-elliptic leaf spring
Bodyframe: Metal monocoque
Transmission: 4-speed manual
Weight: 787kgs

PRICE GUIDE
Launch price: £603
Excellent: £4500
Good: £3500
Average: £1750
Project: £400

MORRIS
Oxford V/VI

Spread right across the BMC range, Morris was just one of five badges to be found on this angular Pininfarina-styled body. The Morris actually differed little from its Austin brother, but was built in another factory. Rear lights are the main visual change, though inside there was a unique dashboard and bench rather than individual front seats. Series VI arrived after just two-and-a-half years with larger engine and wider track for better handling. Rear fins are reduced in height. Usefully spacious estate version was killed off early in 1969.

SPECIFICATIONS
Years produced: 1959-1971 (296,255 in total)
Performance: 0-60mph: 23.6 secs (Top speed: 78mph)
Power & torque: 55bhp / N/A
Engine: Normally aspirated 1489cc in-line four, petrol, carburettor, 8 valves
Drivetrain: Front-engine RWD
Suspension: (F) Independent, coil spring. (R) Beam axle, leaf springs
Bodyframe: Metal monocoque
Transmission: 4-speed manual
Weight: 1054kgs

PRICE GUIDE
Launch price: £816
Excellent: £2900
Good: £2000
Average: £1000
Project: £300

MORRIS
Marina 1.3/1.8

It was never going to be easy, replacing the much-loved Minor. Even if it had been a great car. Unfortunately, the Marina was merely mediocre. A strictly conventional machine, much of its running gear was Minor-based and therefore far from cutting edge for the era. A saloon and coupé were available, with engines in 1275cc or 1798cc sizes, the latter unit from the MGB. That should have made the cars quite sporty, but handling was seriously suspect. Gradual improvement followed until replaced by the visually-similar Ital in 1980.

SPECIFICATIONS

Years produced: 1971-1980 (809,612 in total)
Performance: 0-60mph: 12.1 secs (Top speed: 100mph)
Power & torque: 95bhp / 106lb/ft
Engine: Normally aspirated 1798cc in-line four, petrol, carburettor, 8 valves
Drivetrain: Front-engine RWD
Suspension: (F) Independent, torsion bar. (R) Live axle, semi-elliptic leaf spring
Bodyframe: Metal monocoque
Transmission: 4-speed manual
Weight: 965kgs

PRICE GUIDE

Launch price: £923
Excellent: £1750
Good: £1100
Average: £475
Project: £100

NISSAN
300ZX Turbo

A sharp new look for the 1984 Nissan 300ZX failed to add any excitement to the Z-car line, despite being all-new under the skin, and the first in the line to feature a V6 engine. The familiar looking styling was more aerodynamic than before, boasting a drag co-efficient of just 0.30. In the UK, it was the first to be fitted with a turbo, which managed to deliver lots of straight line pace, if not finesse. Handling was firmer than the sloppy Datsun 280ZX, but still not good enough to be considered a sports car in the traditional sense of the word.

SPECIFICATIONS

Years produced: 1984-1989
Performance: 0-60mph: 7.1 secs (Top speed: 147mph)
Power & torque: 226bhp / 246lb/ft
Engine: Turbocharged 2960cc V6, petrol, electronic fuel injection, 12 valves
Drivetrain: Front-engine RWD
Suspension: (F) Ind. MacPherson strut, coil spring. (R) Ind. semi-trailing arms, coil spring
Bodyframe: Metal monocoque
Transmission: 5-speed manual
Weight: 1324kgs

PRICE GUIDE

Launch price: £16,996
Excellent: £3600
Good: £3000
Average: £2000
Project: £800

NISSAN
Skyline GT-R R32

When Nissan test driver Hiroyoshi Katoh smashed the previous fastest lap for a production car set by a Porsche 944, the world was in shock. This staggering lap time was mainly down to the car's highly sophisticated four-wheel-drive system, which made sure the driver could use all of the 320bhp (officially 276bhp). Nissan intended to take the GT-R racing, so it was built within Japanese Group A regulations. It is almost impossible to find an unmodified R32 in the UK, because they can easily take more power and torque with no fuss.

SPECIFICATIONS

Years produced: 1989-1994
Performance: 0-60mph: 5.6 secs (Top speed: 156mph)
Power & torque: 276bhp / 260lb/ft
Engine: turbocharged 2569cc in-line six, petrol, electronic fuel injection, 24 valves
Drivetrain: front-engine AWD
Suspension: (F) Independent, coil spring, anti-roll bar. (R) Independent, coil spring, anti-roll bar
Bodyframe: Metal monocoque
Transmission: 5-speed manual
Weight: 1430kgs

PRICE GUIDE

Launch price: N/A
Excellent: £10,250
Good: £9000
Average: £6250
Project: £3750

NISSAN
300ZX Turbo (Z32)

This next generation Z-car (known as the Z32) made a clean break stylistically from its predecessors. Favourable comparisons with Porsche were made, and the critics were pleased to see Nissan being brave with its big selling sports car. Like the previous three generations of Z-car (see Datsun), the 300ZX was offered as a two-seat or 2+2, but twin turbos were a new development, making this a very quick car. There are plenty of Japanese imports around now, often with automatic gearboxes, and these are often at very tempting prices.

SPECIFICATIONS

Years produced: 1990-1996 (164,170 in total)
Performance: 0-60mph: N/A (Top speed: N/A)
Power & torque: 276bhp / 274lb/ft
Engine: turbocharged 2960cc V6, petrol, electronic fuel injection, 24 valves
Drivetrain: Front-engine RWD
Suspension: (F) Independent, multi-link, coil spring. (R) Independent, multi-link, coil spring
Bodyframe: Metal monocoque
Transmission: 5-speed manual or 4-speed automatic
Weight: 1520kgs

PRICE GUIDE

Launch price: £34,600
Excellent: £7250
Good: £5500
Average: £3250
Project: £1500

NISSAN
Figaro

Cashing in on the classic car boom in Japan during the 1990s, Nissan sold a series of retro-styled cars in Japan. The BE-1 and S-Cargo were interesting, but it's the Figaro that is the best known in the UK, with floods being imported privately. It's particularly popular with city dwellers, who appreciate its ease of driving. Although it looks pure 1960s, ultra-reliable Micra mechanicals underpin this clever little cabriolet, and most are fitted with automatic transmission. If you're looking for a classic without the tears, a Figaro could be what you're looking for.

SPECIFICATIONS

Years produced: 1991-1991 (20,000 in total)
Performance: 0-60mph: 12.0 secs (Top speed: N/A)
Power & torque: 76bhp / 78lb/ft
Engine: Normally aspirated 988cc in-line four, petrol, electronic fuel injection, 16 valves
Drivetrain: Front-engine FWD
Suspension: (F) Independent, MacPherson strut, coil spring. (R) Ind. multi-link, coil spring
Bodyframe: Metal monocoque
Transmission: 3-speed automatic
Weight: 810kgs

PRICE GUIDE

Launch price: N/A
Excellent: £7250
Good: £6000
Average: £4750
Project: £3000

NSU
Sport Prinz Coupé

Rare and unusual today, the Sport Prinz Coupé was a good looking marriage of Italian style and German engineering that should have done better than it did. The bodywork was styled by Scaglione and built in Italy by Bertone. Powered by the Prinz's aircooled flat-twin the lightweight coupé was capable of 76mph, and seldom felt underpowered on the road. Its handling and roadholding were delightful, and the quick steering was a further positive. Once NSU had been taken over by Volkswagen, the Sport Prinz ceased having a future, and was quickly killed.

SPECIFICATIONS

Years produced: 1958-1967 (20,831 in total)
Performance: 0-60mph: 27.8 secs (Top speed: 78mph)
Power & torque: 30bhp / 33lb/ft
Engine: Normally aspirated 598cc, petrol, carburettor, 4 valves
Drivetrain: Rear-engine RWD
Suspension: (F) Independent, coil spring. (R) Ind. transverse link, coil spring
Bodyframe: Metal monocoque
Transmission: 4-speed manual
Weight: 556kgs

PRICE GUIDE

Launch price: £976
Excellent: £3000
Good: £2250
Average: £1400
Project: £700

NSU
Prinz

When the NSU Prinz arrived in 1961, it was the height of small car fashion. Aside from the Mini, all of the important European baby cars had their engines slung out back, and many were still aircooled. The Prinz was well-built and packed with nice features – disc brakes and a slick all-synchromesh gearbox made it a pleasure to drive. However, time passed it by, and as the opposition went front-wheel-drive, NSU didn't have the resources to develop a suitable replacement. The company run out of money, and was taken over by the Volkswagen group.

SPECIFICATIONS

Years produced: 1958-1972 (664,549 in total)
Performance: 0-60mph: 53.0 secs (Top speed: 66mph)
Power & torque: 20bhp / 30lb/ft
Engine: Normally aspirated 583cc, petrol, carburettor, 4 valves
Drivetrain: Rear-engine RWD
Suspension: (F) Independent, wishbones, coil spring. (R) Independent, swing axle, coil spring
Bodyframe: Metal monocoque
Transmission: 4-speed manual
Weight: 505kgs

PRICE GUIDE

Launch price: £641
Excellent: £2000
Good: £1500
Average: £750
Project: £200

NSU
Wankel Spider

For much of the 1960s, the future of the internal combustion engine remained up in the air. Felix Wankel's rotary design emerged as a credible alternative, being both smooth and compact, and it's no surprise that manufacturers were clamouring to build their own versions. The first production rotary ended being the NSU Wankel Spider, an open-topped variation on the Sport Prinz theme. It was potent little car – the 497cc rotary put out 50bhp and pushed the Spider to over 100mph – but proved too expensive and unreliable for serious sales success.

SPECIFICATIONS

Years produced: 1964-1967 (2375 in total)
Performance: 0-60mph: 17.6 secs (Top speed: 92mph)
Power & torque: 50bhp / 70lb/ft
Engine: Normally aspirated 1500cc, petrol, carburettor, valves
Drivetrain: Rear-engine RWD
Suspension: (F) Independent, wishbones, coil spring. (R) Ind. semi-trailing arms, coil spring
Bodyframe: Metal monocoque
Transmission: 4-speed manual
Weight: 770kgs

PRICE GUIDE

Launch price: £1391
Excellent: £6000
Good: £4750
Average: £3000
Project: £1500

NSU
1000

The NSU 1000 was a larger, more civilised version of the Prinz 4. Powered by a new 1-litre four-cylinder aircooled engine, the 1000 failed to make a sales impact, probably because it too closely resembled the cheaper car it was based upon. The main differences between the Prinz 4 and the 1000 were its longer wheelbase, restyled front end and plastic cooling fins – and just like its smaller brother, it was a great little car to drive. The 1000 survived the Volkswagen takeover, making it to 1973, but its replacement – the Audi 50 – shared no parts with it.

SPECIFICATIONS

Years produced: 1964-1972 (196,000 in total)
Performance: 0-60mph: 20.5 secs (Top speed: 80mph)
Power & torque: 43bhp / 52lb/ft
Engine: Normally aspirated 996cc in-line four, petrol, carburettor, 8 valves
Drivetrain: Rear-engine RWD
Suspension: (F) Independent, coil spring, wishbone. (R) Ind. coil spring, semi-trailing arms
Bodyframe: Metal monocoque
Transmission: 4-speed manual
Weight: 620kgs

PRICE GUIDE

Launch price: £673
Excellent: £2000
Good: £1500
Average: £800
Project: £300

NSU
Ro80

The NSU Ro80 redefined the levels of expectation for buyers in the executive class. It handled beautifully, was huge inside, looked amazing and rode as well as any luxury saloon. It was crowned Car of The Year, and for a while, the NSU Ro80 had the world at its feet. But the problems soon started – its rotary engine was refined but unreliable, and warranty costs had crippled NSU. Modern technology has conquered the rotor tip problem, and a Ro80 is a brilliant classic car to own with the correct support; a constant reminder of what might have been.

SPECIFICATIONS

Years produced: 1966-1977 (37,204 in total)
Performance: 0-60mph: 14.2 secs (Top speed: 117mph)
Power & torque: 114bhp / 139lb/ft
Engine: Normally aspirated 1990cc twin-rotor, petrol, carburettor, valves
Drivetrain: Front-engine FWD
Suspension: (F) Ind. MacPherson strut, coil spring. (R) Ind. semi-trailing arms, coil spring
Bodyframe: Metal monocoque
Transmission: 3-speed semi-automatic
Weight: 1190kgs

PRICE GUIDE

Launch price: £2249
Excellent: £6250
Good: £5000
Average: £2250
Project: £750

NSU
1200 TT/TTS

The NSU 1200TT proved popular with competitive drivers, and was successful in motor sport. Making the most of the basic car's lightness, the TT version was created when the engine was expanded to 1.2-litres. The excellent handling and roadholding of the basic car was beautifully complemented with the additional power, and the NSU 1200 TT/TTS ended up becoming Germany's answer to the Mini Cooper or Simca 1000 Rallye. Due to their high quality construction, a large number have survived in Germany, with rather less in the UK.

SPECIFICATIONS

Years produced: 1967-1972 (63,289/2404 in total)
Performance: 0-60mph: 14.8 secs (Top speed: 96mph)
Power & torque: 64bhp / 65lb/ft
Engine: Normally aspirated 1172cc in-line four, petrol, carburettor, 8 valves
Drivetrain: Rear-engine RWD
Suspension: (F) Independent, coil spring. (R) Independent, coil spring, swing axle
Bodyframe: Metal monocoque
Transmission: 4-speed manual
Weight: 650kgs

PRICE GUIDE

Launch price: £824
Excellent: £3750
Good: £3000
Average: £1500
Project: £750

OPEL
Kadett

Opel waited until 1962 before launching its small car of the post-war era. This was the Kadett A and very successful it was too during its 1962-65 life, though it was never sold in the UK. What came afterwards though was even better. The Kadett B had restyled looks mated to the same chassis, but with a bigger selection of engines, ranging from 1078cc to 1897cc. As well as the saloons and estates, there was a pretty coupé which, in Rallye form, made use of the 1897cc engine with twin carburettors to give 90bhp. These are the ones that excite collectors.

SPECIFICATIONS

Years produced: 1962-1973 (2,311,389 in total)
Performance: 13.8 secs (Top speed: 89mph)
Power & torque: 60bhp / 65lb/ft
Engine: Normally aspirated 1196cc in-line four, petrol, carburettor, 8 valves
Drivetrain: Front-engine RWD
Suspension: (F) Independent, coil springs. (R) Live axle, coil springs
Bodyframe: Metal monocoque
Transmission: 4-speed manual
Weight: 800kgs

PRICE GUIDE

Launch price: £708
Excellent: £3000
Good: £2200
Average: £1200
Project: £400

OPEL
Commodore

The Commodore, launched in 1967, was an upmarket version of the Opel Reckord. Sold as a saloon or coupé, it was only available with six-cylinder engines, initially 2239cc and 2490cc units, although a 2784cc followed in 1970 and was used in the most desirable GS2800 variant, boasting 143bhp. The second generation Commodore came on the scene in 1972, sharing its floorpan with the Vauxhall Victor FE. It upped the luxury inside, with the fuel-injected GS/E model as the flagship from 1974 up until the end of the line in 1977.

SPECIFICATIONS

Years produced: 1967-1977 (156,330 in total)
Performance: 12.1 secs (Top speed: 108mph)
Power & torque: 130bhp / 137lb/ft
Engine: Normally aspirated 2490cc in-line six, petrol, carburettor, 12 valves
Drivetrain: Front-engine RWD
Suspension: (F) Independent, coil springs. (R) Live axle, coil springs
Bodyframe: Metal monocoque
Transmission: 4-speed manual/3-speed automatic
Weight: 1234kgs

PRICE GUIDE

Launch price: £1380
Excellent: £4000
Good: £3000
Average: £1500
Project: £500

OPEL
GT 1900

Given Opel's General Motors heritage, nobody should have been too surprised when the GT popped up in 1968 looking like a shrunken Corvette (although it had been previously seen as a concept car at the 1965 Frankfurt Motor Show). The Kadett provided most of the underpinnings while the body was built by Brissoneau & Lotz in France. The rotating headlamps were manually operated. Most GTs ended up in the US, presumably with owners who couldn't afford to run the full-sized Corvette. Very nimble, very fun, very distinctive.

SPECIFICATIONS

Years produced: 1968-1973 (103,463 in total)
Performance: 11.0 secs (Top speed: 116mph)
Power & torque: 88bhp / 110lb/ft
Engine: Normally aspirated 1897cc in-line four, petrol, carburettor, 8 valves
Drivetrain: Front-engine RWD
Suspension: (F) Independent, wishbone, coil spring. (R) Live axle, trailing arms, coil spring
Bodyframe: Metal monocoque
Transmission: 4-speed manual
Weight: 970kgs

PRICE GUIDE

Launch price: £1882
Excellent: £7000
Good: £5500
Average: £3000
Project: £1000

OPEL
Manta A Coupé

'We want a Capri!' That was the cry of most European manufacturers after Ford launched its coupé in 1969, and the Manta was Opel's attempt to get in on the act. It used the Ascona as its basis, with the same panels as that car up to the windscreen; thereafter it was a well-proportioned coupé. 1584cc and 1897cc overhead camshaft engines did service under the bonnet although mainland Europe also had an 1196cc engine. A small number of turbocharged models, based on the plusher Berlinetta, were built and sold in Britain.

SPECIFICATIONS

Years produced: 1970-1975 (498,553 in total)
Performance: 12.2 secs (Top speed: 105mph)
Power & torque: 90bhp / 108lb/ft
Engine: Normally aspirated 1897cc in-line four, petrol, carburettor, 8 valves
Drivetrain: Front-engine RWD
Suspension: (F) Independent, coil spring. (R) Live axle, coil spring
Bodyframe: Metal monocoque
Transmission: 4-speed manual
Weight: 955kgs

PRICE GUIDE

Launch price: £1475
Excellent: £3750
Good: £3000
Average: £1500
Project: £750

OPEL
Manta GT/E

In 1973, one of the most desirable Manta As was created when Bosch electronic fuel injection was adopted, giving 105bhp from the car's 1196cc engine. Such was the cachet of the GT/E name that it was carried over to the mid-1970s Manta B model, which was closely based on the Ascona (or Cavalier MkI in the UK), was expanded to 1897cc with the new model's arrival before being expanded to 1979cc at the end of '78. A bodykit found its way onto the sporty Opel from '82, and the GT/E remained in production long after the RWD Ascona was put to grass.

SPECIFICATIONS

Years produced:	1975-1988 (603,000 in total)
Performance:	8.5 secs (Top speed: 120mph)
Power & torque:	110bhp / 119lb/ft
Engine:	Normally aspirated 1979cc in-line four, petrol, electronic fuel injection, 8 valves
Drivetrain:	Front-engine RWD
Suspension:	(F) Independent, wishbones, coil spring. (R) Rigid axle (torque tube), coil spring
Bodyframe:	Metal monocoque
Transmission:	5-speed manual
Weight:	1065kgs

PRICE GUIDE

Launch price:	£2370
Excellent:	£3000
Good:	£2200
Average:	£1100
Project:	£350

OPEL
Monza 3.0

What the Royale hatchback coupé was to Vauxhall, so the Monza was to Opel. Based on the big Vauxhall Senator, this 1978-86 'Autobahnstormer' was a good-looking and well-equipped three-door coupé which proved agile despite its bulk. Its dramatic straight line ability – 0-60mph in 8.5 seconds, a top speed of 133mph – was made possible by its fuel-injected six-cylinder engine. Variations on the theme included the ES, with a limited-slip differential to better cope with all that power, and the GSE with Recaro seats, digital instrumentation and a prominent rear spoiler.

SPECIFICATIONS

Years produced:	1978-1985 (43,500 in total)
Performance:	9.3 secs (Top speed: 123mph)
Power & torque:	148bhp / 170lb/ft
Engine:	Normally aspirated 2969cc in-line six, petrol, electronic fuel injection, 12 valves
Drivetrain:	Front-engine RWD
Suspension:	(F) Ind. MacPherson strut, coil spring. (R) Ind. semi-trailing arms, coil spring
Bodyframe:	Metal monocoque
Transmission:	4-speed manual
Weight:	1375kgs

PRICE GUIDE

Launch price:	£9762
Excellent:	£3500
Good:	£2750
Average:	£1200
Project:	£400

PANTHER
J72

The Panther J72 owed its looks to Jaguar's SS100, although it was more parody than replica. This being the 1970s, there was a ready market for such brash expressions of style (or lack of it), and a number of celebrities bought into British businessman Robert Jankel's dream machine. There was little sophistication to the J72, but it was very fast thanks to its Jaguar six-cylinder engines; even more so when the V12 was added in 1974. The J72 stayed in production until 1981, during which time 426 examples of this expensive vintage wannabe were constructed.

SPECIFICATIONS

Years produced:	1972-1981 (426 in total)
Performance:	0-60mph: 6.4 secs (Top speed: 114mph)
Power & torque:	190bhp / 200lb/ft
Engine:	Normally aspirated 4253cc V12, petrol, carburettor, 24 valves
Drivetrain:	Front-engine RWD
Suspension:	(F) Independent, wishbone, coil spring. (R) Live axle, trailing arms, coil spring
Bodyframe:	Chassis and separate body
Transmission:	4-speed manual with overdrive
Weight:	1136kgs

PRICE GUIDE

Launch price:	£4380
Excellent:	£16,500
Good:	£12,500
Average:	£8500
Project:	£5000

PANTHER
De Ville

As if the J72 wasn't enough, Panther then came up with the De Ville in 1974. Fittingly, the character of Cruella DeVil drove one in Disney's *102 Dalmations*. Inspired by the Bugatti Royale, the enormous bonnet hid Jaguar six-cylinder or V12 engines and there were also Jaguar XJ subframes back and front. The wealthy celebrities who bought the De Ville might have been less impressed by the saloon doors coming from an Austin Maxi or the convertibles having MGB ones. Elton John bought a De Ville in 1977. Enough said?

SPECIFICATIONS

Years produced:	1974-1985 (60 in total)
Performance:	0-60mph: 6.5 secs (Top speed: 150mph)
Power & torque:	286bhp / 294lb/ft
Engine:	Normally aspirated 5343cc V12, petrol, carburettor, 24 valves
Drivetrain:	Front-engine RWD
Suspension:	(F) Ind. wishbone, coil spring. (R) Ind. wishbones, radius arm, coil spring
Bodyframe:	Spaceframe
Transmission:	3-speed automatic
Weight:	1982kgs

PRICE GUIDE

Launch price:	£21,965
Excellent:	£30,000
Good:	£25,000
Average:	£15,000
Project:	£8000

PANTHER
Lima

With its Morgan-ish looks, and Vauxhall Magnum floorpan and 2279cc slant-four engine, the Lima was significantly cheaper than its stablemates and could even be ordered through some Vauxhall dealerships. The glassfibre bodywork surrounding an MG Midget centre section made it lightweight and well-behaved, while the 108bhp on offer meant good performance, although even more was offered by the turbocharged variant of 1978. The MkII from 1979 had a box section chassis. A total of 918 were constructed up until the end of manufacture in 1982.

SPECIFICATIONS

Years produced:	1976-1982 (897 in total)
Performance:	0-60mph: 6.7 secs (Top speed: 107mph)
Power & torque:	108bhp / 138lb/ft
Engine:	Normally aspirated 2279cc in-line four, petrol, carburettor, 8 valves
Drivetrain:	Front-engine RWD
Suspension:	(F) Independent, wishbone, coil spring. (R) Live axle, coil spring
Bodyframe:	Spaceframe
Transmission:	4-speed manual
Weight:	862kgs

PRICE GUIDE

Launch price:	£8997
Excellent:	£6250
Good:	£5000
Average:	£2250
Project:	£1250

PANTHER
Kallista

After financial troubles forced owner Robert Jankel to sell Panther, the marque ended up in the hands of a Korean conglomerate. Under them, the Lima evolved into the Kallista. Instead of a glassfibre body, it used aluminium over a steel chassis, and the Vauxhall mechanicals were replaced by a series of Ford engines from four-cylinder 1597cc up to 2935cc V6. Although manufacture came to an end in 1990, the SsangYong Motor Company came back with a badge-engineered version of the roadster in 1992, but a mere 73 were made.

SPECIFICATIONS

Years produced: 1982-1990
Performance: 0-60mph: 7.5 secs (Top speed: 120mph)
Power & torque: 150bhp / 159lb/ft
Engine: Normally aspirated 2792cc V6, petrol, mechanical fuel injection, 12 valves
Drivetrain: Front-engine RWD
Suspension: (F) Independent, wishbone, coil spring. (R) Live axle, coil spring
Bodyframe: Spaceframe
Transmission: 5-speed manual
Weight: 965kgs

PRICE GUIDE

Launch price: £5850
Excellent: £7500
Good: £6000
Average: £3500
Project: £1750

PEERLESS/WARWICK
GT

As an affordable GT, the Peerless certainly met all of its targets. The mixture of space frame with de Dion rear axle, and competent Triumph TR3 running gear was a wonderful set of ingredients with which to build a new sporting car. But like all of these ventures, finance was always the issue, and no matter how promising the car looks and drives, if the company can't afford to develop it properly it's more than likely going to fail. This was the case with the Peerless GT, and although it deserved to do well, it lasted a mere three years and only 325 were made.

SPECIFICATIONS

Years produced: 1958-1962 (325 in total)
Performance: 0-60mph: 12.8 secs (Top speed: 103mph)
Power & torque: 100bhp / N/A
Engine: Normally aspirated 1991cc in-line four, petrol, carburettor, 8 valves
Drivetrain: Front-engine RWD
Suspension: (F) Independent, coil spring. (R) de Dion beam, semi-elliptic leaf spring
Bodyframe: Spaceframe
Transmission: 4-speed manual with overdrive
Weight: 953kgs

PRICE GUIDE

Launch price: £1498
Excellent: £9000
Good: £7500
Average: £4000
Project: £2250

PEUGEOT
203

The 203 was Peugeot's first all-new post-war design and although it lacked the 202's idiosyncratic styling, it was a groundbreaking technical package. The alloy-headed engine and hydraulic brakes were novelties, while the independent front suspension and rack and pinion steering set the company's products on their way towards a reputation for dynamic pleasure. Like all Peugeots for the next 30 years, the 203 enjoyed a long production run – 12 years – and ended up donating much of its platform to its replacement. An endearing French classic.

SPECIFICATIONS

Years produced: 1948-1963 (686,628 in total)
Performance: 0-60mph: N/A (Top speed: 71mph)
Power & torque: 45bhp / 59lb/ft
Engine: Normally aspirated 1290cc in-line four, petrol, carburettor, 8 valves
Drivetrain: Front-engine RWD
Suspension: (F) Independent, coil springs. (R) Live axle, coil springs
Bodyframe: Metal monocoque
Transmission: 4-speed manual
Weight: 930kgs

PRICE GUIDE

Launch price: £986
Excellent: £4500
Good: £3250
Average: £1500
Project: £500

PEUGEOT
403 Saloon

Peugeot's 1950s saloon was little more than a reskin of the 203; it was larger, more luxurious, and ended up being sold alongside the older car as an upgrade for an increasingly affluent market. Pinin Farina assisted with the styling – leading to an enduring partnership – but with full-width bodywork and neat detailing, it struck a chord with the French middle-classes. The popular Familiale version was innovative for offering three rows of seats, while the diesel version sold well in its home country as it was a rugged and reliable workhorse.

SPECIFICATIONS

Years produced: 1955-1966 (1,214,121 in total)
Performance: 0-60mph: 24.0 secs (Top speed: 76mph)
Power & torque: 58bhp / 74lb/ft
Engine: Normally aspirated 1468cc in-line four, petrol, carburettor, 8 valves
Drivetrain: Front-engine RWD
Suspension: (F) Independent, transverse leaf spring. (R) Live axle, coil spring
Bodyframe: Metal monocoque
Transmission: 4-speed manual
Weight: 1300kgs

PRICE GUIDE

Launch price: £1129
Excellent: £3250
Good: £2250
Average: £1250
Project: £400

PEUGEOT
403 Cabriolet

Pininfarina's reputation for producing stylish convertibles and coupés from family cars arguably started here. The 403 Decapotable, to give the car its correct title, shared its wheelbase and running gear with the saloon, but looked a lot more appealing. First shown at the 1956 Paris Salon, it instantly found favour with buyers. The high-compression 1.5-litre engine gave reasonable performance, but this car was always about touring. Values continue to climb, despite (or due to?) endless reruns of TV's *Columbo* – and appearances of his shabby, unkempt version.

SPECIFICATIONS

Years produced: 1957-1961 (2050 in total)
Performance: 0-60mph: 24.0 secs (Top speed: 76mph)
Power & torque: 58bhp / 74lb/ft
Engine: Normally aspirated 1468cc in-line four, petrol, carburettor, 8 valves
Drivetrain: Front-engine RWD
Suspension: (F) Independent, transverse leaf springs. (R) Live axle, coil springs
Bodyframe: Metal monocoque
Transmission: 4-speed manual
Weight: 1300kgs

PRICE GUIDE

Launch price: £N/A
Excellent: £11,000
Good: £9000
Average: £6000
Project: £2000

PEUGEOT
404 Saloon

At first glance, the Farina-styled 404 looks like a copy of BMC's and Fiat's contemporary mid-sized saloons, with 403 underpinnings. In reality, the 404 was a nicer car to drive and offered a clever design as although it looked like a grand saloon it was actually smaller than the car it was supposed to replace. In the end – and in good Peugeot tradition – the 404 and 403 ran concurrently for three years, before the newer car went on to sell millions worldwide. Still a relatively common site in Northern Africa, thanks to solid build and simple DIY.

SPECIFICATIONS	
Years produced:	1960-1978 (1,847,568 in total)
Performance:	0-60mph: 18.1 secs (Top speed: 82mph)
Power & torque:	68bhp / 94lb/ft
Engine:	Normally aspirated 1618cc in-line four, petrol, carburettor, 8 valves
Drivetrain:	Front-engine RWD
Suspension:	(F) Independent, coil spring. (R) Live axle, coil spring
Bodyframe:	Metal monocoque
Transmission:	4-speed manual
Weight:	1070kgs
PRICE GUIDE	
Launch price:	£1297
Excellent:	£2650
Good:	£2000
Average:	£1000
Project:	£300

PEUGEOT
404 Cabriolet

Unlike some Peugeot/Pininfarina collaborations, the 404 Cabriolet and its coupé brother were a full rebody of an existing platform, sharing no external panels. Given such a free rein, it's unsurprising the Italian styling house came up with such a stunning car – and one that, thanks to its scarcity, is in strong demand today. The wheelbase is shared with the saloon, and as a result, the 404 Cabriolet is a full four-seater. Power came from Peugeot's well-regarded 1.6-litre engine, and delivered excellent performance, especially in fuel injected form.

SPECIFICATIONS	
Years produced:	1962-1968 (3728 in total)
Performance:	0-60mph: 12.2 secs (Top speed: 92mph)
Power & torque:	79bhp / 100lb/ft
Engine:	Normally aspirated 1608cc in-line four, petrol, carburettor, 8 valves
Drivetrain:	Front-engine RWD
Suspension:	(F) Independent, coil spring. (R) Live axle, coil spring
Bodyframe:	Metal monocoque
Transmission:	4-speed manual
Weight:	1030kgs
PRICE GUIDE	
Launch price:	£2367
Excellent:	£9500
Good:	£7500
Average:	£4250
Project:	£1500

PEUGEOT
204/304 Coupé

Whereas the Peugeot 204 and 304 have been unfairly consigned to the ranks to the automotive hall of mediocrity, the coupé versions were a further Pininfarina masterclass in product maximisation. The pretty three-door fastback used a hatchback rear door, and comfortable seating for two plus two children, despite a wheelbase shortened by 12 inches. Surviving examples are good to drive and are likely to have been well cared-for, but take care when looking for corrosion – it can strike anywhere, and often does.

SPECIFICATIONS	
Years produced:	1965-1979 (42,756 in total)
Performance:	0-60mph: 18.2 secs (Top speed: 91mph)
Power & torque:	53bhp / 82lb/ft
Engine:	Normally aspirated 1130cc in-line four, petrol, carburettor, 8 valves
Drivetrain:	Front-engine FWD
Suspension:	(F) Ind. MacPherson strut, coil spring, lower wish. (R) Ind. trailing arm, coil spring
Bodyframe:	Metal monocoque
Transmission:	4-speed manual
Weight:	838kgs
PRICE GUIDE	
Launch price:	£983
Excellent:	£4000
Good:	£3000
Average:	£2000
Project:	£650

PEUGEOT
204/304 Saloon

The 204 and 304 were a leap forward for Peugeot as they were the firm's first cars with transverse front engines driving the front wheels. Combined with independent rear suspension, servo-assisted brakes and anti-roll bars, the advanced suspension delivered surefooted roadholding and a comfortable ride, in true French style. The 304 was similar in conception, but with a longer front and rear, plusher interiors and a more powerful 1.3-litre engine it was a lot more satisfying to own. Downsides were few – but lack of glamour was one, as was corrosion.

SPECIFICATIONS	
Years produced:	1965-1980 (1,387,473/1,334,309 in total)
Performance:	0-60mph: 16.2 secs (Top speed: 90mph)
Power & torque:	55bhp / 66lb/ft
Engine:	Normally aspirated 1130cc in-line four, petrol, carburettor, 8 valves
Drivetrain:	Front-engine FWD
Suspension:	(F) Ind. MacPherson strut, coil spring, lower wish. (R) Ind. trailing arm, coil spring
Bodyframe:	Metal monocoque
Transmission:	4-speed manual
Weight:	880kgs
PRICE GUIDE	
Launch price:	£992
Excellent:	£2500
Good:	£1750
Average:	£850
Project:	£300

PEUGEOT
204/304 Cabriolet

Unlike the Coupé, the 204 Cabriolet was never officially sold in the UK, making buying one a lengthy and involved process. But there are a few in the UK, which have quite a cult following thanks to head-turning looks and neat dynamics. However, the 304 did make it here, and examples aren't too difficult to track down thanks to a high survival rate. The newer car's uprated engine delivered sprightly performance and excellent economy, and if you're looking for an easy to drive, appealing rag top that's just a little bit different, this could be ideal for you.

SPECIFICATIONS	
Years produced:	1967-1975 (18,181 in total)
Performance:	0-60mph: 14.5 secs (Top speed: 96mph)
Power & torque:	74bhp / 80lb/ft
Engine:	Normally aspirated 1288cc in-line four, petrol, carburettor, 8 valves
Drivetrain:	Front-engine FWD
Suspension:	(F) Ind. MacPherson strut, coil spring, lower wish. (R) Ind. trailing arm, coil spring
Bodyframe:	Metal monocoque
Transmission:	4-speed manual
Weight:	895kgs
PRICE GUIDE	
Launch price:	£1496
Excellent:	£5250
Good:	£4000
Average:	£2200
Project:	£900

PEUGEOT
504 Saloon

Launched at the Paris Motor Show in 1968, the 504 saloon was Peugeot's mid-sized booted option, slotting in between the new 604 and the ageing 304. The engine was mounted longitudinally, driving the rear wheels, and the combination of soft spring and damper rates with massive suspension travel made the 504 an excellent performer on poor and non-existent road surfaces. European 504s are a rare sight today, but they are still one of the most common forms of transport throughout Africa, due to their simplicity and reliability.

SPECIFICATIONS

Years produced:	1968-1983 (3,073,185 in total)
Performance:	0-60mph: 12.7 secs (Top speed: 106mph)
Power & torque:	93bhp / 124lb/ft
Engine:	Normally aspirated 1971cc in-line four, petrol, carburettor, 8 valves
Drivetrain:	Front-engine FWD
Suspension:	(F&R) Ind. strut, coil spring, lower wish. anti-roll bars (R) semi-trailing arm
Bodyframe:	Metal monocoque
Transmission:	4-speed manual
Weight:	1175kgs
	PRICE GUIDE
Launch price:	£1500
Excellent:	£2500
Good:	£2000
Average:	£800
Project:	£300

PEUGEOT
504 Cabriolet

With a production run of just over 8000, and with a reputation for rust, it's a surprise just how many 504 Cabriolets have survived; yet with such graceful styling and superb road manners, it ended up being a classic the moment it left the production line. Fuel injected, all models proved fast and effective tourers, especially the final five-speed models. Not directly replaced as Peugeot failed to develop the 505, although the 406 Coupé recaptured the spirit of the tin-top version during the late-1990s. Prices are for V6 models, four-cylinder Cabrios will be less.

SPECIFICATIONS

Years produced:	1968-1983
Performance:	0-60mph: 9.9 secs (Top speed: 105mph)
Power & torque:	110bhp / 131lb/ft
Engine:	Normally aspirated 1971cc in-line four, petrol, carburettor, 8 valves
Drivetrain:	Front-engine RWD
Suspension:	(F&R) Ind. strut, coil spring, lower wish. anti-roll bars (R) semi-trailing arm
Bodyframe:	Metal monocoque
Transmission:	4-speed manual
Weight:	1165kgs
	PRICE GUIDE
Launch price:	£1594
Excellent:	£12,500
Good:	£10,000
Average:	£6500
Project:	£2500

PEUGEOT
504 Coupé

The same Peugeot/PininFarina recipe used for the 404 Coupé was used once again for its replacement, which hit the road in 1969. With an all-new body on a slightly shortened 504 platform, the 504 Coupé combined the excellent road manners of this no-nonsense French saloon with a healthy dose of glamorous Italian style. The top of the range version was treated to a PRV Peugeot-Renault V6 (the same engine that saw service in the DeLorean DMC-12 and Alpine A310 V6) in 1974, creating easily the company's most desirable car of the period.

SPECIFICATIONS

Years produced:	1969-1983 (26,477 in total)
Performance:	0-60mph: 10.5 secs (Top speed: 111mph)
Power & torque:	110bhp / 131lb/ft
Engine:	Normally aspirated 1971cc in-line four, petrol, carburettor, 8 valves
Drivetrain:	Front-engine RWD
Suspension:	(F&R) Ind. strut, coil springs, wish, anti-roll bar. (R) Ind. semi-trailing arms
Bodyframe:	Metal monocoque
Transmission:	4-speed manual
Weight:	1165kgs
	PRICE GUIDE
Launch price:	£2609
Excellent:	£6750
Good:	£5000
Average:	£3000
Project:	£1200

PEUGEOT
505

Like the 504 it replaced, with the 505 Peugeot created one of the most recognisable and rugged medium-sized saloons on the planet. The main reason for the car's success in developing countries was its ability to handle rutted and very poor road surfaces; the 505 is still produced in Nigeria, but European production stopped in 1993, when it was made redundant by the smaller 405 and the larger 605. The diesel 505s were always the biggest sellers, and if you opted for the estate it could be fitted with a third row of seats, giving room for eight people.

SPECIFICATIONS

Years produced:	1983-1990
Performance:	0-60mph: 10.0 secs (Top speed: 114mph)
Power & torque:	130bhp / 136lb/ft
Engine:	Normally aspirated 2165cc in-line four, petrol, electronic fuel injection, 8 valves
Drivetrain:	Front-engine FWD
Suspension:	(F&R) Ind. strut, coil springs, anti-roll bars. (R) Ind. oblique semi-trailing arm
Bodyframe:	Metal monocoque
Transmission:	5-speed manual
Weight:	1235kgs
	PRICE GUIDE
Launch price:	£9595
Excellent:	£1750
Good:	£1400
Average:	£900
Project:	£300

PEUGEOT
205 GTi

The best hot hatch ever? Volkswagen may have started the GTi craze in 1976, but many see the 205 as king of the breed. Initially only available with a 1.6-litre engine, in 1986 the 205 received the 130bhp 1905cc engine, instantly giving more rapid acceleration and a higher top speed – although it is still hotly-debated which is the better car. The 1.6 is slightly lighter, and better balanced, but the more powerful 1.9 is ultimately faster. Both variants had a reputation for snap-off oversteer – which is also what attracts many people to the model.

SPECIFICATIONS

Years produced:	1984-1994
Performance:	0-60mph: 8.6 secs (Top speed: 120mph)
Power & torque:	105bhp / 99lb/ft
Engine:	Normally aspirated 1580cc in-line four, petrol, electronic fuel injection, 8 valves
Drivetrain:	Front-engine FWD
Suspension:	(F) Ind. strut, lower wish. coil spring, anti-roll bar. (R) Ind. trailing arms, torsion bar
Bodyframe:	Metal monocoque
Transmission:	5-speed manual
Weight:	850kgs
	PRICE GUIDE
Launch price:	£6295
Excellent:	£3250
Good:	£2400
Average:	£1250
Project:	£450

PEUGEOT
309 GTi

Even though it was full of Peugeot 205 parts, PSA never intended to stick a Peugeot badge to the front of the 309. It started life as the Talbot Arizona – a Horizon replacement – but when PSA decided to kill the Talbot brand in 1985, Peugeot completed the project. The 309 GTi shortly followed, but, unlike the 205, it was only available as a 1.9. It featured uprated front and rear suspension, 15-inch Speedline alloy wheels, and a subtle bodykit. Peugeot only offered the car in three-door form to begin with, but the GTi was later sold as a five-door version as well.

SPECIFICATIONS

Years produced: 1987-1993
Performance: 0-60mph: 8.7 secs (Top speed: 119mph)
Power & torque: 130bhp / 119lb/ft
Engine: Normally aspirated 1905cc in-line four, petrol, electronic fuel injection, 8 valves
Drivetrain: Front-engine FWD
Suspension: (F) Ind. strut, lower wish. coil spring, anti-roll bar. (R) Ind. trailing arm, torsion bar
Bodyframe: Metal monocoque
Transmission: 5-speed manual
Weight: 930kgs

PRICE GUIDE

Launch price: £9595
Excellent: £2500
Good: £1750
Average: £950
Project: £500

PEUGEOT
405 Mi16

The early Mi16 shared its all-alloy 16-valve engine with the Citroën BX 16v. This XU9J4 engine was a mass-produced, normally aspirated 160bhp development of the T16 engine used in Peugeot's Group B 205 rally car. Sadly, due to cost, PSA switched to a cast-iron block in the post-1992 cars. This heavier engine was also less powerful, but the torque figure was up; giving the car a more useable power band. The 405 range was always praised for its handling and ride, and the Mi16 was no exception, but starting at almost £2000 more than its BX sibling, it was an expensive choice at the time.

SPECIFICATIONS

Years produced: 1987-1995
Performance: 0-60mph: 8.2 secs (Top speed: 138mph)
Power & torque: 160bhp / 131lb/ft
Engine: Normally aspirated 1905cc in-line four, petrol, electronic fuel injection, 16 valves
Drivetrain: Front-engine FWD
Suspension: (F) Independent, MacPherson strut. (R) Ind. trailing arm, torsion bars
Bodyframe: Metal monocoque
Transmission: 5-speed manual
Weight: 1108kgs

PRICE GUIDE

Launch price: £14,995
Excellent: £2500
Good: £1750
Average: £1000
Project: £500

PIPER
GTT/P2

The Piper GTT was designed by Tony Hilder after being commissioned by racing driver George Henrotte to create the ultimate GT car. The GTT caused a sensation when it was launched, and that was enough to convince Brian Sherwood's Piper company to put the car into production in kit form, using Ford and Triumph suspension parts, with the engine choice being down to the owner. Initially the car sold well, and quite a few survive today, but Piper fell foul of the introduction of VAT and the 1973 oil crisis, and the company folded the following year.

SPECIFICATIONS

Years produced: 1968-1974 (150 in total)
Performance: 0-60mph: N/A (Top speed: 115mph)
Power & torque: 71bhp / N/A
Engine: Normally aspirated 1298cc in-line four, petrol, carburettor, 8 valves
Drivetrain: Front-engine RWD
Suspension: (F) Independent, coil spring. (R) Beam axle, coil spring
Bodyframe: Spaceframe, glassfibre body
Transmission: 4-speed manual
Weight: N/A

PRICE GUIDE

Launch price: £1435
Excellent: £12,500
Good: £10,000
Average: £7000
Project: £4000

PORSCHE
356

The first 49 Porsches were built in Gmünd, Austria, and though historically important, these underpowered 1100cc cars are best left to collectors. Production proper started at Stuttgart in 1950, with steel bodies. The first year it was all coupés, then cabriolets arrived in 1951, though in sales they were usually outnumbered by coupés about 4:1. Two-piece screens were fitted until April 1952, after which they were one-piece with a bend in the centre. Engine options soon grew to 1100, 1300 and 1500. 'S' version of the latter rated up to 72bhp, but were complex and short-lived.

SPECIFICATIONS

Years produced: 1949-1955 (7627 in total)
Performance: 0-60mph: 17 secs (Top speed: 87mph)
Power & torque: 55bhp / 78lb/ft
Engine: Normally aspirated 1488cc flat 4, petrol, carburettor, 8 valves
Drivetrain: Rear-engine RWD
Suspension: (F) Double trailing arm, torsion bar. (R) Swing axle, torsion bar
Bodyframe: Metal monocoque
Transmission: 4-speed manual
Weight: 830kgs

PRICE GUIDE

Launch price: £1971
Excellent: £37,500
Good: £30,000
Average: £22,500
Project: £15,000

PORSCHE
356 Carrera

With four gear-driven camshafts, dry-sump lubrication, twin spark plugs and even roller-bearing crankshafts on early models, 356 Carreras are not for the faint of heart or wallet. Built with competition in mind, and producing most of their power high up in the rev range, they don't even make good road cars. However, none of that detracts from their collectibility. Even the 1500 versions will hit 120mph. Two-litre Carrera 2 is the ultimate, 126 of which were built starting in 1962. Be aware that this was a year before the arrival of disc brakes for these cars.

SPECIFICATIONS

Years produced: 1955-1962
Performance: 0-60mph: N/A (Top speed: 125mph)
Power & torque: 100bhp / 88lb/ft
Engine: Normally aspirated 1498cc flat 4, petrol, carburettor, 8 valves
Drivetrain: Rear-engine RWD
Suspension: (F) Ind. double trailing arm, torsion bar. (R) Swing axle, torsion bar
Bodyframe: Metal monocoque
Transmission: 4-speed manual
Weight: 850kgs

PRICE GUIDE

Launch price: N/A
Excellent: £65,000
Good: £52,500
Average: £35,000
Project: £20,000

SUPER FLEX®
POLYURETHANE
ADVANCED POLYURETHANE SUSPENSION BUSHES
www.superflex.co.uk
No Compromise - Upgrade to SuperFlex
01749 678152
Mon-Fri 9-5.30
Instigators in Europe of the development and sales of a wide range of Top Quality Polyurethane Suspension Bushes - Primarily for the upgrade of performance and classic cars. - Since 1993.

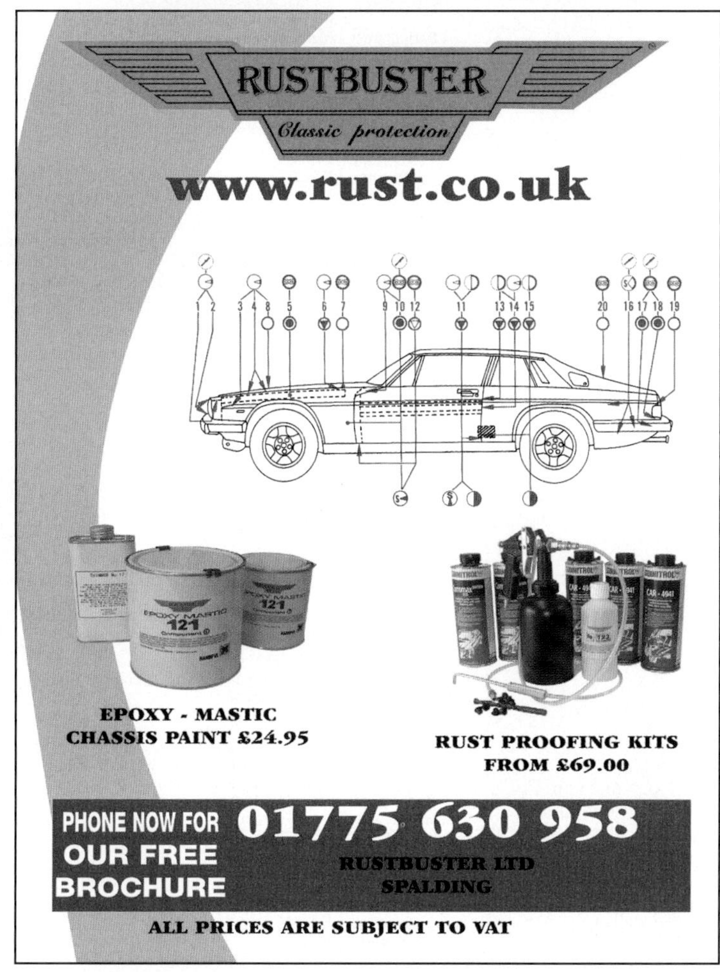
RUSTBUSTER
Classic protection
www.rust.co.uk
EPOXY - MASTIC CHASSIS PAINT £24.95
RUST PROOFING KITS FROM £69.00
PHONE NOW FOR OUR FREE BROCHURE
01775 630 958
RUSTBUSTER LTD
SPALDING
ALL PRICES ARE SUBJECT TO VAT

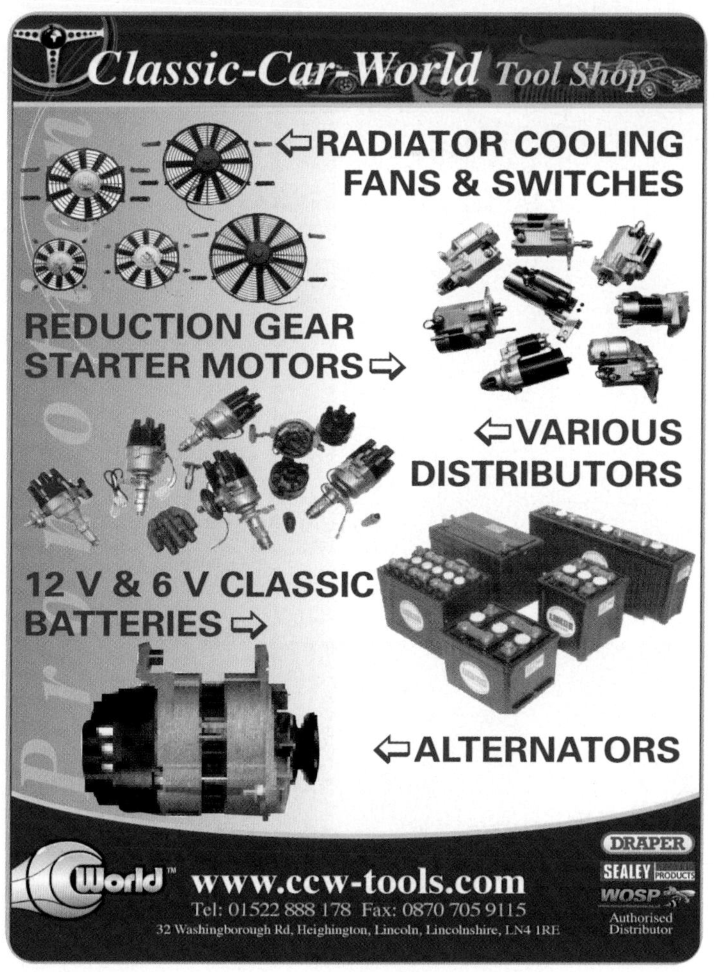
Classic-Car-World Tool Shop
RADIATOR COOLING FANS & SWITCHES
REDUCTION GEAR STARTER MOTORS
VARIOUS DISTRIBUTORS
12 V & 6 V CLASSIC BATTERIES
ALTERNATORS
World
www.ccw-tools.com
Tel: 01522 888 178 Fax: 0870 705 9115
32 Washingborough Rd, Heighington, Lincoln, Lincolnshire, LN4 1RE
DRAPER
SEALEY
WOSP
Authorised Distributor

PORSCHE
356 A/B/C

With body revisions that modernised and prettified the looks, more civilised interiors, and engines increased to 1600cc (although there were still 1300s for some markets), Porsche's 356 hit the big time and sales more than doubled. 'Super' means more power, along with higher prices than those quoted here. The 356B added twin-choke carbs and some styling revisions, the most obvious being larger bumpers and front bonnet chrome. The 356C added disc brakes at last and the lowest powered engine was now 75bhp, up from the 60bhp of the 356B 'Normal'.

SPECIFICATIONS

Years produced: 1955-1965 (68,676 in total)
Performance: 0-60mph: 14.1 secs (Top speed: 102mph)
Power & torque: 60bhp / 81lb/ft
Engine: Normally aspirated 1582cc flat 4, petrol, carburettor, 8 valves
Drivetrain: Rear-engine RWD
Suspension: (F) Ind. double trailing arm, torsion bar. (R) Swing axle, torsion bar
Bodyframe: Metal monocoque
Transmission: 4-speed manual
Weight: 815kgs

PRICE GUIDE

Launch price: £1891
Excellent: £32,500
Good: £27,500
Average: £17,500
Project: £10,000

PORSCHE
356 Speedster

Like their badges, Speedsters have become gold-plated cult classics. Much imitated by replica builders, the originals are high on many collectors' wanted lists and have been known to change hands for six-figure sums, despite nearly 5000 having been built. Most are in America, which is no surprise as that's the market they were built for. They were actually made at the suggestion of US Porsche importer Max Hoffman, who wanted a stripped down version of the 356 that could be driven during the week and raced at weekends, much like later Porsche Club Sports.

SPECIFICATIONS

Years produced: 1956-1956 (2910 in total)
Performance: 0-60mph: 14.5 secs (Top speed: 108mph)
Power & torque: 75bhp / 82lb/ft
Engine: Normally aspirated 1582cc flat 4, petrol, carburettor, 8 valves
Drivetrain: Rear-engine RWD
Suspension: (F) Ind. double trailing arm, torsion bar. (R) Swing axle, torsion bar
Bodyframe: Metal monocoque
Transmission: 4-speed manual
Weight: 760kgs

PRICE GUIDE

Launch price: £1971
Excellent: £92,500
Good: £80,000
Average: £65,000
Project: £50,000

PORSCHE
911 2.0

As the 911 legend has grown, so desire for the pure original short-wheelbase version of Porsche's concept has increased with it. The flat-six engine is only a two-litre, but it's a highly tuned one wearing overhead cams and two triple-choke carbs, Solexes on early car, then Webers from early 1966. Within months of production starting, a 911 came fifth in the Monte Carlo Rally, and these cars are still being successfully campaigned in historic events. Semi-convertible Targa version launched in early 1967, but despite their relative rarity no price premium is attached.

SPECIFICATIONS

Years produced: 1964-1967 (10,753 in total)
Performance: 0-60mph: 8.3 secs (Top speed: 131mph)
Power & torque: 130bhp / 128lb/ft
Engine: Normally aspirated 1991cc Flat 6, petrol, carburettor, 12 valves
Drivetrain: Rear-engine RWD
Suspension: (F) Ind. MacPherson struts, torsion bar (R) Ind. trailing wishbones, torsion bar
Bodyframe: Metal monocoque
Transmission: 5-speed manual
Weight: 1080kgs

PRICE GUIDE

Launch price: £2996
Excellent: £29,500
Good: £25,000
Average: £16,000
Project: £9500

PORSCHE
912/912E

Keen to retain a slightly more affordable car in the range after production of the 356 ended, Porsche installed a 90bhp version of that car's four-cylinder engine in a 911 bodyshell, most fitted with the optional five-speed gearbox. That sounds potentially disappointing, but with light weight and better handling than the 911, this is a fine sports car in its own right. It briefly reappeared in 1975 as the 912E, fitted with a two-litre VW engine. Sold only in the US, this filled gap between the outgoing 914-4 and Porsche's new 924. Prices are similar for either version.

SPECIFICATIONS

Years produced: 1965-1969 + 1975 (30,300/2092 in total)
Performance: 0-60mph: 11.9 secs (Top speed: 119mph)
Power & torque: 90bhp / 90lb/ft
Engine: Normally aspirated 1599cc flat 4, petrol, carburettor, 8 valves
Drivetrain: Rear-engine RWD
Suspension: (F) Ind. MacPherson struts, torsion bar (R) Ind. trailing wishbones, torsion bar
Bodyframe: Metal monocoque
Transmission: 4-speed manual
Weight: 970kgs

PRICE GUIDE

Launch price: £2467
Excellent: £13,000
Good: £10,000
Average: £6500
Project: £3500

PORSCHE
911S

This is the hot one, ready for competition use thanks to forged alloy pistons and wheels, plus vented disc brakes. Output starts at 160bhp, then grows to 170bhp with the 1969 introduction of fuel injection. The following year there's another 10bhp to go with the new 2.2-litre engine capacity, and then we finally arrive at 190bhp with the 2.4-litre 'S' for the 1972 model year. As with the slightly less sporty 911s, both coupé and Targa versions are offered. Pre-1968 short-wheelbase cars are the most sought after by collectors, but the later ones are most fun.

SPECIFICATIONS

Years produced: 1966-1973 (14,841 in total)
Performance: 0-60mph: 8.0 secs (Top speed: 137mph)
Power & torque: 170bhp / 135lb/ft
Engine: Normally aspirated 1991cc flat 6, petrol, carburettor, 12 valves
Drivetrain: Rear-engine RWD
Suspension: (F) Ind. MacPherson struts, torsion bar (R) Ind. trailing wishbones, torsion bar
Bodyframe: Metal monocoque
Transmission: 5-speed manual
Weight: 995kgs

PRICE GUIDE

Launch price: £3556
Excellent: £40,000
Good: £32,500
Average: £20,000
Project: £12,000

PORSCHE
911 L/T/E

From 1967 the regular 130bhp 911 is renamed 911L. This is because there is now not only the sporty 'S' version, but an entry level model with 110bhp called the 911T (for Touring). As standard it has a four- rather than five-speed 'box. From August 1968 the 'B-series' body arrives with the rear wheels moved back by 61mm to lengthen the wheelbase and improve handling. At this point the 911L gains fuel injection, gets wider wheels and becomes the 140bhp 911E. For 1970 there's 2.2 litres and 125/155bhp (T/E). Two years later capacity grows to 2.4 litres and power to 130/165bhp.

SPECIFICATIONS

Years produced: 1967-1973 (62,402 in total)
Performance: 0-60mph: 7.9 secs (Top speed: 140mph)
Power & torque: 125bhp / 131lb/ft
Engine: Normally aspirated 2195cc flat 6, petrol, carburettor, 12 valves
Drivetrain: Rear-engine RWD
Suspension: (F) Ind. MacPherson struts, torsion bar (R) Ind. trailing wishbones, torsion bar
Bodyframe: Metal monocoque
Transmission: 5-speed manual
Weight: 1020kgs

PRICE GUIDE

Launch price: £2745
Excellent: £28,000
Good: £20,000
Average: £11,000
Project: £7000

PORSCHE
914-4

Developed in conjunction with Volkswagen to replace the four-cylinder 912. The engine is borrowed from the VW 411, and being mid- rather than rear-mounted the 914 has excellent handling characteristics, aided by the all-independent suspension. Targa roof clips neatly out of the way to the underside of the bootlid when you want fresh air. From 1973 the 1700 is joined by a 2.0 version, and the following year the smaller engine capacity is raised to 1.8-litres. Low power and that VW connection haven't helped popularity, but they outrank most water-cooled Porsches.

SPECIFICATIONS

Years produced: 1969-1975 (115,646 in total)
Performance: 0-60mph: 14.8 secs (Top speed: 110mph)
Power & torque: 80bhp / 97lb/ft
Engine: Normally aspirated 1679cc flat 4, petrol, carburettor, 8 valves
Drivetrain: Mid-engine RWD
Suspension: (F) Ind. MacPherson strut, torsion bar. (R) Ind. trailing arm, coil spring
Bodyframe: Metal monocoque
Transmission: 5-speed manual
Weight: 898kgs

PRICE GUIDE

Launch price: £2261
Excellent: £8000
Good: £6500
Average: £4000
Project: £2000

PORSCHE
914-6

The main difference between this and the 914-4 is its six-cylinder engine. In fact it's the two-litre flat-six from the 911, though no-one should get over-excited at the thought as, to avoid too much in-house competition, they used the lowest spec version from the 911T with only 110bhp. With only 3360 sold compared to over 100,000 of the 914-4, they are also rare, though those low numbers have something to do with the price hike over their kid brother that made them 50% more expensive than an E-type Jaguar. Most went to America and none was built with right-hand-drive.

SPECIFICATIONS

Years produced: 1969-1972 (3333 in total)
Performance: 0-60mph: 8.3 secs (Top speed: 125mph)
Power & torque: 110bhp / 115lb/ft
Engine: Normally aspirated 1991cc flat 6, petrol, carburettor, 12 valves
Drivetrain: Mid-engine RWD
Suspension: (F) Ind. MacPherson strut, torsion bar. (R) Ind. trailing arm, coil spring
Bodyframe: Metal monocoque
Transmission: 5-speed manual
Weight: 1020kgs

PRICE GUIDE

Launch price: £3475
Excellent: £20,000
Good: £16,000
Average: £11,000
Project: £7500

PORSCHE
911 Carrera 2.7 RSL/RST

A homologation special to qualify Porsche for sub-3.0-litre GT racing. They had to build 500, but wound up selling three times that. The basis was the 2.4S, but with a big-bore engine and every conceivable means of lightening the car, from thinner steel panels to throwing away the rear seats. The first 911 to have wider rear than front wheels, there were 200 RSLs – really a race car you can drive on the road, and 1360 of the slightly softer RST (T for Touring), which actually contained a few creature comforts. Of course the racer is more valuable, so add another 50% for their prices.

SPECIFICATIONS

Years produced: 1972-1973 (200/1360 in total)
Performance: 0-60mph: 6.1 secs (Top speed: 149mph)
Power & torque: 210bhp / 188lb/ft
Engine: Normally aspirated 2687cc flat 6, petrol, carburettor, 12 valves
Drivetrain: Rear-engine RWD
Suspension: (F) Ind. MacPherson struts, torsion bar (R) Ind. trailing wishbones, torsion bar
Bodyframe: Metal monocoque
Transmission: 5-speed manual
Weight: 975kgs

PRICE GUIDE

Launch price: £5825
Excellent: £130,000
Good: £100,000
Average: £80,000
Project: £60,000

PORSCHE
911 2.7

These models represented a change in 911 ethos. Less frantic engines had less power but more torque. K-Jetronic injection made them more economical. The body and wheels are wider, and this is the start of impact bumpers. There's good news, too, in that from August 1975 Porsche became the first manufacturer to produce hot-dip galvanised bodies, so they are very resistant to rust, unlike earlier 911s. There's just the standard car and the 911S in the range now, the latter having an extra 25bhp, and strangely enough 25% higher values in today's market.

SPECIFICATIONS

Years produced: 1973-1977
Performance: 0-60mph: 8.5 secs (Top speed: 130mph)
Power & torque: 148bhp / 173lb/ft
Engine: Normally aspirated 2687cc flat 6, petrol, mechanical fuel injection, 12 valves
Drivetrain: Rear-engine RWD
Suspension: (F) Ind. MacPherson struts, torsion bar (R) Ind. trailing wishbones, torsion bar
Bodyframe: Metal monocoque
Transmission: 5-speed manual
Weight: 1161kgs

PRICE GUIDE

Launch price: £6249
Excellent: £18,000
Good: £15,000
Average: £8500
Project: £5000

PORSCHE
911 Carrera 2.7

The name Carrera is no longer just for racing specials but now denotes the range-topping 911. It has also gone a bit soft compared to the previous 2.7 Carrera; you even got the option of an automatic gearbox. They are easier cars to live with though. The engine might be in the same 210bhp state of tune, but these Carreras don't have lightweight bodies and come fully loaded with all the equipment of the lesser cars, plus electric windows. Their high price limited sales compared to the other 2.7s, though that now simply makes them even more expensive.

SPECIFICATIONS

Years produced: 1974-1977 (3353 in total)
Performance: 0-60mph: 6.3 secs (Top speed: 149mph)
Power & torque: 277bhp / 188lb/ft
Engine: Normally aspirated 2687cc flat 6, petrol, electronic fuel injection, 12 valves
Drivetrain: Rear-engine RWD
Suspension: (F) Ind. MacPherson struts, torsion bar (R) Ind. trailing wishbones, torsion bar
Bodyframe: Metal monocoque
Transmission: 4-speed manual
Weight: 1075kgs

PRICE GUIDE

Launch price: £6993
Excellent: £48,500
Good: £42,500
Average: £25,000
Project: £15,000

PORSCHE
911 Turbo

Not just a fast car but an instant pin-up beloved of teenage boys. Having experimented with turbochargers in racing, Porsche saw this as the way forward for performance road cars, and this rocket was the result. With fat arches to cover the seven- and eight-inch rims, plus that enormous rear spoiler, the Turbo was something of a trend-setter. But what really mattered was how well it went; the incredible acceleration, superb grip and handling, and enormous brakes to match. Surprisingly the gearbox was only a four-speed, but that didn't hold it back.

SPECIFICATIONS

Years produced: 1975-1977 (2873 in total)
Performance: 0-60mph: 6.1 secs (Top speed: 153mph)
Power & torque: 260bhp / 253lb/ft
Engine: turbocharged 2994cc flat 6, petrol, mechanical fuel injection, 12 valves
Drivetrain: Rear-engine RWD
Suspension: (F) Ind. MacPherson struts, torsion bar (R) Ind. trailing wishbones, torsion bar
Bodyframe: Metal monocoque
Transmission: 4-speed manual
Weight: 1195kgs

PRICE GUIDE

Launch price: £14,749
Excellent: £23,000
Good: £19,000
Average: £13,000
Project: £7500

PORSCHE
924

Originally conceived as a replacement for the VW-Porsche 914, Porsche was commissioned to develop the 924 project, then bought the rights to it when VW changed tack. It uses an Audi engine with Porsche cylinder head, and the gearbox is in unit with the rear axle to provide near-perfect 53/47 weight distribution. Build quality is to the usual excellent Porsche standards, and the 924 was in instant sales success, quickly tripling the company's factory output. Best ones to buy are from 1981-on as the whole bodies were hot-zinc-dipped to (successfully) keep rust at bay.

SPECIFICATIONS

Years produced: 1976-1988 (122,304 in total)
Performance: 0-60mph: 9.5 secs (Top speed: 124mph)
Power & torque: 125bhp / 122lb/ft
Engine: Normally aspirated 1984cc in-line four, petrol, electronic fuel injection, 8 valves
Drivetrain: Front-engine RWD
Suspension: (F) Ind. MacPherson struts, coil spring. (R) Ind. trailing wishbones, coil spring
Bodyframe: Metal monocoque
Transmission: 5-speed manual
Weight: 1080kgs

PRICE GUIDE

Launch price: £6999
Excellent: £3750
Good: £2900
Average: £1400
Project: £475

PORSCHE
911 SC 3.0

Gaining the three-litre block from last season's Turbo, the SC becomes Porsche's sole non-turbo 911, though a lengthy options list ensures enough variety. Cast alloy 15in wheels are standard, with forged 16in rims optional as is the Sport option of a Turbo rear spoiler. Power grew quickly from the original 180bhp to 188bhp for the 1980 model year and 204bhp just a year later, though with improvements in economy. From 1982 the Coupé and Targa are joined by a Cabriolet model, Porsche's first full convertible since the 356. Unusually, these only command a small premium.

SPECIFICATIONS

Years produced: 1978-1983
Performance: 0-60mph: 6.5 secs (Top speed: 141mph)
Power & torque: 180bhp / 196lb/ft
Engine: Normally aspirated 2994cc flat 6, petrol, mechanical fuel injection, 12 valves
Drivetrain: Rear-engine RWD
Suspension: (F) Ind. MacPherson struts, torsion bar (R) Ind. trailing wishbones, torsion bar
Bodyframe: Metal monocoque
Transmission: 5-speed manual
Weight: 1160kgs

PRICE GUIDE

Launch price: £14,100
Excellent: £14,500
Good: £12,000
Average: £8500
Project: £5500

PORSCHE
928/S/S2

Porsche's intended replacement for the 911 may not have achieved that goal, but it wasn't for lack of performance or technological wizardry. An alloy V8 was attached to a rear-mounted gearbox and clothed in a galvanised body with aluminium doors and bonnet and body-coloured plastic bumpers – pretty radical for 1977. The original 4.5-litres was upped to 4.7 for the 300bhp 928S in 1982. Two years later, higher compression and a new fuel-injection system saw that rise to 310bhp in the 928 S2, which also offered ABS as an option for the first time on a Porsche.

SPECIFICATIONS

Years produced: 1978-1987 (17,710 in total)
Performance: 0-60mph: 6.2 secs (Top speed: 158mph)
Power & torque: 240bhp / 257lb/ft
Engine: Normally aspirated 4474cc V8, petrol, electronic fuel injection, 16 valves
Drivetrain: Front-engine RWD
Suspension: (F) Ind. double wishbone, coil spring. (R) Ind. Weissach axle, coil springs
Bodyframe: Metal monocoque
Transmission: 5-speed manual
Weight: 1468kgs

PRICE GUIDE

Launch price: £19,499
Excellent: £7500
Good: £6000
Average: £3500
Project: £1500

PORSCHE
911 Turbo

It turns out the short run of original Turbos was merely a warm-up act for the main act. With an extra 300cc and an intercooler built into the rear spoiler, power jumped by another 40bhp, putting the 911 Turbo firmly in the supercar class. It also helped mask the previous car's turbo lag to some extent, though it seems poor by modern standards. Further development to the suspension reduced the car's power-off tail-wagging tendencies and improving safety, but the pay-off is a bone-jarring ride. A five-speed gearbox finally arrived for the 1989 model year.

SPECIFICATIONS

Years produced: 1978-1989 (21,589 in total)
Performance: 0-60mph: 6.1 secs (Top speed: 153mph)
Power & torque: 260bhp / 253lb/ft
Engine: Turbocharged 2994cc flat 6, petrol, electronic fuel injection, 12 valves
Drivetrain: Rear-engine RWD
Suspension: (F) Ind. MacPherson struts, torsion bar (R) Ind. trailing wishbones, torsion bar
Bodyframe: Metal monocoque
Transmission: 4-speed manual
Weight: 1195kgs

PRICE GUIDE

Launch price: £23,200
Excellent: £24,000
Good: £19,000
Average: £13,500
Project: £8000

PORSCHE
924 Turbo

With Porsche at the forefront of turbo technology, and the 924 chassis ripe for exploitation with more power, this car's development was inevitable. Thanks to a 45bhp power boost that raised top speed by nearly 20mph, a five-speed gearbox and uprated suspension, the 924 Turbo was very well received and over 12,000 were sold over a five-year period. Easily identified by the row of four extra air intakes in the nose panel and NACA duct in the bonnet, they also got five- rather than four-bolt wheels and were the first 924s to use the discreet but effective rear lip spoiler.

SPECIFICATIONS

Years produced: 1979-1983 (12,385 in total)
Performance: 0-60mph: 7.7 secs (Top speed: 142mph)
Power & torque: 174bhp / 184lb/ft
Engine: Turbocharged 1984cc in-line four, petrol, carburettor, 8 valves
Drivetrain: Front-engine RWD
Suspension: (F) Ind. MacPherson struts, coil spring. (R) Ind. semi-trailing arms, coil spring
Bodyframe: Metal monocoque
Transmission: 4-speed manual
Weight: 1180kgs

PRICE GUIDE

Launch price: £13,629
Excellent: £5000
Good: £4000
Average: £1800
Project: £850

PORSCHE
924 Carrera GT

Based around prototype ideas for the forthcoming 944, which you can see in the distinctive bloated wheelarches, fabricated from flexible polyurethane. Porsche built 406 Carrera GTs to homologate the 924 for racing at Le Mans. Based on the 924 Turbo, engine output was boosted by another 40bhp thanks to an intercooler and internal modifications. The Carrera GT was sold only in red, silver or black, and just 75 right-hand-drive examples were built for the UK market. No surprise then that prices have been rising here in recent years as their rarity and abilities are recognised.

SPECIFICATIONS

Years produced: 1980-1981 (406 in total)
Performance: 0-60mph: 6.5 secs (Top speed: 150mph)
Power & torque: 207bhp / 207lb/ft
Engine: Turbocharged 1984cc in-line four, petrol, electronic fuel injection, 8 valves
Drivetrain: Front-engine RWD
Suspension: (F) Ind. MacPherson struts, coil spring. (R) Ind. semi-trailing arm, coil spring
Bodyframe: Metal monocoque
Transmission: 5-speed manual
Weight: 1179kgs

PRICE GUIDE

Launch price: £19,210
Excellent: £18,000
Good: £15,000
Average: £9000
Project: £5000

PORSCHE
944

It might share the 924's profile, but the flared arches, wider wheels and deeper front valance turn the older car's delicacy into aggression. A 2.5-litre engine that was effectively half a 928's V8 delivered on the promise. Handling and grip was very assured, and the 944 went on to outsell even the 924, keeping Porsche afloat in the early 1990s. Interior revisions in 1985 gave it an oval dashboard and revised door panels. For 1988-89 – the last year of 'plain' 944 production – engine capacity rose to 2.7 litres, offering little in the way of bhp, but handy low-down pulling power.

SPECIFICATIONS

Years produced: 1982-1989 (117,790 in total)
Performance: 0-60mph: 8.3 secs (Top speed: 138mph)
Power & torque: 163bhp / 151lb/ft
Engine: Normally aspirated 2479cc in-line four, petrol, electronic fuel injection, 8 valves
Drivetrain: Front-engine RWD
Suspension: (F) Ind. MacPherson struts, coil spring. (R) Ind. semi-trailing arm, torsion bar
Bodyframe: Metal monocoque
Transmission: 5-speed manual
Weight: 1180kgs

PRICE GUIDE

Launch price: £12,999
Excellent: £5000
Good: £4000
Average: £2400
Project: £1100

PORSCHE
911 Carrera 3.2

Last of the second generation 911s and still a viable daily driver if that's what you want. The choice of Coupé, Targa and Cabriolet (worth perhaps £2000 more now) continues from the SC, though all now have 150mph capability. Even better, fuel economy has been further improved and beats practically everything else in this class. Can be had with either the standard or wider Turbo-look body complete with spoilers and wide wheels. Despite more drag and an extra 50kg blunting performance, this was the bigger seller. The 1987 model year gets an improved five-speed gearbox.

SPECIFICATIONS

Years produced: 1984-1989 (76,473 in total)
Performance: 0-60mph: 5.6 secs (Top speed: 153mph)
Power & torque: 231bhp / 209lb/ft
Engine: Normally aspirated 3164cc flat 6, petrol, electronic fuel injection, 12 valves
Drivetrain: Rear-engine RWD
Suspension: (F) Ind. MacPherson struts, torsion bar (R) Ind. trailing wishbones, torsion bar
Bodyframe: Metal monocoque
Transmission: 5-speed manual
Weight: 1210kgs

PRICE GUIDE

Launch price: £23,366
Excellent: £16,750
Good: £13,500
Average: £10,000
Project: £6500

PORSCHE
924S

A master of subtlety, the 924S appeals to those who are fond of the 'Q-car' concept – there's a lot more going on than the body leads you to believe. Aside from the Teledial wheels and extra 'S' on the badge at the rear, nothing gives the game away that this is virtually a 944 wearing the 924's slimline bodyshell. However, it's all there, from the new 2.5-litre overhead-cam engine to the four-wheel vented disc brakes. Engine power was raised from 150bhp to 160bhp for the 1988 model year, at the same time as Le Mans editions in black or white were offered with lowered, uprated suspension.

SPECIFICATIONS

Years produced: 1985-1988 (16,282 in total)
Performance: 0-60mph: 7.9 secs (Top speed: 136mph)
Power & torque: 160bhp / 155lb/ft
Engine: Normally aspirated 2479cc in-line four, petrol, electronic fuel injection, 8 valves
Drivetrain: Front-engine RWD
Suspension: (F) Ind. MacPherson struts, coil spring. (R) Ind. semi-trailing arms, coil spring
Bodyframe: Metal monocoque
Transmission: 5-speed manual
Weight: 1164kgs

PRICE GUIDE

Launch price: £21,031
Excellent: £4000
Good: £3000
Average: £1750
Project: £900

PORSCHE
944 Turbo

As with the 924, a turbo version was always on the cards. Here it boosts the 2.5-litre engine by nearly 60bhp, with the clutch and gearbox uprated to suit. The chassis got thicker anti-roll bars and four-pot brake calipers. A smoother nose panel and larger rear spoiler distinguish it from the 944. For 1988 only, Turbo SE is offered with 250bhp thanks to a larger turbocharger. The transmission is further beefed up, a limited-slip diff is standard, brakes are uprated and Koni dampers fitted. For 1989-91 the SE specification was adopted for the normal 944 Turbo.

SPECIFICATIONS

Years produced: 1985-1991 (25,245 in total)
Performance: 0-60mph: 5.9 secs (Top speed: 152mph)
Power & torque: 220bhp / 243lb/ft
Engine: Turbocharged 2479cc in-line four, petrol, electronic fuel injection, 8 valves
Drivetrain: Front-engine RWD
Suspension: (F) Ind. MacPherson struts, coil spring. (R) Ind. semi-trailing arm, torsion bar
Bodyframe: Metal monocoque
Transmission: 5-speed manual
Weight: 1280kgs

PRICE GUIDE

Launch price: £25,311
Excellent: £8500
Good: £7000
Average: £4500
Project: £2400

PORSCHE
911 Carrera Club Sport

Harking back to the 1973 Carrera 2.7s, this was a stripped out version of the 3.2, made some 100kg lighter than most by stripping out non-essentials like the rear seats, sound deadening, electric windows, and even the passenger's sun visor. The engine puts out the same power but revs more freely, and 300rpm higher, thanks to lightweight inlet valves and a reprogrammed ECU. Just 340 examples were made, and only 53 of those were in right-hand-drive for the UK market. Available here in any colour you like, as long as what you like is Grand Prix White with red wheel centres.

SPECIFICATIONS

Years produced: 1987-1988 (340 in total)
Performance: 0-60mph: 5.6 secs (Top speed: 149mph)
Power & torque: 210bhp / 188lb/ft
Engine: Normally aspirated 3164cc flat 6, petrol, mechanical fuel-injection, 12 valves
Drivetrain: Rear-engine RWD
Suspension: (F) Ind. MacPherson struts, torsion bar (R) Ind. trailing wishbones, torsion bar
Bodyframe: Metal monocoque
Transmission: 5-speed manual
Weight: 960kgs

PRICE GUIDE

Launch price: £34,389
Excellent: £29,000
Good: £25,000
Average: £19,000
Project: £15,000

PORSCHE
959

Conceived for the short-lived Group B motor sport formula, the 959 was Porsche's riposte to the Ferrari 288GTO. Unlike the boisterous but largely conventional Italian supercar, this was a technological tour-de-force with permanent four-wheel-drive and twin sequential turbos. This set-up went some way to eliminating the dreaded lag which typified forced-induction when the car was originally dreamed up in the early 1980s. Unusually – bizarrely even – the front tyres were larger than the rear items, with 80% of the drive going to the back wheels. All cars were made in left-hand-drive.

SPECIFICATIONS

Years produced: 1987-1988 (250 in total)
Performance: 0-60mph: 3.6 secs (Top speed: 197mph)
Power & torque: 444bhp / 369lb/ft
Engine: Turbocharged 2849cc Flat 6, petrol, electronic fuel injection, 24 valves
Drivetrain: Rear-engine AWD
Suspension: (F&R) Independent, double wishbones, coil springs, anti-roll bars
Bodyframe: Metal monocoque
Transmission: 6-speed manual
Weight: 1350kgs

PRICE GUIDE

Launch price: £155,266
Excellent: £160,000
Good: £135,000
Average: £100,000
Project: £70,000

PORSCHE
944S

For those wanting more power from a 944 without the drama and cost of a Turbo, Porsche sent in the 944S to plug the gap for a couple of years. Apart from badges, it was visually the same as the 944, though the Turbo's rear undertray was added later in production. Under the bonnet, however, was the 16-valve twin-cam head developed for the 1981 924 GTP Le Mans racer. This puts power output bang-slap in-between the standard and Turbo 944s. Never a great seller, more fragile valve gear and complicated belt and chain-drive for camshafts makes them expensive to fix.

SPECIFICATIONS

Years produced: 1987-1989 (12,831 in total)
Performance: 0-60mph: 7.5 secs (Top speed: 141mph)
Power & torque: 188bhp / 170lb/ft
Engine: Normally aspirated 2479cc in-line four, petrol, electronic fuel injection, 16 valves
Drivetrain: Front-engine RWD
Suspension: (F) Ind. MacPherson struts, coil spring. (R) Ind. semi-trailing arm, torsion bar
Bodyframe: Metal monocoque
Transmission: 5-speed manual
Weight: 1275kgs

PRICE GUIDE

Launch price: £23,977
Excellent: £6250
Good: £5000
Average: £2750
Project: £1750

PORSCHE
928 S4

In an even greater technical tour de force than before, the V8 engine has grown to five litres and now has twin-cam heads with four valves per cylinder. Power goes up to 320bhp, but the big difference is low-end pulling power. The popular automatic gearbox option is now a Mercedes four-speed. Intelligent cooling system features louvres in the air intake that are computer-controlled to change their angle in line with coolant temperature. When closed the car is more aerodynamic. Smoother front and rear bumpers give the looks a lift, and there's a much larger rear spoiler.

SPECIFICATIONS

Years produced: 1987-1991 (16,213 in total)
Performance: 0-60mph: 5.7 secs (Top speed: 170mph)
Power & torque: 316bhp / 317lb/ft
Engine: Normally aspirated 4957cc V8, petrol, electronic fuel injection, 32 valves
Drivetrain: Front-engine RWD
Suspension: (F) Ind. double wishbones, coil spring. (R) Ind. Weissach axle, coil spring
Bodyframe: Metal monocoque
Transmission: 5-speed manual
Weight: 1538kgs

PRICE GUIDE

Launch price: £30,679
Excellent: £8500
Good: £7000
Average: £4500
Project: £2750

PORSCHE
911 Speedster

A retro-styled homage to the Fifties' 356 Speedster. Strictly a two-seater, it's all 3.2 Carrera underneath, but above the waist there's a shorter and steeply raked windscreen and a hard tonneau cover that gave the back a bit of a hump. Weather protection was on the rudimentary side, but that didn't matter too much as the bulk of the two thousand or so produced headed to America. The car also became an instant collectible, so few Speedsters were pressed into daily service. That makes finding a good example pretty easy, though paying for it may be another matter.

SPECIFICATIONS

Years produced: 1988-1989 (2100 in total)
Performance: 0-60mph: 6.1 secs (Top speed: 152mph)
Power & torque: 228bhp / 210lb/ft
Engine: Normally aspirated 3464cc flat 6, petrol, mechanical fuel injection, 12 valves
Drivetrain: Rear-engine RWD
Suspension: (F) Ind. MacPherson struts, torsion bar (R) Ind. trailing wishbones, torsion bar
Bodyframe: Metal monocoque
Transmission: 5-speed manual
Weight: 1140kgs

PRICE GUIDE

Launch price: £57,852
Excellent: £40,000
Good: £35,000
Average: £26,500
Project: £17,500

PORSCHE
911 Carrera 2/4 (964)

It might still look like any other 911, but underneath that familiar body is an entirely new structure designed to meet ever-changing technical and safety requirements. With integrated bumpers and other tricks, the body is a great deal more aerodynamic too. And there's the gadget man's dream of a rear spoiler that pops up automatically at 50mph. Launched first in four-wheel-drive Carrera 4 form, the rear-drive Carrera 2 was released a year later and was by far the best-selling version. As with past 911s, the range featured the choice of Coupe, Targa and Cabriolet.

SPECIFICATIONS

Years produced: 1989-1993 (55,682 in total)
Performance: 0-60mph: 5.7 secs (Top speed: 162mph)
Power & torque: 246bhp / 229lb/ft
Engine: Normally aspirated 2600cc flat 6, petrol, electronic fuel injection, 12 valves
Drivetrain: Rear-engine, RWD
Suspension: (F) Ind. MacPherson struts, torsion bar (R) Ind. trailing wishbones, torsion bar
Bodyframe: Metal monocoque
Transmission: 5-speed manual/semi-automatic
Weight: 1075kgs

PRICE GUIDE

Launch price: £53,995
Excellent: £19,000
Good: £16,000
Average: £12,000
Project: £7500

PORSCHE
944 S2

For the 1989 model year the S2 replaced both standard and 'S' spec 944s. A new aluminium cylinder block employing Formula One technology allowed a capacity increase to three litres. Power was up 21bhp on even the 944S, and torque took an even bigger jump. Externally the S2 adopted the lower drag nose and tail panels from the Turbo, which along with a taller final drive ratio helped it to hit almost 150mph. The Turbo's braking system was also adopted. For the final two years of production a Cabriolet version was also offered. Add 25% for those.

SPECIFICATIONS

Years produced: 1989-1993 (19,120 in total)
Performance: 0-60mph: 6.7 secs (Top speed: 149mph)
Power & torque: 208bhp / 207lb/ft
Engine: Normally aspirated 2990cc in-line four, petrol, electronic fuel injection, 16 valves
Drivetrain: Front-engine RWD
Suspension: (F) Ind. MacPherson struts, coil spring. (R) Ind. semi-trailing arm, torsion bar
Bodyframe: Metal monocoque
Transmission: 5-speed manual
Weight: 1320kgs

PRICE GUIDE

Launch price: £31,304
Excellent: £7000
Good: £5750
Average: £4000
Project: £2250

PORSCHE
928 GT/GTS

GT is a slightly sportier version of the S4 with an extra 10bhp and a short-shifting close-ratio five-speed manual gearbox and sports seats, but standard suspension settings. Rare and sought after. However, the GTS that replaced it in 1992 was the ultimate 928. The engine has a long-stroke crank to take it out to 5.4 litres and 350bhp, while the body is revised with widened rear arches to take larger 'Cup' design 17in alloy wheels. A body-colour rear spoiler and teardrop mirrors also help bring the styling up to date. Both manual and automatic versions were offered.

SPECIFICATIONS

Years produced: 1989-1995 (4451 in total)
Performance: 0-60mph: 5.6 secs (Top speed: 170mph)
Power & torque: 325bhp / 317lb/ft
Engine: Normally aspirated 4957cc V8, petrol, electronic fuel injection, 32 valves
Drivetrain: Front-engine RWD
Suspension: (F) Ind. double wishbones, coil spring. (R) Ind. Weissach axle, coil spring
Bodyframe: Metal monocoque
Transmission: 5-speed manual
Weight: 1565kgs

PRICE GUIDE

Launch price: £62398
Excellent: £15,000
Good: £11,000
Average: £8000
Project: £5250

PORSCHE
911 Turbo (964)

Reintroduced for 1991 in a hurry to boost flagging sales. The lack of development time meant reviving the previous Turbo's 3.3-litre engine, which with a larger intercooler and other tweaks managed to put out 320bhp. This gave Porsche two years of breathing space in which to develop the turbocharged version of the 3.6 that arrived in early 1993 with another 40bhp and a massive boost in torque. This new version rolled on 18in wheels and could hit 100mph in under ten seconds. Turbos are easily distinguished from other 964s by their fixed rear spoiler.

SPECIFICATIONS

Years produced:	1991-1994 (6427 in total)
Performance:	0-60mph: 4.7 secs (Top speed: 168mph)
Power & torque:	315bhp / 332lb/ft
Engine:	Turbocharged 3299cc flat 6, petrol, electronic fuel injection, 12 valves
Drivetrain:	Rear-engine RWD
Suspension:	(F) Ind. MacPherson strut, coil spring. (R) Ind. semi-trailing arm, coil spring
Bodyframe:	Metal monocoque
Transmission:	5-speed manual
Weight:	1232kgs
PRICE GUIDE	
Launch price:	£72,993
Excellent:	£32,500
Good:	£26,000
Average:	£22,000
Project:	£17,000

PORSCHE
968

Launched in late 1991, the UK had to wait until May 1992 for right-hand-drive versions of this ultimate development of the 944 theme. It continues with the 944 S2's three-litre engine, but with variable valve timing to improve power, torque and economy. Visually it was the biggest change to the range, with only doors, roof and tailgate surviving unchanged from the 944. Inside, all trim materials were standardised with the 911 and 928, raising the impression of quality. Sales were disappointing, but 1993's stripped out Club Sport version got buyers back into the showrooms.

SPECIFICATIONS

Years produced:	1991-1995 (11,602 in total)
Performance:	0-60mph: 6.1 secs (Top speed: 158mph)
Power & torque:	240bhp / 225lb/ft
Engine:	Normally aspirated 2990cc in-line four, petrol, electronic fuel injection, 16 valves
Drivetrain:	Front-engine RWD
Suspension:	(F) Ind. MacPherson struts, coil spring. (R) Ind. semi-trailing arm, torsion bar
Bodyframe:	Metal monocoque
Transmission:	6-speed manual
Weight:	1420kgs
PRICE GUIDE	
Launch price:	£34,945
Excellent:	£12,000
Good:	£10,000
Average:	£8000
Project:	£5250

PORSCHE
911 Turbo 4 (993)

Once again there was a pause in Turbo production while the normally aspirated models were launched, but as it ever it proved worth the wait. Slightly flared wheelarches cover 10in and 8in wide rims that have hollow spokes to reduce unsprung weight, and a large rear spoiler confirms the car's identity. As the '4' in the name suggests, this Turbo has four-wheel-drive, which means it can make the most of the 408bhp generated with the aid of twin turbochargers. The six-speed gearbox is a beefed-up version of that in the Carrera 4. Only a coupé version is offered.

SPECIFICATIONS

Years produced:	1995-1998
Performance:	0-60mph: 3.9 secs (Top speed: 180mph)
Power & torque:	402bhp / 398lb/ft
Engine:	Turbocharged 3600cc flat 6, petrol, electronic fuel injection, 12 valves
Drivetrain:	Rear-engine RWD
Suspension:	(F) Ind. MacPherson strut, coil spring. (R) Ind. semi-trailing arm, coil spring
Bodyframe:	Metal monocoque
Transmission:	6-speed manual
Weight:	1500kgs
PRICE GUIDE	
Launch price:	£91,950
Excellent:	£50,000
Good:	£45,000
Average:	£37,500
Project:	£32,500

PORSCHE
Boxster

An affordable mid-engined car from Porsche, and a convertible to boot, was always going to be a success, but the Boxster has exceeded all expectations in its popularity. Initially only sold in 2.5-litre form to distance it from the 911, pressure from customers for more power meant that from 1999 the base model's capacity was upped to 2.7 and the 3.2-litre Boxster S joined the party. Finally the car had enough power to properly challenge the excellent chassis dynamics. High production numbers means these are destined to be affordable classics, but parts costs can be high.

SPECIFICATIONS

Years produced:	1996-2004
Performance:	0-60mph: 6.4 secs (Top speed: 157mph)
Power & torque:	228bhp / 192lb/ft
Engine:	Normally aspirated 2687cc Flat 6, petrol, electronic fuel injection, 24 valves
Drivetrain:	Mid-engine RWD
Suspension:	(F) Ind. MacPherson strut, coil spring. (R) Ind. MacPherson strut, coil spring
Bodyframe:	Metal monocoque
Transmission:	5-speed manual
Weight:	1275kgs
PRICE GUIDE	
Launch price:	£31,140
Excellent:	£21,000
Good:	£17,500
Average:	£11,500
Project:	£5750

RANGE ROVER
Classic

Inventor of the SUV and a classless conveyance, the Range Rover introduced the joys of off-roading to a whole new clienetele. Powered by Rover's ex-Buick V8 and using similar chassis technology as the Land Rover, its off-road ability was beyond reproach, while the hose-clean interior proved just the ticket for those with an active lifestyle. The styling was so clean that the Range Rover was at home in the politest places. It became more luxurious through the years, but its appeal remained undimmed during a 25-year production run.

SPECIFICATIONS

Years produced:	1970-1995
Performance:	14.2 secs (Top speed: 99mph)
Power & torque:	135bhp / 185lb/ft
Engine:	Normally aspirated 3528cc V8, petrol, carburettor, 16 valves
Drivetrain:	Front-engine AWD
Suspension:	(F) Live axle, coil spring. (R) Live axle, coil spring
Bodyframe:	Chassis and separate body
Transmission:	4-speed manual/3-speed automatic
Weight:	1760kgs
PRICE GUIDE	
Launch price:	£1998
Excellent:	£3250
Good:	£2500
Average:	£1000
Project:	£350

RELIANT
Sabre

The Reliant Sabre actually started out as a car designed as a Ford 'special' from Ashley, which Autocars of Israel then bought the rights to. Reliant was called in to engineer the car, originally called the Sabra, for production – and introduction into the USA – using Ford Consul power and a ZF gearbox. Once ready, Reliant sold the car as the Sabre in the UK, where it failed to make much of an impression at all, while the rest were sent to Israel in kit form. After two years in production, a total of 100 Sabres and Sabras were built.

SPECIFICATIONS	
Years produced:	1961-1964 (285 in total)
Performance:	14.4 secs (Top speed: 93mph)
Power & torque:	90bhp / 91lb/ft
Engine:	Normally aspirated 1703cc in-line four, petrol, carburettor, 8 valves
Drivetrain:	Front-engine RWD
Suspension:	(F) Independent, coil springs. (R) Live axle, coil springs
Bodyframe:	Chassis and glassfibre body
Transmission:	4-speed manual
Weight:	797kgs
PRICE GUIDE	
Launch price:	£1165
Excellent:	£9500
Good:	£7500
Average:	£2500
Project:	£1000

RELIANT
Scimitar SE4 Coupé

Reliant's next attempt at a sports car was the Scimitar SE4 and it was a lot more successful. The handsome coupé was originally designed by Ogle, and first shown on a Daimler SP250 chassis, but Reliant was so impressed with the design that it bought the rights and immediately set about putting it into production using the Sabre Six's running gear and an all-new steel chassis. In 1964, it went on sale and sold well. Subsequent Ford 'Essex' V6 powered versions kept the factory busy until 1970, when it was phased out in favour of the Scimitar GTE.

SPECIFICATIONS	
Years produced:	1964-1970 (1004 in total)
Performance:	11.4 secs (Top speed: 117mph)
Power & torque:	120bhp / 140lb/ft
Engine:	Normally aspirated 2553cc in-line six, petrol, carburettor, 12 valves
Drivetrain:	Front-engine RWD
Suspension:	(F) Independent, coil spring. (R) Live axle, coil spring
Bodyframe:	Chassis and glassfibre body
Transmission:	4-speed manual
Weight:	1003kgs
PRICE GUIDE	
Launch price:	£1292
Excellent:	£6750
Good:	£5000
Average:	£3000
Project:	£850

RELIANT
Scimitar GTE SE5

Reliant scored a major hit with the Scimitar GTE. It had been Reliant's idea to ask Ogle's Tom Karen to redesign the SE4 into a sporting estate, and when it subsequently appeared, the new car proved highly successful. As well as being good looking and usefully commodious, the 3-litre Ford V6 gave the GTE plenty of performance. The body style proved such a trendsetter that other manufacturers raced to produce their own versions, with Volvo's P1800ES and Lancia's Beta HPE being the most faithful homages. Despite that, values remain criminally low.

SPECIFICATIONS	
Years produced:	1968-1975 (5127 in total)
Performance:	8.9 secs (Top speed: 121mph)
Power & torque:	119bhp / 144lb/ft
Engine:	Normally aspirated 2495cc V6, petrol, carburettor, 12 valves
Drivetrain:	Front-engine RWD
Suspension:	(F) Independent, coil spring. (R) Live axle, coil spring
Bodyframe:	Chassis and glassfibre body
Transmission:	4-speed manual
Weight:	991kgs
PRICE GUIDE	
Launch price:	£1759
Excellent:	£4750
Good:	£3500
Average:	£1500
Project:	£500

RELIANT
Scimitar GTE SE6/SE6a

The GTE formula was so right that when Reliant came to replacing it, the job was impossible. So instead, it was made wider, given a longer wheelbase and sported new chassis settings that erred on the side of comfort. It continued to sell handsomely and remained Reliant's main money earner. In 1979, the 2.8-litre V6 Ford 'Cologne' engine was introduced, adding little to the mix, other than continued supply. Of more significance was the galvanised chassis that was phased in during 1981 – rust prevention became a whole lot easier from this point.

SPECIFICATIONS	
Years produced:	1976-1982 (4420 in total)
Performance:	10.0 secs (Top speed: 119mph)
Power & torque:	135bhp / 192lb/ft
Engine:	Normally aspirated 2994cc V6, petrol, carburettor, 12 valves
Drivetrain:	Front-engine RWD
Suspension:	(F) Independent, wishbone, coil spring. (R) Live axle, coil spring
Bodyframe:	Chassis and glassfibre body
Transmission:	4-speed manual (+O/D)/3-speed auto
Weight:	1293kgs
PRICE GUIDE	
Launch price:	£4367
Excellent:	£4600
Good:	£3400
Average:	£1400
Project:	£500

RELIANT
Scimitar GTC

The Scimitar GTC should have been another money spinner for Reliant. When it emerged in 1980, it had the market all to itself – the Triumph Stag had been dead three years. It was the large Triumph that obviously provided inspiration – with its T-piece targa arrangement and removable hardtop – and just like Triumph, Reliant struggled to meet ambitious sales expectations. The main problem wasn't the product at all, which was very good, but the fact it was launched in the middle of a recession. By the time the economy had recovered, the GTC was old hat...

SPECIFICATIONS	
Years produced:	1980-1985 (442 in total)
Performance:	9.7 secs (Top speed: 114mph)
Power & torque:	135bhp / 152lb/ft
Engine:	Normally aspirated 2792cc V6, petrol, carburettor, 12 valves
Drivetrain:	Front-engine RWD
Suspension:	(F) Independent, wishbone, coil spring. (R) Live axle, coil spring
Bodyframe:	Chassis and glassfibre body
Transmission:	4-speed manual with overdrive
Weight:	1265kgs
PRICE GUIDE	
Launch price:	£10,324
Excellent:	£7500
Good:	£6000
Average:	£3500
Project:	£1750

RELIANT
Scimitar GTE SE6b

The final generation of Reliant produced GTEs failed to replicate the success of the earlier models. The design may have aged gracefully, but demand tailed off (as it did for all large engined cars) during the recession in the early 1980s, and the GTE then simply faded away. The last models were a real improvement over the earlier SE6s, though, as they were lighter and stiffer and more comprehensively equipped. The GTE was later resurrected by Middlebridge, but failed to take off, despite Princess Anne buying one, and disappeared from view in 1990.

SPECIFICATIONS

Years produced:	1982-1986 (437 in total)
Performance:	10.0 secs (Top speed: 119mph)
Power & torque:	135bhp / N/A
Engine:	Normally aspirated 2792cc in-line four, petrol, carburettor, 12 valves
Drivetrain:	Front-engine RWD
Suspension:	(F) Ind., coil spring, wishbone. (R) Live axle, trailing-arms, coil spring
Bodyframe:	Chassis and glassfibre body
Transmission:	4-speed manual with overdrive
Weight:	1293kgs
	PRICE GUIDE
Launch price:	£10,324
Excellent:	£5500
Good:	£4000
Average:	£1750
Project:	£650

RELIANT
Scimitar SS1/SST

A brave experiment that didn't quite make the grade despite being ahead of its time. The Scimitar SS1 was designed to plug the gap in the market vacated by the MGB and TR7 when they went out of production, and should have been a massive success. It was simple, cheap and fun – and handled well thanks to its all-independent suspension. However, the Michelotti styling was a mess, the Ford CVH engines underpowered and panel fit of the glassfibre panels was terrible. As a result, it never came close to selling in the numbers once envisaged.

SPECIFICATIONS

Years produced:	1984-1990
Performance:	11.2 secs (Top speed: 111mph)
Power & torque:	95bhp / 97lb/ft
Engine:	Normally aspirated 1597cc in-line four, petrol, carburettor, 8 valves
Drivetrain:	Front-engine RWD
Suspension:	(F) Independent, coil springs. (R) Ind. semi-trailing arms, coil springs
Bodyframe:	Steel chassis, plastic body
Transmission:	5-speed manual
Weight:	887kgs
	PRICE GUIDE
Launch price:	£6995
Excellent:	£4250
Good:	£2750
Average:	£1000
Project:	£500

RENAULT
4CV

With Renault's 4CV developed in secret in occupied France during the war, it's tempting to believe that this rear-engined car was influenced by certain German machines. The 4CV was launched in 1946 with an 18bhp 760cc four-cylinder engine, all-independent suspension and very chic and cuddly styling. More power – albeit from a smaller 747cc engine – came in 1950, and the gradual advancements continued until 1961. Most intriguing was the R1063 Sport, with 42bhp. Not that much maybe, but in a car this light and small, more than enough to turn it into a real terrier.

SPECIFICATIONS

Years produced:	1947-1961 (1,105,547 in total)
Performance:	N/A (Top speed: 57mph)
Power & torque:	19bhp / 33lb/ft
Engine:	Normally aspirated 760cc in-line four, petrol, carburettor, 8 valves
Drivetrain:	Rear-engine RWD
Suspension:	(F) Independent, wishbone, coil spring. (R) Ind. swinging half axle, coil spring
Bodyframe:	Metal monocoque
Transmission:	3-speed manual
Weight:	560kgs
	PRICE GUIDE
Launch price:	£474
Excellent:	£4250
Good:	£3250
Average:	£1750
Project:	£750

RENAULT
Dauphine

The 4CV lived on in the stylish Dauphine. Born in 1956, this was a development of the 4CV with bigger rear-engine, chassis and bodywork. It sold almost twice as many (2,120,000) as the car which it grew out of. Intriguing features were the Ferlec transmission – giving finger-touch changes – and Aerostable semi-pneumatic variable suspension, plus disc brakes on all four wheels from 1964. The 37-40bhp Gordini (add 50% to prices) and the 49bhp 1093cc Rallye (not imported to UK) gave Mini Cooper-esque performance. The latter even had natty racing stripes!

SPECIFICATIONS

Years produced:	1956-1967 (2,150,738 in total)
Performance:	45.7 secs (Top speed: 70mph)
Power & torque:	30bhp / 43lb/ft
Engine:	Normally aspirated 845cc in-line four, petrol, carburettor, 8 valves
Drivetrain:	Rear-engine RWD
Suspension:	(F) Independent, wishbone, coil spring. (R) Swing axle, coil spring, anti-roll bar
Bodyframe:	Metal monocoque
Transmission:	3- or 4-speed manual, 3-speed automatic
Weight:	650kgs
	PRICE GUIDE
Launch price:	£769
Excellent:	£3250
Good:	£2500
Average:	£1200
Project:	£600

RENAULT
Floride coupé/convertible

Dauphine underneath, coupé or convertible on top. The design was by Frua and almost merited the hefty price tag. However, those expecting the looks to have some substance were to be disappointed, for the underpinnings were Dauphine, which meant just 38bhp from the rear-mounted four-cylinder engine. The Floride S of 1962 injected some vigour thanks to a 956cc engine giving 51bhp, but that was only available as a convertible. Nevertheless, the often 'interesting' handling probably meant that the car's speed was just the right side of manageable. Add 30% for convertible prices.

SPECIFICATIONS

Years produced:	1959-1962
Performance:	28.7 secs (Top speed: 83mph)
Power & torque:	36bhp / 44lb/ft
Engine:	Normally aspirated 845cc in-line four, petrol, carburettor, 8 valves
Drivetrain:	Rear-engine RWD
Suspension:	(F) Independent, wishbone, coil springs. (R) Swing axle, coil spring, anti-roll bar
Bodyframe:	Metal monocoque
Transmission:	4-speed manual
Weight:	805kgs
	PRICE GUIDE
Launch price:	£1296
Excellent:	£3750
Good:	£2750
Average:	£1500
Project:	£600

RENAULT
R4

If any Renault was a true 2CV rival, then this was it. Long-lived – built from 1961 to 1992 – and utterly simple in some places yet complex in others, this was Renault's first front-wheel-drive car. Quirks included the gearlever sprouting from the dashboard – necessary because the transmission was mounted in front of the engine – plus a different wheelbase on each side! The six engines available ranged from 603cc to 1108cc, but power stayed between the limits of 23bhp and 34bhp. As well as the saloon, there was also a 4x4 and a beach car known as the Plein Air.

SPECIFICATIONS

Years produced:	1961-1980 (8,135,424 in total)
Performance:	38.1 secs (Top speed: 70mph)
Power & torque:	30bhp / 41lb/ft
Engine:	Normally aspirated 845cc in-line four, petrol, carburettor, 8 valves
Drivetrain:	Front-engine FWD
Suspension:	(F) Ind. wishbones, lower arms, coil springs. (R) Ind. trailing arms, torsion bar
Bodyframe:	Metal monocoque
Transmission:	3-speed manual
Weight:	597kgs
	PRICE GUIDE
Launch price:	£539
Excellent:	£1750
Good:	£1250
Average:	£600
Project:	£125

RENAULT
Caravelle

America knew the Floride as the Caravelle. But from 1962, the name was used in Europe for a facelifted version, available as a coupé and convertible. The shape was largely the same, although some of the over-fussy ornamentation was dispensed with and passengers in the coupe had more headroom. The 956cc engine of the Floride S was initially used, still rear-mounted, but after a year, capacity rose to 1108cc. With 54bhp on tap, top speed rose to within a whisper of 90mph, but Renault never managed to resolve the handling issues. Add 25% for convertibles.

SPECIFICATIONS

Years produced:	1962-1968
Performance:	17.6 secs (Top speed: 89mph)
Power & torque:	54bhp / 65lb/ft
Engine:	Normally aspirated 1108cc in-line four, petrol, carburettor, 8 valves
Drivetrain:	Rear-engine RWD
Suspension:	(F) Ind. wishbone, coil spring. (R) Swing axle, trailing radius arm, coil spring
Bodyframe:	Metal monocoque
Transmission:	4-speed manual
Weight:	800kgs
	PRICE GUIDE
Launch price:	£1168
Excellent:	£4000
Good:	£3250
Average:	£1700
Project:	£700

RENAULT
R8 Gordini 1100/1300

When it comes to mad Renaults, the 8 Gordini takes some beating. Launched in 1964, this rear-engined car was tuned up to a whopping 90bhp, rather more than its rear-engined chassis could cope with despite the lowered suspension. The servo-assisted disc brakes at least gave it the ability to stop quickly. More madness was to follow though, for in 1967, the engine was upped to 1255cc, giving it 103bhp and the ability to easily top the ton. Originally, Gordinis were only available in blue with white stripes; other identifiers were spotlamps and four headlamps on the 1255cc R1135 types.

SPECIFICATIONS

Years produced:	1964-1970 (12,203 in total)
Performance:	12.3 secs (Top speed: 100mph)
Power & torque:	95bhp / 72lb/ft
Engine:	Normally aspirated 1108cc in-line four, petrol, carburettor, 8 valves
Drivetrain:	Rear-engine RWD
Suspension:	(F) Ind. wishbone, coil spring. (R) Ind. swing axle, trailing arm, coil spring
Bodyframe:	Metal monocoque
Transmission:	4-speed manual
Weight:	853kgs
	PRICE GUIDE
Launch price:	£984
Excellent:	£5750
Good:	£4500
Average:	£3000
Project:	£1500

RENAULT
R8

Renault persisted with a rear-engined layout for the 8, the successor to the Dauphine. Unveiled in 1962, it was an altogether more angular car. The 956cc engine was larger than before, suspension was independent all around, and there were disc brakes on each wheel... which certainly wasn't usual for most cars of this class at the time. They were more justified on faster, more powerful versions such as 1964's 8-1100 – also known as the 8 Major – with 1108cc, and the 8S of 1968, which could boast 53bhp and had a quad-headlamp front to show off its sportier pretensions.

SPECIFICATIONS

Years produced:	1964-1972 (1,316,134 in total)
Performance:	16.5 secs (Top speed: 81mph)
Power & torque:	45bhp / 65lb/ft
Engine:	Normally aspirated 1108cc in-line four, petrol, carburettor, 8 valves
Drivetrain:	Rear-engine RWD
Suspension:	(F) Ind. wishbone, coil springs. (R) Ind. swing axles, trailing arm, coil spring
Bodyframe:	Metal monocoque
Transmission:	4-speed manual
Weight:	767kgs
	PRICE GUIDE
Launch price:	£764
Excellent:	£2750
Good:	£2200
Average:	£1100
Project:	£400

RENAULT
16

The 16 can lay major claim to being the first modern hatchback. Its 1964 design seems to be a blueprint for much that came after it, with a lifting tailgate, two-box shape with a roomy interior, front-wheel-drive, lively alloy engine and disc brakes up at the head. There was even what could be regarded as a hot hatch from 1973, two years before the Golf GTI popularised the genre. This was the TX with a 1647cc 93bhp engine, five-speed transmission and quad-headlights. A very forward-thinking and well-behaved machine with a lot of typically French quirks to make it even more intriguing.

SPECIFICATIONS

Years produced:	1965-1979 (1,846,000 in total)
Performance:	12.3 secs (Top speed: 101mph)
Power & torque:	83bhp / 88lb/ft
Engine:	Normally aspirated 1470cc in-line four, petrol, carburettor, 8 valves
Drivetrain:	Front-engine FWD
Suspension:	(F) Independent, torsion bar. (R) Ind. trailing arm, torsion bar
Bodyframe:	Metal monocoque
Transmission:	4-speed manual
Weight:	980kgs
	PRICE GUIDE
Launch price:	£949
Excellent:	£3000
Good:	£2250
Average:	£1000
Project:	£350

RENAULT
R10

Renault stuck extra length onto the boot and bonnet of the 8 to create the 10. Quite what the reason for this was is unclear, and perhaps even Renault themselves didn't know, for the model only lasted three years from 1969 to 1971, and was still known as the 8 in some countries. However, in its homeland, it was a 10, as it was in the UK too. Aside from the big nose and plumper rump, changes from the 8 were minimal save for the fitment of a five-bearing 1289cc engine at the rear to give a top speed of 82mph from its 48bhp. Handling was better too.

SPECIFICATIONS

Years produced:	1969-1971 (699,490 in total)
Performance:	17.0 secs (Top speed: 88mph)
Power & torque:	52bhp / 72lb/ft
Engine:	Normally aspirated 1289cc in-line four, petrol, carburettor, 8 valves
Drivetrain:	Rear-engine RWD
Suspension:	(F) Independent, coil spring, (R) Independent, coil spring
Bodyframe:	Metal monocoque
Transmission:	4-speed manual
Weight:	792kgs
	PRICE GUIDE
Launch price:	£776
Excellent:	£2500
Good:	£1750
Average:	£900
Project:	£400

RENAULT
15/17

After Ford launched the Capri in 1969, other European manufacturers launched cheap and cheerful coupés. The 15 and 17 were Renault's. Based on the chassis of the 12, the 15 was the lower-spec model with single headlamps and conventional side windows, while the 17 had four lights and louvred rear quarter windows, which gave it a strangely beguiling appearance. The range of engines encompassed 1289cc, 1565cc, 1605cc and 1647cc capacities, the latter used in the top-dog 108bhp 17 Gordini. Convertible versions were actually coupés with a full-length roll-top roof to let the sun in.

SPECIFICATIONS

Years produced:	1972-1978 (207,854/92,589 in total)
Performance:	13.6 secs (Top speed: 108mph)
Power & torque:	90bhp / 90lb/ft
Engine:	Normally aspirated 1289cc in-line four, petrol, carburettor, 8 valves
Drivetrain:	Front-engine FWD
Suspension:	(F) Independent, wishbone, coil spring. (R) Independent, coil spring
Bodyframe:	Metal monocoque
Transmission:	4-speed manual
Weight:	965kgs
	PRICE GUIDE
Launch price:	£1325
Excellent:	£3000
Good:	£2000
Average:	£900
Project:	£400

RENAULT
5 Gordini/Turbo

Known as the Renault 5 Alpine in Continental Europe, the Gordini was one of the first generation hot hatches, predating the Golf GTi by a year. The car's 1397cc engine produced 93bhp, more than double the power of the standard 5. However, this was a time of rapidly expanding power figures, and the Gordini was quickly outgunned by its new-found rivals. Renault's solution to this problem, as with its F1 car, was forced induction. Bolting a single Garrett T3 turbocharger onto the Gordini instantly gave the car a handy increase in power and torque.

SPECIFICATIONS

Years produced:	1976-1984
Performance:	10.7 secs (Top speed: 107mph)
Power & torque:	93bhp / 85lb/ft
Engine:	Normally aspirated 1397cc in-line four, petrol, carburettor, 8 valves
Drivetrain:	Front-engine, FWD
Suspension:	(F) Independent MacPherson strut, coil spring. (R) Ind., trailing arms
Bodyframe:	Metal monocoque
Transmission:	5-speed manual
Weight:	850kgs
	PRICE GUIDE
Launch price:	£4149
Excellent:	£3500
Good:	£2500
Average:	£1250
Project:	£500

RENAULT
Fuego Turbo

After eight years of moderate coupé sales with the 15/17, Renault needed something fresh. The Fuego was distinctive. Novel too, it being the first car ever to be fitted with a PLIP, or remote central locking. In 1982, after two years at the top of the sales charts in Europe, Renault introduced a 132bhp Fuego Turbo, which could sprint from 0-60 mph in 9.5 seconds. Clad with Turbo decals, and BBS alloys, it was less than subtle, but UK sales proved surprisingly strong. Renault stopped importing the Fuego into Great Britain in 1986.

SPECIFICATIONS

Years produced:	1980-1985
Performance:	8.9 secs (Top speed: 120mph)
Power & torque:	132bhp / 147lb/ft
Engine:	Turbocharged 1565cc in-line four, petrol, carburettor, 8 valves
Drivetrain:	Front-engine FWD
Suspension:	(F) Independent, MacPherson strut, coil spring. (R) Ind., trailing arms, coil spring
Bodyframe:	Metal monocoque
Transmission:	5-speed manual
Weight:	1050kgs
	PRICE GUIDE
Launch price:	£8700
Excellent:	£1750
Good:	£1250
Average:	£600
Project:	£150

RENAULT
5 Turbo 2

The first 400 Renault 5 Turbos were built in-line with Group 4 regulations with the intention of going rallying. This homologation special would have cost Renault too much money to put into full-scale production as there were so many lightweight aluminium parts unique to the mid-engined rally car. That is why Renault brought out the R5 Turbo 2. This more production-friendly car shared most of its components with the front-engined Gordini Turbo. The Turbo 2 was almost as fast as the Group 4 car, but it didn't cost Renault anywhere near as much to build.

SPECIFICATIONS

Years produced:	1983-1986 (3576 in total)
Performance:	6.6 secs (Top speed: 124mph)
Power & torque:	160bhp / 163lb/ft
Engine:	Turbocharged 1397cc in-line four, petrol, electronic fuel injection, 8 valves
Drivetrain:	Mid-engine RWD
Suspension:	(F) Independent, wishbones, torsion bars. (R) Ind., wishbones, anti-roll bar
Bodyframe:	Metal and glassfibre monocoque
Transmission:	5-speed manual
Weight:	970kgs
	PRICE GUIDE
Launch price:	£N/A
Excellent:	£16,500
Good:	£14,000
Average:	£10,000
Project:	£6500

RENAULT
5 GT Turbo

When the Gordini Turbo was phased out in 1984 with the facelift of the 5, Renault had to come up with a replacement. The GT Turbo used the same basic engine as the Gordini, but a smaller Garrett T2 turbocharger and a few other minor modifications to the induction system saw power rise to 113 bhp, and again to 118bhp in 1987. This power figure on its own isn't that impressive, but the Renault 5 only tipped the scales at 850kg, giving the tiny hot hatch truly staggering acceleration. That and fun, rear inside wheel-lifting handling.

SPECIFICATIONS

Years produced: 1985-1991
Performance: 7.1 secs (Top speed: 123mph)
Power & torque: 115bhp / 121lb/ft
Engine: turbocharged 1397cc in-line four, petrol, carburettor, 8 valves
Drivetrain: Front-engine FWD
Suspension: [F] Independent, MacPherson strut. [R] Ind., trailing arms, torsion bar
Bodyframe: Metal monocoque
Transmission: 5-speed manual
Weight: 820kgs

PRICE GUIDE

Launch price: £7630
Excellent: £3500
Good: £2750
Average: £1650
Project: £750

RENAULT
Clio Williams

Even though it was called the Clio Williams, the F1 team played a minimal role in the development of this car. It started out as a standard Clio 16V, and the transformation was carried out by Renault Sport, the firm's motor sport arm. Originally, a limited run of 500 Clio Williams was planned, but, due to overwhelming demand, Renault saw an opportunity and continued building them – much to the annoyance of those believing they'd bought a limited edition car. Over the course of its life, the Williams put on weight which blunted appeal.

SPECIFICATIONS

Years produced: 1993-1995
Performance: 7.8 secs (Top speed: 134mph)
Power & torque: 145bhp / 129lb/ft
Engine: Normally aspirated 1998cc in-line four, petrol, electronic fuel injection, 16 valves
Drivetrain: Front-engine FWD
Suspension: [F] Independent, MacPherson strut, coil spring. [R] Ind., trailing arms
Bodyframe: Metal monocoque
Transmission: 5-speed manual
Weight: 1010kgs

PRICE GUIDE

Launch price: £13,275
Excellent: £4750
Good: £3600
Average: £2500
Project: £1500

RENAULT
Sport Spider

The plan with the Sport Spider was similar to that of the mid-engined 5 Turbo a decade earlier. The Spider was used in various one-make motorsport championships, the aluminium chassis and composite bodyshell keeping weight down to 854kg. The road car was slightly heavier than the racing version, but still retained all the ingredients of a competition tool, albeit one with a rock-hard ride quality that soon proved wearisome. Power came from the 150bhp Clio 16v engine, which propelled the Spider to 60mph in 6.5-seconds.

SPECIFICATIONS

Years produced: 1995-1999
Performance: 6.5 secs (Top speed: 131mph)
Power & torque: 144bhp / 136lb/ft
Engine: Normally aspirated 1998cc in-line four, petrol, electronic fuel injection, 16 valves
Drivetrain: Mid-engine RWD
Suspension: [F] Independent, double wishbone, coil spring. [R] Ind., wishbones, coil spring
Bodyframe: Spaceframe chassis, composite body
Transmission: 5-speed manual
Weight: 930kgs (road car)

PRICE GUIDE

Launch price: £25,000
Excellent: £16,750
Good: £15,500
Average: £14,000
Project: £12,500

RILEY
RMA/RME

The immediate post-war Rileys continued with their traditional method of a separate chassis and ash-frame construction. 1945's RMA was a handsome streamlined saloon, its lively twin-camshaft 1496cc engine giving effective performance while the independent front suspension meant effective handling as well. It metamorphosed into the RME in 1952, with hydraulic brakes – one of the areas where the RMA had been weak – plus a larger rear window. A year before the end of production (in 1954) wheel spats were added but the running boards were dispensed with.

SPECIFICATIONS

Years produced: 1946-1955 (13,950 in total)
Performance: 25.1 secs (Top speed: 81mph)
Power & torque: 55bhp / 76lb/ft
Engine: Normally aspirated 1496cc in-line four, petrol, carburettor, overhead valves
Drivetrain: Front-engine RWD
Suspension: (F) Independent, torsion bar (R) Beam axle, leaf spring
Bodyframe: Chassis and separate body
Transmission: 4-speed manual
Weight: 1422kgs

PRICE GUIDE

Launch price: £710
Excellent: £8750
Good: £6500
Average: £3750
Project: £1750

RILEY
RMB/RMF

A step upwards from the RMA was the RMB, with its 2443cc engine offering enhanced potential. The 'B kept the same basic look as the 'A, but had a longer wheelbase and bonnet. When launched in 1946, 90bhp was available, but this went up to 100bhp in 1948. By happy coincidence, this also brought top speed up to 100mph as well. 1952's RMF was an almost identical-looking replacement with improved suspension, hydraulic brakes in place of the previous hydromechanical ones and a larger, curved rear screen. Manufacture continued until 1953.

SPECIFICATIONS

Years produced: 1946-1953 (8959 in total)
Performance: 15.2 secs (Top speed: 95mph)
Power & torque: 90bhp / N/A
Engine: Normally aspirated 2443cc in-line four, petrol, carburettor, 8 valves
Drivetrain: Front-engine RWD
Suspension: (F) Independent, torsion bar (R) Beam axle, leaf spring
Bodyframe: Chassis and separate body
Transmission: 4-speed manual
Weight: 1211kgs

PRICE GUIDE

Launch price: £1125
Excellent: £10,500
Good: £9000
Average: £5000
Project: £2250

RILEY
RMC Roadster

The rarest of the RM variants, especially in Britain, was the RMC, a three-seater, two-door roadster version of the RMB. The sleek lines were even more attractive sans roof, especially with the windscreen folded flat, and the more compact interior meant a larger boot could be fitted. The engine was the same as that of the RMB – a 2443cc overhead valve unit – and also tuned to give 100bhp. The RMC was intended for overseas markets, with most going to North America. Only 507 were constructed up until the end of the line in 1950.

SPECIFICATIONS

Years produced: 1948-1950 (507 in total)
Performance: 19.0 secs (Top speed: 98mph)
Power & torque: 100bhp / N/A
Engine: Normally aspirated 2443cc in-line four, petrol, carburettor, 8 valves
Drivetrain: Front-engine RWD
Suspension: (F) Independent, torsion bar. (R) Live axle, leaf springs
Bodyframe: Chassis and separate body
Transmission: 4-speed manual
Weight: 1219kgs

PRICE GUIDE

Launch price: £1225
Excellent: £23,000
Good: £18,500
Average: £12,500
Project: £6500

RILEY
RMD Convertible

More practical than the RMC Roadster was the four-seater RMD. Introduced at the same time as the RMC, this elegant drophead coupé would turn out to be the final open-top car to wear the Riley name, aside from the specially-converted Elf convertibles of the 1960s. The RMD kept much the same lines as the RMB, so no fold-flat one-piece windscreen or enlarged boot. It did have distinctive grab irons on its hood though. Production continued one year past the RMC until 1951 but, by the end of its three year life, only 502 had found homes.

SPECIFICATIONS

Years produced: 1948-1951 (502 in total)
Performance: 15.2 secs (Top speed: 95mph)
Power & torque: 100bhp / N/A
Engine: Normally aspirated 2443cc in-line four, petrol, carburettor, 8 valves
Drivetrain: Front-engine RWD
Suspension: (F) Independent, torsion bar (R) Live axle, leaf spring
Bodyframe: Chassis, separate body
Transmission: 4-speed manual
Weight: 1239kgs

PRICE GUIDE

Launch price: £1382
Excellent: £17,500
Good: £14,000
Average: £9000
Project: £4000

RILEY
Pathfinder/2.6

The sleek Pathfinder brought Riley into the modern age, though its twin-cam four-cylinder engine was carried over from the traditional and upright RMF. Right-hand floor shift for the gearchange can take some getting used to, as can the handling. Later car got leaf rather than coil rear springs and were better in this respect. The 2.6 that replaced it was of similar style but taller, and was really a Wolseley 6/90 with a Riley grille and an extra 4bhp from its BMC C-series six-cylinder engine. Both are rare now, but offer a large slice of 1950s British wood and leather luxury.

SPECIFICATIONS

Years produced: 1953-1958 (8959/2000 in total)
Performance: 16.7 secs (Top speed: 100mph)
Power & torque: 110bhp / 135lb/ft
Engine: Normally aspirated 2443cc in-line four, petrol, carburettor, 8 valves
Drivetrain: Front-engine RWD
Suspension: (F) Independent, torsion bar. (R) Live axle, semi-elliptic leaf spring
Bodyframe: Chassis and separate body
Transmission: 4-speed manual
Weight: 1500kgs

PRICE GUIDE

Launch price: £1382
Excellent: £4500
Good: £3250
Average: £1850
Project: £750

RILEY
1.5

Originally intended as a Morris Minor successor, the One-Point-Five emerged in 1957 instead as the sassier sister to the Wolseley 1500. The shell was the same albeit with differences in trim and the front end, where Riley's traditional grille was fitted. It was under the bonnet where the real fun lay, for the BMC B-series 1489cc had an extra carburettor fitted, boosting output to 62bhp over the Wolseley's 43bhp. Coupled with Morris Minor running gear, the One-Point-Five was a nimble and entertaining car to drive. The luxurious interior also befitted the Riley image.

SPECIFICATIONS

Years produced: 1957-1965 (39,568 in total)
Performance: 17.4 secs (Top speed: 84mph)
Power & torque: 62bhp / 82lb/ft
Engine: Normally aspirated 1489cc in-line four, petrol, carburettor, 8 valves
Drivetrain: Front-engine RWD
Suspension: (F) Independent, torsion bar. (R) Live axle, semi-elliptic leaf spring
Bodyframe: Metal monocoque
Transmission: 4-speed manual
Weight: 864kgs

PRICE GUIDE

Launch price: £864
Excellent: £4000
Good: £3000
Average: £1400
Project: £450

RILEY
4/68, 4/72

Or, as Shakespeare might have said, a Farina by any other name... The Riley-badged version of BMC's mid-sized Farina-penned saloons of 1959 to 1969 was arguably the most desirable, for it blended the performance of the MG with the interior luxury of the Wolseley. The car was based on the MG Magnette so had cut-back fins from its birth in 1959 plus the same twin-carburettor, four-cylinder engine of 66.5bhp. The 4/72 in 1961 put that figure at 68bhp; there was also a wider track, increased wheelbase and anti-roll bars to try and control the body roll all Farinas suffered from.

SPECIFICATIONS

Years produced: 1959-1969 (10,940/14,151 in total)
Performance: 20.6 secs (Top speed: 84mph)
Power & torque: 66bhp / 85lb/ft
Engine: Normally aspirated 1489cc in-line four, petrol, carburettor, 8 valves
Drivetrain: Front-engine RWD
Suspension: (F) Independent, coil spring (R) Live axle, leaf spring
Bodyframe: Metal monocoque
Transmission: 4-speed manual
Weight: 1092kgs

PRICE GUIDE

Launch price: £1028
Excellent: £3500
Good: £2500
Average: £1250
Project: £350

RILEY
Elf

Continuing Riley's adventures in badge engineering was the Elf of 1961 to 1969. It looked like a Mini on steroids, with an extended rump framed by fins and an old school Riley front end grafted on. Occupants could delight in a less spartan interior with a full-length burr walnut dash. The MkII in 1963 made use of the bigger 998cc A-series engine and Hydrolastic suspension from 1964 and the MkIII introduced winding windows, better ventilation and a remote-control gearbox. Despite selling well, the Elf was discontinued when British Leyland killed off Riley.

SPECIFICATIONS
Years produced: 1961-1969 (30,912 in total)
Performance: 32.3 secs (Top speed: 71mph)
Power & torque: 34bhp / N/A
Engine: Normally aspirated 848cc in-line four, petrol, carburettor, 8 valves
Drivetrain: Front-engine FWD
Suspension: (F) Independent, rubber spring. (R) Independent, rubber spring
Bodyframe: Metal monocoque
Transmission: 4-speed manual
Weight: 660kgs
PRICE GUIDE
Launch price: £694
Excellent: £3650
Good: £2850
Average: £1500
Project: £500

RILEY
Kestrel

The last Riley of all was the Kestrel (and subsequent 1300 upgrade). It wasn't really a Riley though, being just a rebadged BMC 1100 with the 55bhp specification of the MG plus the now-expected individual grille and side whiskers. A walnut veneer dashboard upgraded the interior. When the 1275cc A-series was installed under the bonnet in 1967, power rose first to 65bhp, then 70bhp a year later. The car was de-named in 1968, becoming just the Riley 1300. This suggested the writing was on the wall for the marque. It was, for the car and the life of Riley ended a year later.

SPECIFICATIONS
Years produced: 1965-1969 (21,529 in total)
Performance: 18.4 secs (Top speed: 85mph)
Power & torque: 55bhp / 62lb/ft
Engine: Normally aspirated 1098cc in-line four, petrol, carburettor, 8 valves
Drivetrain: Front-engine FWD
Suspension: (F) Independent, wishbone, rubber spring. (R) Ind., rubber spring,
Bodyframe: Metal monocoque
Transmission: 4-speed manual
Weight: 832kgs
PRICE GUIDE
Launch price: £781
Excellent: £2600
Good: £1900
Average: £1000
Project: £350

ROCHDALE
GT

Rochdale made a success of supplying bodies for the specialist car industry. Its glassfibre shells were found adorning a number of specials – so much so that it started making full cars. The best selling GT (a coupé version of the Rochdale F racing body), was designed specifically to work with Ford Popular running gear. It was an advanced design, with sleek styling, a curved windscreen, and doors and bonnet that came ready fitted. One of the main bonus of the coupé roof was the lack of chassis flex – a lesson learned for subsequent models.

SPECIFICATIONS
Years produced: 1957-1961 (1350 in total)
Performance: (Top speed:)
Power & torque: bhp / N/A
Engine: Normally aspirated 1172cc in-line four, petrol, carburettor, 8 valves
Drivetrain: Front-engine RWD
Suspension: [F] Independent, torsion bar. [R] Live axle, coil spring
Bodyframe: Chassis and separate body
Transmission: 4-speed manual
Weight: 650kgs
PRICE GUIDE
Launch price: Not known
Excellent: £4250
Good: £3250
Average: £1850
Project: £500

ROCHDALE
Olympic

When it appeared in 1960, the Olympic was only the second car to feature a glassfibre monocoque – following hot on the heels of the Lotus Elite. The Olympic was bulbous and lacked the glamour of its rival, but it was well-engineered and handled assuredly thanks to its coil spring set-up. Production endured a critical setback following a fire at the factory a year after launch, but picked up slowly afterwards, being offered in component form or as a complete car. The Olympic II of 1963 moved to Ford (from BMC) for its running gear.

SPECIFICATIONS
Years produced: 1960-1962 (21,529 in total)
Performance: 11.9 secs (Top speed: 102 mph)
Power & torque: 60 bhp / N/A
Engine: Normally aspirated 1498cc in-line four, petrol, carburettor, 8 valves
Drivetrain: Front-engine RWD
Suspension: [F] Independent, torsion bar. [R] Live axle, coil spring
Bodyframe: Glassfibre monocoque
Transmission: 4-speed manual
Weight: 700 kgs
PRICE GUIDE
Launch price: Not known
Excellent: £6000
Good: £4750
Average: £2500
Project: £1000

ROLLS-ROYCE
Silver Wraith

Rolls-Royce re-emerged after World War Two with the Silver Wraith, based on the 1939 (non-Silver) Wraith model. At first, it was only available for export, Great Britain having to wait until 1948 before sales commenced. The Wraith was offered as a bare chassis only; it was up to the affluent owner to have a coachbuilder construct the body, with Mulliner outlines the most popular option. Initially, motive power was a 4257cc straight-six engine, but this rose to 4566cc in 1951 and then jumped to 4887cc in 1954 .

SPECIFICATIONS
Years produced: 1946-1959 (1783 in total)
Performance: 16.2 secs (Top speed: 88mph)
Power & torque: N/A / N/A
Engine: Normally aspirated 4566cc in-line six, petrol, carburettor, Overhead valves
Drivetrain: Front-engine RWD
Suspension: [F] Independent coil springs. [R] Beam axle, half (semi)-elliptic leaf spring
Bodyframe: Chassis and separate body
Transmission: 4-spd/Auto
Weight: 2359kgs
PRICE GUIDE
Launch price: £4190
Excellent: £30,000
Good: £25,000
Average: £15,000
Project: £9500

ROLLS-ROYCE
Silver Dawn

Before WW2, most Rolls-Royces had been large and imposing chauffeur-driven palaces on wheels. But the world was changing, and Rolls-Royce felt the need to change with it. Thus the Silver Dawn was a more compact Rolls, aimed at owners who also drove themselves. It was based on the Bentley MkVI. Engines were less powerful than their Bentley counterparts, and Rolls-Royce never let on the power output figures, at least not to the public. Most cars had standard Pressed Steel bodies, but there were some coachbuilt specials – some more special than others.

SPECIFICATIONS

Years produced:	1949-1955 (761 in total)
Performance:	16.2 secs (Top speed: 87mph)
Power & torque:	N/A / N/A
Engine:	Normally aspirated 4556cc in-line six, petrol, carburettor, 12 valves
Drivetrain:	Front-engine RWD
Suspension:	[F] Independent, coil springs. [R] Beam axle, semi-elliptic leaf spring
Bodyframe:	Chassis and separate body
Transmission:	4-speed manual
Weight:	1842kgs
PRICE GUIDE	
Launch price:	£3250
Excellent:	£32,500
Good:	£26,000
Average:	£15,000
Project:	£8500

ROLLS-ROYCE
Silver Cloud I

A new era for Rolls-Royce was ushered in with the Silver Cloud in 1955. The company started building bodies in-house, although many customers still preferred to have their favourite coachbuilder construct something special. But such was the imposing elegance of the Cloud's standard body that many buyers never felt the need to shop elsewhere. The 4887cc engine was an enlargement of that which had been used in previous models. In addition to the standard 123-inch wheelbase cars, a 127-inch limousine was offered with bodywork by Park Ward.

SPECIFICATIONS

Years produced:	1955-1959 (2359 in total)
Performance:	13.0 secs (Top speed: 106mph)
Power & torque:	N/A / N/A
Engine:	Normally aspirated 4887cc in-line six, petrol, carburettor, 12 valves
Drivetrain:	Front-engine RWD
Suspension:	[F] Independent, coils springs. [R] Beam axle, semi-elliptic leaf spring
Bodyframe:	Chassis and separate body
Transmission:	4-speed automatic
Weight:	2032kgs
PRICE GUIDE	
Launch price:	£3385
Excellent:	£29,000
Good:	£21,500
Average:	£11,000
Project:	£6500

ROLLS-ROYCE
Silver Cloud II

V8 power reached Rolls-Royce with the Silver Cloud II of 1959. The company's new 6230cc V8 brought power, flexibility and smoothness to these commanding heavyweights. Although actual horsepower was never revealed, it was estimated to be around the 200bhp, or 25 per cent greater than in the six-cylinder Cloud. Other changes included the adoption of power-assisted steering and a new facia. The standard saloons and Park Ward limousines were now complimented by the choice of a Mulliner drophead coupé, although its price was just as fabulous as its looks.

SPECIFICATIONS

Years produced:	1959-1965 (5013 in total)
Performance:	11.5 secs (Top speed: 113mph)
Power & torque:	N/A / N/A
Engine:	Normally aspirated 6230cc V8, petrol, carburettor, 16 valves
Drivetrain:	Front-engine RWD
Suspension:	[F] Independent, leaf springs. [R] Independent, semi-trailing arms
Bodyframe:	Chassis and separate body
Transmission:	4-speed automatic
Weight:	2109kgs
PRICE GUIDE	
Launch price:	£5802
Excellent:	£30,000
Good:	£22,500
Average:	£11,500
Project:	£6500

ROLLS-ROYCE
Phantom V Limousine

The Phantom V was the first Rolls-Royce to use the company's new V8 engine. And boy, did it need it. This ultra-luxurious leviathan weighed just under three tonnes and the huge rear passenger compartment was made possible by the elongated 12-foot wheelbase. Everything about the Phantom was designed to pamper; aside from the acres of wood and leather, power steering and automatic transmission came as standard. The styling was closely related to the Cloud on which the Phantom was based, with few cars being bodied by outside coachbuilders.

SPECIFICATIONS

Years produced:	1959-1968 (516 in total)
Performance:	13.8 secs (Top speed: 101mph)
Power & torque:	N/A / N/A
Engine:	Normally aspirated 6223cc V8, petrol, carburettor, 16 valves
Drivetrain:	Front-engine, RWD
Suspension:	[F] Independent, leaf springs. [R] Independent, semi-trailing arms
Bodyframe:	Chassis and separate body
Transmission:	4-speed automatic
Weight:	2540kgs
PRICE GUIDE	
Launch price:	£8905
Excellent:	£60,000
Good:	£50,000
Average:	£32,500
Project:	£22,500

ROLLS-ROYCE
Silver Cloud III

The adoption of the V8 engine for the Cloud II was universally regarded as an improvement. Not everybody was convinced by the 1962 facelift that created the Cloud III, though. It modernised the looks but old school aficionados bemoaned the loss of the traditional 'face'. However, it didn't offend the 'new money' celebrities who were now buying into the Rolls-Royce dream; John Lennon even had his Cloud III painted in a psychedelic colour scheme. A raised compression ratio resulted in more power although, predictably, how much more remained a secret.

SPECIFICATIONS

Years produced:	1962-1965 (2359 in total)
Performance:	10.8 secs (Top speed: 116mph)
Power & torque:	N/A / N/A
Engine:	Normally aspirated 6230cc V8, petrol, carburettor, 16 valves
Drivetrain:	Front-engine RWD
Suspension:	[F] Independent, leaf springs. [R] Independent, semi-trailing arms
Bodyframe:	Chassis and separate body
Transmission:	4-speed automatic
Weight:	2109kgs
PRICE GUIDE	
Launch price:	£5517
Excellent:	£32,500
Good:	£25,000
Average:	£13,500
Project:	£7500

ROLLS-ROYCE
Silver Shadow

If ever there was a Rolls-Royce for the masses, then the Shadow was it. It was revolutionary for the company, with unitary construction, all-round disc brakes and self-levelling suspension. The modern lines reflected contemporary car design, yet also managed to retain Rolls-Royce's upper class air. The 6230cc V8 rose in capacity to 6750cc in 1970, and the Shadow II fell victim to rubber bumpers and a front air dam in 1977. The Silver Wraith name was used from the same year to distinguish the long wheelbase version.

SPECIFICATIONS

Years produced: 1965-1980 (27,915 in total)
Performance: 10.9 secs (Top speed: 118mph)
Power & torque: N/A / N/A
Engine: Normally aspirated 6230cc V8, petrol, carburettor, overhead valves
Drivetrain: Front-engine RWD
Suspension: [F] Independent coils spring. [R] Ind., semi-trailing arms
Bodyframe: Metal monocoque
Transmission: Automatic
Weight: 2114kgs

PRICE GUIDE

Launch price: £6670
Excellent: £14,000
Good: £11,000
Average: £6250
Project: £1750

ROLLS-ROYCE
Phantom VI Limousine

The existing Phantom metamorphosed into the even more magnificent Phantom VI in 1968, a car that Rolls-Royce would continue to build – to special order only – right up until 1992. Despite this, and the rise of its V8 engine to 6750cc in 1978, it had drum brakes right until the end. However, this most stately of British limousines wasn't intended for speed, more for cruising along gently while those inside basked in the glory of being incredibly rich. During its quarter of a century existence, a mere 373 were constructed, ownership reading like a who's who of the global elite.

SPECIFICATIONS

Years produced: 1968-1992 (373 in total)
Performance: 13.2 secs (Top speed: 112mph)
Power & torque: N/A / N/A
Engine: Normally aspirated 6750cc V8, petrol, carburettor, 16 valves
Drivetrain: Front-engine RWD
Suspension: [F] Independent, wishbone, coil spring. [R] beam axle, semi-elliptic leaf spring,
Bodyframe: Chassis and separate body
Transmission: 4/3-speed automatic
Weight: 2722kgs

PRICE GUIDE

Launch price: £8905
Excellent: £80,000
Good: £67,500
Average: £47,500
Project: £30,000

ROLLS-ROYCE
Corniche I

One of the few coachbuilders to create special versions of the Shadow was Mulliner Park Ward, although as it was owned by Rolls-Royce, it was well-placed to do so. Its two-door coupé and convertible had been around since 1965, but became known officially as Corniches in 1971. Britain's most expensive car at the time echoed the mechanical layout of the Shadow, but with even more lavish levels of equipment. Despite the saloon becoming the Shadow II a year later, the Corniche's title wasn't amended at the same time. Dropheads nowadays command a sizable premium.

SPECIFICATIONS

Years produced: 1971-1987
Performance: 9.7 secs (Top speed: 126mph)
Power & torque: N/A / N/A
Engine: Normally aspirated 6750cc V8, petrol, carburettor, 16 valves
Drivetrain: Front-engine RWD
Suspension: [F] Independent, coil spring. [R] Ind., semi-trailing arms
Bodyframe: Metal monocoque
Transmission: 4/3-speed automatic
Weight: 2184kgs

PRICE GUIDE

Launch price: £11,556
Excellent: £22,000
Good: £17,500
Average: £11,000
Project: £6500

ROLLS-ROYCE
Camargue

Rolls-Royce tried to pull something special out of the bag with the Camargue, which, at £29,250 in 1975, took over from the Corniche as the UK's most expensive car. Based on the Shadow platform, Italian styling house Pininfarina produced the car's razor-edged silhouette. The resemblance to its earlier Fiat 130 Coupé and Ferrari GT4 2+2 designs was palpable; not quite what was expected for a flagship Rolls! The 6750cc V8 engine had extra (undisclosed) power, too, but in ten years of production, just 530 Camargues were made with no Bentley-badged sister models.

SPECIFICATIONS

Years produced: 1975-1986 (530 in total)
Performance: 10.9 secs (Top speed: 118mph)
Power & torque: 220bhp / 330lb/ft
Engine: Normally aspirated 6750cc V8, petrol, carburettor, 16 valves
Drivetrain: Front-engine RWD
Suspension: [F] Independent, coil spring. [R] Ind., semi-trailing arms
Bodyframe: Metal and aluminium monocoque
Transmission: 3-speed GM400 automatic
Weight: 2390kgs

PRICE GUIDE

Launch price: £29,250
Excellent: £28,000
Good: £22,000
Average: £14,000
Project: £7500

ROLLS-ROYCE
Silver Spirit/Silver Spur

In 1980, Rolls-Royces pensioned off the 15-year-old Shadow and replaced it with the Silver Spirit. Except the Shadow lived on in spirit for the new car was effectively the old car with a fresh skin. The angular body was completely new, while an update in 1989 resulted in fuel-injection, more power, anti-lock brakes and a revised interior. The Silver Spur was a long wheelbase offshoot and outlasted the short wheelbase cars on which it was based. In 1994, the Flying Spur was added to the range, complete with Bentley-esque turbocharging.

SPECIFICATIONS

Years produced: 1980-1993
Performance: 10.4 secs (Top speed: 126mph)
Power & torque: N/A / N/A
Engine: Normally aspirated 6750cc V8, petrol, carburettor, overhead valves
Drivetrain: Front-engine RWD
Suspension: [F] Independent, coil spring. [R]Ind., semi-trailing arms
Bodyframe: Metal monocoque
Transmission: 4-speed GM400 automatic
Weight: 2285kgs

PRICE GUIDE

Launch price: £85,609
Excellent: £15,000
Good: £12,000
Average: £7000
Project: £3750

ROLLS-ROYCE
Corniche II

The Corniche lived on beyond the Silver Shadow saloon on which it was based, surviving well into the Silver Spirit era. Although coupés were discontinued in 1982, the convertibles were updated enough for 1987 to justify a small change of name to Corniche II. Alloy and rubber bumpers replaced the chrome items and fuel-injection became standard for all markets, as did ABS brakes. Subsequent incarnations remained largely unchanged: 1989's Corniche III had colour-coded bumpers and better suspension while the end-of-the-line Corniche S in 1995 incorporated a turbocharger.

SPECIFICATIONS

Years produced: 1987-1994 (452 in total)
Performance: 17.1 secs (Top speed: 120mph)
Power & torque: 215bhp / 325lb/ft
Engine: Normally aspirated 6750cc V8, petrol, electronic fuel-injection, 16 valves
Drivetrain: Front-engine RWD
Suspension: [F] Independent coil spring. [R] Ind., semi-trailing arms
Bodyframe: Metal monocoque
Transmission: 3-speed automatic
Weight: 1430kgs

PRICE GUIDE

Launch price: £11566
Excellent: £60,000
Good: £50,000
Average: £40,000
Project: £20,000

ROVER
P3

Rover's first new post-war car was visually similar to its predecessors, with only detail changes over the 10, 12, 14 and 16hp models. However, the ash frame construction of the older cars was dropped in favour of an all-steel arrangement for its shorter chassis. New inlet-over-exhaust engines were fitted as well as all-independent front suspension. It was a nice, conventional model that majored on Rover's core values of solidity and quality. But the P3 stayed in production for a mere 18 months, its new parts being used more effectively on the P4.

SPECIFICATIONS

Years produced: 1948-1949 (9109 in total)
Performance: 29.4 secs (Top speed: 75mph)
Power & torque: 72bhp / N/A
Engine: Normally aspirated 2103cc in-line six, petrol, carburettor, 12 valves
Drivetrain: Front-engine RWD
Suspension: [F] Independent, coil springs. [R] Live axle, semi-elliptic leaf spring
Bodyframe: chassis and separate body
Transmission: 4-speed manual
Weight: 1346kgs

PRICE GUIDE

Launch price: £1080
Excellent: £7250
Good: £5500
Average: £2750
Project: £825

ROVER
P4 75 'Cyclops'

With the exciting new P4, Rover wiped its pre-war slate clean and presented a confident US inspired – if rather upright – façade for the 1950s. The original P4 'Cyclops' model may have shared its chassis and engines with the P3, but it appeared radically different, its most striking feature being the centrally-mounted headlight in the radiator grille, hence the nickname. Power was supplied by a 2.1-litre straight-six engine noted for its smoothness, allied to a four-speed column shift manual transmission.

SPECIFICATIONS

Years produced: 1949-1959 (43,241 in total)
Performance: 23.1 secs (Top speed: 82mph)
Power & torque: 75bhp / 111lb/ft
Engine: Normally aspirated 2103cc in-line six, petrol, carburettor, 12 valves
Drivetrain: Front-engine RWD
Suspension: [F] Independent, coil spring. [R] live axle, semi-elliptic leaf spring
Bodyframe: Chassis and separate body
Transmission: 4-speed manual
Weight: 1451kgs

PRICE GUIDE

Launch price: £1106
Excellent: £7500
Good: £5500
Average: £2600
Project: £900

ROVER
P4 60/80

In 1953, the appeal of the P4 was widened considerably by the arrival of the four-cylinder model. The 2-litre engine was also used in the Land Rover, and after the smoothness of the straight-six proved something of a disappointment. However, it wasn't much slower than the standard car, and proved slightly more economical. The 60bhp engine remained in the P4 until 1959, when it made way for the more powerful 2.2-litre 80bhp engine – reason enough to re-designate the car the P4 80 in its final three seasons.

SPECIFICATIONS

Years produced: 1952-1962
Performance: 0-60mph: 19.3 secs (Top speed: 88mph)
Power & torque: 60bhp / 101lb/ft
Engine: Normally aspirated 1997cc in-line four, petrol, carburettor, 8 valves
Drivetrain: Front-engine RWD
Suspension: [I] Independent, coil spring. [R] Live axle, semi-elliptic leaf spring
Bodyframe: Chassis and separate body
Transmission: 4-speed manual
Weight: 1481kgs

PRICE GUIDE

Launch price: £1163
Excellent: £5600
Good: £3900
Average: £1850
Project: £500

ROVER
P4 90/95/100/110

The six-cylinder P4 was offered in a wide variety of forms throughout its life. After its first facelift, the 2.6-litre IOE engine producing 90bhp was installed, giving it a 90mph top speed and effortless motorway cruising. However, that made way for the more powerful P4 100 in 1960. Although the engine capacities were similar, the new engine was a short-stroke version of the P5 3-Litre, and even smoother in service. Performance was up and overdrive improved refinement at speed. All are refined, high quality classics and currently undervalued.

SPECIFICATIONS

Years produced: 1954-1964 (60,724 in total)
Performance: 18.4 secs (Top speed: 90mph)
Power & torque: 93bhp / 138lb/ft
Engine: Normally aspirated 2638cc in-line four, petrol, carburettor, 8 valves
Drivetrain: Front-engine RWD
Suspension: [F] Independent, coil spring. [R] Live axle, semi-elliptic leaf spring
Bodyframe: Chassis and separate body
Transmission: 4-speed manual
Weight: 1486kgs

PRICE GUIDE

Launch price: £1297
Excellent: £7000
Good: £4500
Average: £2100
Project: £600

ROVER
P4 105R/S

Top dogs in the Rover P4 range, the R and S models boasted the most power, and easily topped the magic 'ton'. Introduced in 1956, the P4 105R and P4 105S shared the same engine as the P4 90, but had a high compression cylinder head and twin SU carburettors to boost power to a very respectable 108bhp. The R and S designations referred to their transmissions – the 105R featured a Roverdrive automatic transmission, while the 105S had a four-speed manual with overdrive. Both were luxuriously equipped and are in demand among marque fans.

SPECIFICATIONS

Years produced: 1957-1959 (8755 in total)
Performance: 15.9 secs (Top speed: 94mph)
Power & torque: 108bhp / 152lb/ft
Engine: Normally aspirated 2638cc in-line six, petrol, carburettor, 8 valves
Drivetrain: Front-engine RWD
Suspension: [F] Independent, coil spring. [R] Live axle, semi-elliptic leaf spring
Bodyframe: Chassis and separate body
Transmission: 4-speed manual
Weight: 1486kgs

PRICE GUIDE

Launch price: £1569
Excellent: £7000
Good: £5000
Average: £2400
Project: £650

ROVER
P5

Introduced in 1959, the Rover P5 became the company's flagship, easily slotting in above the P4 105 models. In the process, it became the favoured transport of British prime ministers and royalty. The new styling had been penned by David Bache while the monocoque body (Rover's first) had been engineered by Spen King and Gordon Bashford. Power was from a 2995cc version of the IOE that had first seen service in the P3, but which continued to deliver supreme smoothness and refinement. The cabin was predictably awash with wood and leather.

SPECIFICATIONS

Years produced: 1958-1967 (48,541 in total)
Performance: 16.2 secs (Top speed: 96mph)
Power & torque: 115bhp / 164lb/ft
Engine: Normally aspirated 2995cc in-line six, petrol, carburettor, 12 valves
Drivetrain: Front-engine RWD
Suspension: [F] Independent, coil spring. [R] Live axle, semi-elliptic leaf spring
Bodyframe: Metal monocoque
Transmission: 4-speed manual
Weight: 1613kgs

PRICE GUIDE

Launch price: £1764
Excellent: £6000
Good: £4500
Average: £2200
Project: £650

ROVER
P5B

The P5 was continuously developed during its life, first with the arrival of the more powerful 'Weslake Head' version, and then with the arrival of the handsome coupé. However, the most exciting addition to the P5 range came in 1967, when the new ex-Buick V8 engine was squeezed under the bonnet to create the P5B. The gutsy new engine immediately improved performance, and economy too, although the appealing straight-six soundtrack had been replaced by a charismatic V8 rumble. For many, this was Rover's high watermark, never to be topped.

SPECIFICATIONS

Years produced: 1967-1973 (20,600 in total)
Performance: 12.4 secs (Top speed: 108mph)
Power & torque: 151bhp / 201lb/ft
Engine: Normally aspirated 3528cc V8, petrol, carburettor, 16 valves
Drivetrain: Front-engine RWD
Suspension: [F] Independent, coil spring. [R] Live axle, semi-elliptic leaf spring
Bodyframe: Metal monocoque
Transmission: 3-speed automatic
Weight: 1586kgs

PRICE GUIDE

Launch price: £2009
Excellent: £8250
Good: £6500
Average: £2850
Project: £800

ROVER
P6 2000/2200

In the UK the Rover and Triumph 2000 pairing created the executive car class as we know it today. Less bulky than the luxury cars of old, but just as comfortable, and a whole lot more economical. But when it first appeared, the P6 was rather radical, with its skeletal structure and modern styling. The company gambled that it would appeal to traditionally conservative Rover customers, as well as attracting new ones. It worked, and the Rover P6 went on to become a huge success. It was a none too shabby, if improbable, rally car, too.

SPECIFICATIONS

Years produced: 1963-1977 (213,890 in total)
Performance: 11.9 secs (Top speed: 112mph)
Power & torque: 113bhp / 126lb/ft
Engine: Normally aspirated 1978cc in-line four, petrol, carburettor, 8 valves
Drivetrain: Front-engine RWD
Suspension: [F] Independent, coil springs. [R] de Dion axle, coil spring
Bodyframe: Metal monocoque
Transmission: 4-speed manual
Weight: 1222kgs

PRICE GUIDE

Launch price: £1264
Excellent: £3000
Good: £2200
Average: £1200
Project: £300

ROVER
P6B 3500

Although the Rover 2000 was capable, in no way could it be described as quick. However with the insertion of the ex-Buick V8 it became Rover's first Q-car, offering Jaguar matching pace and poise. The P6B caught on rapidly, selling in huge numbers despite its loftier price tag than the four-cylinder models. Initially offered in automatic guise only, the more sporting 3500S with four-speed manual gearbox appeared in 1971 which redressed the balance. Take care when buying as clean body panels can hide many horrors beneath.

SPECIFICATIONS

Years produced: 1968-1976 (79,057 in total)
Performance: 9.5 secs (Top speed: 117mph)
Power & torque: 144bhp / 197lb/ft
Engine: Normally aspirated 3532cc V8, petrol, carburettor, 16 valves
Drivetrain: Front-engine RWD
Suspension: [F] Independent, coil spring. [R] de Dion axle, coil spring
Bodyframe: Metal monocoque
Transmission: 3-speed automatic
Weight: 1272kgs

PRICE GUIDE

Launch price: £1801
Excellent: £3500
Good: £2500
Average: £1400
Project: £400

ROVER
SD1 3500/VDP

The SD1 was the final flowering of the Rover V8 line first masterminded by Spen King, Gordon Bashford and David Bache, although looking at its swooping Ferrari Daytona-inspired styling and BL vintage build quality, it's hard to see the connection. Initially sold like hot cakes, but the shoddy quality soon started putting buyers off. Improved during its life, so the final models were fast, appealing and genuinely desirable, but always tarnished by the BL connection. Nowadays, there's excellent parts availability and club support.

SPECIFICATIONS

Years produced: 1976-1986 (37,900 in total)
Performance: 8.6 secs (Top speed: 126mph)
Power & torque: 155bhp / 198lb/ft
Engine: Normally aspirated 3528cc V8, petrol, carburettor, 16 valves
Drivetrain: Front-engine RWD
Suspension: [F] Independent, MacPherson strut, coil spring. [R] Live axle, coil spring
Bodyframe: Metal monocoque
Transmission: 5-speed manual
Weight: 1313kgs

PRICE GUIDE

Launch price: £7511
Excellent: £3250
Good: £2500
Average: £850
Project: £250

ROVER
SD1 Vitesse

Once referred to as 'the poor man's Aston Martin' by *Motor* magazine, the Rover Vitesse remains a fast and effective bruiser of a sports saloon, despite the relatively paltry horsepower figure. Extrovert spoilers and racy trim completed the Vitesse transformation, and, despite the SD1 having been around for six years when it first appeared, it was a surprise success for Rover. Later twin plenum version homologation special, developed with help from Lotus, was more powerful. TWR-prepared touring car racers won at international level.

SPECIFICATIONS

Years produced: 1982-1986
Performance: 7.1 secs (Top speed: 135mph)
Power & torque: 187bhp / 220lb/ft
Engine: Normally aspirated 3532cc V8, petrol, mechanical fuel injection, 16 valves
Drivetrain: Front-engine RWD
Suspension: [F] Independent, MacPherson strut, coil spring. [R] Live axle, coil spring
Bodyframe: Metal monocoque
Transmission: 5-speed manual
Weight: 1440kgs

PRICE GUIDE

Launch price: £14,950
Excellent: £4500
Good: £3500
Average: £1650
Project: £800

SAAB
95/96 two-stroke

The Saab 96 might have been marketed as a new car when launched in 1960, but it was very closely related to the original two-stroke front-wheel-drive 92 that had been around since 1949 and had proved to be a massive breakthrough in design. More than ten years on and the 96, with its aerodynamic styling, independent suspension and tenacious roadholding still seemed ultra-modern despite being a facelift. The 841cc two-stroke developed enough power to push the 96 to over 80mph while the standard seat belts appealed to safety-conscious drivers.

SPECIFICATIONS

Years produced: 1960-1968 (253,305 in total)
Performance: 0-60mph: 24.1 secs (Top speed: 79mph)
Power & torque: 38bhp / 60lb/ft
Engine: Normally aspirated 841cc in-line three, petrol, carburettor, Two-stroke valves
Drivetrain: Front-engine FWD
Suspension: [F] Independent, double wishbone, coil springs, [R] beam axle, coil spring
Bodyframe: Metal monocoque
Transmission: 3/4-speed manual
Weight: 803kgs

PRICE GUIDE

Launch price: £885
Excellent: £4500
Good: £3500
Average: £1500
Project: £550

SAAB
96 Sport/Monte Carlo

Introduced in 1962, the 96 Sport model was the raciest of the breed and reflected its competition breeding. The shrieking two-stroke pushed out a heady 57bhp and the model soon proved its mettle in rallying. Factory driver Erik Carlsson won the 1960, 1961 and 1962 RAC rallies in addition to the 1962 and '63 Monte Carlo classics. Three years later, the Sport was renamed Monte Carlo to reflect its top-level success. As marketing opportunities went, it was a case of too little too late, although this special edition is highly-prized today.

SPECIFICATIONS

Years produced: 1962-1968 (2412/2453 in total)
Performance: 0-60mph: 19.3 secs (Top speed: 88mph)
Power & torque: 57bhp / 67lb/ft
Engine: Normally aspirated 841cc in-line three, petrol, carburettor, two-stroke valves
Drivetrain: Front-engine FWD
Suspension: [F] Independent, double wishbone, coil spring. [R] beam axle, coil spring
Bodyframe: Metal monocoque
Transmission: 4-speed manual
Weight: 888kgs

PRICE GUIDE

Launch price: £1059
Excellent: £6750
Good: £5000
Average: £3000
Project: £1500

SAAB
Sonett II/III

The Sonett was an unusual addition to the Saab line-up. The Bjorn Karlstrom-penned two-seater coupé was powered initially by the 96's two-stroke but in 1967 received Ford's unlovely V4 power for increased performance. The Sonett II made way for the heavily-revised, Sergio Coggiola-styled Sonett III in 1970. The new car retained the same centre section and, despite a more powerful 1.7-litre V4, it delivered near identical performance due to its extra heft. The Sonett was phased out in 1974, having failed to find favour in the lucrative Stateside market.

SPECIFICATIONS

Years produced: 1967-1974 (10,236 in total)
Performance: 0-60mph: 14.4 secs (Top speed: 100mph)
Power & torque: 75bhp / 94lb/ft
Engine: Normally aspirated 1699cc V4, petrol, carburettor, 8 valves
Drivetrain: Front-engine FWD
Suspension: [F] Independent, wishbone, coil spring. [R] beam axle, coil spring
Bodyframe: Metal and glassfibre monocoque
Transmission: 4-speed manual
Weight: 810kgs

PRICE GUIDE

Launch price: £N/A
Excellent: £7000
Good: £5500
Average: £3500
Project: £1250

SAAB
96/95 V4

In 1967, the two-stroke that had served so well for 15 years was joined by a V4. The four-stroke 1498cc Ford Taunus V4 engine had been installed to take the 96 further upmarket, but also acted as an insurance against the threat of US-style emissions regulations in Europe. The first V4 96s produced 55bhp and 65bhp, and usefully boosted performance. Top speed was now over 90mph. It was in this form that the 96 remained to the end, gaining more equipment and impact absorbing bumpers before finally being retired in 1980.

SPECIFICATIONS

Years produced: 1967-1980 (326,570/77,873 in total)
Performance: 0-60mph: 16.5 secs (Top speed: 96mph)
Power & torque: 65bhp / 85lb/ft
Engine: Normally aspirated 1498cc V4, petrol, carburettor, 8 valves
Drivetrain: Front-engine FWD
Suspension: [F] Independent, double wishbone. [R] beam axle, coil spring
Bodyframe: Metal monocoque
Transmission: 4-speed manual
Weight: 873kgs

PRICE GUIDE

Launch price: £801
Excellent: £3500
Good: £2500
Average: £1200
Project: £450

SAAB
99

Although the 92 and 96 had done well for Saab, the firm's bosses knew that in order to retain customers, it would need to introduce a larger car. The 99 ended up being the perfect car to head the range as it was also innovative, quirky and individual. The wraparound screen and impressive aerodynamics packaged a front-wheel-drive car of commendable dynamic prowess. Its 1.7-litre engine had been developed in tandem with Triumph and UK engineering company Ricardo, although Saab developed it further to overcome a number of design faults.

SPECIFICATIONS

Years produced: 1968-1984 (588,643 in total)
Performance: 0-60mph: 15.2 secs (Top speed: 97mph)
Power & torque: 80bhp / N/A
Engine: Normally aspirated 1709cc in-line four, petrol, carburettor, 8 valves
Drivetrain: Front-engine FWD
Suspension: [F] Independent, coil spring, wishbone. [R] Dead axle, Panhard rod
Bodyframe: Metal monocoque
Transmission: 4-speed manual
Weight: 925kgs

PRICE GUIDE

Launch price: £1288
Excellent: £1750
Good: £1250
Average: £700
Project: £200

SAAB
99 Turbo

During its lifetime, the 99 had received regular upgrades, first a larger version of its slant-four engine, then fuel-injection to create the effective EMS sports saloon. However, in 1978, the Saab created a legend – the 145bhp 99 Turbo. An early adopter of forced-induction, Saab's fast but laggy 99 Turbo hit the market at just the right time – the second energy crisis of 1979 witnessed many people trading down from larger cars, and the seemingly economical new car offered all of the pace without the fuel consumption of the multi-cylinder opposition.

SPECIFICATIONS

Years produced: 1978-1981 (10,607 in total)
Performance: 0-60mph: 8.9 secs (Top speed: 121mph)
Power & torque: 145bhp / 174lb/ft
Engine: Turbocharged 1985cc in-line four, petrol, electronic fuel injection, 8 valves
Drivetrain: Front-engine FWD
Suspension: [F] Independent, coil spring, wishbone. [R] Dead axle, Panhard rod
Bodyframe: Metal monocoque
Transmission: 4-speed manual
Weight: 1130kgs

PRICE GUIDE

Launch price: £7850
Excellent: £3000
Good: £2200
Average: £1000
Project: £450

SAAB
900 Turbo

Saab cleverly evolved its models and augmented platforms, so when it launched the 900 in 1979, it was clear that it was based heavily on the ten-year-old 99. But given that car's continued popularity, this was no handicap. The 900 majored on safety, and its impact absorbing bumpers, crumple zones and padded interior were touted as major selling points. But the star of the range was the 900 Turbo – a car that thanks to consistent development remained competitive throughout its life, and is still seen as superior to the GM-based car that replaced it.

SPECIFICATIONS

Years produced: 1979-1993 (202,284 in total)
Performance: 0-60mph: 7.5 secs (Top speed: 135mph)
Power & torque: 175bhp / 205lb/ft
Engine: Turbocharged 1985cc in-line four, petrol, electronic fuel injection, 16 valve
Drivetrain: Front-engine FWD
Suspension: [F] Independent, coil spring, wishbone. [R] Dead axle, Panhard rod
Bodyframe: Metal monocoque
Transmission: 5-speed manual
Weight: 1340kgs

PRICE GUIDE

Launch price: £8675
Excellent: £2400
Good: £1800
Average: £900
Project: £375

SAAB
9000 Carlsson/Aero

Saab's first all-new car since the 99 was part of a joint venture between Fiat, Lancia and Alfa Romeo. The Giugiaro-styled 9000 lacked the immediate quirkiness of its forebears, but was the right product for the time. Powered by the same four-cylinder engines that had powered the 900 so effectively, the 9000 had plenty of pace and refinement, especially in turbocharged form. Constantly revised, and outliving the rest of the Type Four cars, the ultimate performance models were the 2.3-litre Carlsson and Aero models, which produced 225bhp and can top 150mph.

SPECIFICATIONS

Years produced: 1992-1997
Performance: 0-60mph: 6.5 secs (Top speed: 153mph)
Power & torque: 225bhp / 258lb/ft
Engine: Turbocharged 2290cc in-line four, petrol, electronic fuel injection, 16 valve
Drivetrain: Front-engine FWD
Suspension: [F] Independent, coil spring, wishbone. [R] Dead axle, Panhard rod
Bodyframe: Metal monocoque
Transmission: 5-speed manual
Weight: 1460kgs

PRICE GUIDE

Launch price: £26,995
Excellent: £4000
Good: £3000
Average: £1750
Project: £650

SHELBY
Mustang GT350

The GT350 was the brainchild of former chicken farmer and Le Mans winner, Carroll Shelby. He took near-finished fastback coupés from Ford and reworked them into altogether more convincing sports cars at his California works. Chief among changes was a hike in horsepower from 271bhp to 306bhp from the existing 4724cc V8 engines, in addition to a weightier steering set-up and revised suspension geometry. Most appeared in the Wimbledon White with blue racing stripes, the 350R edition being an off-the-peg competition version.

SPECIFICATIONS

Years produced:	1965-1967 (4117 in total)
Performance:	0-60mph: 6.7 secs (Top speed: 134mph)
Power & torque:	306bhp / 329lb/ft
Engine:	Normally aspirated 4727cc V8, petrol, carburettor, 16 valves
Drivetrain:	Front-engine RWD
Suspension:	[F] Independent, wishbone, coil spring, anti-roll bar. [R] Live axle, leaf spring
Bodyframe:	Chassis and separate body
Transmission:	4-speed manual
Weight:	1265kgs
PRICE GUIDE	
Launch price:	£N/A
Excellent:	£125,000
Good:	£100,000
Average:	£60,000
Project:	£40,000

SIMCA
Aronde

The conventionally-engineered Aronde was the car that carried Simca into the world of constructors, the French firm having hitherto assembled licence-built Fiats (the Aronde retained a Fiat-conceived engine). The model proved popular in its home market, competing strongly with the Peugeot 203, and paved the way for a long line of middle-market Simcas. It was of monocoque construction with a typically soft Gallic ride. Understandably rare in France, rust being a major enemy of these cars, finding one won't be the work of a moment.

SPECIFICATIONS

Years produced:	1951-1964
Performance:	0-60mph: 29.4 secs (Top speed: 73mph)
Power & torque:	45bhp / 61lb/ft
Engine:	Normally aspirated 1221cc in-line four, petrol, carburettor, 8 valves
Drivetrain:	Front-engine RWD
Suspension:	[F] Independent, coil springs. [R] Live axle, semi-elliptic leaf spring
Bodyframe:	Metal monocoque
Transmission:	4-speed manual
Weight:	1140kgs
PRICE GUIDE	
Launch price:	£896
Excellent:	£2750
Good:	£1850
Average:	£1000
Project:	£500

SIMCA
1000/1200 Coupé

In its desire to create a sporting version of the 1000, Simca turned to Bertone – and chief stylist Giorgetto Giugiaro – to fashion this chic coupé's outline. Under the skin, changes from the 1000 saloon were limited to the adoption of all-round disc brakes, with the donor car's robust 944cc engine/gearbox package being carried straight over. The model was upgraded to 1200S specification in 1967, by now packing an 80bhp 1204cc engine. This pert device achieved little in the way of success outside of its homeland, due largely to its maker's near total lack of promotion.

SPECIFICATIONS

Years produced:	1962-1971
Performance:	0-60mph: 13.6 secs (Top speed: 107mph)
Power & torque:	80bhp / 76lb/ft
Engine:	Normally aspirated 1204cc in-line four, petrol, carburettor, 8 valves
Drivetrain:	Rear-engine RWD
Suspension:	[F] Independent, leaf spring. [R] Ind., semi-trailing arm
Bodyframe:	metal monocoque
Transmission:	4-speed manual
Weight:	891kgs
PRICE GUIDE	
Launch price:	£1493
Excellent:	£3200
Good:	£2500
Average:	£1200
Project:	£600

SIMCA
1000 GLS/Special

The Simca Mille was more than a baby car for a generation of young French families; it was a way of life. The rear-engined saloon boasted four doors, reasonable cabin space, as well as a large front luggage compartment. However, handling was 'interesting' due to its rearward weight bias. Later GLS and Special models had additional equipment and were powered by 1.1- and 1.3-litre engines. The improved performance made them easier to live with as a result. These cars suffer from widespread rust but are bulletproof mechanically.

SPECIFICATIONS

Years produced:	1969-1978
Performance:	0-60mph: 16.4 secs (Top speed: 88mph)
Power & torque:	40bhp / 47lb/ft
Engine:	Normally aspirated 944cc in-line four, petrol, carburettor, 8 valves
Drivetrain:	Rear-engine RWD
Suspension:	[F] Independent, leaf springs. [R] Independent, semi-trailing arm
Bodyframe:	Metal monocoque
Transmission:	4-speed manual
Weight:	796kgs
PRICE GUIDE	
Launch price:	£758
Excellent:	£1750
Good:	£1250
Average:	£700
Project:	£250

SINGER
Nine Roadster/4A/4B

Inhabiting the same territory as MG's T-series, Singer's Nine Roadster used the beam axle and leaf spring suspension as found on the Ten and Twelve. It featured a vintage-looking open body with flowing wings and running boards. The 1074cc overhead-camshaft engine of 36bhp was lively enough in this wood-framed tourer although the mechanical brakes left a lot to be desired. 1949's 4A changed the three-speed transmission for one with four ratios, while a year later the 4AB arrived with more compliant coil-over independent front suspension and better brakes.

SPECIFICATIONS

Years produced:	1939-1952 (7623 in total)
Performance:	0-60mph: 37.6 secs (Top speed: 65mph)
Power & torque:	36bhp / 48lb/ft
Engine:	Normally aspirated 1074cc in-line four, petrol, carburettor, 8 valves
Drivetrain:	Front-engine RWD
Suspension:	[F] Independent, coil springs, [R] Beam axle, leaf springs
Bodyframe:	Chassis and separate body
Transmission:	3/4-speed manual
Weight:	840kgs
PRICE GUIDE	
Launch price:	£493
Excellent:	£8750
Good:	£7000
Average:	£4500
Project:	£2500

SINGER
SM 1500/Hunter

For a small company like Singer, the SM1500 saloon was a brave step; its blocky and slab-sided styling reflecting contemporary American trends. However, whatever the good intentions, the result was a very unappealing car with a row of slats instead of a front grille and a very plain appearance. The 1506cc overhead-cam engine was sprightly enough, as was the 1497cc version fitted from 1951 (but which had more power). The 1954 update into the Hunter saw a more attractive and traditional look, with a proper grille but some glassfibre panels.

SPECIFICATIONS

Years produced: 1949-1956 (17,382/4772 in total)
Performance: 0-60mph: 33.7 secs (Top speed: 71mph)
Power & torque: 48bhp / 72lb/ft
Engine: Normally aspirated 1497cc in-line four, petrol, carburettor, 8 valves
Drivetrain: Front-engine RWD
Suspension: (F) Independent, coil spring. (R) Live axle, semi-elliptic leaf spring
Bodyframe: Chassis and separate body
Transmission: 4-speed manual
Weight: 1184kgs

PRICE GUIDE

Launch price: £799
Excellent: £3400
Good: £2600
Average: £1400
Project: £700

SINGER
SM Roadster 4AD

The SM Roadster – a progression of the Nine Roadster – came along in 1951 to fight against MG's TD model, a car it bore rather a striking resemblance to. With an SM1500 overhead-cam engine reduced in size to 1497cc (to allow it to enter under-1500cc motorsport events), it had less power than the MG but similar performance thanks to its light weight. However, the battle lines were more evenly drawn from 1952 when twin carburettors became an option. With the extra carb, 58bhp was the more satisfying output. Some cars had bodies by Bertone, but these are very rare.

SPECIFICATIONS

Years produced: 1951-1955 (3440 in total)
Performance: 0-60mph: 23.6 secs (Top speed: 73mph)
Power & torque: 48bhp / 72lb/ft
Engine: Normally aspirated 1497cc in-line four, petrol, carburettor, 8 valves
Drivetrain: Front-engine RWD
Suspension: (F) Independent, coil spring. (R) Live axle, semi-elliptic leaf spring
Bodyframe: Chassis and separate body
Transmission: 4-speed manual
Weight: 840kgs

PRICE GUIDE

Launch price: £724
Excellent: £9750
Good: £8000
Average: £5500
Project: £3250

SINGER
Gazelle

With the Rootes Group now in control of Singer, the marque was set to become another exercise in badge engineering, pitched between Hillman and Humber in the pecking order. However, in the new Gazelle of 1956 – a plusher version of the Hillman Minx – Singer's 1497cc OHC engine was used at first, but was replaced in 1958 by Rootes' own OHV unit. Saloons, estates (rare and worth 25% more) and convertibles (pay double for those) were all available. Rootes updated the Gazelle almost every year until production ended in 1967, by then it had a 1725cc engine and less curves.

SPECIFICATIONS

Years produced: 1955-1967 (83,061 in total)
Performance: 0-60mph: 21.4 secs (Top speed: 82mph)
Power & torque: 53bhp / 87lb/ft
Engine: Normally aspirated 1592cc in-line four, petrol, carburettor, 8 valves
Drivetrain: Front-engine RWD
Suspension: (F) Independent, coil spring. (R) Live axle, semi-elliptic leaf spring
Bodyframe: Metal monocoque
Transmission: 4-speed manual
Weight: 1043kgs

PRICE GUIDE

Launch price: £898
Excellent: £2650
Good: £2000
Average: £1000
Project: £350

SINGER
Vogue

In Singer form, Rootes' new medium-sized family car was christened the Vogue. Originally intended as a replacement for the Gazelle, this slightly larger car kept the family resemblance and was quite comfortably appointed inside. Powered by a 1592cc OHV engine, Rootes' policy of constant change resulted in front disc brakes from 1962 and a flatter roof and changes to the window arrangement from 1964. A year later, the 1725cc engine from the Humber Sceptre found its way under the bonnet, meaning a generous jump in power to 85bhp.

SPECIFICATIONS

Years produced: 1961-1966 (47,769 in total)
Performance: 0-60mph: 14.1 secs (Top speed: 91mph)
Power & torque: 85bhp / 106lb/ft
Engine: Normally aspirated 1725cc in-line four, petrol, carburettor, 8 valves
Drivetrain: Front-engine RWD
Suspension: (F) Independent, coil spring. (R) Live axle, semi-elliptic leaf spring
Bodyframe: Metal monocoque
Transmission: 4-speed manual, overdrive optional
Weight: 1092kgs

PRICE GUIDE

Launch price: £929
Excellent: £2600
Good: £1950
Average: £850
Project: £300

SINGER
Chamois

Alongside the mainstream Hillman Imp, Rootes also launched sportier versions of its small car. The Singer version, from 1964, was dubbed the Chamois and followed the usual marque policy of walnut veneer inside and extra brightwork outside, including, from 1968, quad headlamps. All models had chrome grilles at the front, for appearance's sake only since the Chamois was rear-engined. Still, it looked good. In 1966 a Sport version was launched. It had a 51bhp engine instead of the standard saloon's 39bhp. From 1967, there was also a pretty fastback Coupé.

SPECIFICATIONS

Years produced: 1964-1970 (97,567 in total)
Performance: 0-60mph: 25.4 secs (Top speed: 78mph)
Power & torque: 39bhp / 52lb/ft
Engine: Normally aspirated 875cc in-line four, petrol, carburettor, 8 valves
Drivetrain: Rear-engine RWD
Suspension: (F) Independent, swing axle, coil spring. (R) Ind. semi-trailing arm, coil spring
Bodyframe: Monocoque
Transmission: 4-speed manual
Weight: 711kgs

PRICE GUIDE

Launch price: £582
Excellent: £2100
Good: £1600
Average: £800
Project: £250

SINGER
New Gazelle/Vogue

Chrysler-controlled Rootes swept aside all its old cars in the latter half of the Sixties and replaced them with the new 'Arrow' range. The boxy design wasn't too imaginative. The new Vogue was a Hillman Hunter given plusher touches and a touched-up nose; a year after its 1966 birth came the Gazelle. The chief differences between the two were that the Vogue had a 1725cc, 68bhp engine while the Gazelle only had 60bhp from its 1496cc engine (unless an automatic, in which case it got the 1725cc engine). Both models were dropped in 1970, along with the Singer name.

SPECIFICATIONS

Years produced: 1966-1970 (79,137 in total)
Performance: 0-60mph: 14.6 secs (Top speed: 90mph)
Power & torque: 61bhp / 81lb/ft
Engine: Normally aspirated 1496cc in-line four, petrol, carburettor, 8 valves
Drivetrain: Front-engine RWD
Suspension: (F) Ind. coil spring, MacPherson strut. (R) Live axle, semi-elliptic leaf spring
Bodyframe: Metal monocoque
Transmission: 4-speed manual
Weight: 955kgs

PRICE GUIDE

Launch price: £798
Excellent: £1950
Good: £1400
Average: £700
Project: £200

SKODA
Felicia Convertible

The Felicia might not have been the most exciting technical package, being based on the Octavia saloon, and it wasn't quick, with just 53bhp on tap. But that didn't stop it being one of the most desirable cars produced in the Soviet Pact countries. A separate chassis and swing axle suspension meant that handling could be unpredictable, but its styling largely made up for the lack of dynamic fizz. It was sold in the UK – the first Skoda to find its way over here – and was met with an apathetic response, despite its low price and overall reliability.

SPECIFICATIONS

Years produced: 1959-1964
Performance: 0-60mph: 24.5 secs (Top speed: 85mph)
Power & torque: 53bhp / 55lb/ft
Engine: Normally aspirated 1089cc in-line four, petrol, carburettor, 8 valves
Drivetrain: Front-engine RWD
Suspension: (F) Independent, coil spring. (R) Live axle, transverse leaf spring
Bodyframe: Chassis and separate body
Transmission: 4-speed manual
Weight: 863kgs

PRICE GUIDE

Launch price: £809
Excellent: £4000
Good: £3250
Average: £1750
Project: £750

SKODA
Octavia

So-called because it was the eighth model line produced by the Czech manufacturer, the Octavia was a rugged, dependable and tough family car. Thoroughly conventional in its engineering, the Octavia was a development of the 1954 440 model. The car was improved during its five-year production run with the 50bhp 1221cc engines in the Super and TS models giving a welcome performance lift over the standard car. Today, there are a surprising number of Octavias still on the road in the UK, and they have an enthusiastic following.

SPECIFICATIONS

Years produced: 1959-1964
Performance: 0-60mph: 29 secs (Top speed: 78mph)
Power & torque: 43bhp / 51lb/ft
Engine: Normally aspirated 1089cc in-line four, petrol, carburettor, 8 valves
Drivetrain: Front-engine RWD
Suspension: (F) Independent, coil spring. (R) Live axle, transverse leaf spring
Bodyframe: Chassis and separate body
Transmission: 4-speed manual
Weight: 920kgs

PRICE GUIDE

Launch price: £745
Excellent: £3500
Good: £2750
Average: £1300
Project: £450

SKODA
1000MB/1100MB

The rear-engined Skoda 1000MB represented the beginning of a very dark period in Skoda's history. It was considered a joke in the West but in its home land, the practical, reliable and easy-to-work-on 1000MB was a car with a waiting list. Of course, that was due to other factors, but what is easily forgotten is that the car, which was basically a reskinned Renault Dauphine, was cheap to buy, cheap to run, and motorised a generation of Czechs and Slovaks. The 1000MB was one of the cheapest new cars you could buy in the UK, and plenty of people did.

SPECIFICATIONS

Years produced: 1965-1977
Performance: 0-60mph: 30.8 secs (Top speed: 78mph)
Power & torque: 48bhp / 55lb/ft
Engine: Normally aspirated 988cc in-line four, petrol, carburettor, 8 valves
Drivetrain: Rear-engine RWD
Suspension: (F) Independent, coil spring. (R) Independent, coil spring
Bodyframe: Metal monocoque
Transmission: 4-speed manual
Weight: 787kgs

PRICE GUIDE

Launch price: £580
Excellent: £2000
Good: £1500
Average: £750
Project: £200

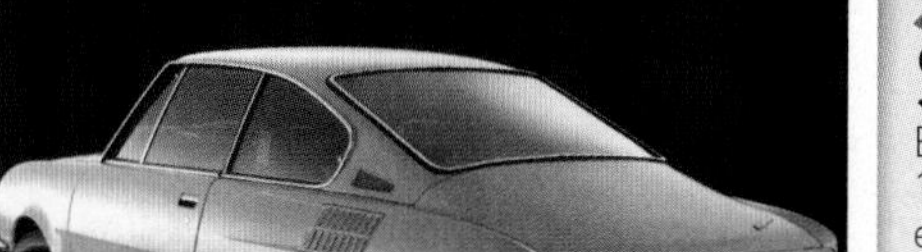

SKODA
S110R

Based on the S100 saloon, which itself was a revised 1000MB, the S110R coupé probably shouldn't have excited too many enthusiasts. However, its introduction in the West coincided with a long rallying career that resulted in class wins on the RAC Rally on an almost annual basis. Powered by a 1107cc water-cooled four, mounted in the rear, the pretty S110R was also great value, even if its swing-axle rear suspension caused a few white knuckles on wet roundabouts. They have a strong following on the classic scene.

SPECIFICATIONS

Years produced: 1970-1980
Performance: 0-60mph: 17.7 secs (Top speed: 90mph)
Power & torque: 52bhp / 64lb/ft
Engine: Normally aspirated 1107cc in-line four, petrol, carburettor, 8 valves
Drivetrain: Rear-engine RWD
Suspension: (F) Independent, coil spring. (R) Independent, coil spring
Bodyframe: Metal monocoque
Transmission: 4-speed manual
Weight: 840kgs

PRICE GUIDE

Launch price: £1050
Excellent: £4750
Good: £3500
Average: £1500
Project: £500

SKODA
Rapid Coupé

In the mid-1980s, Skoda introduced a coupé version of its almost universally-hated Estelle in the UK. No one expected very much of it, least of all Skoda, marketing it strongly as the cheapest coupé in Britain – not a strong message. However, halfway through the life of the Estelle, the rear suspension was improved, taming the handling – and in 1988, *Autocar* magazine put the 136R Coupé on the cover, comparing its handling favourably with the Porsche 911. Few examples remain, and those that do in the UK are cherished by their owners.

SPECIFICATIONS

Years produced:	1984-1991
Performance:	0-60mph: 15.0 secs (Top speed: 95mph)
Power & torque:	61bhp / 74lb/ft
Engine:	Normally aspirated 1289cc in-line four, petrol, carburettor, 8 valves
Drivetrain:	Rear-engine RWD
Suspension:	(F) Independent, coil spring. (R) Independent, coil spring
Bodyframe:	Metal monocoque
Transmission:	5-speed manual
Weight:	920kgs
	PRICE GUIDE
Launch price:	£3751
Excellent:	£3000
Good:	£2200
Average:	£1000
Project:	£300

SS-JAGUAR
SS100

Although not the first car from William Lyons' Swallow Sidecar Company, the SS100 was a landmark in the development of the Jaguar marque. Powered by a 125bhp version of the Standard engine, this pretty roadster had the power to match its looks. Initially conceived as an image-building exercise for competition, the SS100 proved so appealing that buyers flocked to it, and Lyons ended up building over 300. The post-war cars that followed, wearing the Jaguar badge, were direct descendents of this car.

SPECIFICATIONS

Years produced:	1936-1939 (308 in total)
Performance:	0-60mph: 10.4 secs (Top speed: 101mph)
Power & torque:	125bhp / N/A
Engine:	Normally aspirated 3486cc in-line six, petrol, carburettor, 12 valves
Drivetrain:	front-engine RWD
Suspension:	(F) Beam axle, semi-elliptic leaf spring. (R) Live axle, semi-elliptic leaf spring
Bodyframe:	Chassis and separate body
Transmission:	4-speed manual
Weight:	1220kgs
	PRICE GUIDE
Launch price:	£385
Excellent:	£200,000
Good:	£175,000
Average:	£140,000
Project:	£110,000

STANDARD
Flying 8

Standard's small car offering was surprisingly lively considering its one-litre sidevalve engine. Built either side of WW2, the later cars lost the 'Flying' part of their name and are visually distinguished by a lack of bonnet louvres. Perhaps more significantly, they all gained a four-speed gearbox in place of the old three-speed unit. All used Bendix cable brakes, which are fine as long as they are set up correctly. Tourer and drophead coupé models were also offered, but these are even harder to find. When you do, expect to pay at least 50% more than for a saloon.

SPECIFICATIONS

Years produced:	1938-1948 (59,099 in total)
Performance:	0-60mph: N/A (Top speed: 58mph)
Power & torque:	28bhp / 44lb/ft
Engine:	Normally aspirated 1009cc in-line four, petrol, carburettor, 8 valves
Drivetrain:	Front-engine RWD
Suspension:	(F) Independent, leaf spring. (R) Live axle, leaf spring
Bodyframe:	Chassis and separate body
Transmission:	3-speed manual
Weight:	762kgs
	PRICE GUIDE
Launch price:	£314
Excellent:	£4250
Good:	£3250
Average:	£1500
Project:	£500

STANDARD
Flying 12 & 14/12 & 14HP

The 12 and 14hp Standards were introduced in 1936, although revised in 1938 with a notchback instead of fastback appearance. After the hiatus of the war, they bounced back in 1945 with three-inch wider bodies giving more interior space. These sidevalve machines; were simply-engineered but robust. The 12 had a 1609cc engine while the more desirable 14 boasted 1776cc (which gave it a top speed of 70mph), but was initially for export only. The vast majority of 12s and 14s appeared as saloons, although drophead coupés and estates were also available.

SPECIFICATIONS

Years produced:	1936-1948
Performance:	0-60mph: 36.0 secs (Top speed: 65mph)
Power & torque:	44bhp / 69lb/ft
Engine:	Normally aspirated 1609cc in-line four, petrol, carburettor, 8 valves
Drivetrain:	Front-engine RWD
Suspension:	(F) Independent, leaf spring. (R) Live axle, leaf spring
Bodyframe:	Chassis and separate body
Transmission:	4-speed manual
Weight:	1130kgs
	PRICE GUIDE
Launch price:	£480
Excellent:	£5000
Good:	£4000
Average:	£1750
Project:	£600

STANDARD
Vanguard I

With its modern beetle-back styling, the Vanguard replaced Standard's entire range of pre-war offerings in one go – there would be no more small cars from Standard until 1953. A full six-seater with a split windscreen, it introduced the world to the tough wet-liner four-cylinder engine that would go on to power everything from Triumph TRs to Ferguson tractors. Now-rare estate model was introduced in 1950, and all get a lower bonnet line and larger rear window from October '51. Try and find one with overdrive – it makes a big difference to fuel consumption.

SPECIFICATIONS

Years produced:	1948-1953 (184,799 in total)
Performance:	0-60mph: 22.0 secs (Top speed: 78mph)
Power & torque:	68bhp / 108lb/ft
Engine:	Normally aspirated 2088cc in-line four, petrol, carburettor, 8 valves
Drivetrain:	Front-engine RWD
Suspension:	(F) Independent, coil spring. (R) Live axle, leaf spring
Bodyframe:	chassis and separate body
Transmission:	3-speed manual with optional overdrive
Weight:	1188kgs
	PRICE GUIDE
Launch price:	£544
Excellent:	£4000
Good:	£3000
Average:	£1400
Project:	£550

STANDARD Vanguard II

The revised and more conventional three-box styling of the Phase II Vanguard may lack some of the character of the original, but it does provide better headroom and something in the region of 50% more luggage space. Getting in and out is easier too, as the front doors are longer. Suspension is stiffer, but the anti-roll bar has been deleted, so despite wider tyres the handling is still not a Vanguard strong point. With this car, Standard also became the first British manufacturer to offer a diesel engine (with a claimed 37mpg), though surviving examples are rare.

SPECIFICATIONS

Years produced: 1953-1955 (81,074 in total)
Performance: 0-60mph: 19.9 secs (Top speed: 80mph)
Power & torque: 68bhp / 108lb/ft
Engine: Normally aspirated 2088cc in-line four, petrol, carburettor, 8 valves
Drivetrain: Front-engine RWD
Suspension: (F) Independent, coil spring. (R) Live axle, leaf spring
Bodyframe: Chassis and separate body
Transmission: 3-speed manual with optional overdrive
Weight: 1270kgs

PRICE GUIDE

Launch price: £919
Excellent: £3250
Good: £2500
Average: £1200
Project: £450

STANDARD 8/10/Pennant

These were Standard's entries in the popular Minor/A30/Ford 100E market, and they are worthy rivals. The 8 only came with an 803cc engine and was very basically equipped: you didn't even get winding windows until 1954, or an opening bootlid until 1957. The better-selling 10 did have these features from its inception in 1954 (except on the rare base-spec Family 10), and also a 948cc engine. The Pennant is a luxury 10 but with lengthened wings, two-tone paint, hooded headlamps and more equipment. They are outnumbered about five-to-one by the other models.

SPECIFICATIONS

Years produced: 1953-1961 (351,727 in total)
Performance: 0-60mph: 38.3 secs (Top speed: 69mph)
Power & torque: 35bhp / 48lb/ft
Engine: Normally aspirated 948cc in-line four, petrol, carburettor, 8 valves
Drivetrain: Front-engine RWD
Suspension: (F) Independent, coil spring. (R) Live axle, leaf spring
Bodyframe: Metal monocoque
Transmission: 4-speed manual
Weight: 762kgs

PRICE GUIDE

Launch price: £481
Excellent: £2400
Good: £1800
Average: £950
Project: £300

STANDARD Vanguard III

Not only was there an all-new and much lower body for the Phase III, but at last Standard did away with the separate chassis and embraced the concept of monocoque construction. As a result, the new car was lighter, with taller gearing that makes it quicker too. An eight inch longer wheelbase aided ride and handling, but otherwise the running gear was pretty much as before. A curved glass windscreen in place of the old split-screen added another touch of modernity, and from 1957 an automatic gearbox option was available.

SPECIFICATIONS

Years produced: 1955-1958 (37,194 in total)
Performance: 0-60mph: 22.2 secs (Top speed: 77mph)
Power & torque: 62bhp / 113lb/ft
Engine: Normally aspirated 2088cc in-line four, petrol, carburettor, 8 valves
Drivetrain: Front-engine RWD
Suspension: (F) Independent, coil spring. (R) Beam axle, leaf spring
Bodyframe: Metal monocoque
Transmission: 3-speed manual with optional overdrive
Weight: 1194kgs

PRICE GUIDE

Launch price: £850
Excellent: £3000
Good: £2250
Average: £1000
Project: £400

STANDARD Vanguard Sportsman

This sporty variation on the Vanguard theme is the most distinctive car in the range. Never mind the standard two-tone paint – the main standout is that small-mouth grille that looks to have been an inspiration for the MG 1100. It's there because this was supposed to have been a new Triumph, but the company changed its plans at the last minute. It does have a TR3 engine and bigger brakes. A real rarity now, the number of survivors in the UK is thought to be in single figures, hence the large price difference from other Vanguards.

SPECIFICATIONS

Years produced: 1956-1958 (901 in total)
Performance: 0-60mph: 19.2 secs (Top speed: 91mph)
Power & torque: 90bhp / 122lb/ft
Engine: Normally aspirated 2088cc in-line four, petrol, carburettor, 8 valves
Drivetrain: Front-engine RWD
Suspension: (F) Independent, coil spring. (R) Live axle, semi-elliptic leaf spring
Bodyframe: Metal monocoque
Transmission: 3-speed manual
Weight: 1283kgs

PRICE GUIDE

Launch price: £1231
Excellent: £5000
Good: £3750
Average: £1750
Project: £700

STANDARD Ensign/Ensign De Luxe

The Ensign started out as a stripped-down version of the Vanguard, lacking much of that car's chrome trim and using cheaper materials inside. It was also fitted with a small-bore engine of just 1670cc. After four-cylinder Vanguard production ended in 1961, the Ensign was revitalised as the De Luxe. That kept the cheap Ensign's grille, but had more chrome, a larger capacity engine than the Vanguard, and all came with a four-speed floor shift. Overdrive was also an option, and most came with disc brakes too. Unlike the cheap Ensign, there was an estate option for the De Luxe.

SPECIFICATIONS

Years produced: 1957-1963 (18,852/2318 in total)
Performance: 0-60mph: 24.4 secs (Top speed: 78mph)
Power & torque: 60bhp / 91lb/ft
Engine: Normally aspirated 1670cc in-line four, petrol, carburettor, 8 valves
Drivetrain: Front-engine RWD
Suspension: (F) Independent, coil spring. (R) Live axle, leaf spring
Bodyframe: Metal monocoque
Transmission: 4-speed manual
Weight: 762kgs

PRICE GUIDE

Launch price: £900
Excellent: £2650
Good: £1850
Average: £950
Project: £350

STANDARD
Vignale/Luxury Six

That Vignale tag adds a hint of glamour, really this is nothing more than a Vanguard Phase IV. Changes over the previous model were limited to bigger front and rear windows along with a new grille and rear lights, though you also got the option of a floor-mounted gearchange. More significant changes came with 1960's Luxury Six. By now it was all over for the old four-cylinder lump, which has been replaced by the smooth twin-carb straight-six heading for the Triumph 2000. Longer rear springs improved the ride, and disc brakes were offered from 1961.

SPECIFICATIONS

Years produced: 1958-1963 (36,229 in total)
Performance: 0-60mph: 22.2 secs (Top speed: 83mph)
Power & torque: 62bhp / 113lb/ft
Engine: Normally aspirated 2088cc in-line four, petrol, carburettor, 8 valves
Drivetrain: Front-engine RWD
Suspension: (F) Independent, coil spring. (R) Live axle, leaf springs
Bodyframe: Metal monocoque
Transmission: 4-speed manual
Weight: 1194kgs

PRICE GUIDE

Launch price: £1021
Excellent: £3000
Good: £2250
Average: £1200
Project: £400

SUBARU
SVX

Styled by Giorgetto Giugiaro, the Subaru SVX was undoubtedly a handsome car. It was powered by a normally-aspirated flat-6 Boxer engine, and used Subaru's symmetrical all-wheel drive system - standard on all models (apart from the short lived 'base spec' front wheel drive SVX in 1994-95). The sleek shape gave the car an impressive drag coefficient of .29 cd. Only 24,965 SVXs were officially imported into Europe, so finding a genuine UK car can be difficult – the market is rife with grey imports. Engines and drivetrain are strong,

SPECIFICATIONS

Years produced: 1991-1997 (24,965 in total)
Performance: 0-60mph: 8.7 secs (Top speed: 144mph)
Power & torque: 226bhp / 228lb/ft
Engine: Normally aspirated 3319cc flat 6, petrol, electronic fuel injection, 24 valves
Drivetrain: Front-engine AWD
Suspension: (F) Ind. MacPherson strut, anti-roll bar. (R) Ind. MacPherson strut, trailing arm
Bodyframe: Metal monocoque
Transmission: 5-speed manual
Weight: 1600kgs

PRICE GUIDE

Launch price: £27,999
Excellent: £3650
Good: £3000
Average: £2000
Project: £1200

SUBARU
Impreza Turbo

There is no doubt that Subaru really made its name in Europe through rallying. Partnered up with Prodrive, the company created one of the most recognisable rally cars in history, the Impreza Turbo. After Colin McRae won the World Rally Championship in 1995, the Impreza was an instant classic. There are so many different variations of the Impreza, that it can be difficult making sense of it all, but if you avoid grey imports and go for an original UK-spec STi, you can't go far wrong.

SPECIFICATIONS

Years produced: 1993-2001
Performance: 0-60mph: 5.6 secs (Top speed: 143mph)
Power & torque: 215bhp / 214lb/ft
Engine: Turbocharged 1994cc flat 4, petrol, electronic fuel injection, 16 valves
Drivetrain: Front-engine AWD
Suspension: (F) Ind. MacPherson strut, anti-roll bar. (R) Ind. MacPherson struts, anti-roll bar
Bodyframe: Metal monocoque
Transmission: 5-speed manual
Weight: 1235kgs

PRICE GUIDE

Launch price: £21,450
Excellent: £7000
Good: £5500
Average: £3000
Project: £1250

SUNBEAM
Alpine

The original Sunbeam Alpine was a stylish two-seater convertible version of the Sunbeam-Talbot 90. It shared the saloon's effective suspension set-up, but was powered by an 80bhp 2.3-litre in-line-four also used in the Humber Hawk. It was a heavy car, and didn't offer sparkling performance, but it proved good enough to take outright victory in the 1955 Monte Carlo Rally. The Alpine was designed with the American market in mind, hence its soft ride, but failed to make the grade there, dropping out of production after just two years.

SPECIFICATIONS

Years produced: 1953-1955 (3000 in total)
Performance: 0-60mph: 18.9 secs (Top speed: 95mph)
Power & torque: 80bhp / 120lb/ft
Engine: Normally aspirated 2267cc in-line four, petrol, carburettor, 8 valves
Drivetrain: Front-engine RWD
Suspension: (F) Independent, coil spring. (R) Panhard rod, semi-elliptic leaf spring
Bodyframe: Chassis and separate body
Transmission: 4-speed manual
Weight: 1270kgs

PRICE GUIDE

Launch price: £1269
Excellent: £22,500
Good: £19,500
Average: £12,500
Project: £8000

SUNBEAM
Rapier I-V

In design and engineering terms, the Rapier was a two-door version of the Hillman Minx. But the stylish Sunbeam was definitely the glamorous cousin to the family Hillman. During its production run, the Rapier went through four facelifts, starting out with 1494cc and ending up as a rapid 1592cc sporting saloon that continues to prove itself in competition. Like all Rootes Group cars of its era, build quality was good, and the construction tough – and that's why so many survive today, and why the Rapier is such a popular classic choice.

SPECIFICATIONS

Years produced: 1955-1965 (76,954 in total)
Performance: 0-60mph: 21.7 secs (Top speed: 85mph)
Power & torque: 63bhp / 74lb/ft
Engine: Normally aspirated 1390cc in-line four, petrol, carburettor, 8 valves
Drivetrain: Front-engine RWD
Suspension: (F) Independent, coil spring. (R) Live axle, semi-elliptic leaf spring
Bodyframe: Metal monocoque
Transmission: 4-speed manual
Weight: 1070kgs

PRICE GUIDE

Launch price: £1044
Excellent: £5000
Good: £4000
Average: £1750
Project: £700

SUNBEAM
Alpine Sports

The second car to bear the Sunbeam Alpine name was a very different proposition to its more portly predecessor. The new roadster was designed to compete with the MGA and appeal to US buyers. That meant a comfortable interior, and sharp styling, but lack of a suitably sporting power plant and Hillman Husky underpinnings were always going to count against the Alpine. Sales were disappointing, and the final nail in the Alpine's coffin was probably the appearance of the 1.8-litre MGB, which was a far more complete all-round package.

SPECIFICATIONS

Years produced: 1959-1968 (69,251 in total)
Performance: 0-60mph: 14.0 secs (Top speed: 98mph)
Power & torque: 78bhp / 74lb/ft
Engine: Normally aspirated 1494cc in-line four, petrol, carburettor, 8 valves
Drivetrain: Front-engine RWD
Suspension: (F) Independent, coil spring. (R) Live axle, semi-elliptic leaf spring
Bodyframe: Metal monocoque
Transmission: 4-speed manual
Weight: 966kgs

PRICE GUIDE

Launch price: £972
Excellent: £7500
Good: £6250
Average: £3250
Project: £1100

SUNBEAM
Harrington Alpine GT

Made famous at the Le Mans 24 Hour race, the Harrington GT was essentially a Sunbeam Alpine GT with a swept back hardtop that turned the roadster into a pretty-convincing looking coupé. Of course, the reason for that shape was down do aerodynamics, and with the Harrington GT roof on it, the Sunbeam Alpine was faster down the Mulsanne straight than it would have been with the standard-steel hardtop. When the Harrington was sold as a standalone model, though, it struggled on the market, failing to dent the success of the MGB.

SPECIFICATIONS

Years produced: 1961-1963 (425 in total)
Performance: 0-60mph: 12.7 secs (Top speed: 99mph)
Power & torque: 93bhp / N/A
Engine: Normally aspirated 1592cc in-line four, petrol, carburettor, 8 valves
Drivetrain: Front-engine RWD
Suspension: (F) Independent, coil spring. (R) Live axle, semi-elliptic leaf spring
Bodyframe: Metal monocoque
Transmission: 4-speed manual
Weight: 972kgs

PRICE GUIDE

Launch price: £1225
Excellent: £9750
Good: £8000
Average: £4000
Project: £2000

SUNBEAM
Tiger 260

Long before Ken Costello came up with the idea of stuffing an American V8 under the bonnet of a British sports car to produce the MGB GT V8, Rootes came up with the plan of fitting a 4.2-litre Ford V8 in the Sunbeam Alpine, to produce the Tiger. Sales took off in the USA far more than in the UK, where the underdeveloped suspension set-up was far more evident, but before the Tiger got into its stride, the plug was pulled and the car went out of production. Why? Because Chrysler took a controlling stake in Rootes, and its own engine didn't fit in the Tiger.

SPECIFICATIONS

Years produced: 1964-1968 (7085 in total)
Performance: 0-60mph: 7.8 secs (Top speed: 117mph)
Power & torque: 164bhp / 258lb/ft
Engine: Normally aspirated 4261cc V8, petrol, carburettor, 16 valves
Drivetrain: Front-engine RWD
Suspension: (F) Independent, coil spring, wishbone (R) Live axle, semi-elliptic leaf spring
Bodyframe: Metal monocoque
Transmission: 4-speed manual
Weight: 1163kgs

PRICE GUIDE

Launch price: £1446
Excellent: £22,500
Good: £18,000
Average: £12,000
Project: £6000

SUNBEAM
Imp Sport

When Rootes decided to build a hot version of the Imp, it was logical to market it as a Sunbeam, the group's most flamboyant marque. What we got was a car closely related to the original, but thanks to the fitment of twin carburettors and wider wheels, not only was it faster in a straight line, but it was more fun in the corners. Another surprising success given the dominance of the Mini Cooper in the sector, but the Imp Sport's smooth little engine and beautifully set-up engine made it a rewarding drive for press-on drivers. Well worth seeking out now.

SPECIFICATIONS

Years produced: 1966-1976 (10,000 in total)
Performance: 0-60mph: 16.3 secs (Top speed: 90mph)
Power & torque: 51bhp / 52lb/ft
Engine: Normally aspirated 875cc in-line four, petrol, carburettor, 8 valves
Drivetrain: Rear-engine RWD
Suspension: (F) Independent, coil spring. (R) Independent, coil spring
Bodyframe: Metal monocoque
Transmission: 4-speed manual
Weight: 747kgs

PRICE GUIDE

Launch price: £665
Excellent: £2100
Good: £1600
Average: £900
Project: £300

SUNBEAM
Stiletto

Of all the Imp variants offered by the Rootes Group, the Sunbeam Stiletto remains by far the most desirable with collectors. The combination of the Hillman Californian's pretty bodyshell and Imp Sport's engine created a desirable sporting baby. Handling was further improved over the Imp Sport thanks to geometry changes to the front suspension, making this the best of the lot to drive. The jazzed-up interior with bespoke dashboard and reclining seats were further attractions, as was the ever-attractive quad headlamp nose.

SPECIFICATIONS

Years produced: 1967-1973 (10,000 in total)
Performance: 0-60mph: 17.6 secs (Top speed: 87mph)
Power & torque: 51bhp / 52lb/ft
Engine: Normally aspirated 875cc in-line four, petrol, carburettor, 8 valves
Drivetrain: Rear-engine RWD
Suspension: (F) Independent, coil spring. (R) Independent, coil spring
Bodyframe: Metal monocoque
Transmission: 4-speed manual
Weight: 711kgs

PRICE GUIDE

Launch price: £726
Excellent: £2350
Good: £1800
Average: £1150
Project: £400

SUNBEAM
Rapier Fastback

Although its designer, Roy Axe, will tell you that it was pure coincidence that the Rapier looks similar to the Plymouth Barracuda, the resemblance between the half cousins is striking. Based on the Hillman Hunter, but not sharing a single panel, the Rapier (and its cheaper Alpine sister) were striking-looking cars that were well engineered, handled tidily and, in Holbay tuned H120 form, quick. This model died when Chrysler rationalised the range, overshadowed today by its '60s forebear, and undervalued as a consequence.

SPECIFICATIONS

Years produced:	1967-1976 (46,204 in total)
Performance:	0-60mph: 13.2 secs (Top speed: 103mph)
Power & torque:	79bhp / 93lb/ft
Engine:	Normally aspirated 1598cc in-line four, petrol, carburettor, 8 valves
Drivetrain:	Front-engine RWD
Suspension:	(F) Independent, coil spring, lower wishbone. (R) Live axle, leaf spring
Bodyframe:	Metal monocoque
Transmission:	4-speed manual
Weight:	1016kgs
	PRICE GUIDE
Launch price:	£1200
Excellent:	£3500
Good:	£2400
Average:	£1200
Project:	£375

SUNBEAM-TALBOT
80

Introduced in 1948, the Sunbeam-Talbot 80 was the stylish entry level model in a range that didn't fit easily within the Rootes Group. Effectively, Sunbeam-Talbots were touring versions of Humbers and Hillmans and ended up being phased out in favour of the standalone Sunbeam. Although it was a stylish vehicle it was powered by the 1.2-litre engine also found in the Minx, a vehicle not known for its sparkling performance. Despite that, it sold reasonably well to those looking for the style and image of the Sunbeam-Talbot 90 without the price.

SPECIFICATIONS

Years produced:	1948-1950 (3500 in total)
Performance:	0-60mph: 36.4 secs (Top speed: 73mph)
Power & torque:	47bhp / 61lb/ft
Engine:	Normally aspirated 1185cc in-line four, petrol, carburettor, 8 valves
Drivetrain:	Front-engine RWD
Suspension:	(F) Beam axle, semi-elliptic leaf spring. (R) Live axle, semi-elliptic leaf spring
Bodyframe:	Chassis and separate body
Transmission:	4-speed manual
Weight:	1184kgs
	PRICE GUIDE
Launch price:	£889
Excellent:	£6000
Good:	£4000
Average:	£2250
Project:	£800

SUNBEAM-TALBOT
90

With an uninspiring suspension set-up comprising of a beam-axle front and semi-elliptic springs all round, the Sunbeam-Talbot 90 shouldn't have been memorable to drive, and certainly not worthy of the great marque. However, its reasonably powerful 2-litre overhead valve engine upfront produced enough grunt to allow the well set-up chassis to entertain its driver. The MkII of 1950 was a much better effort thanks to its chassis with coils and wishbone suspension, a fact proved in rallying, where the car did rather well.

SPECIFICATIONS

Years produced:	1948-1954 (22,631 in total)
Performance:	0-60mph: 22.5 secs (Top speed: 80mph)
Power & torque:	64bhp / 101lb/ft
Engine:	Normally aspirated 1944cc in-line four, petrol, carburettor, 8 valves
Drivetrain:	Front-engine RWD
Suspension:	(F) Ind. semi-elliptic leaf spring. (R) Live axle, semi-elliptic leaf spring
Bodyframe:	Chassis and separate body
Transmission:	4-speed manual
Weight:	1235kgs
	PRICE GUIDE
Launch price:	£991
Excellent:	£8000
Good:	£6000
Average:	£2750
Project:	£1000

SUZUKI
Cappuccino

Appealing little roadster that emerged during a particularly fertile period in Japanese design. Powered by a mid-mounted 660cc turbocharged three-cylinder engine, the Cappuccino was designed to qualify for Japanese Kei-Car regulations that entitled it to low tax and insurance in its home market. Although a niche car, it proved popular in Europe, where small, light roadsters were at a premium. Today, these cars remain very much in demand, as buyers switch on to their low running costs, reliability and excellent build quality.

SPECIFICATIONS

Years produced:	1991-1997
Performance:	0-60mph: 11.3 secs (Top speed: 93mph)
Power & torque:	63bhp / 63lb/ft
Engine:	Turbocharged 657cc in-line three, petrol, electronic fuel injection, 12 valves
Drivetrain:	Front-engine RWD
Suspension:	(F) Ind. double wishbone, coil spring. (R) Ind. double wishbone, coil spring
Bodyframe:	Metal monocoque
Transmission:	5-speed manual
Weight:	679kgs
	PRICE GUIDE
Launch price:	£11,995
Excellent:	£4200
Good:	£3500
Average:	£2500
Project:	£1200

SWALLOW
Doretti

The Triumph TR2 based Swallow Doretti is one of the most sought-after British specials of the 1950s because of its combination of simple, elegant style, and rugged Triumph TR2 mechanicals. The bodyshell was handbuilt sheet steel skin with aluminium panels attached, mated to a tubular frame chassis. The car was as good to drive as the TR2 it was based on, and the leather-trimmed interior was well-made – but its advantages over the Triumph weren't sufficient enough to warrant the hefty premium.

SPECIFICATIONS

Years produced:	1954-1955 (250 in total)
Performance:	0-60mph: 12.3 secs (Top speed: 100mph)
Power & torque:	90bhp / 117lb/ft
Engine:	Normally aspirated 1991cc in-line four, petrol, carburettor, 8 valves
Drivetrain:	Front-engine RWD
Suspension:	(F) Independent, coil spring, wishbone. (R) Live axle, semi-elliptic leaf spring
Bodyframe:	Chassis and separate body
Transmission:	4-speed manual with overdrive
Weight:	864kgs
	PRICE GUIDE
Launch price:	£1102
Excellent:	£17,500
Good:	£14,000
Average:	£8000
Project:	£4000

TALBOT
Sunbeam 1600Ti

In 1977, and thanks to a UK government bailout, Chrysler UK introduced the Sunbeam. Although it was little more than a shortened Avenger with a stylish new liftback body, the model sold enough to sustain the company's Linwood factory for another five years. Most were dull to drive, but the 1600Ti version was an interesting proposition, as it was effectively, a shortened, lightened Avenger Tiger. Performance was rapid thanks to the 100bhp 1.6-litre engine running twin Weber carburettors, and proved a popular entrant in club-level rallying.

SPECIFICATIONS

Years produced:	1979-1981 (10,113 in total)
Performance:	0-60mph: 10.7 secs (Top speed: 107mph)
Power & torque:	100bhp / 96lb/ft
Engine:	Normally aspirated 1598cc in-line four, petrol, carburettor, 8 valves
Drivetrain:	Front-engine RWD
Suspension:	(F) Independent, MacPherson strut. (R) Live axle, coil spring
Bodyframe:	Metal monocoque
Transmission:	4-speed manual
Weight:	920kgs

PRICE GUIDE

Launch price:	£3779
Excellent:	£4000
Good:	£3250
Average:	£1500
Project:	£750

TALBOT
Sunbeam Lotus

Chrysler commissioned Lotus to produce an effective entrant for international rallying. Lotus took a 1.6GLS shell, installed its own slant-four 2.2-litre 160bhp 16 valve engine and a ZF gearbox, fitted light alloy wheels, and uprated the suspension. It proved effective in rallying, winning the 1980 RAC event. The roadgoing version proved quick and balanced, although it was priced higher than the comparable Vauxhall Chevette HS or Escort RS2000 – and currently, values are a long way ahead of the homologation special-style opposition.

SPECIFICATIONS

Years produced:	1979-1983 (2308 in total)
Performance:	0-60mph: 7.4 secs (Top speed: 121mph)
Power & torque:	150bhp / 150lb/ft
Engine:	Normally aspirated 2174cc in-line four, petrol, carburettor, 16 valves
Drivetrain:	Front-engine RWD
Suspension:	(F) Independent, coil spring. (R) Live axle, coil spring, radius arm
Bodyframe:	Metal monocoque
Transmission:	5-speed manual
Weight:	960kgs

PRICE GUIDE

Launch price:	£6995
Excellent:	£7250
Good:	£6000
Average:	£3250
Project:	£1750

TOYOTA
Celica 1600 ST

When new, these sporting coupés were considered the dynamic inferiors to their European rivals, but considering the A20/35 generation Celica was to the Carina what the Capri was to the Cortina, they were very much the same thing. Sold in huge numbers in Japan and the USA, the Celica was a braver choice over here, although bulletproof reliability made ownership a painless experience. Rust and indifference killed most, but their chitzy mid-Atlantic styling has made these cult cars in the burgeoning Jap car scene.

SPECIFICATIONS

Years produced:	1970-1977
Performance:	0-60mph: 11.5 secs (Top speed: 104mph)
Power & torque:	105bhp / 101lb/ft
Engine:	Normally aspirated 1588cc in-line four, petrol, carburettor, 8 valves
Drivetrain:	Front-engine RWD
Suspension:	(F) Independent, MacPherson strut. (R) Live axle, trailing arm, coil spring
Bodyframe:	Metal monocoque
Transmission:	4-speed manual
Weight:	1100kgs

PRICE GUIDE

Launch price:	£1362
Excellent:	£5250
Good:	£4000
Average:	£1750
Project:	£850

TOYOTA
Celica GT

The facelifted RA25 and R28 Celicas introduced the popular liftback bodystyle (pictured here in American specification), and provided Toyota with the perfect weapon to go Capri chasing. Referred to by many as the 'Mustang' shape car, the GT version was a genuinely quick car with its 124bhp twin cam 1600. Sales were limited due to the high price and lack of badge kudos in the UK. Japanese market cars were also treated to a mighty two-litre Yamaha-headed power unit, dubbed the 18R-GU, that pushed out 134bhp.

SPECIFICATIONS

Years produced:	1974-1977
Performance:	0-60mph: 8.8 secs (Top speed: 120mph)
Power & torque:	124bhp / 113lb/ft
Engine:	Normally aspirated 1588cc in-line four, petrol, carburettor, 8 valves
Drivetrain:	Front-engine RWD
Suspension:	(F) Independent, MacPherson strut. (R) Live axle, trailing arm, coil spring
Bodyframe:	Metal monocoque
Transmission:	5-speed manual
Weight:	1116kgs

PRICE GUIDE

Launch price:	£2345
Excellent:	£6500
Good:	£5000
Average:	£2750
Project:	£1350

TOYOTA
Celica Supra

Known as the Celica XX in Japan, the Celica Supra was heavily based on the Toyota Celica range. The major difference between the two was the use of an in-line six cylinder engine up front, which gave Toyota a direct rival to the Capri 2.8i and Alfa GTV6 in Europe. The power output started out at a reasonable 174bhp, but this rose to 178bhp later in the Supra's life. Even with this power output, the Celica Supra was always more of a luxury barge than a sports car. Once popular in the 'drift' scene, these cars are now emerging as true classics.

SPECIFICATIONS

Years produced:	1982-1985 (863,700 in total)
Performance:	0-60mph: 8.7 secs (Top speed: 131mph)
Power & torque:	168bhp / 169lb/ft
Engine:	Normally aspirated 2759cc in-line six, petrol, mech fuel injection, 12 valves
Drivetrain:	Front-engine RWD
Suspension:	(F) Ind. MacPherson strut, anti-roll bar. (R) Independent, semi-trailing arm
Bodyframe:	Metal monocoque
Transmission:	5-speed manual
Weight:	1265kgs

PRICE GUIDE

Launch price:	£9888
Excellent:	£3600
Good:	£2750
Average:	£1400
Project:	£650

TOYOTA
MR2 MkI

A shock to Japan, and the rest of the world, Toyota brought the mid-engined MR2 to the table in 1984. No Japanese car manufacturer had ever attempted to sell a mid-engined car before. The standard MR2 came with the 1.6 16-valve engine first seen in the Corolla GT, which gave it brisk performance. Sadly, the supercharged MR2 was never officially sold in Europe, but we did get the removable roof panels and improved suspension package from that model. Like most other Toyotas, the MR2 was a very reliable car – the main thing to watch out for is rust.

SPECIFICATIONS
Years produced: 1984-1989 (166,104 in total)
Performance: 0-60mph: 7.7 secs (Top speed: 116mph)
Power & torque: 122bhp / 105lb/ft
Engine: Normally aspirated 1588cc in-line four, petrol, electronic fuel injection, 16 valves
Drivetrain: Mid-engine RWD
Suspension: (F) Independent, coil spring (R) Independent, coil spring
Bodyframe: Metal monocoque
Transmission: 5-speed manual
Weight: 1052kgs
PRICE GUIDE
Launch price: £9295
Excellent: £3250
Good: £2500
Average: £1250
Project: £500

TOYOTA
Supra/Supra Turbo

This was Toyota's third incarnation of the Supra, but unlike the previous two, this 'New' Supra was not directly related to the Celica. Available as a 200bhp normally aspirated in-line-six at launch, the turbocharged version arrived shortly after in 1987, boasting a more impressive 230bhp. The car was very advanced, and offered (as an expensive optional extra) a clever set of electronically controlled dampers. All the gadgets in the world could not disguise the car's weight however, and for this reason the Supra was more of a grand tourer.

SPECIFICATIONS
Years produced: 1986-1993 (970,000/407,950 in total)
Performance: 0-60mph: 6.9 secs (Top speed: 144mph)
Power & torque: 232bhp / 254lb/ft
Engine: Turbocharged 2954cc in-line six, petrol, electronic fuel injection, 24 valves
Drivetrain: Front-engine RWD
Suspension: (F) Independent, wishbone, coil spring. (R) Independent, wishbone, coil spring
Bodyframe: Metal monocoque
Transmission: 5-speed manual
Weight: 1603kgs
PRICE GUIDE
Launch price: £15,299
Excellent: £3500
Good: £2500
Average: £1000
Project: £500

TRIUMPH
1800/2000 Roadster

It's impossible to write this without mentioning the *Bergerac* connection, especially as so many that come up for sale claim to have appeared in the Jersey-based TV detective series. There's reasonable evidence to suggest that five cars did, but don't pay a premium for one without checking its provenance. There were 1800 and 2000 versions, the former using a Triumph unit with a four-speed 'box, the latter adopting more powerful Standard Vanguard running gear, though that means you only get a three-speed gearbox. The stiffer chassis and better brakes make up for it, though.

SPECIFICATIONS
Years produced: 1946-1949 (2501/2000 in total)
Performance: 0-60mph: 24.8 secs (Top speed: 77mph)
Power & torque: 68bhp / 108lb/ft
Engine: Normally aspirated 2088cc in-line four, petrol, carburettor, 8 valves
Drivetrain: Front-engine RWD
Suspension: (F) Independent, coil spring. (R) Beam axle, semi-elliptic leaf spring
Bodyframe: Chassis and separate body
Transmission: 3-/4-speed manual
Weight: 1283kgs
PRICE GUIDE
Launch price: £991
Excellent: £16,000
Good: £14,000
Average: £9000
Project: £4500

TRIUMPH
1800/2000/Renown

Proper coachbuilt cars in the great British tradition, with sharp-edged aluminium bodies on an ash frame, mounted to a steel chassis. The 1800s use a Triumph four-cylinder engine and four-speed gearbox (column-change, as all versions would be) and transverse leaf front suspension. The 2000 was only produced during 1949 and had switched to the Standard 2088cc engine and three-speed gearbox. The Renown saw the same body mounted on a lengthened Standard Vanguard chassis, complete with its coil spring front suspension. From 1952 this was lengthened by three inches.

SPECIFICATIONS
Years produced: 1946-1954 (4000/2000/9301 in total)
Performance: 0-60mph: 25.1 secs (Top speed: 75mph)
Power & torque: 68bhp / 108lb/ft
Engine: Normally aspirated 2088cc in-line four, petrol, carburettor, 8 valves
Drivetrain: Front-engine RWD
Suspension: (F) Independent, transverse leaf spring. (R) Live axle, semi-elliptic leaf spring
Bodyframe: Chassis and separate body
Transmission: 3-speed manual with overdrive
Weight: 1283kgs
PRICE GUIDE
Launch price: £889
Excellent: £6750
Good: £5750
Average: £2750
Project: £1250

TRIUMPH
Mayflower

A peculiar little car with shrunken Roll-Royce styling that doesn't quite fit the short wheelbase. It is, however, roomy and comfortable, and assembled from good-quality materials. As long as you are in no real hurry, the unique-to-this-model aluminium-headed 1250cc sidevalve engine has enough torque to make decent progress, though its maximum speed is 55-60mph. It is very economical though, and enthusiastic club back-up is there to keep it on the road. Just as when it was new, this makes an intriguing alternative to a Minor or Austin Devon.

SPECIFICATIONS
Years produced: 1949-1953 (34,000 in total)
Performance: 0-60mph: N/A (Top speed: 63mph)
Power & torque: 38bhp / 58lb/ft
Engine: Normally aspirated 1247cc in-line four, petrol, carburettor, 8 valves
Drivetrain: Front-engine RWD
Suspension: (F) Independent, coil springs. (R) Live axle, semi-elliptic leaf spring
Bodyframe: Chassis and separate body
Transmission: 3-speed manual
Weight: 914kgs
PRICE GUIDE
Launch price: £480
Excellent: £3500
Good: £2750
Average: £1200
Project: £600

TRIUMPH TR2

Did Triumph know what it was starting? The TR2 practically defined the new wave of British sports cars that came along in the '50s: quick, basic, admirably strong, and under the bonnet, a well-proven engine from a saloon car with an extra carburettor bolted on. Instantly distinguished from later cars by its deeply recessed grille, the TR2 will easily pass 100mph, won rallies in its day, and is still popular for classic rallying. A strong seller, it could be worth hanging out for one built after October 1954. These got shorter doors so you could at last get out next to kerbs.

SPECIFICATIONS

Years produced: 1953-1955 (8628 in total)
Performance: 0-60mph: 11.9 secs (Top speed: 103mph)
Power & torque: 90bhp / 117lb/ft
Engine: Normally aspirated 1991cc in-line four, petrol, carburettor, 8 valves
Drivetrain: Front-engine RWD
Suspension: (F) Independent, coil spring. (R) Live axle, semi-elliptic leaf spring
Bodyframe: Chassis and separate body
Transmission: 4-speed with overdrive
Weight: 838kgs

PRICE GUIDE

Launch price: £787
Excellent: £17,000
Good: £14,250
Average: £8500
Project: £4500

TRIUMPH TR3/3A

The TR3 had been in production for almost a year before it gained its great claim to automotive fame. In September 1956 this became the first production car to be fitted as standard with front disc brakes, beating the Jaguar XK150 by four months. Egg-crate grille marks out the TR3, which also gained an extra 5bhp over the TR2 thanks to larger carbs. Sales were even better, and 90% were exported. The 3A is easily distinguished by its full-width grille and headlamps that were recessed further into the front panel. Public demand brought the welcome addition of external door handles.

SPECIFICATIONS

Years produced: 1955-1961 (13,377/58,236 in total)
Performance: 0-60mph: 11.4 secs (Top speed: 106mph)
Power & torque: 100bhp / 117lb/ft
Engine: Normally aspirated 1991cc in-line four, petrol, carburettor, 8 valves
Drivetrain: Front-engine RWD
Suspension: (F) Independent, coil spring. (R) Live axle, semi-elliptic leaf spring
Bodyframe: Chassis and separate body
Transmission: 4-speed manual with overdrive
Weight: 902kgs

PRICE GUIDE

Launch price: £976
Excellent: £16,000
Good: £13,750
Average: £8250
Project: £4250

TRIUMPH Herald

One of the new small family car stars of the 1959 Motor Show, the Herald was a bit more upmarket than the Mini or Anglia. All that really held it back was the lack of power from its 948cc engine, even in the twin-carb form used in the convertible launched in 1960 (worth a 25% premium) and soon offered as an option for the saloon. There was also a Herald S launched in 1961, but don't go thinking that stands for Sport. It was actually a stripped-out budget model that continued for some time after the 1200 arrived and, though rarer, is the least valuable of the range.

SPECIFICATIONS

Years produced: 1959-1964 (76,860 in total)
Performance: 0-60mph: 31.1 secs (Top speed: 71mph)
Power & torque: 35bhp / 41lb/ft
Engine: Normally aspirated 948cc in-line four, petrol, carburettor, 8 valves
Drivetrain: Front-engine RWD
Suspension: (F) Independent, coil springs. (R) Independent, transverse leaf spring
Bodyframe: Chassis and separate body
Transmission: 4-speed manual
Weight: 870kgs

PRICE GUIDE

Launch price: £702
Excellent: £2400
Good: £1650
Average: £850
Project: £350

TRIUMPH Herald Coupé

By a couple of weeks, this was actually the first Herald model to be launched, and was what Michelotti's Herald prototype had looked like. Initially all Coupés were sold with a twin-carb version of the 948cc engine, though this was increased to a single-carb 1147cc along with the rest of the range in 1961. Front disc brakes became optional just before the engine swap. All but very early cars had strengthening ribs on the hardtop behind the side windows. Though undoubtedly pretty and sought after today, the Coupé proved a poor seller and was discontinued in 1964.

SPECIFICATIONS

Years produced: 1959-1964 (20,472 in total)
Performance: 0-60mph: 23.6 secs (Top speed: 77mph)
Power & torque: 39bhp / 41lb/ft
Engine: Normally aspirated 948cc in-line four, petrol, carburettor, 8 valves
Drivetrain: Front-engine RWD
Suspension: (F) Independent, coil spring. (R) Independent, transverse leaf spring
Bodyframe: Chassis and separate body
Transmission: 4-speed manual
Weight: 749kgs

PRICE GUIDE

Launch price: £731
Excellent: £3000
Good: £2400
Average: £1600
Project: £650

TRIUMPH TR4/4A

Michelotti's radically-restyled body on a widened TR3A chassis so frightened American dealers that they ordered another 3000-odd TR3As for 1962 instead. Everyone else took well to the sharp modern lines, though there were a few purist mutterings about it having gone soft, what with the wind-up windows and face-level air vents (the first British car to have them). Other benefits included rack and pinion steering, all-synchro gearbox and an extra 150cc in engine capacity. From 1964 the TR4A was more of the same, but with independent rear suspension.

SPECIFICATIONS

Years produced: 1961-1967 (40,253/28,465 in total)
Performance: 0-60mph: 11.4 secs (Top speed: 109mph)
Power & torque: 104bhp / 132lb/ft
Engine: Normally aspirated 2138cc in-line four, petrol, carburettor, 8 valves
Drivetrain: Front-engine RWD
Suspension: (F) Independent, coil spring. (R) Independent, coil spring
Bodyframe: Chassis and separate body
Transmission: 4-speed manual with overdrive
Weight: 1016kgs

PRICE GUIDE

Launch price: £968
Excellent: £14,500
Good: £12,000
Average: £7250
Project: £3750

TRIUMPH
Herald 1200

The backbone ordinary model that was easily the Herald range's best-seller and continued almost to the end of production. The 1147cc engine produced less bhp than the smaller twin-carb engine it replaced, but gave much better torque figures, so it always felt more powerful. A higher axle ratio was fitted for easier cruising and this time there's an estate version as well as a convertible. Either of those can command up to 50% more than the saloon. Fittings were more luxurious than earlier Heralds and disc brakes were an option worth looking out for now.

SPECIFICATIONS

Years produced: 1961-1970 (284,256 in total)
Performance: 0-60mph: 28.6 secs (Top speed: 74mph)
Power & torque: 39bhp / 51lb/ft
Engine: Normally aspirated 948cc in-line four, petrol, carburettor, 8 valves
Drivetrain: Front-engine RWD
Suspension: (F) Independent, coil spring. (R) Independent, transverse leaf spring
Bodyframe: Chassis and separate body
Transmission: 4-speed manual
Weight: 800kgs

PRICE GUIDE

Launch price: £708
Excellent: £2400
Good: £1600
Average: £825
Project: £300

TRIUMPH
Vitesse 1600

Largely a Herald with an extra two cylinders, twin headlamps and a beefed up chassis, but then all those things can be considered improvements. Though by far the most numerous Vitesses from a production point of view, the classic car movement came too late to save many and the 1600 is now the hardest to find. The small bore engine was never used in this capacity in another Triumph. Overdrive was an optional extra worth paying more for now, on which subject there was a convertible version that you should budget an extra 35% over the saloon prices quoted here.

SPECIFICATIONS

Years produced: 1962-1966 (31,278 in total)
Performance: 0-60mph: 17.6 secs (Top speed: 91mph)
Power & torque: 70bhp / 92lb/ft
Engine: Normally aspirated 1596cc in-line six, petrol, carburettor, 12 valves
Drivetrain: Front-engine RWD
Suspension: (F) Independent, coil spring. (R) Independent, transverse leaf spring
Bodyframe: Chassis and separate body
Transmission: 4-speed manual with overdrive
Weight: 909kgs

PRICE GUIDE

Launch price: £839
Excellent: £3250
Good: £2500
Average: £1250
Project: £550

TRIUMPH
Spitfire 4/MkII

Inspired by the success of the Frogeye Sprite, and Triumph's firm belief that it could build something better, the Spitfire was born in 1962, after the Frogeye had gone, but in time to tackle the MG Midget head-to-head. With similar performance and the benefit of independent rear suspension it fulfilled that task with great success. Overdrive became an option from October '63, and was something else the Midget never got. The MkII arrived in March 1965 with la new grille and improved interior, but there was an extra 4bhp thanks to a new cam and tubular exhaust manifold.

SPECIFICATIONS

Years produced: 1962-1967 (45,753/37,409 in total)
Performance: 0-60mph: 15.5 secs (Top speed: 92mph)
Power & torque: 67bhp / 67lb/ft
Engine: Normally aspirated 1147cc in-line four, petrol, carburettor, 8 valves
Drivetrain: Front-engine RWD
Suspension: (F) Independent, coil spring. (R) Independent, transverse leaf spring
Bodyframe: Chassis and separate body
Transmission: 4-speed manual with overdrive
Weight: 711kgs

PRICE GUIDE

Launch price: £730
Excellent: £4250
Good: £3500
Average: £2000
Project: £900

TRIUMPH
Herald 12/50

Best thought of as a GT version of the Herald 1200, the 12/50 has become the most popular saloon version as it combines the prettier looks of the early cars with almost the performance of the blander Herald 13/60 that replaced it. A higher compression ratio and other tweaks took power from 39 to 51bhp, disc brakes were standard, as was a Webasto folding sunroof. A fine-barred aluminium grille and '12/50' badges were the only other external giveaways, though you did also get a padded dashtop. Perhaps due to the sunroof, Triumph never built a convertible version.

SPECIFICATIONS

Years produced: 1963-1967 (54,807 in total)
Performance: 0-60mph: 25.2 secs (Top speed: 78mph)
Power & torque: 51bhp / 63lb/ft
Engine: Normally aspirated 1147cc in-line four, petrol, carburettor, 8 valves
Drivetrain: Front-engine RWD
Suspension: (F) Independent, coil spring. (R) Independent, transverse leaf spring
Bodyframe: Chassis and separate body
Transmission: 4-speed manual
Weight: 841kgs

PRICE GUIDE

Launch price: £635
Excellent: £2800
Good: £2100
Average: £1000
Project: £450

TRIUMPH
2000

The demise of the Standard brand saw the Vanguard's replacement wearing a Triumph badge - and bearing no relation to its predecessor apart from the two-litre engine that was passed on. Michelotti's styling took a brave leap into the Sixties, and Triumph now had a credible Rover 2000 rival with all-independent suspension in what would become known as the executive saloon class. A MkII arrived in 1969 with more of an edge to the styling, and longer bonnet and boot. Relatively few estates were built, but they make a practical and interesting classic if you can find one.

SPECIFICATIONS

Years produced: 1963-1977 (219,816 in total)
Performance: 0-60mph: 14.9 secs (Top speed: 96mph)
Power & torque: 84bhp / 100lb/ft
Engine: Normally aspirated 1998cc in-line six, petrol, carburettor, 12 valves
Drivetrain: Front-engine RWD
Suspension: (F) Independent, coil spring. (R) Independent, coil spring
Bodyframe: Monocoque
Transmission: 4-speed manual with overdrive
Weight: 1188kgs

PRICE GUIDE

Launch price: £1412
Excellent: £2600
Good: £1900
Average: £850
Project: £250

TRIUMPH 1300/1500 fwd

This small, well appointed front-wheel-drive saloon was another radical departure for Triumph that it subsequently retreated from. Engine is the same as the Herald 13/60's, but it was joined in 1967 by a twin-carb version in the sportier 1300TC. That got an extra 14bhp, plus a brake servo to help cope with it. Both were replaced by the 1500 in 1970, an elegant restyle that saw the car grow seven inches in length and acquire twin headlamps. Wood and deep carpets added to the attractions, but its days were numbered as Triumph already had a rear-wheel-drive alternative.

SPECIFICATIONS

Years produced: 1965-1973
Performance: 0-60mph: 15.9 secs (Top speed: 93mph)
Power & torque: 75bhp / 75lb/ft
Engine: Normally aspirated 1296cc in-line four, petrol, carburettor, 8 valves
Drivetrain: Front-engine FWD
Suspension: (F) Independent, coil spring. (R) Independent, coil spring
Bodyframe: Metal monocoque
Transmission: 4-speed manual
Weight: 914kgs

PRICE GUIDE

Launch price: £874
Excellent: £1650
Good: £1200
Average: £600
Project: £200

TRIUMPH Vitesse 2-Litre MkI

The whole world loves a small car with more power than is strictly good for it, and that pretty well sums up why a Vitesse costs so much more than a Herald. Though the Vitesse is much more of success now than when it was new and outsold by the Herald by nearly ten-to-one. The 2-litre was an inevitable development of the 1600, as the larger engine was already in use in other Triumphs. As well as taller gearing and wider wheels, the 2-litre was also treated to larger front brake discs. The suspension was left unchanged, and that power can overstretch its abilities.

SPECIFICATIONS

Years produced: 1966-1968 (10,830 in total)
Performance: 0-60mph: 12.6 secs (Top speed: 95mph)
Power & torque: 95bhp / 117lb/ft
Engine: Normally aspirated 1998cc in-line six, petrol, carburettor, 12 valves
Drivetrain: Front-engine RWD
Suspension: (F) Independent, coil spring. (R) Independent, transverse leaf spring
Bodyframe: Chassis and separate body
Transmission: 4-speed manual with overdrive
Weight: 946kgs

PRICE GUIDE

Launch price: £839
Excellent: £3400
Good: £2650
Average: £1350
Project: £550

TRIUMPH TR5/TR250

In a search for greater power and refinement, Triumph dropped a long-stroke version of its six-cylinder engine into the TR4A body and created the 2.5-litre TR5. Most of the world got the Lucas fuel-injected 150bhp engine. America was different. To get round emissions regulations Triumph sent them a twin-carb version with just 104bhp and called it the TR250. It sounds like a terrible idea, but these outsold the TR5 by almost three-to-one. It's not unusual to find examples that have been repatriated to the UK and fitted with the injection engine from the much-less-valuable TR6.

SPECIFICATIONS

Years produced: 1967-1968 (2947 in total)
Performance: 0-60mph: 8.8 secs (Top speed: 120mph)
Power & torque: 150bhp / 164lb/ft
Engine: Normally aspirated 2498cc in-line six, petrol, carburettor, 12 valves
Drivetrain: Front-engine RWD
Suspension: (F) Independent, coil spring. (R) Independent, coil spring
Bodyframe: Chassis and separate body
Transmission: 4-speed with overdrive
Weight: 1029kgs

PRICE GUIDE

Launch price: £1212
Excellent: £27,500
Good: £20,000
Average: £12,000
Project: £6500

TRIUMPH Spitfire Mk III

Instantly recognisable by the raised front bumper (by nine inches) that adds a hint of Lotus Elan, the MkIII Spitfire may count as the only car in history to have its looks improved by trying to meet American regulations. The soft-top is also much improved, in both looks and ease of operation. But the best change lies under the bonnet: a 1296cc engine with an eight-port cylinder head based on the FWD Triumph 1300 unit. This adds up to a 12% power increase (with better economy), so a stronger clutch and larger brake calipers join the party, along with stiffer front springs.

SPECIFICATIONS

Years produced: 1967-1970 (65,320 in total)
Performance: 0-60mph: 14.5 secs (Top speed: 95mph)
Power & torque: 75bhp / 75lb/ft
Engine: Normally aspirated 1296cc in-line four, petrol, carburettor, 8 valves
Drivetrain: Front-engine RWD
Suspension: (F) Independent, coil spring. (R) Independent, transverse leaf spring
Bodyframe: Chassis and separate body
Transmission: 4-speed with overdrive
Weight: 749kgs

PRICE GUIDE

Launch price: £717
Excellent: £4500
Good: £4000
Average: £2250
Project: £1000

TRIUMPH
Herald 13/60

The final and most powerful Herald got a single-carb version of the 1300 engine. That makes it the most useable of the range, and you'll usually find it in any magazine's list of the top ten starter classics, as they combine driveability with ease of maintenance. There's a new dashboard and more space for rear passengers, but the most noticeable change is to a single headlamp version of the Vitesse's bonnet. Saloon production ended in 1970, with convertibles and estates lasting another year. Both can be worth 50% more than saloons.

SPECIFICATIONS

Years produced:	1967-1971 (82,650 in total)
Performance:	0-60mph: 17.7 secs (Top speed: 84mph)
Power & torque:	58bhp / 73lb/ft
Engine:	Normally aspirated 1296cc in-line four, petrol, carburettor, 8 valves
Drivetrain:	Front-engine RWD
Suspension:	(F) Independent, coil springs. (R) Independent, transverse leaf spring
Bodyframe:	Chassis and separate body
Transmission:	4-speed manual
Weight:	838kgs
	PRICE GUIDE
Launch price:	£700
Excellent:	£2500
Good:	£1700
Average:	£900
Project:	£400

TRIUMPH
GT6 MkI/II

Conceived as a Spitfire GT, with the same four-cylinder running gear, it was quickly discovered that the extra weight of the fastback resulted in less performance. The solution was the six-cylinder Triumph 2000 engine, also creating an instant rival for the newly launched MGB GT. An E-type-like bonnet bulge completed the visual move upmarket. Great in a straight line, but that extra power highlights the deficiencies of the MkI's swing-axle rear suspension. Lift-off oversteer means they must be driven with a modicum of respect. An improved system makes the MkII a much better car.

SPECIFICATIONS

Years produced:	1968-1970 (15,818/12,066 in total)
Performance:	0-60mph: 10.0 secs (Top speed: 107mph)
Power & torque:	104bhp / 117lb/ft
Engine:	Normally aspirated 1998cc in-line six, petrol, carburettor, 12 valves
Drivetrain:	Front-engine RWD
Suspension:	(F) Independent, coil spring. (R) Independent, transverse leaf spring
Bodyframe:	Chassis and separate body
Transmission:	4-speed manual with overdrive
Weight:	864kgs
	PRICE GUIDE
Launch price:	£1125
Excellent:	£6500
Good:	£5000
Average:	£2750
Project:	£900

TRIUMPH
Vitesse 2-Litre MkII

Engine revisions left the capacity changed for the MkII Vitesse, but power was up by almost 10%. Thankfully this time Triumph saw fit to revise the rear suspension with lower wishbones, making the handling safer near the limit. Visually, a three-bar grille is the instant giveaway that you're looking at a MkII. It was a poor seller as people were by now attracted to more modern cars like the identically priced Hillman Hunter (how times change). Convertibles are worth a 50% premium, but make sure you buy a real one. The commission plate should have the code 'CV' on it.

SPECIFICATIONS

Years produced:	1968-1971 (9121 in total)
Performance:	0-60mph: 11.3 secs (Top speed: 100mph)
Power & torque:	95bhp / 115lb/ft
Engine:	Normally aspirated 1998cc in-line six, petrol, carburettor, 12 valves
Drivetrain:	Front-engine RWD
Suspension:	(F) Independent, coil spring. (R) Independent, transverse leaf spring
Bodyframe:	Chassis and separate body
Transmission:	4-speed manual
Weight:	927kgs
	PRICE GUIDE
Launch price:	£951
Excellent:	£4250
Good:	£3000
Average:	£1500
Project:	£650

TRIUMPH
TR6

It might look like a new car but all Triumph did was get Karmann to reshape the front and rear panelwork in a more modern style. The doors and windscreen are still TR4. Wider wheels are now more commonly steel with chrome trim rings, and the seats have a bit more padding, but under the bonnet things continued as with the TR5/TR250, with a fuel-injected 150bhp for most of the world and 104bhp with carbs for the US, where most were sold. That differential was reduced in 1972 when the injected cars' output was cut to 125bhp to aid refinement, and US cars were re-rated at 106bhp.

SPECIFICATIONS

Years produced:	1968-1976 (91,850 in total)
Performance:	0-60mph: 8.2 secs (Top speed: 119mph)
Power & torque:	150bhp / 164lb/ft
Engine:	Normally aspirated 2498cc in-line six, petrol, carburettor, 12 valves
Drivetrain:	Front-engine RWD
Suspension:	(F) Independent, coil spring. (R) Independent, coil spring
Bodyframe:	Chassis and separate body
Transmission:	4-speed manual with overdrive
Weight:	1122kgs
	PRICE GUIDE
Launch price:	£1334
Excellent:	£14,000
Good:	£11,000
Average:	£6500
Project:	£3250

TRIUMPH
2.5PI/2500TC/2500S

Think Triumph 2000 with TR5 engine, which made this Britain's first family car to be fitted with fuel injection. After little over a year it got the MkII bodyshell, but neither had the best reputation for reliability – mostly fuel injection problems, though you can expect those to have been sorted out by now. This led Triumph back to using carburettors again in 1974 for the 2500TC, which had 99bhp, lower spec, and was cheaper than the 2.5PI. Then in 1975 the 2500S fully replaced the PI with a 106bhp carburettor engine, stiffer suspension and Stag alloys. This is the one to have.

SPECIFICATIONS

Years produced:	1968-1977 (47,455 in total)
Performance:	0-60mph: 11.5 secs (Top speed: 106mph)
Power & torque:	132bhp / 153lb/ft
Engine:	Normally aspirated 2498cc in-line six, petrol, carburettor, 12 valves
Drivetrain:	Front-engine RWD
Suspension:	(F) Independent, coil spring. (R) Independent, coil spring
Bodyframe:	Metal monocoque
Transmission:	4-speed manual with overdrive
Weight:	1252kgs
	PRICE GUIDE
Launch price:	£1595
Excellent:	£3250
Good:	£2400
Average:	£1250
Project:	£300

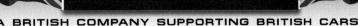

TRIUMPH
GT6 MkIII

Visual changes were made in line with the MkIV Spitfire, though if anything they are more successful on the GT6, whose fastback styling suits the new cut-off tail. At the front, the bonnet bulge remains, in a flatter and wider form. Rear side windows are reprofiled for a cleaner look. There was no significant change to the two-litre power unit, but switching to the DIN standard of power measurement drops quoted power output from 104bhp to 98bhp. The rear axle was changed to the cheaper Spitfire system for 1973 – but you won't notice the difference.

SPECIFICATIONS

Years produced:	1970-1973 (13,042 in total)
Performance:	0-60mph: 10 secs (Top speed: 112mph)
Power & torque:	104bhp / 117lb/ft
Engine:	Normally aspirated 1998cc in-line six, petrol, carburettor, 12 valves
Drivetrain:	Front-engine RWD
Suspension:	(F) Independent, coil spring. (R) Independent, transverse leaf spring
Bodyframe:	Chassis and separate body
Transmission:	4-speed manual with overdrive
Weight:	921kgs
	PRICE GUIDE
Launch price:	£1287
Excellent:	£7250
Good:	£5500
Average:	£3000
Project:	£1000

TRIUMPH
Spitfire MkIV

Michelotti restyled the Spitfire for the 1970s using many cues from the recently launched Stag. Only the sills and door skins were carried over from the MkIII, A change to swing-spring rear suspension made a vast difference to roadholding. The engine is often said to have been de-tuned from Mk3 spec, but in fact only the system of measuring output changed – from SAE to DIN – so the drop from 75bhp to 63bhp was not a real one. The MkIV was slower though, thanks to both extra weight and the taller gearing used to improve economy.

SPECIFICATIONS

Years produced:	1970-1974 (70,021 in total)
Performance:	0-60mph: 16.2 secs (Top speed: 90mph)
Power & torque:	63bhp / 69lb/ft
Engine:	Normally aspirated 1296cc in-line four, petrol, carburettor, 8 valves
Drivetrain:	Front-engine RWD
Suspension:	(F) Independent, coil spring. (R) Independent, transverse leaf spring
Bodyframe:	Chassis and separate body
Transmission:	4-speed manual with overdrive
Weight:	779kgs
	PRICE GUIDE
Launch price:	£985
Excellent:	£4000
Good:	£3400
Average:	£1850
Project:	£750

TRIUMPH
Stag

Triumph's four-seater V8 tourer stumbled at the hurdles marked 'development budget' and 'build quality.' The good news is that all the teething troubles are now well known and a large proportion of surviving Stags have been put together properly, with specialist knowledge. That leaves us free to describe it as a stylish, strong and refined grand tourer that's simple and cheap to maintain and has one of the best exhaust notes this side of a street rod event. Common with a three-speed auto, but the manual/overdrive version is preferred, not just because it uses less fuel.

SPECIFICATIONS

Years produced:	1970-1977 (25,939 in total)
Performance:	0-60mph: 9.7 secs (Top speed: 117mph)
Power & torque:	145bhp / 170lb/ft
Engine:	Normally aspirated 2997cc V8, petrol, carburettor, 16 valves
Drivetrain:	Front-engine RWD
Suspension:	(F) Independent, coil spring. (R) Independent, coil spring
Bodyframe:	Metal monocoque
Transmission:	4-speed manual with overdrive
Weight:	1273kgs
	PRICE GUIDE
Launch price:	£1996
Excellent:	£13,000
Good:	£10,000
Average:	£5000
Project:	£2250

TRIUMPH
Toledo/1500TC/Dolomite

Are you sitting comfortably? The Toledo was a 1300cc rear-wheel drive car that used the front-wheel-drive 1500's body with a shorter nose and tail, but was launched at the same time. These rear-drive underpinning were used in the 1500's replacement, the 1500TC, in 1973. That got the 1500's full-length body. Both were renamed Dolomite in 1976, when you could have either 1300 or 1500 engines and rectangular headlamps, or, for driveway one-upmanship, the 1500HL with twin headlamps, more gauges and a better standard of trim. A cheap starter classic.

SPECIFICATIONS

Years produced:	1970-1981 (220,017 in total)
Performance:	0-60mph: 14.2 secs (Top speed: 91mph)
Power & torque:	71bhp / 84lb/ft
Engine:	Normally aspirated 1493cc in-line four, petrol, carburettor, 8 valves
Drivetrain:	Front-engine RWD
Suspension:	(F) Independent, coil spring. (R) Live axle, coil spring
Bodyframe:	Metal monocoque
Transmission:	4-speed manual
Weight:	980kgs
	PRICE GUIDE
Launch price:	£2441
Excellent:	£1750
Good:	£1250
Average:	£700
Project:	£200

TRIUMPH
Dolomite 1850

A woefully under-rated sporting saloon that was a genuine BMW contender in its day, but has come to be overshadowed by the Sprint. In essence it's a 1500TC fitted with an 1854cc version of the overhead-cam slant-four engine Triumph had been building for the Saab 99. Wishbone front suspension and live rear axle was all very conventional, but tightened up for the 1850 it created a sweet-handling and friendly machine that could be driven hard. Plusher 1850HL from 1976, and from 1973 all could be had with automatic transmission or manual with overdrive.

SPECIFICATIONS

Years produced:	1972-1980 (79,010 in total)
Performance:	0-60mph: 11.6 secs (Top speed: 100mph)
Power & torque:	91bhp / 105lb/ft
Engine:	Normally aspirated 1854cc in-line four, petrol, carburettor, 8 valves
Drivetrain:	Front-engine RWD
Suspension:	(F) Independent, coil springs. (R) Live axle, coil springs
Bodyframe:	Metal monocoque
Transmission:	4-speed manual with overdrive
Weight:	965kgs
	PRICE GUIDE
Launch price:	£1399
Excellent:	£2100
Good:	£1500
Average:	£850
Project:	£250

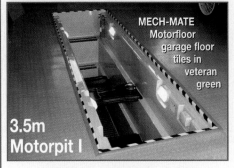

TRIUMPH
Dolomite Sprint

With a strong background in touring car racing winning it the accolade of BL's most successful competition car of the Seventies, by rights the Dolomite Sprint should be valued as highly as its old rivals: Alfa GTV, BMW 2002tii or Escort RS2000. But it's not, which must make it a bargain. Those others may all be two-doors, but the Dolly is the only one with a 16-valve head. Well equipped in street trim, they come with plenty of wood trim, tinted glass, overdrive as standard from May 1975, plus that most 1970s of items, a vinyl roof. With around 400 UK survivors, choice is good.

SPECIFICATIONS

Years produced: 1973-1980 (22,941 in total)
Performance: 0-60mph: 8.7 secs (Top speed: 115mph)
Power & torque: 127bhp / 124lb/ft
Engine: Normally aspirated 1998cc in-line four, petrol, carburettor, 16 valves
Drivetrain: Front-engine RWD
Suspension: (F) Independent, coil spring. (R) Beam axle, coil spring
Bodyframe: Monocoque
Transmission: 4-speed manual with overdrive
Weight: 1004kgs

PRICE GUIDE

Launch price: £1740
Excellent: £5000
Good: £4000
Average: £2000
Project: £500

TRIUMPH
Spitfire 1500

Aside from the very obvious Spitfire 1500 decals on the nose and tail, you'd need to be a devout anorak-wearer to spot the external differences between this and a MkIV. Silver rather than black wheel centres are probably the most obvious. The real change comes under the bonnet. The new capacity came from a longer stroke crankshaft which rather blunted the engine's will to rev, and made life tougher for the crank bearings, but it punches out a lot more mid-range power and the taller gearing it allowed made the Spitfire a genuine 100mph car at last.

SPECIFICATIONS

Years produced: 1974-1980 (91,137 in total)
Performance: 0-60mph: 13.2 secs (Top speed: 100mph)
Power & torque: 71bhp / 82lb/ft
Engine: Normally aspirated 1493cc in-line four, petrol, carburettor, 8 valves
Drivetrain: Front-engine RWD
Suspension: (F) Independent, coil spring. (R) Independent, transverse leaf spring
Bodyframe: Chassis and separate body
Transmission: 4-speed with overdrive
Weight: 794kgs

PRICE GUIDE

Launch price: £1360
Excellent: £4400
Good: £3500
Average: £2000
Project: £750

TRIUMPH
TR7

After the TR6 this was a disappointment for purists, having gained a roof but lost two cylinders, 500cc and independent rear suspension. It really wasn't a true TR, until the convertible version arrived in 1979 – those initials simply meant Triumph Roadster. But for all the criticism over these points and the still controversial 'wedge' styling, it sold faster than the TR6 had ever done. It's a much easier car to live with, driving more like a two-seater saloon than a sports car. It's also by far the cheapest way to join the ranks of Triumph TR ownership.

SPECIFICATIONS

Years produced: 1975-1981 (112,375 in total)
Performance: 0-60mph: 9.1 secs (Top speed: 109mph)
Power & torque: 105bhp / 119lb/ft
Engine: Normally aspirated 1998cc in-line four, petrol, carburettor, 8 valves
Drivetrain: Front-engine RWD
Suspension: (F) Independent, coil spring. (R) Live axle, coil spring
Bodyframe: Metal monocoque
Transmission: 4/5-speed manual/3-speed auto
Weight: 1000kgs

PRICE GUIDE

Launch price: £3000
Excellent: £3000
Good: £2000
Average: £1000
Project: £400

TRIUMPH
TR8

This was the car the TR7 should have been – it was designed to accept the Rover V8 engine from the outset. Sadly it arrived too late, was in production for less than two years and nearly all were left-hand drive examples for the US market. A handful of UK cars escaped into the wild – many more have since been created on a DIY basis (you can buy a kit from Rimmer Bros). Some price guides carry an entry for these conversions. There are few other differences apart from bigger brakes, radiator and modified crossmember. They might not be original, but are probably the best bet for UK buyers.

SPECIFICATIONS

Years produced: 1979-1981 (2722 in total)
Performance: 0-60mph: 8.4 secs (Top speed: 120mph)
Power & torque: 137bhp / 168lb/ft
Engine: Normally aspirated 3528cc V8, petrol, mechanical fuel injection, 16 valves
Drivetrain: Front-engine RWD
Suspension: (F) Ind. MacPherson strut, lower wishbone. (R) Live axle, trailing arms
Bodyframe: Metal monocoque
Transmission: 5-speed manual
Weight: 1163kgs

PRICE GUIDE

Launch price: £N/A
Excellent: £11,000
Good: £9750
Average: £6000
Project: £3000

TURNER
803/950 Sports

Jack Turner started out making specials, but such was the quality of his work that others would ask him to make cars for them. Before he knew it, he'd become a car constructor. The 803 and 950 Sports were powered by Austin A30 and A35 A-series engines, and suspension was by torsion bars and trailing arms. It was a simple but effective recipe, that appeared a while before the Austin-Healey Sprite. BMC ended up refusing to supply parts directly, pushing up the price of the final product, but like all Turners, it was available in kit form.

SPECIFICATIONS

Years produced: 1955-1959 (260 in total)
Performance: 0-60mph: 12.0 secs (Top speed: 94mph)
Power & torque: 34bhp / 50lb/ft
Engine: Normally aspirated 803cc in-line four, petrol, carburettor, 8 valves
Drivetrain: Front-engine RWD
Suspension: (F) Independent, coil spring. (R) Live axle, torsion bar
Bodyframe: Spaceframe
Transmission: 4-speed manual
Weight: 560kgs

PRICE GUIDE

Launch price: £789
Excellent: £6000
Good: £4500
Average: £2750
Project: £1000

TURNER
Climax

All Turners shared the same ingredients as the original 803 Sports, and from the 950 Sports onwards, the excellent Climax FWA and 1220cc 90bhp FWE engines were made an optional extra to create the Turner-Climax. Considering it was a low volume special, the Turner-Climax was very well finished, and drove every bit as well as the Austin-Healey Sprite that it was often compared against. In truth, the special car was far quicker, but because it cost at least a third more than its BMC rival, sales were slow.

SPECIFICATIONS

Years produced:	1959-1966
Performance:	0-60mph: 12.8 secs (Top speed: 99mph)
Power & torque:	85bhp / 75lb/ft
Engine:	Normally aspirated 1216cc in-line four, petrol, carburettor, 8 valves
Drivetrain:	Front-engine RWD
Suspension:	(F) Independent, coil spring. (R) Live axle, torsion bar
Bodyframe:	Spaceframe
Transmission:	4-speed manual
Weight:	600kgs
	PRICE GUIDE
Launch price:	£N/A
Excellent:	£12,000
Good:	£10,000
Average:	£6250
Project:	£3000

TURNER
MkI/II/III

Of all the Turners, it was this model that sold the most. In 1960, the Austin A30 front suspension was replaced by Triumph Herald coil springs and double wishbones to give a more compliant ride. The curvaceous body styling largely remained intact, although the bonnet scoop fitted to accommodate the larger engines now being fitted took away some of the design purity of the older cars. Ford engines replaced the BMC A-series for the basic models – with most Turners being fitted with Anglia and Cortina power units. Back to basics thrills.

SPECIFICATIONS

Years produced:	1959-1966 (400 in total)
Performance:	0-60mph: 12.0 secs (Top speed: 90mph)
Power & torque:	34bhp / N/A
Engine:	Normally aspirated 948cc in-line four, petrol, carburettor, 8 valves
Drivetrain:	Front-engine RWD
Suspension:	(F) Independent, coil spring. (R) Live axle, coil spring
Bodyframe:	Spaceframe
Transmission:	4-speed manual
Weight:	612kgs
	PRICE GUIDE
Launch price:	£840
Excellent:	£8500
Good:	£6500
Average:	£4000
Project:	£1750

TVR
Grantura I-1800S

Trevor Wilkinson's company started out like so many other sports car manufacturers in the UK – marrying lightweight special bodies with tried-and-tested mechanicals to produce affordable kit cars that could be enjoyed by many. What set TVR apart, though, was its staying power, and most of that was down to the appeal of early models like the Grantura, and the sheer number of permutations you could buy it in – with engines ranging from the 1172cc Ford Popular engine to the 1798cc twin carburettor MGB engine, there was bound to be a TVR for you.

SPECIFICATIONS

Years produced:	1957-1967 (800 approx in total)
Performance:	0-60mph: 10.0 secs (Top speed: 111mph)
Power & torque:	95bhp / N/A
Engine:	Normally aspirated 1799cc in-line four, petrol, carburettor, 8 valves
Drivetrain:	front-engine RWD
Suspension:	(F) Torsion bar. (R) Live axle, torsion bar.
Bodyframe:	Chassis and glassfibre body
Transmission:	4-speed manual
Weight:	864kgs
	PRICE GUIDE
Launch price:	£1426
Excellent:	£10,000
Good:	£8000
Average:	£4500
Project:	£2750

TVR
Griffith V8

American racing driver Jack Griffith approached TVR with a proposal to produce a V8-engined Grantura for competition. TVR agreed and supplied Grantura bodies and chassis for Griffith to fit 4727cc Ford V8s in to. These cars were badged as the Griffith in the USA and were offered with either a manual or automatic gearbox. Performance was predictably swift. Some models could top 150mph and hit 60 in around six seconds. In truth, they were overpowered – and only remained in production for a couple of years. A great idea for the future, though...

SPECIFICATIONS

Years produced:	1963-1965 (300 in total)
Performance:	0-60mph: 6.9 secs (Top speed: 140mph)
Power & torque:	195bhp / 282lb/ft
Engine:	Normally aspirated 4727cc V8, petrol, carburettor, 16 valves
Drivetrain:	Front-engine RWD
Suspension:	(F) Ind, double wishbone, coil spring. (R) Ind, double wishbone, coil spring
Bodyframe:	Chassis and glassfibre body
Transmission:	4-speed manual
Weight:	864kgs
	PRICE GUIDE
Launch price:	£1620
Excellent:	£25,000
Good:	£20,000
Average:	£15,000
Project:	£9000

TVR
Tuscan V6

Here's a car that probably deserves greater respect and collector interest than it currently receives, especially with such low build numbers. And if the Tuscan looks rather like the Vixen, that's because in effect it is one, but with a Ford three-litre V6 from the Zodiac, plus larger brakes and a heavy-duty rear axle. Uncompromisingly sporty, it's light, rides hard and delivers strong performance with very acceptable economy figures, especially if fitted with the optional overdrive gearbox. Can be hard to find, but worth the effort.

SPECIFICATIONS

Years produced:	1969-1971 (101 in total)
Performance:	0-60mph: 8.3 secs (Top speed: 125mph)
Power & torque:	128bhp / 173lb/ft
Engine:	Normally aspirated 2994cc V6, petrol, carburettor, 12 valves
Drivetrain:	Front-engine RWD
Suspension:	(F) Independent, coil spring. (R) Independent, coil spring
Bodyframe:	Spaceframe
Transmission:	4-speed manual with overdrive
Weight:	907kgs
	PRICE GUIDE
Launch price:	£1930
Excellent:	£6750
Good:	£5500
Average:	£3500
Project:	£2000

TVR
Vixen S1-S4

Early Vixens were really just Granturas with a Cortina GT engine in place of the old MGB unit. The improved S2 from October 1968 came with a longer wheelbase - and longer doors to go with it. It is easily distinguishable by its Cortina MkII tail-lights. A year later the S3 brought further upgrades, including a Capri-spec engine, cast alloy wheels, and grilles to cover the engine bay cooling vents. Twenty-three S4 Vixens were built on the new M-series chassis to use up old bodies. Quite quick, but with a hard ride and quite twitchy handling.

SPECIFICATIONS

Years produced:	1970-1972 (746 in total)
Performance:	0-60mph: 10.5 secs (Top speed: 109mph)
Power & torque:	88bhp / 96lb/ft
Engine:	Normally aspirated 1599cc in-line four, petrol, carburettor, 8 valves
Drivetrain:	Front-engine RWD
Suspension:	(F) Independent, coil spring. (R) Independent, coil spring
Bodyframe:	Spaceframe
Transmission:	4-speed manual
Weight:	762kgs
	PRICE GUIDE
Launch price:	£1387
Excellent:	£6500
Good:	£5000
Average:	£3250
Project:	£1500

TVR
2500/3000M

The need for two different engines in the Tuscan's replacement was due to the UK market's three-litre Ford V6 not meeting US emissions standards. So cars heading that way were fitted with the already-approved TR6 engine, with carburettors and smog gear, and quite a few bhp less than the fuel-injected versions the UK was used to. Though most of those went to America, a few did find British homes, but 3000Ms are what you will mostly find. Thanks to the TR6's demise, 2500M production ended in 1977. The 3000M soldiered on for another two years.

SPECIFICATIONS

Years produced:	1971-1979 (947/654 in total)
Performance:	0-60mph: 7.7 secs (Top speed: 124mph)
Power & torque:	86bhp / 92lb/ft
Engine:	Normally aspirated 1599cc in-line six, petrol, carburettor, 12 valves
Drivetrain:	Front-engine RWD
Suspension:	(F) Independent coil spring. (R) Independent coil spring
Bodyframe:	Spaceframe
Transmission:	4-speed manual
Weight:	907kgs
	PRICE GUIDE
Launch price:	£2170
Excellent:	£6900
Good:	£5500
Average:	£3750
Project:	£2000

TVR
1600M

Cleverly restyled from the waist down, the M-series TVRs (the M is for TVR boss Martin Lilley) were wider and nine inches longer, mostly in the nose, and built on a dynamically improved, stronger and better protected chassis. Still using the Capri GT 'Kent' engine, the 1600M was a poor seller compared to its more powerful brethren and was dropped in 1973 after less than a year on sale, but reintroduced with a mild restyle and bigger alloys in 1975 in the wake of an energy crisis. The return of such concerns once again makes the 1600M an interesting alternative.

SPECIFICATIONS

Years produced:	1972-1977 (148 in total)
Performance:	0-60mph: 10.4 secs (Top speed: 106mph)
Power & torque:	86bhp / 92lb/ft
Engine:	Normally aspirated 1599cc in-line four, petrol, carburettor, 8 valves
Drivetrain:	Front-engine RWD
Suspension:	(F) Ind. double wishbone, anti-roll bar. (R) Ind. double wishbone, coils springs
Bodyframe:	Spaceframe
Transmission:	4-speed manual
Weight:	907kgs
	PRICE GUIDE
Launch price:	£1886
Excellent:	£6000
Good:	£4750
Average:	£3000
Project:	£1750

TVR
Taimar

Sold alongside the 3000M for three years, the Taimar finally answered a long-asked question of TVRs and provided proper external access to the boot via a large hatchback. A vast improvement compared to leaning over the seats. This added a mere 9kgs in extra weight, and otherwise the cars were identical. Their appeal was obvious and despite a price premium, the Taimar was a strong seller. Of special note is the Taimar Turbo, of which around 30 were built. Alongside a handful of 3000Ms, these were the first British production cars to be turbocharged. Prices are commensurately higher.

SPECIFICATIONS

Years produced:	1976-1979 (395 in total)
Performance:	0-60mph: 7.7 secs (Top speed: 121mph)
Power & torque:	142bhp / 174lb/ft
Engine:	Normally aspirated 2994cc V6, petrol, carburettor, 12 valves
Drivetrain:	Front-engine RWD
Suspension:	(F) Independent, coil spring. (R) Independent, coil spring
Bodyframe:	Spaceframe
Transmission:	4-speed manual
Weight:	1025kgs
	PRICE GUIDE
Launch price:	£4260
Excellent:	£6500
Good:	£5250
Average:	£3750
Project:	£2250

TVR
3000S

Soft-top version of the 3000M, called simply Convertible at the time, but it was no simple roof-chop. In fact not much more than the chassis, engine and bonnet are shared. The windscreen is new, and the roof detaches completely to stow in the boot. Removing the side windows leaves cutaways in the doors at comfortable elbow height. Even the dashboard joins in the game, with centrally-mounted instruments. Underneath, all Convertibles got a much stronger XJ6 rear axle as supplies of the TR6 unit used in the 3000M had dried up.

SPECIFICATIONS

Years produced:	1978-1979 (258 in total)
Performance:	0-60mph: 7.7 secs (Top speed: 125mph)
Power & torque:	142bhp / 174lb/ft
Engine:	Normally aspirated 2994cc V6, petrol, carburettor, 12 valves
Drivetrain:	Front-engine RWD
Suspension:	(F) Independent coil spring. (R) Independent coil spring
Bodyframe:	Spaceframe
Transmission:	4-speed manual
Weight:	1098kgs
	PRICE GUIDE
Launch price:	£6390
Excellent:	£10,000
Good:	£8000
Average:	£5000
Project:	£3000

TVR
Tasmin/280i

All change for the 1980s as TVR adopt radical new wedge-shaped bodies from the pen of former Lotus designer Oliver Winterbottom. Launched as a two-seater coupé, the range expanded with a 2+2 and convertible in 1981. The former was short lived, but when it was dropped, the larger body, sans rear seats, was used for the coupé. Engine was from Ford again – the Cologne V6 from the Capri 2.8i. From 1983 a five-speed gearbox was introduced; the following year the Tasmin was rebadged 280i. There was a Pinto-powered Tasmin 200 for a short time, but this was not popular.

SPECIFICATIONS

Years produced:	1981-1988
Performance:	0-60mph: 9.7 secs (Top speed: 134mph)
Power & torque:	145bhp / 150lb/ft
Engine:	Normally aspirated 2792cc V6, petrol, electronic fuel injection, 12 valves
Drivetrain:	Front-engine RWD
Suspension:	(F) Ind. coils spring, anti-roll bar. (R) Ind. trailing arm, coil spring
Bodyframe:	Spaceframe
Transmission:	5-speed manual
Weight:	1143kgs
	PRICE GUIDE
Launch price:	£15,540
Excellent:	£6000
Good:	£4000
Average:	£2250
Project:	£1250

TVR
350i

The arrival of Peter Wheeler at the helm of TVR brought excitement to the marque. He started by bolting a Rover V8 into the Tasmin, (it was known as the Tasmin V8 at first, then simplified to 350i). Tubular exhaust manifolds turned up the volume to what would become a TVR trademark, the much lighter engine, along with revisions to the suspension, brought a significant handling improvement. There was a Series II version from 1985 with larger rear lights and a lack of bonnet vents. Perhaps surprisingly there's only around a 10% premium for the convertible.

SPECIFICATIONS

Years produced:	1983-1986
Performance:	0-60mph: 6.5 secs (Top speed: 134mph)
Power & torque:	197bhp / 220lb/ft
Engine:	Normally aspirated 3528cc V8, petrol, electronic fuel injection, 16 valves
Drivetrain:	Front-engine RWD
Suspension:	(F) Ind, double wishbone, coil spring. (R) Ind, lower wishbone, coil spring
Bodyframe:	Spaceframe
Transmission:	5-speed manual
Weight:	1004kgs
	PRICE GUIDE
Launch price:	£16,975
Excellent:	£6500
Good:	£4750
Average:	£2750
Project:	£1500

TVR
390/420SE

With the Rover V8 bored out to 3.9 litres and expertly fiddled with by racer Andy Rouse to extract serious horsepower, TVR's wedge really staked its claim as a performance car. To prevent it being too much of a handful, the rear axle received a Torsen limited-slip diff, ducts were added for brake cooling, and the aerodynamics were tweaked to keep the wheels in better touch with the tarmac. The result was raved about in the press, but 390SE sales were restricted by it being more expensive than a Lotus Esprit, without the heritage. All models were convertibles.

SPECIFICATIONS

Years produced:	1985-1988
Performance:	0-60mph: 4.9 secs (Top speed: 144mph)
Power & torque:	275bhp / 270lb/ft
Engine:	Normally aspirated 3905cc V8, petrol, mechanical fuel injection, 16 valves
Drivetrain:	Front-engine RWD
Suspension:	(F) Ind, double wishbone, coil spring (R) Ind, wishbone, coil spring
Bodyframe:	Spaceframe
Transmission:	5-speed manual
Weight:	1107kgs
	PRICE GUIDE
Launch price:	£19,700
Excellent:	£7500
Good:	£6250
Average:	£4250
Project:	£2500

TVR
420/450 SEAC

The AC on the end stands for Aramid Composite, which translates to mean a body created using much carbon fibre and Kevlar to shave off a lot of weight. Racing version cemented TVR's bad-boy image – it was banned for being too fast, a marketing man's dream ticket. Around 40 of the 300bhp 420SEACs were built, along with another 17 of the 450 version, which added another 25bhp. The huge rear wing does nothing for the car's appearance, but an awful lot for high-speed stability. Rumours abound of upgraded SEs, so make sure you buy the real thing.

SPECIFICATIONS

Years produced:	1986-1988 (40/17 in total)
Performance:	0-60mph: 5.0 secs (Top speed: 165mph)
Power & torque:	300bhp / 290lb/ft
Engine:	Normally aspirated 4228cc V8, petrol, carburettor, 16 valves
Drivetrain:	Front-engine RWD
Suspension:	(F) Independent coil spring. (R) Independent coil spring
Bodyframe:	Spaceframe
Transmission:	5-speed manual
Weight:	1130kgs
	PRICE GUIDE
Launch price:	£31,000
Excellent:	£12,500
Good:	£10,000
Average:	£8000
Project:	£6000

TVR
S1-S3

The Convertible S range was introduced as an entry-level traditional sports car, specifically aimed at those who thought TVRs had grown too fast and too expensive. Pitched 30% cheaper than the 350i, they found a ready market. Early versions used the same Ford 2.8-litre Cologne V6 as the 280i, but this was replaced from 1988 in the S2 by Ford's new 2.9-litre Granada V6. For 1990, the S3 got a better interior and four-inch longer doors for easier access. There were also around 40 S4Cs – basically a V8S with the V6 engine fitted.

SPECIFICATIONS

Years produced:	1986-1994
Performance:	0-60mph: 7.6 secs (Top speed: 128mph)
Power & torque:	160bhp / 162lb/ft
Engine:	Normally aspirated 2792cc V6, petrol, electronic fuel injection, 12 valves
Drivetrain:	Front-engine RWD
Suspension:	(F) Independent, coil spring (R)Independent, coil spring
Bodyframe:	Spaceframe
Transmission:	5-speed manual
Weight:	987kgs
	PRICE GUIDE
Launch price:	£12,995
Excellent:	£7250
Good:	£5500
Average:	£3500
Project:	£1600

TVR 400/450SE

These bigger engined TVRs succeeded the 390/420SE and were in effect glassfibre versions of the lightweight SEAC cars, aimed at those with a little less money and a little more sanity. Not that they were that much slower, as you can see from the figures. They can prove to be quite a handful on a wet road too, so it's not a bad idea to check the car and its history for past accident damage. Interiors were improved, with better seats and materials, and more curves. TVRs were getting away from the hint of kit-car that had affected their earlier offerings.

SPECIFICATIONS

Years produced:	1988-1991
Performance:	0-60mph: 5.0 secs (Top speed: 150mph)
Power & torque:	275bhp / 270lb/ft
Engine:	Normally aspirated 3998cc V8, petrol, carburettor, 16 valves
Drivetrain:	Front-engine RWD
Suspension:	(F) Independent, wishbone, coil spring. (R) Independent, wishbone, coil spring
Bodyframe:	Spaceframe
Transmission:	5-speed manual
Weight:	1150kgs
	PRICE GUIDE
Launch price:	£24,995
Excellent:	£10,250
Good:	£8500
Average:	£6000
Project:	£4000

TVR V8S

It was inevitable that the Rover V8 would find its way into an 'S', and it proved an effective way to bridge the gap between the outgoing 'wedges' and the new generation of TVRs that kicked off properly in 1992. That's not to dismiss the V8S, which is a fantastic car in its own right, benefiting from a stiffer chassis, rear disc brakes, larger front ones and a limited-slip diff. A large bonnet bulge sets it apart from the V6-engined S-series cars, but on the road the V8S is streets ahead and should be considered more of a match for the Chimaera that replaced it.

SPECIFICATIONS

Years produced:	1991-1993
Performance:	0-60mph: 4.9 secs (Top speed: 146mph)
Power & torque:	240bhp / 275lb/ft
Engine:	Normally aspirated 3948cc V8, petrol, carburettor, 16 valves
Drivetrain:	Front-engine RWD
Suspension:	(F) Independent coil spring. (R) Independent coil spring
Bodyframe:	Spaceframe
Transmission:	5-speed manual
Weight:	1019kgs
	PRICE GUIDE
Launch price:	£23,595
Excellent:	£10,500
Good:	£8750
Average:	£7000
Project:	£4750

TVR Griffith 4.0/4.3

It has been hailed as one of the purest sports car bodies ever, and who's to argue with TVR's incredible transformation from producing wedges with bits stuck on to the organic one-ness of the Griffith. Using a spaceframe chassis based on that developed under the Tuscan racecar, the first run of Griffiths used Rover V8s reworked to give a choice of either 240bhp 4.0 or 280bhp 4.3 form. A healthy (for TVR) 600 of them were built in 1992, but production was stopped in 1993 to allow the Chimaera to be put into production. The Griffith would be back though...

SPECIFICATIONS

Years produced:	1991-2000
Performance:	0-60mph: 4.6 secs (Top speed: 161mph)
Power & torque:	280bhp / 305lb/ft
Engine:	Normally aspirated 4280cc V8, petrol, electronic fuel injection, 16 valves
Drivetrain:	front-engine RWD
Suspension:	(F) Independent, coil spring. (R) Independent, coil spring
Bodyframe:	Spaceframe
Transmission:	5-speed manual
Weight:	1045kgs
	PRICE GUIDE
Launch price:	£28,295
Excellent:	£14,000
Good:	£12,000
Average:	£9750
Project:	£6500

TVR Chimaera 4.0/4.3

Though sharing much with the Griffith, the Chimaera's proposition is as a slightly bigger and more comfortable touring car. And it does that, though you'll never mistake it for a Jaguar: soft is a relative term in TVR-speak, and they are still dangerously fast in the wrong hands. Engines were certainly shared with the Griffith, starting out with the 4.0, but soon adding the 4.3. Later versions of the Chimaera even adopted 4.5 and five-litre versions of the Rover V8. Oh yes, and that tall tale about Ned the dog styling the sidelight opening by biting the clay model – it's true!

SPECIFICATIONS

Years produced:	1993-1998
Performance:	0-60mph: 5.2 secs (Top speed: 158mph)
Power & torque:	240bhp / 275lb/ft
Engine:	Normally aspirated 3947cc V8, petrol, electronic fuel injection, 16 valves
Drivetrain:	Front-engine RWD
Suspension:	(F) Independent, coil spring. (R) Independent, coil spring
Bodyframe:	Spaceframe
Transmission:	5-speed manual
Weight:	1060kgs
	PRICE GUIDE
Launch price:	£26,250
Excellent:	£13,000
Good:	£11,000
Average:	£8000
Project:	£5000

TVR Griffith 500

Though originally designed to use TVR's own AJP V8 engine, a more expedient route was chosen to get the Griffith back into production: a well tweaked five-litre incarnation of the Rover V8. In keeping with the stunning performance this provided, the 'new' Griffith also came with better brakes, Koni dampers and an even stiffer chassis. To the relief of many, in 1994 a Borg-Warner T5 gearbox replaced the old Rover SD1 unit. The raft of new customers TVR was now attracting were offered such previously-unthinkable luxuries including air-conditioning and heated seats.

SPECIFICATIONS

Years produced:	1993-2000
Performance:	0-60mph: 4.1 secs (Top speed: 161mph)
Power & torque:	340bhp / 350lb/ft
Engine:	Normally aspirated 4988cc V8, petrol, electronic fuel injection, 16 valves
Drivetrain:	Front-engine RWD
Suspension:	(F) Independent, coil spring (R) Independent, coil spring
Bodyframe:	Spaceframe
Transmission:	5-speed manual
Weight:	1075kgs
	PRICE GUIDE
Launch price:	£32,995
Excellent:	£17,500
Good:	£15,000
Average:	£11,000
Project:	£7750

TVR
Cerbera

In many ways the Cerbera is a spiritual successor to the E-type Jaguar – a stunning British coupé with amazing performance. It has also confounded the sceptics by using TVRs own AJP engines and becoming their best selling car of all time. Launched with a 360bhp 4.2-litre V8, this was joined in 1998 by a 4.5 with 420bhp. A year later came the Cerbera Speed Six with, as the name suggests, a straight-six of four litres and 350bhp. The glassfibre body was based on the Chimaera, with eight inches added to the wheelbase, hence those enormous doors.

SPECIFICATIONS

Years produced: 1996-2003
Performance: 0-60mph: 4.0 secs (Top speed: 185mph)
Power & torque: 350bhp / 320lb/ft
Engine: Normally aspirated 4185cc V8, petrol, electronic fuel injection, 32 valves
Drivetrain: Front-engine RWD
Suspension: (F) Independent, coil spring. (R) Independent, coil spring
Bodyframe: Spaceframe
Transmission: 5-speed manual
Weight: 1177kgs

PRICE GUIDE

Launch price: £37,000
Excellent: £15,500
Good: £13,000
Average: £10,500
Project: £6750

VANDEN PLAS
Princess 4-Litre Limo

What had been the Austin A135 Princess in 1952 became a Vanden Plas model in 1957, the prestigious badge being regarded as a way of making it seem even more upmarket. This cut-price Rolls-Royce had much to recommend it, becoming a particular favourite of mayors and successful businessman across Britain. Its 3993cc six-cylinder 122bhp engine made it a capable cruiser, and it could be had in three body styles; saloon, six-seater limousine or landaulette. An offshoot was the Princess IV of 1956, an expensive grand touring version intended to compete with Jaguar.

SPECIFICATIONS

Years produced: 1957-1968 (3344 in total)
Performance: 0-60mph: 26.0 secs (Top speed: 75mph)
Power & torque: 120bhp / 185lb/ft
Engine: Normally aspirated 3990cc in-line six, petrol, carburettor, 12 valves
Drivetrain: Front-engine RWD
Suspension: (F) Independent, coil spring. (R) Live axle, semi-elliptic leaf spring
Bodyframe: Chassis and separate body
Transmission: 4-speed manual or 3-speed automatic
Weight: 2121kgs

PRICE GUIDE

Launch price: £3047
Excellent: £7500
Good: £6000
Average: £4000
Project: £2000

VANDEN PLAS
3-Litre

Farina styling reached Vanden Plas in 1959 with the 3-Litre model. The VP was top dog of the trio that also included the Austin Westminster and Wolseley 6/99. It was packed with even more wood and leather and offered silent refinement from its extensive soundproofing, which successfully drowned out the burble of the six-cylinder 2912cc C-series engine. The MkII of 1961 gave more power – 120bhp – and the ability to sail past 100mph at last, plus a four-speed floor-mounted transmission. As well as the standard saloon, a touring limousine could also be specified.

SPECIFICATIONS

Years produced: 1959-1964 (12,703 in total)
Performance: 0-60mph: 17.9 secs (Top speed: 97mph)
Power & torque: 108bhp / 165lb/ft
Engine: Normally aspirated 2912cc in-line six, petrol, carburettor, 12 valves
Drivetrain: Front-engine RWD
Suspension: (F) Independent, coil spring. (R) Live axle, semi-elliptic leaf spring
Bodyframe: Metal monocoque
Transmission: 3-speed manual
Weight: 1530kgs

PRICE GUIDE

Launch price: £1396
Excellent: £5250
Good: £4000
Average: £1800
Project: £500

VANDEN PLAS
Princess 1100/1300

BMC badge engineering ran amok with the 1100 and 1300 range, but the flagship Vanden Plas Princess variant was quite a superior machine. For its size, it managed to pack in a lot of cosseting. All the trimming was done at the Vanden Plas factory in London and, as well as all the expected wood and leather touches, VP also fitted extra sound deadening and picnic tables for rear seat passengers. The initial 1098cc engine gave 55bhp, this rose to 65bhp with the MkII of 1967 (but only after BMC upgraded it from single- to twin-carb in 1968). Probably the most desirable of all BMC 1100s.

SPECIFICATIONS

Years produced: 1963-1974 (43,741 in total)
Performance: 0-60mph: 21.1 secs (Top speed: 85mph)
Power & torque: 55bhp / 60lb/ft
Engine: Normally aspirated 1098cc in-line four, petrol, carburettor, 8 valves
Drivetrain: Front-engine FWD
Suspension: (F) Independent, Hydrolastic. (R) Independent, Hydrolastic
Bodyframe: Metal monocoque
Transmission: 4-speed manual
Weight: 832kgs

PRICE GUIDE

Launch price: £895
Excellent: £3500
Good: £2500
Average: £1350
Project: £400

VANDEN PLAS
4-Litre R

A brief encounter between Rolls-Royce and BMC led to the Vanden Plas 4-Litre R of 1964. The 'R' of the name was shorthand for the 3909cc Rolls-Royce six-cylinder engine under the bonnet of a modified 3-Litre bodyshell. The 175bhp of the all-alloy unit meant an easy car to drive – even without the extra refinement from the Borg Warner automatic transmission, power steering and servo-assisted front disc brakes. There was even more wood and leather inside than in the 3-Litre cars. Rolls-Royce even considered building its own version as a Bentley but then decided against it.

SPECIFICATIONS

Years produced: 1964-1968 (6999 in total)
Performance: 0-60mph: 12.7 secs (Top speed: 106mph)
Power & torque: 175bhp / 218lb/ft
Engine: Normally aspirated 3909cc in-line six, petrol, carburettor, 12 valves
Drivetrain: Front-engine RWD
Suspension: (F) Independent, coil spring. (R) Live axle, semi-elliptic leaf spring
Bodyframe: Metal monocoque
Transmission: 3-speed automatic
Weight: 1575kgs

PRICE GUIDE

Launch price: £1994
Excellent: £5500
Good: £4000
Average: £2000
Project: £600

VANDEN PLAS
1500/1750

Yes, it's an Allegro. With a faux-Bentley grille and a rather pretentious air. When the Allegro superseded the 1300 range, it seemed only logical that a posh version would follow to satisfy British Leyland devotees who prized luxury motoring in a small package. The disproportionate grille did little for the Allegro's already inelegant looks but it had a great interior. Those picnic tables were there, alongside the walnut veneer and hide. Most cars had 1485cc OHC engines of 68bhp but in the final couple of years there was a 90bhp 1748cc unit, only mated to automatic transmission.

SPECIFICATIONS

Years produced:	1974-1980 (11,840 in total)
Performance:	0-60mph: 16.7 secs (Top speed: 90mph)
Power & torque:	69bhp / 77lb/ft
Engine:	Normally aspirated 1485cc in-line four, petrol, carburettor, 8 valves
Drivetrain:	Front-engine FWD
Suspension:	(F) Independent, Hydragas. (R) Independent, Hydragas
Bodyframe:	Monocoque
Transmission:	5-speed manual
Weight:	850kgs
PRICE GUIDE	
Launch price:	£1951
Excellent:	£1800
Good:	£1300
Average:	£600
Project:	£100

VAUXHALL
Wyvern/Velox L

You had to look twice at Vauxhall's 1948 Wyvern and Velox before its true origins became apparent; for this was a 12/14 model with a different nose and tail grafted on. At the front, the longer wings now incorporated the headlamps and a rear-hinged bonnet plus an Art Deco-ish slatted grille, while the sleeker rear allowed a bigger boot. The lower-class Wyvern had a 1442cc four-cylinder engine while the higher-spec Velox had a 2275cc six-cylinder. Despite the big difference in engine sizes, the gap in power was slight; 33bhp versus 54bhp. These stopgap Vauxhalls kept going until 1951.

SPECIFICATIONS

Years produced:	1948-1951 (55,409/76,919 in total)
Performance:	0-60mph: 22.9 secs (Top speed: 64mph)
Power & torque:	35bhp / 68lb/ft
Engine:	Normally aspirated 1442cc in-line four, petrol, carburettor, 8 valves
Drivetrain:	Front-engine RWD
Suspension:	(F) Independent, coil spring, torsion bar. (R) Live axle, semi-elliptic leaf spring
Bodyframe:	Chassis and separate body
Transmission:	3-speed manual
Weight:	993kgs
PRICE GUIDE	
Launch price:	£448
Excellent:	£3500
Good:	£2500
Average:	£1500
Project:	£500

VAUXHALL
Velox/Cresta E

Moving upmarket from the Wyvern were Vauxhall's Velox and Cresta, six-cylinder models with considerably enhanced creature comforts. Launched in 1951, the monocoque-construction Velox had a 2275cc engine and Chevrolet-inspired looks, with a significant amount of chrome on the exterior. After one year, a 2262cc engine made an appearance; although smaller in capacity, it had more power (from 58bhp to 64 or 69bhp). The Cresta joined the line-up in 1954 as an even more prestigious model; from the outside it could be distinguished by its two-tone paint.

SPECIFICATIONS

Years produced:	1951-1957 (251,800 in total)
Performance:	0-60mph: 20.9 secs (Top speed: 80mph)
Power & torque:	55bhp / 106lb/ft
Engine:	Normally aspirated 2275cc in-line six, petrol, carburettor, 12 valves
Drivetrain:	Front-engine RWD
Suspension:	(F) Independent, coil spring, wishbone. (R) Live axle, semi-elliptic leaf spring
Bodyframe:	Metal monocoque
Transmission:	3-speed manual
Weight:	1021kgs
PRICE GUIDE	
Launch price:	£803
Excellent:	£5250
Good:	£4000
Average:	£2000
Project:	£800

VAUXHALL
Wyvern E

Along with the closely-related Velox and Cresta, the Wyvern EIX was the first completely new postwar Vauxhall. The 1442cc engine was carried over from the previous Wyvern but the bodywork was thoroughly modern and very American in its look, with a lot of flashy chrome up front and a curved windscreen, something unusual for the era. The increased weight of the new styling blunted performance so, from 1952, a 1507cc engine was fitted. This increased power from 35bhp to 40 or 48bhp. Aside from tweaks to its exterior, the Wyvern continued in this form until 1957.

SPECIFICATIONS

Years produced:	1951-1957 (5315 in total)
Performance:	0-60mph: 37.2 secs (Top speed: 71mph)
Power & torque:	35bhp / 68lb/ft
Engine:	Normally aspirated 1442cc in-line four, petrol, carburettor, 8 valves
Drivetrain:	Front-engine RWD
Suspension:	(F) Independent, wishbone, coil spring (R) Live axle, semi-elliptic leaf spring
Bodyframe:	Metal monocoque
Transmission:	3-speed manual
Weight:	1001kgs
PRICE GUIDE	
Launch price:	£495
Excellent:	£4000
Good:	£3000
Average:	£1500
Project:	£500

VAUXHALL
Velox/Cresta PA

British restraint went completely out of the window with the Velox and Cresta of 1957. Flamboyant American design was wholeheartedly embraced, with fins, a dogleg wraparound windscreen, two-tone paint schemes (on the Cresta) and cascades of chrome. The 2262cc six-cylinder engine was shared by both, so the Cresta only stood out from the cheaper Velox by its greater levels of luxury and equipment inside. In 1960, engine size went up to 2651cc and front disc brakes became available to cope with the extra power; the fins also grew in stature.

SPECIFICATIONS

Years produced:	1957-1962 (173,759 in total)
Performance:	0-60mph: 18.0 secs (Top speed: 87mph)
Power & torque:	83bhp / 124lb/ft
Engine:	Normally aspirated 2651cc in-line six, petrol, carburettor, 12 valves
Drivetrain:	Front-engine RWD
Suspension:	(F) Independent, coil spring. (R) Live axle, semi-elliptic leaf springs
Bodyframe:	Metal monocoque
Transmission:	3-speed manual
Weight:	1193kgs
PRICE GUIDE	
Launch price:	£984
Excellent:	£5500
Good:	£4500
Average:	£2250
Project:	£850

VAUXHALL
Victor FB

More restrained and sensible styling marked the 1961-64 FB Victor incarnation, albeit still with leanings across the Atlantic. But the new look was neat, handsome and inoffensive and helped make this mid-sized family car one of Vauxhall's big successes of the 1960s. Four-door saloons and five-door estates were available, with the first cars (1961-63) sporting the same 1507cc engine as the F-type, but those from September 1963 until the end of production had a 1595cc engine of 58.5bbhp, when front disc brakes were also adopted. 328,640 were built up until 1964.

SPECIFICATIONS	
Years produced:	1961-1964 (328,640 in total)
Performance:	0-60mph: 22.6 secs (Top speed: 76mph)
Power & torque:	55bhp / 80lb/ft
Engine:	Normally aspirated 1508cc in-line four, petrol, carburettor, 8 valves
Drivetrain:	Front-engine RWD
Suspension:	(F) Independent, coil spring. (R) Live axle, semi-elliptic leaf spring
Bodyframe:	Metal monocoque
Transmission:	3-speed manual
Weight:	953kgs
PRICE GUIDE	
Launch price:	£574
Excellent:	£3250
Good:	£2400
Average:	£1100
Project:	£400

VAUXHALL
VX4/90 FB

As well as the standard Victor FB there was, for the first time, a performance-orientated version of the type, dubbed the VX 4/90. Twin carburettors and a high-compression 1507cc engine boosted power from 50bhp to 71bhp, while a floor-mounted transmission and servo front disc brakes allowed the sporty Vauxhall driver to make the most of this extra potential. Spotters could recognise a VX4/90 by its contrasting colour side stripe and a vertical bar grille. When a 1595cc engine was fitted in 1963, power rose to 74bhp, with a wood-panelled dash to make up for this meagre increase.

SPECIFICATIONS	
Years produced:	1961-1964 (328,640 (All FB) in total)
Performance:	0-60mph: 16.4 secs (Top speed: 90mph)
Power & torque:	71bhp / 92lb/ft
Engine:	Normally aspirated 1508cc in-line four, petrol, carburettor, 8 valves
Drivetrain:	Front-engine RWD
Suspension:	(F) Independent, coil spring. (R) Live axle, semi-elliptic leaf spring
Bodyframe:	Metal monocoque
Transmission:	3-speed manual
Weight:	990kgs
PRICE GUIDE	
Launch price:	£674
Excellent:	£3750
Good:	£3000
Average:	£1350
Project:	£550

VAUXHALL
Velox/Cresta PB

Vauxhall toned things down for the 1962-65 PB generation of Velox and Cresta. There was still a US influence and imposing size, but with a more UK flavour overall. Front disc brakes were standard but the traditional three-speed column-mounted transmission persisted; there was also a three-speed Hydramatic automatic which changed to a two-speed Powerglide in 1965. Futuristic names were then all the rage of course. Initially, the 2651cc six-cylinder engine was carried over from the PA, but this jumped to 3294cc in 1964, the 115bhp providing a much-needed shot of adrenalin.

SPECIFICATIONS	
Years produced:	1962-1965 (87,047 in total)
Performance:	0-60mph: 19.5 secs (Top speed: 92mph)
Power & torque:	95bhp / 149lb/ft
Engine:	Normally aspirated 2651cc in-line six, petrol, carburettor, 12 valves
Drivetrain:	Front-engine RWD
Suspension:	(F) Independent, coil spring. (R) Live axle, half-elliptic leaf spring
Bodyframe:	Metal monocoque
Transmission:	3-speed manual or auto
Weight:	1220kgs
PRICE GUIDE	
Launch price:	£805
Excellent:	£3000
Good:	£2250
Average:	£1100
Project:	£350

VAUXHALL
Viva HA

The British small car market was swelled in 1963 by the belated entry of Vauxhall with its Viva HA. Stylistically, it was nothing to get excited about; the angular looks were bland by comparison with rivals. However, the mechanical package was neat enough with a four-speed all-synchromesh gearbox, sharp rack-and-pinion steering and front disc brakes as an option. The more desirable variants – the De Luxe and the SL90 – boasted 54bhp from their 1057cc engines, but the Viva's main claim to fame was in being the first UK car with acrylic lacquer paint. Which doesn't make it that memorable...

SPECIFICATIONS	
Years produced:	1963-1966 (309,538 in total)
Performance:	0-60mph: 19.6 secs (Top speed: 78mph)
Power & torque:	44bhp / 56lb/ft
Engine:	Normally aspirated 1057cc in-line four, petrol, carburettor, 8 valves
Drivetrain:	Front-engine RWD
Suspension:	(F) Ind. double wishbone, leaf spring. (R) Live axle, half-elliptic leaf spring
Bodyframe:	Metal monocoque
Transmission:	4-speed manual
Weight:	709kgs
PRICE GUIDE	
Launch price:	£578
Excellent:	£1750
Good:	£1400
Average:	£600
Project:	£150

VAUXHALL
Victor FC 101

Marketed as the 101, the third incarnation of Victor was a spacious car with a number of novel design features such as curved side windows, ridged wing tops and front indicators/sidelights incorporated in the bumper. The 1595cc engine was carried over from the preceding type, although there was more power for the FC. As before, the VX4/90 did duty as the racier model, with twin carburettors, higher compression, enhanced suspension and more instrumentation inside, as well as a wood-panelled dashboard. This extra appeal means 25% can be added onto standard FC prices.

SPECIFICATIONS	
Years produced:	1964-1967 (219,814 (All FC) in total)
Performance:	0-60mph: 17.1 secs (Top speed: 85mph)
Power & torque:	60bhp / 86lb/ft
Engine:	Normally aspirated 1594cc in-line four, petrol, carburettor, 8 valves
Drivetrain:	Front-engine RWD
Suspension:	(F) Independent, coil spring. (R) Live axle, semi-elliptic leaf spring
Bodyframe:	Metal monocoque
Transmission:	4-speed manual
Weight:	1086kgs
PRICE GUIDE	
Launch price:	£655
Excellent:	£2400
Good:	£1750
Average:	£750
Project:	£250

VAUXHALL
Cresta PC/Viscount

The PC was only available with a 3294cc six-cylinder engine. At first, the Cresta De Luxe, with its four headlamps and extra brightwork, did service as the most luxurious model, but then came the 1966 Viscount with its vinyl roof, power steering and windows, plus those essential plush touches of wood and leather inside. Most Viscounts came with automatic transmission, which was improved considerably once the two-speed Powerglide gearbox was ditched in favour of a General Motors three-speeder.

SPECIFICATIONS	
Years produced:	1965-1972 (66,937 in total)
Performance:	0-60mph: 12.6 secs (Top speed: 97mph)
Power & torque:	123bhp / 175lb/ft
Engine:	Normally aspirated 3294cc in-line six, petrol, carburettor, 12 valves
Drivetrain:	Front-engine RWD
Suspension:	(F) Independent, coil spring. (R) Live axle, semi-elliptic leaf spring
Bodyframe:	Metal monocoque
Transmission:	2-speed or 3-speed automatic
Weight:	1179kgs
PRICE GUIDE	
Launch price:	£956
Excellent:	£2500
Good:	£1800
Average:	£950
Project:	£250

VAUXHALL
Viva HB

The Viva got more attractive and trendy in HB form. Not only was it larger, but it also featured distinctive 'Coke bottle' side styling, one of the first UK cars to do so. Aside from the engine, an enlarged (1159cc) version of the HA unit, little was carried over from the previous model. The suspension was totally new and quite advanced, resulting in impressive handling. This could be better enjoyed in the high compression SL90, with 59.5bhp. When the Viva started to lag behind its rivals in the late Sixties, the overhead-cam 1599cc engine from the Victor was added to the mix.

SPECIFICATIONS	
Years produced:	1966-1970 (566,391 in total)
Performance:	0-60mph: 19.7 secs (Top speed: 80mph)
Power & torque:	47bhp / 62lb/ft
Engine:	Normally aspirated 1159cc in-line four, petrol, carburettor, 8 valves
Drivetrain:	Front-engine RWD
Suspension:	(F) Independent, coil spring, wishbone. (R) Live axle, trailing arm, coil spring
Bodyframe:	Metal monocoque
Transmission:	4-speed manual
Weight:	777kgs
PRICE GUIDE	
Launch price:	£508
Excellent:	£1650
Good:	£1200
Average:	£500
Project:	£100

VAUXHALL
Viva Brabham HB

If BMC could do it with Cooper and Ford with Lotus, then why shouldn't Vauxhall do it with Brabham? That was the thinking behind 1967's Brabham HB Viva, developed with world racing champion Jack Brabham. The hotted-up 1159cc engine had twin Stromberg carburettors, reworked exhaust manifolds and an uprated camshaft, combining to give 69bhp. The interior trim was different as well, with bodywork embellished by black stripes running from the bonnet and around the front wings to the doors. Nice! It was in production for just a year before being replaced by the Viva 1600.

SPECIFICATIONS	
Years produced:	1967-1968
Performance:	0-60mph: 14.4 secs (Top speed: 90mph)
Power & torque:	68bhp / 66lb/ft
Engine:	Normally aspirated 1159cc in-line four, petrol, carburettor, 8 valves
Drivetrain:	Front-engine RWD
Suspension:	(F) Independent, coil spring, wishbone. (R) Live axle, trailing arm, coil spring
Bodyframe:	Metal monocoque
Transmission:	4-speed manual
Weight:	777kgs
PRICE GUIDE	
Launch price:	£690
Excellent:	£3750
Good:	£2750
Average:	£1750
Project:	£750

VAUXHALL
Victor FD

The FD Victor's 'Coke bottle' kink on its rear doors reflected contemporary American trends, just as previous Victors before it had done. Thus the looks were bold and brash, with quad-headlamp styling and the continuation (on some models) of the three-speed column-mounted gearchange and front bench seating that Vauxhall had persisted with for years. Two new hemispherical-head overhead-cam engines, of 1599cc and 1975cc, were introduced, with servo-assisted front brakes for the latter. The VX 4/90 was the sporty model, with twin carburettors, overdrive and Rostyle wheels.

SPECIFICATIONS	
Years produced:	1967-1972 (198,085 in total)
Performance:	0-60mph: 14.0 secs (Top speed: 95mph)
Power & torque:	83bhp / 90lb/ft
Engine:	Normally aspirated 1599cc in-line four, petrol, carburettor, 8 valves
Drivetrain:	Front-engine RWD
Suspension:	(F) Independent, coil spring, wishbone. (R) Panhard rod, trailing arm
Bodyframe:	Metal monocoque
Transmission:	3-speed/4-speed manual
Weight:	1066kgs
PRICE GUIDE	
Launch price:	£819
Excellent:	£2250
Good:	£1600
Average:	£600
Project:	£150

VAUXHALL
Viva GT

The Viva Brabham was a half-hearted effort at injecting some vigour into the HB range but the same couldn't be said of the 1968 Viva GT. For this was a storming machine that gave the Viva a heady degree of sportiness absent before. To achieve this, Vauxhall dropped in the 1975cc engine from the Victor, adorned with twin carburettors and mated with a close ratio gearbox. This unleashed 104 horses on the small car, giving 100mph. The suspension was uprated, while bonnet scoops, a black grille, black bonnet and contrasting white body made it look the part. Vauxhall's equivalent of the Lotus Cortina.

SPECIFICATIONS
Years produced: 1968-1970 (4606 in total)
Performance: 0-60mph: 14.4 secs (Top speed: 100mph)
Power & torque: 104bhp / 117lb/ft
Engine: Normally aspirated 1975cc in-line four, petrol, carburettor, 8 valves
Drivetrain: Front-engine RWD
Suspension: (F) Independent, coil spring, wishbone. (R) Panhard rod, coil spring
Bodyframe: Metal monocoque
Transmission: 4-speed manual
Weight: 925kgs
PRICE GUIDE
Launch price: £1062
Excellent: £3500
Good: £2500
Average: £1600
Project: £600

VAUXHALL
Ventora FD/FE

Vauxhall continued its obsession with the letter 'V' in 1968, with the launch of the Ventora. It wasn't a new car though, just the amalgam of two existing machines; the Victor FD and the Cresta PC. The body was taken from the former, the 3294cc six-cylinder 123bhp engine came from the latter, while enhanced trim levels raised the car above normal Victor standards of comfort and equipment. The car continued as an FE model from 1972, using the same engine with the same level of power. Slightly bizarrely though, estate versions were badged as Victor 3300s rather than Ventoras until 1973.

SPECIFICATIONS
Years produced: 1970-1975 (25,185 in total)
Performance: 0-60mph: 12.1 secs (Top speed: 107mph)
Power & torque: 123bhp / 176lb/ft
Engine: Normally aspirated 3294cc in-line six, petrol, carburettor, 12 valves
Drivetrain: Front-engine RWD
Suspension: (F) Ind. coil spring, wishbone. (R) Panhard rod, coil spring, radius arm
Bodyframe: Metal monocoque
Transmission: 4-speed manual
Weight: 1124kgs
PRICE GUIDE
Launch price: £1102
Excellent: £2100
Good: £1600
Average: £675
Project: £175

VAUXHALL
Viva HC

Little changed underneath the Viva HC when it appeared in 1970, for the engines and platform were carried over from the HB. However, the bodies – available as saloons, estates and coupés – were restyled for the new decade, adopting a square-cut style (on the saloons) more reminiscent of the HA than the HB. Within a few years, a range of new engines was introduced; 1256cc, 1759cc and 2279cc. To make the higher-powered cars stand out, they were badged as Magnums from 1973, the coupés were also known by this name for just over a year as well.

SPECIFICATIONS
Years produced: 1970-1979 (640,863 in total)
Performance: 0-60mph: 20.6 secs (Top speed: 78mph)
Power & torque: 60bhp / 87lb/ft
Engine: Normally aspirated 1159cc in-line four, petrol, carburettor, 8 valves
Drivetrain: Front-engine RWD
Suspension: (F) Independent, coil spring, wishbone. (R) Live axle, trailing arm, coil spring
Bodyframe: Metal monocoque
Transmission: 4-speed manual
Weight: 817kgs
PRICE GUIDE
Launch price: £783
Excellent: £1400
Good: £1000
Average: £450
Project: £100

VAUXHALL
Firenza

The success of Ford's Capri prompted other manufacturers to offer similar models. The Firenza coupé was Vauxhall's effort, launched in 1971. It bore a family resemblance to the Viva HC it was based on, but had more rounded, fastback styling; arguably, it was a more attractive creation than the Capri. Engines ranged from an insipid 1159cc to a rather enjoyable 1975cc, but changes in 1972 introduced 1256cc, 1759cc units, as well as the thoroughly entertaining 2279cc powerhouse of 110bhp. In 1973, the coupes became known as Magnums instead.

SPECIFICATIONS
Years produced: 1971-1973 (18,352 in total)
Performance: 0-60mph: 22.0 secs (Top speed: 84mph)
Power & torque: 62bhp / 65lb/ft
Engine: Normally aspirated 1159cc in-line four, petrol, carburettor, 8 valves
Drivetrain: Front-engine RWD
Suspension: (F) Independent, coil spring, wishbone. (R) Live axle, trailing arm, coil spring
Bodyframe: Metal monocoque
Transmission: 4-speed manual
Weight: 856kgs
PRICE GUIDE
Launch price: £1017
Excellent: £1850
Good: £1400
Average: £700
Project: £150

VAUXHALL
Victor FE/VX1800/2300

British Vauxhalls started to lose their individuality with the Victor FE of 1972, for this car also shared some of its underpinnings with the Opel Rekord, albeit with different suspension and engines. The latter were 1759cc and 2279cc four-cylinder overhead-cam units, giving these mid-sized models effective performance, while front disc brakes meant they also stopped well too. The sportier Rostyle wheel-decorated variant was known as the VX 4/90 and managed 116bhp from its twin-carb 2.3-litre engine. From 1976, the cars became known as VX1800s or VX2300s.

SPECIFICATIONS
Years produced: 1972-1978 (80,610 in total)
Performance: 0-60mph: 12.4 secs (Top speed: 97mph)
Power & torque: 110bhp / 138lb/ft
Engine: Normally aspirated 2278cc in-line six, petrol, carburettor, 12 valves
Drivetrain: Front-engine RWD
Suspension: (F) Ind. Wishbone, coil spring. (R) Panhard rod, trailing link
Bodyframe: Metal monocoque
Transmission: 4-speed manual
Weight: 1178kgs
PRICE GUIDE
Launch price: £1299
Excellent: £2000
Good: £1350
Average: £500
Project: £100

VAUXHALL
Firenza Droopsnoot

The Firenza departed even further from the standard Viva HC formula with the unveiling of the Firenza HP – nicknamed the Droopsnoot – in 1973. This was the HC coupé body with a glassfibre nose cone and injected with 131bhp courtesy of its tweaked 2279cc engine. The streamlined front was more than just show as top speed was raised to 120mph. However, the car wasn't a success. Just 204 had been built by the time it was dropped in 1975, against estimates of 1000 a year. Resourcefully, Vauxhall then used the left-over noses on 197 HC estate cars, dubbed Sportshatches.

SPECIFICATIONS

Years produced: 1973-1975 (204 in total)
Performance: 0-60mph: 9.4 secs (Top speed: 120mph)
Power & torque: 131bhp / 145lb/ft
Engine: Normally aspirated 2279cc in-line four, petrol, carburettor, 8 valves
Drivetrain: Front-engine RWD
Suspension: (F) Ind. wishbone, coil spring. (R) Live axle, coil spring
Bodyframe: Metal monocoque
Transmission: 5-speed manual
Weight: 1015kgs

PRICE GUIDE

Launch price: £2625
Excellent: £5000
Good: £4000
Average: £2000
Project: £850

VAUXHALL
Chevette 2300HS

The Chevette, of course, was pure family car. The HS and HSR versions were very different beasts though. Built for rally homologation purposes, road versions went on sale in 1978, equipped with a 2279cc twin-cam engine and Getrag five-speed transmission. With 135bhp on tap and the potential for 120mph, this put it head-to-head with Ford's RS Escorts. Front and rear spoilers and wide alloy wheels marked it out from the Chevette herd. The HSR Evolution in 1979 went the whole hog with flared wheelarches and a bodykit, plus 150bhp. Double the prices shown for one of those.

SPECIFICATIONS

Years produced: 1976-1980 (450 in total)
Performance: 0-60mph: 8.8 secs (Top speed: 117mph)
Power & torque: 135bhp / 134lb/ft
Engine: Normally aspirated 2279cc in-line four, petrol, carburettor, 16 valves
Drivetrain: Front-engine RWD
Suspension: (F) Independent, wishbone, coil spring. (R) Panhard rod, trailing arm
Bodyframe: Metal monocoque
Transmission: 5-speed manual
Weight: 970kgs

PRICE GUIDE

Launch price: £5107
Excellent: £6500
Good: £5000
Average: £2750
Project: £1500

VAUXHALL
Royale

Topping off the Vauxhall tree of the late-1970s were the Royale saloons and coupés, Anglicised versions of Opel's Senator and Monza models. Aside from the front grille and badges, they were identical to their Opel counterparts and were even built in Germany. The saloons were four-door, coupés had two with a hatchback. The 2784cc six-cylinder engine gave a reassuring 138bhp, but the big bruiser was 1980's 2968cc fuel-injected version, with a dramatic rise in power to 180bhp and, with it, the ability to top 130mph. Less kudos than an Opel but still sought-after.

SPECIFICATIONS

Years produced: 1978-1982 (7119 in total)
Performance: 0-60mph: 11.4 secs (Top speed: 118mph)
Power & torque: 140bhp / 161lb/ft
Engine: Normally aspirated 2784cc in-line six, petrol, carburettor, 12 valves
Drivetrain: Front-engine RWD
Suspension: (F) Ind. MacPherson strut, coil spring. (R) Ind. semi-trailing arms, coil spring
Bodyframe: Metal monocoque
Transmission: 4-speed manual
Weight: 1370kgs

PRICE GUIDE

Launch price: £8248
Excellent: £2650
Good: £2000
Average: £1000
Project: £350

VAUXHALL
VX220

From a mainstream company like Vauxhall, the VX220 was something of a shock. For this was an out-and-out, very raw sportscar, a Lotus Elise Series 2 sporting a different Vauxhall (and Opel) body. Built by Lotus, the Targa-topped road racer was launched in 2000 with a mid-mounted Vauxhall Astra 2196cc all-alloy engine of 145bhp, followed in 2003 by a 1998cc turbocharged model, with 197bhp. This would have given any car blistering performance, but in such a lightweight machine as the VX220, acceleration was an incredible 4.9 seconds for the 0-60 dash, with a 151mph top speed.

SPECIFICATIONS

Years produced: 2000-2005
Performance: 0-60mph: 5.9 secs (Top speed: 137mph)
Power & torque: 147bhp / 140lb/ft
Engine: Normally aspirated 2200cc in-line four, petrol, electronic fuel injection, 16 valves
Drivetrain: Mid-engine RWD
Suspension: (F) Ind. wishbone, coil spring. (R) Ind. wishbone, coil spring
Bodyframe: Chassis and separate body
Transmission: 5-speed manual
Weight: 930kgs

PRICE GUIDE

Launch price: £26,495 (Turbo)
Excellent: £12,000
Good: £10,000
Average: £8000
Project: £6000

VOLKSWAGEN
Beetle (split-screen)

Adolf Hitler had the idea for the 'Volkswagen' (People's Car) and Ferdinand Porsche designed it, for the purposes of getting Nazi Germany mobile. Who would have thought that from such a troubled birth, the Beetle would go on to conquer the world? After the war, the British army restarted production and gradually the car started to grow more refined, finding itself exported globally. The original split-rear window models were built until 1953 and featured an 1131cc rear-mounted air-cooled engine of just 25bhp. A simple, charming and ruggedly-reliable motoring legend.

SPECIFICATIONS

Years produced: 1946-1953
Performance: 0-60mph: N/A (Top speed: 62mph)
Power & torque: 24bhp / 49lb/ft
Engine: Normally aspirated 1131cc flat four, petrol, carburettor, 8 valves
Drivetrain: Rear-engine RWD
Suspension: (F) Independent, torsion bar. (R) Independent, torsion bar
Bodyframe: Chassis and separate body
Transmission: 4-speed manual
Weight: 749kgs

PRICE GUIDE

Launch price: £690
Excellent: £10,500
Good: £9000
Average: £6000
Project: £4000

VOLKSWAGEN Beetle (Oval)

Poor visibility was always an issue with the original Beetle and its split back window. Volkswagen addressed this in March 1953 when the screen was replaced by a larger single-piece oval one. This important change coincided with the beginning of sales in the UK, and all but the very first of the 'Oval Beetles' benefitted from the first increase in engine size since 1945 when an 1192cc unit added 5bhp. With 30bhp to play with now, 66mph was possible... not much on paper but, of course, a Beetle could happily cruise at this speed all day. Add 25% for Cabriolet prices.

SPECIFICATIONS

Years produced: 1953-1957
Performance: 0-60mph: 47.6 secs (Top speed: 66mph)
Power & torque: 24.5bhp / 49lb/ft
Engine: Normally aspirated 1131cc flat four, petrol, carburettor, 8 valves
Drivetrain: Rear-engine RWD
Suspension: (F) Independent, torsion bar. (R) Independent, torsion bar
Bodyframe: Chassis and separate body
Transmission: 4-speed manual
Weight: 711kgs

PRICE GUIDE

Launch price: £690
Excellent: £9250
Good: £7500
Average: £4750
Project: £3000

VOLKSWAGEN Kombi/Camper

The initial idea for a VW-based van was in 1947, but it wasn't until 1950 that the officially designated Type 2 appeared. Many different variants were available but the most popular and numerous were the Kombi (Kombinationskraftwagen – a windowed combination of passenger and cargo vehicle, usually referred to as a 'bus') and the Camper. Westfalia created most of the latter. Nicknamed 'Split' or 'Splittie' due to their divided windscreen, VW updated the mechanical side of the vehicles constantly while leaving their looks mostly untouched... at least until 1968.

SPECIFICATIONS

Years produced: 1954-1967
Performance: 0-60mph: N/A (Top speed: 65mph)
Power & torque: 30bhp / 56lb/ft
Engine: Normally aspirated 1192cc flat four, petrol, carburettor, 8 valves
Drivetrain: Rear-engine RWD
Suspension: (F) Ind. torsion bar, trailing link. (R) Independent swing axle, torsion bar
Bodyframe: Chassis and separate body
Transmission: 4-speed manual
Weight: 1105kgs

PRICE GUIDE

Launch price: £N/A (Dependent on variant)
Excellent: £25,000
Good: £20,000
Average: £10,000
Project: £5000

VOLKSWAGEN Karmann-Ghia Coupé

With the Beetle so easy to put different bodies on – after all, this was how Porsche started out – it was almost inevitable that Volkswagen would come up with a sportscar. Actually, it was coachbuilder Karmann which had the idea and VW jumped at the chance when it saw the pretty coupé body that Ghia designed. The public liked it too, and this sleeker Beetle sold well. However, it was a sheep in wolf's clothing, for its underpinnings were pure Beetle, with anemic performance. The original 1192cc engine was increased in stages up to 1584cc by 1974.

SPECIFICATIONS

Years produced: 1955-1974 (364,401 in total)
Performance: 0-60mph: 26.5 secs (Top speed: 77mph)
Power & torque: 30bhp / 56lb/ft
Engine: Normally aspirated 1192cc flat four, petrol, carburettor, 8 valves
Drivetrain: Rear-engine RWD
Suspension: (F) Independent, torsion bar. (R) Independent, torsion bar
Bodyframe: Chassis and separate body
Transmission: 4-speed manual
Weight: 730kgs

PRICE GUIDE

Launch price: £1235
Excellent: £9000
Good: £7000
Average: £5000
Project: £2500

VOLKSWAGEN Beetle 1200/1300

For the 1200, Volkswagen finally went the full Monty and put a proper rectangular back window on the Beetle, almost twice the size of what had been there before. With a bigger windscreen too, visibility was much improved. The company then continued with constant but subtle improvements. Power also rose gradually; 34bhp in 1960 followed by 40bhp from a 1285cc engine in 1965. A year later, 44bhp came from 1493cc capacity. These Beetles also got front discs so their 78mph performance could be more easily reined in. Cabriolets are worth double saloon prices.

SPECIFICATIONS

Years produced: 1957-1968
Performance: 0-60mph: 32.1 secs (Top speed: 72mph)
Power & torque: 40bhp / 65lb/ft
Engine: Normally aspirated1192cc flat four, petrol, carburettor, 8 valves
Drivetrain: Rear-engine RWD
Suspension: (F) Independent, torsion bar. (R) Independent, torsion bar
Bodyframe: Chassis and separate body
Transmission: 4-speed manual
Weight: 739kgs

PRICE GUIDE

Launch price: £617
Excellent: £4750
Good: £3500
Average: £1900
Project: £900

VOLKSWAGEN Karmann-Ghia Convertible

After the hardtop version of the Karmann-Ghia proved such a success, Volkswagen and Karmann didn't take too long to come up with a convertible version. It was unveiled in late-1957 to much the same level of appreciation as its tin-lid sister. Extra strengthening made the convertible heavier and therefore slower than the coupé, but that didn't matter to those who admired this fresh air fashion statement; America of course loved it. The car started life with a rear-mounted air-cooled 1192cc engine, which gradually increased in size through 1285cc and 1493cc to 1584cc.

SPECIFICATIONS

Years produced: 1958-1974 (80,899 in total)
Performance: 0-60mph: 27.0 secs (Top speed: 80mph)
Power & torque: 39bhp / 68lb/ft
Engine: Normally aspirated 1285cc flat four, petrol, carburettor, 8 valves
Drivetrain: Rear-engine RWD
Suspension: (F) Independent, torsion bar. (R) Independent, torsion bar
Bodyframe: Chassis and separate body
Transmission: 4-speed manual
Weight: 830kgs

PRICE GUIDE

Launch price: £1196
Excellent: £11,000
Good: £9000
Average: £6250
Project: £3500

VOLKSWAGEN 1500/1600 Type 3

The Type 3 was a spin off from the Beetle, intended to address some of its perceived shortcomings of being old-fashioned, cramped and having poor luggage capacity. And it was a more modern-looking machine, with extra space inside and a boot front and rear. Initially available as a two-door saloon with a 1493cc engine, a two-door estate – unflatteringly known as the Variant – came along in 1962, with a fastback saloon in 1965. By this time there was also a 1584cc engine too. Very prized these days by air-cooled VW modifiers.

SPECIFICATIONS

Years produced: 1961-1973 (1,813,600 in total)
Performance: 0-60mph: 25.3 secs (Top speed: 78mph)
Power & torque: 44bhp / 72lb/ft
Engine: Normally aspirated 1493cc flat four, petrol, carburettor, 8 valves
Drivetrain: Rear-engine RWD
Suspension: (F) Independent, torsion bar. (R) Independent, torsion bar
Bodyframe: Chassis and separate body
Transmission: 4-speed manual
Weight: 860kgs

PRICE GUIDE

Launch price: £998
Excellent: £5000
Good: £4250
Average: £2000
Project: £650

VOLKSWAGEN Karmann-Ghia Type 34

From 1961, there was another Karmann-Ghia coupé alongside the more familiar type. An offshoot of VW's Type 3, Ghia styled the vaguely BMW-ish-looking machine while coachbuilder Karmann built it. Although less pretty than its stablemate, it was still very attractive and the wider floorpan and 1493cc engine gave it more practicality and performance too. However, it was never a big seller, even when a 1584cc engine of 54bhp was added, along with front disc brakes, in 1965. A high price, thirst for fuel and not being sold in the USA were the main reasons for this.

SPECIFICATIONS

Years produced: 1962-1969 (42,563 in total)
Performance: 0-60mph: 21.3 secs (Top speed: 85mph)
Power & torque: 65bhp / 87lb/ft
Engine: Normally aspirated 1585cc flat four, petrol,carburettor, 8 valves
Drivetrain: Rear-engine RWD
Suspension: (F) Independent, torsion bar. (R) Independent, torsion bar
Bodyframe: Chassis and separate body
Transmission: 4-speed manual
Weight: 920kgs

PRICE GUIDE

Launch price: £1330
Excellent: £7000
Good: £5500
Average: £3250
Project: £1750

VOLKSWAGEN 411/412

One of the main issues with Volkswagen's passenger cars of the 1960s was that none had four doors. The 411 of 1968 changed all this; it managed to squeeze all the requisite doors onto a four-inch stretched wheelbase Beetle chassis but kept the faith with the rear-engined layout. However, at the front were MacPherson struts and disc brakes, meaning the 411 was a better-behaved machine than the Beetle. The 1679cc engine received fuel injection in 1969 and the gawky styling was reworked in 1972 for the 412. A 1795cc engine was adopted in 1973.

SPECIFICATIONS

Years produced: 1968-1974 (367,728 in total)
Performance: 0-60mph: 16.8 secs (Top speed: 96mph)
Power & torque: 80bhp / 97lb/ft
Engine: Normally aspirated 1679cc flat four, petrol, electronic fuel injection, 8 valves
Drivetrain: Rear-engine RWD
Suspension: (F) Ind. MacPherson strut, wishbone. (R) Ind. semi-trailing arm, coil spring
Bodyframe: Chassis and separate body
Transmission: 4-speed manual
Weight: 1030kgs

PRICE GUIDE

Launch price: £1290
Excellent: £3000
Good: £2250
Average: £1000
Project: £500

VOLKSWAGEN Beetle 1200/1500

The Beetle moved even further away from its pre-war origins in 1968 when more safety-conscious features were incorporated. Sloping headlamps were dispensed with in favour of upright ones and thicker bumpers fitted. Mechanical changes included – at last – 12-volt electrics and dual-circuit brakes, plus a fuel tank that didn't have to be filled by via the front boot. There was less focus on the antiquated Beetle once VW's new range of water-cooled cars but it lingered on, with minor improvements, until 1978. Building continued in Mexico until 2003.

SPECIFICATIONS

Years produced: 1968-1978
Performance: 0-60mph: 21.9 secs (Top speed: 81mph)
Power & torque: 53bhp / 78lb/ft
Engine: Normally aspirated 1493cc flat four, petrol, carburettor, 8 valves
Drivetrain: Rear-engine RWD
Suspension: (F) Independent, torsion bar. (R) Independent, torsion bar
Bodyframe: Chassis and separate body
Transmission: 4-speed manual
Weight: 820kgs

PRICE GUIDE

Launch price: £697
Excellent: £4250
Good: £3000
Average: £1650
Project: £650

VOLKSWAGEN Beetle 1302/1303

Although they looked the same as previous models, the 1302 and 1303 'Super' Beetles were the most radical reworks of the car during its long life. MacPherson strut front suspension was adopted, which allowed more front boot space and improved handling. The struts also allowed front disc brakes to be fitted too. The 1303, from 1972, had a more safety-conscious padded dashboard and wraparound windscreen, plus bigger tail lights. Engines were the usual air-cooled units of 1285cc and 44bhp, and 1584cc and 50bhp. Not quite as liked as other Bugs.

SPECIFICATIONS

Years produced: 1970-1975
Performance: 0-60mph: 18.3 secs (Top speed: 81mph)
Power & torque: 50bhp / 78lb/ft
Engine: Normally aspirated 1584cc flat four, petrol, carburettor, 8 valves
Drivetrain: Rear-engine RWD
Suspension: (F) Ind. MacPherson strut, trailing arm. (R) Ind. semi-swing axle, trailing arm
Bodyframe: Chassis and separate body
Transmission: 4-speed manual
Weight: 870kgs

PRICE GUIDE

Launch price: £875
Excellent: £3750
Good: £2750
Average: £1600
Project: £600

VOLKSWAGEN
Camper (Bay)

In 1968, the second generation of Type 2 thoroughly (and, some might say, belatedly) modernised the looks, with a single piece windscreen, thus earning the model the nickname of the 'Bay Window.' Although with less character to their styling, these VWs were easier to drive with improved suspension and larger engines; at introduction there was a 1584cc unit with a 1679cc one from 1971, when disc brakes also appeared. By the time European assembly came to an end in 1978, the Camper sported a 1970cc engine. Endowed with 70bhp, it was almost fast...

SPECIFICATIONS

Years produced: 1968-1979
Performance: 0-60mph: N/A (Top speed: 75mph)
Power & torque: 70bhp / 90lb/ft
Engine: Normally aspirated 1970cc flat four, petrol, carburettor, 8 valves
Drivetrain: Rear-engine RWD
Suspension: (F) Ind. torsion bar, trailing link. (R) Ind. swing axle, torsion bar
Bodyframe: Chassis and separate body
Transmission: 4-speed manual
Weight: 1105kgs

PRICE GUIDE

Launch price: £N/A (Dependent on variant)
Excellent: £8750
Good: £7000
Average: £3500
Project: £1500

VOLKSWAGEN
Scirocco MkI/II

The first in Volkswagen's new front-wheel-drive generation, the Scirocco emerged as a smart and desirable Capri alternative. Styled by Giorgetto Giugiaro and engineered by Audi, it was a major departure for the Wolfsburg company that previewed the ultra-successful Golf. In fuel injected form (it shared its engine with the Golf GTI), it was quick and flighty. MkII version arrived in the early 1980s, and was far duller to look at, but less likely to rot, and as a consequence, there are many more around despite being less desirable.

SPECIFICATIONS

Years produced: 1973-1988 (504,200)
Performance: 0-60mph: 8.5 secs (Top speed: 118mph)
Power & torque: 115bhp / 181lb/ft
Engine: Normally aspirated 1588cc in-line four, petrol, electronic fuel injection, 8 valves
Drivetrain: Front-engine FWD
Suspension: (F) Ind. MacPherson strut, coil spring. (R) Ind. trailing arm, coil spring
Bodyframe: Monocoque
Transmission: 5-speed manual
Weight: 865kgs

PRICE GUIDE

Launch price: £1995
Excellent: £2500
Good: £2000
Average: £800
Project: £300

VOLKSWAGEN
Golf GTI MkI

Having scored such huge global success with the Beetle, Volkswagen then annoyed its rivals by repeating the same trick with its small hatchback Golf. This Giugiaro-designed masterpiece was exactly the right car at the right time, but it was in GTI form, from 1975, that it was most impressive. The car that invented the term 'hot hatch' used a Bosch fuel-injected 1588cc engine to pump 110bhp through its front wheels and the tight and nimble handling meant all this could be used to the max. A 1781cc engine and quad headlamps marked out 1982's 1800 model.

SPECIFICATIONS

Years produced: 1976-1984 (600,000 in total)
Performance: 0-60mph: 8.7 secs (Top speed: 112mph)
Power & torque: 110bhp / 96lb/ft
Engine: Normally aspirated 1588cc in-line four, petrol, electronic fuel injection, 8 valves
Drivetrain: Front-engine FWD
Suspension: (F) Ind. MacPherson strut, coil spring. (R) Ind. trailing arm, coil spring
Bodyframe: Metal monocoque
Transmission: 4-speed manual
Weight: 830kgs

PRICE GUIDE

Launch price: £3707
Excellent: £4200
Good: £3000
Average: £1700
Project: £650

VOLKSWAGEN
Golf Cabriolet

The MkI Cabriolet was a latecomer to the Golf scene, not seeing the light of day until 1979. However, it would far outlast the saloon on which it was based. Built by Karmann, the four-seater Cabriolet had body strengthening, a transverse roll bar and enhanced trim. Earlier cars had manually-operated hoods but these eventually graduated to power-operated ones. The GTI equivalent was known as the GLi until 1984 but proved slower and less rigid than the saloon. Because of the high costs of building a MkII version, the roofless MkI continued through until 1993.

SPECIFICATIONS

Years produced: 1979-1993 (400,871 in total)
Performance: 0-60mph: 14.2 secs (Top speed: 94mph)
Power & torque: 54bhp / 71lb/ft
Engine: Normally aspirated 1272cc in-line four, petrol, carburettor, 8 valves
Drivetrain: Front-engine FWD
Suspension: (F) Ind. MacPherson strut, coil spring. (R) Ind. Trailing arm, coil spring
Bodyframe: Metal monocoque
Transmission: 4-speed manual
Weight: 845kgs

PRICE GUIDE

Launch price: £6985
Excellent: £4000
Good: £3000
Average: £1500
Project: £500

VOLKSWAGEN
Corrado G60

Volkswagen's 1988 replacement for the Scirocco successfully updated its predecessor's three-door hatchback style with a brooding and imposing persona. Closely related to the Golf Mk2, it debuted with a 1781cc engine. Topping the range initially was the G60, a supercharged monster of 158bhp that took just 7.8 seconds to reach 60mph and ultimately reached 140mph. And then came the VR6 version, a 187bhp fire-breather that encroached on supercar territory, with a maximum speed of 143mph and the dash from zero to 60 taking a mere 6.2 seconds.

SPECIFICATIONS

Years produced: 1988-1993
Performance: 0-60mph: 7.8 secs (Top speed: 140mph)
Power & torque: 160bhp / 166lb/ft
Engine: Supercharged 1781cc in-line four, petrol, electronic fuel injection, 8 valves
Drivetrain: Front-engine FWD
Suspension: (F) Ind. MacPherson strut, coil spring. (R) Ind. trailing arm, coil spring
Bodyframe: Metal monocoque
Transmission: 5-speed manual
Weight: 1115kgs

PRICE GUIDE

Launch price: £19,907
Excellent: £5500
Good: £4250
Average: £2500
Project: £1250

VOLVO 121/122S

The 120-series brought Volvo cars to Britain as well as raised the marque's profile elsewhere. Rugged and reliable, with handsome but traditional looks, the unburstable reputation, putting it in the same category as the Beetle on the worldwide stage. The 121 cars were the lower-specification four-door machines with less powerful engines, 122S versions had better performance and equipment levels, and were initially intended for export only. The Amazon name was officially only used in Sweden, but it seemed to suit the cars so the rest of the planet soon adopted it too.

SPECIFICATIONS

Years produced: 1955-1967
Performance: 0-60mph: 17 secs (Top speed: 85mph)
Power & torque: 66bhp / 76lb/ft
Engine: Normally aspirated 1582cc in-line four, petrol, carburettor, 8 valves
Drivetrain: Front-engine RWD
Suspension: (F) Ind. wishbone, coil spring. (R) Panhard rod, coil spring
Bodyframe: Metal monocoque
Transmission: 4-speed manual
Weight: 1000kgs

PRICE GUIDE

Launch price: £1197
Excellent: £4300
Good: £3500
Average: £1800
Project: £750

VOLVO PV544

Volvo's first model to be exported in any great numbers was the PV444 of 1947. When the time came to replace it, in 1958, Volvo simply modified the curvaceous and sturdy bodyshell slightly – with bigger front and rear windows – and dubbed the new model the PV544 (to signify that this 'personvagn' could now seat four instead of five). Two engines were used; a 1583cc unit and, from 1960, a 1778cc one. Sport models boasted twin carburettors and extra levels of equipment. The PV was meant to be superseded by the 120 but lasted seven years alongside it.

SPECIFICATIONS

Years produced: 1959-1965
Performance: 0-60mph: 19 secs (Top speed: 87mph)
Power & torque: 66bhp / 86lb/ft
Engine: Normally aspirated 1584cc in-line four, petrol, carburettor, 8 valves
Drivetrain: Front-engine RWD
Suspension: (F) Independent, wishbone, coil spring. (R) Independent, Live axle, coil spring
Bodyframe: Metal monocoque
Transmission: 5-speed manual
Weight: 940kgs

PRICE GUIDE

Launch price: £N/A in UK
Excellent: £5600
Good: £4250
Average: £2500
Project: £900

VOLVO 131/132

Don't look for a Volvo with 131 or 132 badging, because you won't find one. This designation was used by the factory – and diehard enthusiasts – only to denote two-door versions of the 120-series. Introduced in 1961, these more stylish but less practical variants injected a touch of verve into the Amazon's conservative appearance. 131s had a single carburettor while 132s, logically enough, had two. From 1968, the two-door cars became the only saloon style available, as Volvo had recently launched its new 140-series and was keen on boosting its four-door appeal.

SPECIFICATIONS

Years produced: 1961-1970
Performance: 0-60mph: 17.6 secs (Top speed: 90mph)
Power & torque: 75bhp / 101lb/ft
Engine: Normally aspirated 1778cc in-line four, petrol, carburettor, 8 valves
Drivetrain: Front-engine RWD
Suspension: (F) Independent, coil spring, wishbone. (R) Panhard rod, coil spring
Bodyframe: Metal monocoque
Transmission: 4-speed manual
Weight: 1090kgs

PRICE GUIDE

Launch price: £1022
Excellent: £5200
Good: £4000
Average: £2250
Project: £850

VOLVO P1800/S/E

Volvo gets racy! Or at least looked it. The P1800, designed by Frua and launched in 1960, was a startling-looking creation and British eyebrows were raised when Roger Moore drove one as *The Saint*. But the swept-back glamour disguised little more than 120 mechanics, which gave reasonable enough performance but fell short of being exhilarating. Post-1963, the name was changed to 1800S as power increased to 108 and 115bhp. A bit more wolf and less sheepish was the fuel-injected 1800E of 1969 to 1972; its 130bhp gave performance that went with the looks.

SPECIFICATIONS

Years produced: 1961-1972
Performance: 0-60mph: 13.2 secs (Top speed: 104mph)
Power & torque: 115bhp / 108lb/ft
Engine: Normally aspirated 1780cc in-line four, petrol, carburettor, 8 valves
Drivetrain: Front-engine RWD
Suspension: (F) Ind. wishbone, coil spring. (R) Panhard rod, coil spring
Bodyframe: Metal monocoque
Transmission: 4-speed manual
Weight: 1070kgs

PRICE GUIDE

Launch price: £1836
Excellent: £9000
Good: £7500
Average: £3750
Project: £1500

VOLVO 122 B18

In 1961, Volvo gave the 120-series cars more power to cope with their heavyweight engineering. The B18 engine was a fresh design, which would soon earn a reputation for longevity. Sized at 1778cc, it provided the single carburettor 121 with 75 or 85bhp, while 122 cars, with their twin carburettors, enjoyed fruitier 90, 95 and 100bhp outputs. Even more power and performance was supplied courtesy of the B20 engine. This was a bored-out version of the B18 with a capacity of 1998cc, and resulted in the most powerful 120 of all, the 1968-1970 122S with 118bhp and 100mph potential.

SPECIFICATIONS

Years produced: 1962-1967
Performance: 0-60mph: 13.8 secs (Top speed: 104mph)
Power & torque: 115bhp / 112lb/ft
Engine: Normally aspirated 1778cc in-line four, petrol, carburettor, 8 valves
Drivetrain: Front-engine RWD
Suspension: (F) Independent, coil spring, wishbone. (R) Panhard rod, coil spring
Bodyframe: Metal monocoque
Transmission: 4-speed manual
Weight: 1090kgs

PRICE GUIDE

Launch price: £1022
Excellent: £4850
Good: £4000
Average: £2000
Project: £750

VOLVO 123GT

Thanks to their inherent strength and reliability, Amazons proved natural rally cars. To capitalise on this, Volvo gave the go-faster world of 1966 the 123GT. Its twin-carburettor 1778cc engine came from the more sporty 1800S coupé and it had servo-assisted front disc brakes and bumper-mounted spotlamps while, inside, the driver could revel in his special steering wheel and dash-mounted rev counter. Only available as a two-door, this Swedish grand tourer proved a potent tool. British tuner Ruddspeed offered a package to boost power to an entertaining 132bhp.

SPECIFICATIONS

Years produced: 1967-1968
Performance: 0-60mph: 12.5 secs (Top speed: 109mph)
Power & torque: 115bhp / 107lb/ft
Engine: Normally aspirated 1778cc in-line four, petrol, carburettor, 8 valves
Drivetrain: Front-engine RWD
Suspension: (F) Independent, coil spring, wishbone. (R) Panhard rod, semi-elliptic leaf spring
Bodyframe: Metal monocoque
Transmission: 4-speed manual
Weight: 1050kgs

PRICE GUIDE

Launch price: £1372
Excellent: £6000
Good: £4750
Average: £2750
Project: £1200

VOLVO 144/145/142

Volvo's reputation for safety first, style second started in earnest with the 140-series. These big and boxy cars, built from 1967 to 1974, were uncompromising in their looks but thoroughly protected their occupants. The third figure of the model designation denoted the number of doors; thus the 142 had two, the 144 had four, and the 145 was the five-door estate. At first, the 1778cc engine was all that was available, albeit with twin carburettors on the S models, but 1986cc engines became standard in 1968. Best was the 1970's GL, with fuel injection and leather upholstery.

SPECIFICATIONS

Years produced: 1967-1974
Performance: 0-60mph: 10.1 secs (Top speed: 106mph)
Power & torque: 124bhp / 123lb/ft
Engine: Normally aspirated 1986cc in-line four, petrol, mechanical fuel injection, 8 valve
Drivetrain: Front-engine RWD
Suspension: (F) Independent, wishbone, coil spring. (R) Panhard rod, radius arm, coil spring
Bodyframe: Metal monocoque
Transmission: 4-speed manual
Weight: 1290kgs

PRICE GUIDE

Launch price: £1354
Excellent: £1850
Good: £1400
Average: £700
Project: £200

VOLVO 164

Seeking to enter the luxury realms of Jaguar and Mercedes-Benz, Volvo unveiled the 164 in 1968. It was based on the 140-series, albeit with a longer body and 2978cc six-cylinder engine lurking behind its much grander grille, plus generous equipment. On the TE, owners got leather, air conditioning and power steering. The cars started with 145bhp, but when fuel injection arrived in 1971, this rose to 175bhp. The fitment of built-in foglamps from 1969 was a very Jaguar touch, but the 164 failed to appeal as much as the prettier Jags it wanted to emulate, despite the better build quality.

SPECIFICATIONS

Years produced: 1968-1975
Performance: 0-60mph: 11 secs (Top speed: 110mph)
Power & torque: 145bhp / 163lb/ft
Engine: Normally aspirated 2978cc in-line six, petrol, carburettor, 12 valves
Drivetrain: Front-engine RWD
Suspension: (F) Independent, wishbone, coil spring. (R) Live axle, radius arm, coil spring
Bodyframe: Metal monocoque
Transmission: 4-speed manual
Weight: 1320kgs

PRICE GUIDE

Launch price: £1791
Excellent: £2100
Good: £1600
Average: £850
Project: £300

VOLVO 1800ES

One of the most intriguing of all Volvos appeared in 1971, with the 1800ES. Cast in the mould of Reliant's Scimitar GTE, this was the 1800 given an estate rear as a way of updating its dated appearance for the 1970s. It was a gamble that worked, for this idiosyncratic load-lugger proved very popular, despite its nickname of 'Snow White's hearse.' The 130bhp fuel-injected engine still gave good performance – 115mph was possible for the antiques dealer or heavy shopper in a hurry – while the trademark large glass frameless hatchback was a theme that Volvo would return to again...

SPECIFICATIONS

Years produced: 1971-1973 (8077 in total)
Performance: 0-60mph: 9.7 secs (Top speed: 112mph)
Power & torque: 130bhp / 123lb/ft
Engine: Normally aspirated 1986cc in-line four, petrol, carburettor, 8 valves
Drivetrain: Front-engine RWD
Suspension: (F) Independent, wishbone, coil spring. (R) Panhard rod, coil spring, anti-roll bar
Bodyframe: Metal monocoque
Transmission: 4-speed manual
Weight: 1130kgs

PRICE GUIDE

Launch price: £2650
Excellent: £8250
Good: £7000
Average: £3250
Project: £1250

VOLVO 264/265

Alongside the four-cylinder cars, Volvo also weighed in with six-cylinder variants using the same 240 bodyshell. The 264 saloon was launched at the same time, the 265 estate followed a year later. Both used the brand new 2664cc V6 engine developed with Peugeot and Renault; a smooth and mighty motor especially when in 140bhp fuel-injected form. This went up to 2849cc in 1981, which added an extra 14bhp. Flagship was the 264TE, a Bertone-built stretched limousine, complete with a telephone and a fridge. As ABBA used one, it must have been special!

SPECIFICATIONS

Years produced: 1974-1979 (169,127 in total)
Performance: 0-60mph: 12.7 secs (Top speed: 108mph)
Power & torque: 148bhp / 161lb/ft
Engine: Normally aspirated 2664cc V6, petrol, electronic fuel injection, 12 valves
Drivetrain: Front-engine RWD
Suspension: (F) Ind. MacPherson strut, coil spring. (R) Panhard rod, trailing arm, coil spring
Bodyframe: Metal monocoque
Transmission: 4-speed manual with overdrive
Weight: 1456kgs

PRICE GUIDE

Launch price: £3799
Excellent: £1800
Good: £1400
Average: £600
Project: £200

VOLVO 244/245

The Flying Brick, Swedish Tank... nicknames for Volvo's Lego-like 240 were hardly complimentary. But what this tough-mobile lacked in style, it more than made up for in safety and sales. The cars – the 244 was the four-door saloon, the 245 the estate – were based on the 140. However, the fronts were re-engineered for MacPherson strut suspension and a new nose. Aside from Volvo's existing 1986cc engine, a new overhead-cam 2127cc unit featured; this rose to 2315cc in 1978. The last were built in 1993; as durable in lifespan as they were in quality and strength.

SPECIFICATIONS

Years produced: 1974-1993 (3,000,000+ in total)
Performance: 0-60mph: 11.4 secs (Top speed: 106mph)
Power & torque: 123bhp / 125lb/ft
Engine: Normally aspirated 2127cc in-line four, petrol, electronic fuel injection, 8 valves
Drivetrain: Front-engine RWD
Suspension: (F) Ind. MacPherson strut, coil spring. (R) Panhard rod, trailing arm, coil spring
Bodyframe: Metal monocoque
Transmission: 4-speed manual with overdrive
Weight: 1404kgs

PRICE GUIDE

Launch price: £2155
Excellent: £1750
Good: £1300
Average: £600
Project: £175

VOLVO 262C

The 262C was a wildcard in the Volvo pack, an attempt to build a luxury coupé. Certainly it was distinctive, although the lowered black-vinyl clad roof with swept-back and chunky rear pillars plonked on top of a 260 lower body gave a distinctly tank-like appearance. However, the sumptuous leather-bound interior certainly pampered any occupants. Engines were the same as the standard 260s; thus a 140bhp 2664cc V6 at first, followed by a 155bhp 2849cc V6 towards the end of production. Definitely mean and moody but not all that magnificent, although Volvo aficionados adore them.

SPECIFICATIONS

Years produced: 1978-1981 (5622 in total)
Performance: 0-60mph: 11.1 secs (Top speed: 109mph)
Power & torque: 148bhp / 161lb/ft
Engine: Normally aspirated 2664cc V6, petrol, electronic fuel injection, 12 valves
Drivetrain: Front-engine RWD
Suspension: (F) Ind. MacPherson strut, coil spring. (R) Panhard rod, trailing arm, coil spring
Bodyframe: Metal monocoque
Transmission: 3-speed automatic
Weight: 1450kgs

PRICE GUIDE

Launch price: £13,000
Excellent: £3500
Good: £2750
Average: £1400
Project: £600

VOLVO 480 ES/Turbo

As a belated successor to the 1800ES, the quirky 480ES echoed its predecessor's frameless glass hatchback but, from the front, looked like no Volvo before. The design was a dramatic and sleek wedge with pop-up headlamps and a tiny Volvo-badged grille hiding under the front bumper. Front-wheel-drive was a first for the marque and there were faddish features such as door pillar-mounted locks and an electronic information centre. 1721cc and 1998cc engines featured and there was a turbocharged version from 1989. An oddball in the Volvo canon but an intriguing creation.

SPECIFICATIONS

Years produced: 1986-1995 (80,463 in total)
Performance: 0-60mph: 8.6 secs (Top speed: 124mph)
Power & torque: 120bhp / 129lb/ft
Engine: Turbocharged 1721cc in-line four, petrol, electronic fuel injection, 8 valves
Drivetrain: Front-engine FWD
Suspension: (F) Ind. MacPherson strut, wishbone. (R) Panhard rod, Watt linkage
Bodyframe: Metal monocoque
Transmission: 5-speed manual
Weight: 900kgs

PRICE GUIDE

Launch price: £10,850
Excellent: £1250
Good: £1000
Average: £500
Project: £200

VOLVO 850 T5/T5-R

The launch of the 850 marked a turning point for Volvo. Although it kept the family resemblance, it seemed to have been designed using something other than a ruler and was a more gentle, rounded shape. High equipment levels pushed the car upmarket, but it was the 850 T5-R of 1994 that really caused people to sit up and take notice. With a tyre-shredding 250bhp from its turbocharged 2435cc engine, pumped through the front wheels, here was a Volvo that was both safe and practical yet also fast and a little sexy. The company even took estate versions racing!

SPECIFICATIONS

Years produced: 1992-1997
Performance: 0-60mph: 7.2 secs (Top speed: 140mph)
Power & torque: 240bhp / 300lb/ft
Engine: Turbocharged 2319cc in-line five, petrol, electronic fuel injection, 20 valves
Drivetrain: Front-engine FWD
Suspension: (F) Ind. wishbone, coil spring. (R) Ind. trailing arm, coil spring
Bodyframe: Metal monocoque
Transmission: 5-speed manual
Weight: 1450kgs

PRICE GUIDE

Launch price: £26,995
Excellent: £4500
Good: £3500
Average: £2500
Project: £1500

WILLYS Jeep

The Willys Jeep was designed and built with the sole purpose of mobilising the US army in the heat of World War II. The Overland Jeep revolutionised off-road driving for soldiers, and demand soon outstripped supply. Supply shortages meant Ford stepped in and built the Jeep under licence from Willys, adopting the instantly recognisable seven-slotted grille, which was much cheaper to produce than the original. After the war, Willys decided to offer the Jeep to civilians, and the CJ (Civilian Jeep) was born.

SPECIFICATIONS

Years produced: 1941-1945
Performance: 0-60mph: N/A (Top speed: N/A)
Power & torque: 54bhp / 95lb/ft
Engine: Normally aspirated 2199cc in-line four, petrol, carburettor, 8 valves
Drivetrain: Front-engine AWD
Suspension: (F) Live axle, semi-elliptic leaf spring. (R) Live axle, semi-elliptic leaf spring
Bodyframe: Chassis and separate body
Transmission: 4-speed manual
Weight: 1113kgs

PRICE GUIDE

Launch price: £N/A
Excellent: £9000
Good: £7500
Average: £5000
Project: £3000

WOLSELEY
12/48, 14/60

Wolseley's status as a luxury-orientated marque meant that its big pre-war car cars went back into production soon after the end of the war. The 12/48 was a heavy and conventionally-engineered saloon with a 44bhp 4-cylinder 1548cc engine which struggled to shift the car's bulk adequately. Slightly more lively was the longer-bonneted 14/60, its extra length necessary to accommodate the extra two cylinders of its 1818cc six-pot engine, giving 55bhp. These stately old school machines were built until 1948 when they were replaced by the Wolseley 4/50 and 6/80 ranges.

SPECIFICATIONS

Years produced: 1938-1948 (11,331 in total)
Performance: 0-60mph: 36.2 secs (Top speed: 70mph)
Power & torque: 55bhp / 77lb/ft
Engine: Normally aspirated 1818cc in-line six, petrol, carburettor, 8 valves
Drivetrain: Front-engine RWD
Suspension: (F) Beam axle, semi-elliptic leaf spring. (R) Live axle, semi-elliptic leaf spring
Bodyframe: Chassis and separate body
Transmission: 4-speed manual
Weight: 1397kgs

PRICE GUIDE

Launch price: £614
Excellent: £5000
Good: £3750
Average: £2000
Project: £750

WOLSELEY
18/85

Another large pre-war Wolseley that re-emerged after the end of the war was the 18/85. Practically identical to the 14/60, it justified its higher price by having a bigger 2322cc six-cylinder engine. With 85bhp available, performance was good and it became well-known as a police car. A novel feature was the 'Nightpass' lights, an anti-dazzle, dipped head and driving lamp arrangement. The 18/85's bulletproof reputation was well-justified; one managed to break the London to Cape Town record despite falling 30-foot off a bridge in the Congo. Now that's build quality...

SPECIFICATIONS

Years produced: 1938-1948 (8213 in total)
Performance: 0-60mph: 25.4 secs (Top speed: 75mph)
Power & torque: 85bhp / 99lb/ft
Engine: Normally aspirated 2322cc in-line six, petrol, carburettor, 12 valves
Drivetrain: Front-engine RWD
Suspension: (F) Beam axle, semi-elliptic leaf spring. (R) Live axle, semi-elliptic leaf spring
Bodyframe: Chassis and separate body
Transmission: 4-speed manual
Weight: 1422kgs

PRICE GUIDE

Launch price: £680
Excellent: £5250
Good: £4000
Average: £2000
Project: £750

WOLSELEY
Eight

At first glance, the Wolseley Eight of 1946 looked like nothing more than a Morris Eight with a Wolseley bonnet and grille transplanted. However, it was more than just that, for a smoother 918cc overhead-valve engine of 33bhp was installed in place of the pedestrian 30bhp sidevalve engine of the Morris. A four-speed transmission and hydraulic brakes also featured. A plusher wood and leather interior helped to raise the Wolseley above its humbler Morris sibling and make any passengers feel they were in something a bit special.

SPECIFICATIONS

Years produced: 1946-1948 (5344 in total)
Performance: 0-60mph: N/A (Top speed: 63mph)
Power & torque: 33bhp / 45lb/ft
Engine: Normally aspirated 918cc in-line four, petrol, carburettor, 8 valves
Drivetrain: Front-engine RWD
Suspension: (F) Beam axle, semi-elliptic leaf spring. (R) Live axle, semi-elliptic leaf spring
Bodyframe: Chassis and separate body
Transmission: 4-speed manual
Weight: 864kgs

PRICE GUIDE

Launch price: £416
Excellent: £3600
Good: £2800
Average: £1400
Project: £600

WOLSELEY
4/50

The Nuffield Organisation introduced greater levels of rationalisation among their constituents postwar, and Wolseley was one of the marques that lost its individuality as a result. The 4/50, of 1948, was to all intents and purposes a Morris Oxford MO wearing traditional Wolseley identity tags. Thus, the more stately Wolseley grille was installed, with interior fitments upgraded to suit middle class sensibilities. The Wolseley also junked the Morris' sidevalve engine and had its own 1476cc overhead-cam four-cylinder of 51bhp instead. Handling wasn't a strong point though.

SPECIFICATIONS

Years produced: 1948-1953 (8925 in total)
Performance: 0-60mph: 31.6 secs (Top speed: 74mph)
Power & torque: 51bhp / 72lb/ft
Engine: Normally aspirated 1476cc in-line four, petrol, carburettor, 8 valves
Drivetrain: Front-engine RWD
Suspension: (F) Independent, torsion bar, wishbone. (R) Live axle, semi-elliptic leaf spring
Bodyframe: Metal monocoque
Transmission: 4-speed manual
Weight: 1181kgs

PRICE GUIDE

Launch price: £704
Excellent: £3650
Good: £2850
Average: £1400
Project: £600

WOLSELEY
6/80

While the closely-related Wolseley 4/50 was a Morris Oxford MO in drag, the 6/80 was a Morris Six in an evening dress with a Pinocchio nose. The prominent snout was needed to accommodate the hefty 2215cc six-cylinder engine which offered more power than its Morris equivalent (72bhp versus 66bhp) thanks to an extra carburettor. The engineering - independent front suspension and unitary construction – was also modern for its day. Obviously, as befitted a Wolseley, the cabin featured sufficient wood and leather to justify its illuminated grille badge and higher price tag.

SPECIFICATIONS

Years produced: 1948-1954 (25,281 in total)
Performance: 0-60mph: 27.8 secs (Top speed: 81mph)
Power & torque: 72bhp / 102lb/ft
Engine: Normally aspirated 2215cc in-line six, petrol, carburettor, 12 valves
Drivetrain: Front-engine RWD
Suspension: (F) Independent, torsion bar, wishbone. (R) Live axle, semi-elliptic leaf spring
Bodyframe: Metal monocoque
Transmission: 4-speed manual
Weight: 1308kgs

PRICE GUIDE

Launch price: £767
Excellent: £4400
Good: £3500
Average: £1800
Project: £700

WOLSELEY 4/44, 15/50

This time, it was the Wolseley that was built before any other badge-engineering took place; the equivalent MG Magnette ZA didn't appear for a year after the 4/44's 1952 birth. The Wolseley focused more on opulence than performance, with just a single carburettor on its MG-derived 1250cc overhead valve engine. Nevertheless, its handling was adept thanks to the independent front suspension and rack-and-pinion steering and the sleek lines gave it a rakish persona. In 1956, it was upgraded into the 15/50; identical in looks but with a 1489cc B-series engine.

SPECIFICATIONS

Years produced: 1953-1958 (42,198 in total)
Performance: 0-60mph: 24.3 secs (Top speed: 78mph)
Power & torque: 50bhp / 78lb/ft
Engine: Normally aspirated 1250cc in-line four, petrol, carburettor, 8 valves
Drivetrain: Front-engine RWD
Suspension: (F) Ind. wishbone, coil spring. (R) Live axle, semi-elliptic leaf spring
Bodyframe: Metal monocoque
Transmission: 4-speed manual
Weight: 1118kgs

PRICE GUIDE

Launch price: £997
Excellent: £3750
Good: £3000
Average: £1400
Project: £500

WOLSELEY 6/90 Saloon

Riley introduced its Pathfinder in 1953, Wolseley followed suit in 1954 with the visually-similar 6/90. Aside from minor trim, the two cars looked one and the same. However, the Wolseley boasted two extra cylinders from its 2.6-litre six-pot C-series engine, borrowed from the Austin Westminster. This gave 90bhp as well as 90mph. The Series II of 1956 brought in semi-elliptic rear suspension and a floor-mounted gearchange, but only lasted a year before the Series III added a larger rear window and servo-assisted brakes.

SPECIFICATIONS

Years produced: 1954-1959 (11,852 in total)
Performance: 0-60mph: 18.1 secs (Top speed: 94mph)
Power & torque: 95bhp / 133lb/ft
Engine: Normally aspirated 2639cc in-line six, petrol, carburettor, 12 valves
Drivetrain: Front-engine RWD
Suspension: (F) Independent, torsion bar, wishbone. (R) Live axle, semi-elliptic leaf spring
Bodyframe: Metal monocoque
Transmission: 4-speed manual
Weight: 1492kgs

PRICE GUIDE

Launch price: £1064
Excellent: £3850
Good: £3000
Average: £1450
Project: £500

WOLSELEY 1500

After a Morris Minor replacement project was aborted, the resultant small car became the Riley 1.5 and Wolseley 1500 in 1957 instead. The Minor's floorpan and suspension were retained, but with a new, well-rounded and smart-looking body. The Wolseley was the comfortable cruiser of the pair and thus gave a lower 43bhp from its single-carburettor BMC B-series 1489cc engine. The 1960 MkII hid the bonnet and boot hinges, while the 1961 MkIII lowered the suspension, changed the tail lamps and tweaked the grille. Quite a characterful small classic today.

SPECIFICATIONS

Years produced: 1957-1965 (100,722 in total)
Performance: 0-60mph: 24.4 secs (Top speed: 78mph)
Power & torque: 43bhp / 71lb/ft
Engine: Normally aspirated 1489cc in-line four, petrol, carburettor, 8 valves
Drivetrain: Front-engine RWD
Suspension: (F) Independent, torsion bar, wishbone. (R) Live axle, semi-elliptic leaf spring
Bodyframe: Metal monocoque
Transmission: 4-speed manual
Weight: 1129kgs

PRICE GUIDE

Launch price: £759
Excellent: £3500
Good: £2750
Average: £1250
Project: £400

WOLSELEY 6/99, 6/110

The sharp lines of the BMC Farina range worked well on the large Wolseley 6/99 and 6/110. Sharing the same engine and bodyshell as the Austin Westminster and the Vanden Plas 3-Litre, the 6/99 was quite a prestigious and luxurious machine with its big 2912cc C-series engine giving a lazy but smooth 103bhp. All the extra Wolseley trim and interior touches were in place to pamper occupants. In 1961, a revamp saw the car metamorphose into the 6/110, with more power (120bhp) and improved handling from a Panhard rod back end and power-assisted steering.

SPECIFICATIONS

Years produced: 1959-1968 (37,209 in total)
Performance: 0-60mph: 14.4 secs (Top speed: 98mph)
Power & torque: 103bhp / 158lb/ft
Engine: Normally aspirated 2912cc in-line six, petrol, carburettor, 12 valves
Drivetrain: Front-engine RWD
Suspension: (F) Ind. Coil spring (R) Panhard rod, semi-elliptic leaf spring
Bodyframe: Metal monocoque
Transmission: 3-speed manual
Weight: 1530kgs

PRICE GUIDE

Launch price: £1255
Excellent: £4750
Good: £4000
Average: £2000
Project: £600

WOLSELEY 15/60, 16/60

BMC badge engineering ran riot with the family-sized fintastic Farinas; there were Austin, Morris, MG, Wolseley and Riley versions. Wolseley, as usual, performed the luxury duties, which meant a higher quality cabin of hide and walnut and the trademark grille. So as not to detract from the MG and Riley versions though, it shared the 52bhp single carburettor 1489cc engine of the Austin and Morris machines. In 1961, the type metamorphosed into the 16/60, with a 1622cc engine of 61bhp, anti-roll bars to rein in the excessive body roll and the fins cut down.

SPECIFICATIONS

Years produced: 1959-1971 (87,661 in total)
Performance: 0-60mph: 24.3 secs (Top speed: 77mph)
Power & torque: 52bhp / 82lb/ft
Engine: Normally aspirated 1489cc in-line four, petrol, carburettor, 8 valves
Drivetrain: Front-engine RWD
Suspension: (F) Independent, coil spring, wishbone. (R) Live axle, semi-elliptic leaf spring
Bodyframe: Metal monocoque
Transmission: 4-speed manual
Weight: 1118kgs

PRICE GUIDE

Launch price: £991
Excellent: £3000
Good: £2250
Average: £1000
Project: £350

WOLSELEY Hornet

With the Mini a big success, BMC decided to extend its appeal even further in 1961 with the Wolseley Hornet, sister model to the Riley Elf. This was a far less utilitarian version than the original though. So there was a rather flamboyant chrome-laden front, a larger boot framed by small fins and a three-instrument dashboard surrounded by wood veneer. In 1963, the MkII Hornet introduced the 998cc A-series engine to the Mini for the first time and Hydrolastic suspension replaced the bouncy rubber cone type. The MkIII (1966) had winding windows and improved ventilation.

SPECIFICATIONS

Years produced: 1961-1969 (28,455 in total)
Performance: 0-60mph: 32.3 secs (Top speed: 71mph)
Power & torque: 34bhp / 44lb/ft
Engine: Normally aspirated 848cc in-line four, petrol, carburettor, 8 valves
Drivetrain: Front-engine FWD
Suspension: (F) Ind. rubber cone, later Hydrolastic. (R) Ind. rubber cone, later Hydrolastic
Bodyframe: Metal monocoque
Transmission: 4-speed manual
Weight: 624kgs

PRICE GUIDE

Launch price: £672
Excellent: £3400
Good: £2650
Average: £1400
Project: £450

WOLSELEY 1100/1300

BMC badge engineering reached its zenith with the 1100/1300 range. The Wolseley was a comparative latecomer, not being launched until 1965, three years after the first-born Morris. Mechanically, it played with the same 55bhp as the Riley and MG versions and also had the option of attractive two-tone paintwork. In 1967, the 1300 appeared, with a 1275cc engine instead of a 1098. This had an all-synchromesh gearbox and 70bhp from its twin-carburettor engine, unless with an automatic gearbox, in which case, there was only one.

SPECIFICATIONS

Years produced: 1965-1973 (44,867 in total)
Performance: 0-60mph: 18.4 secs (Top speed: 85mph)
Power & torque: 55bhp / 61lb/ft
Engine: Normally aspirated 1098cc in-line four, petrol, carburettor, 8 valves
Drivetrain: Front-engine FWD
Suspension: (F) Independent, Hydrolastic. (R) Independent, Hydrolastic
Bodyframe: Metal monocoque
Transmission: 4-speed manual
Weight: 832kgs

PRICE GUIDE

Launch price: £754
Excellent: £2400
Good: £1750
Average: £850
Project: £200

WOLSELEY 18/85, Six

Top of the Landcrab tree was the Wolseley 18/85, introduced in 1967. This ultimate Issigonis enlargement of the front-wheel-drive theme begun with the Mini was a capacious car and, in Wolseley form, offered a lot to please class-conscious customers with leather, wood and high quality carpeting. Naturally, there was the usual Wolseley grille with its trademark illuminated centre badge. The 18/85S of 1969 had 96bhp to the standard car's 85bhp. Four cylinders grew to six in 1972 with the fitment of a 2227cc overhead-cam engine.

SPECIFICATIONS

Years produced: 1967-1975 (35,597 in total)
Performance: 0-60mph: 17.1 secs (Top speed: 90mph)
Power & torque: 85bhp / 99lb/ft
Engine: Normally aspirated 1798cc in-line four, petrol, carburettor, 8 valves
Drivetrain: Front-engine FWD
Suspension: (F) Independent, Hydrolastic. (R) Independent, Hydrolastic
Bodyframe: Metal monocoque
Transmission: 4-speed manual
Weight: 1155kgs

PRICE GUIDE

Launch price: £1040
Excellent: £2600
Good: £1850
Average: £1000
Project: £250

WOLSELEY Six (Wedge)

The 1975 Six was the final Wolseley to be built. Designed by Harris Mann, the car that would forever become known as 'The Wedge' was the posh version of its Austin and Morris lookalikes, available only with the 2227cc six-cylinder engine (its humbler siblings were also available with four cylinders). At the front was a much shrunken version of the traditional Wolseley grille and light-up badge, the distinctive shape of the car dictating no room for anything larger. After just six months, the entire range was de-badged and the cars just named Princesses.

SPECIFICATIONS

Years produced: 1975-1975 (3800 in total)
Performance: 0-60mph: 13.5 secs (Top speed: 104mph)
Power & torque: 110bhp / 125lb/ft
Engine: Normally aspirated 2227cc in-line six, petrol, carburettor, 12 valves
Drivetrain: Front-engine FWD
Suspension: (F) Independent, Hydragas. (R) Independent, Hydragas
Bodyframe: Metal monocoque
Transmission: 4-speed manual
Weight: 1215kgs

PRICE GUIDE

Launch price: £2838
Excellent: £2400
Good: £1500
Average: £650
Project: £150